Glencoe

Geometry

Integration
Applications
Connections

Solutions Manual

GLENCOE

McGraw-Hill

New York, New York   Columbus, Ohio   Woodland Hills, California   Peoria, Illinois

Glencoe/McGraw-Hill

A Division of The McGraw·Hill Companies

Send all inquiries to:
Glencoe/McGraw-Hill
936 Eastwind Drive
Westerville, OH 43081-3374

ISBN: 0-02-825296-9

Geometry
Solutions Manual

5 6 7 8 9 10 066 03 02 01 00 99

Contents

To the Teacher

As with all areas of mathematics, there are frequently multiple methods of solving any given problem. This is especially true in geometry. Every effort has been made to present solutions to the problems in the student edition that might be expected from a student studying this course. There may be other approaches or methods for solving a problem that differ from the one given in this document, but are just as valid as the one presented. Every proof in this Solutions Manual might be considered a sample answer, because there are many approaches and orders of statements that lead to the same valid conclusion.

CHAPTER 1   Discovering Points, Lines, Planes, and Angles

1-1   Integration: Algebra
The Coordinate Plane

Pages 8–9 Check for Understanding

1. The first coordinate tells how far to go right (+) or left (−) of the origin. From that point, the second coordinate tells how far up (+) or down (−) to go before plotting the point.

2. Sample answer: The vertical axis goes down, but is positive.

3.

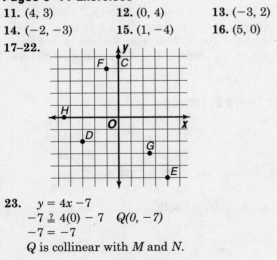

4. (−4, 4)   **5.** (−4, −3)

6–7.

8a. II   **8b.** I   **8c.** y-axis
8d. B   **8e.** B

9. $y = x + 2$
   $-2 \overset{?}{=} (-3) + 2$
   $-2 \ne -1$
   Z is noncollinear with A and B.

10a. (135°, 34.5°)   **10b.** Tokyo

Pages 9–11 Exercises

11. (4, 3)   **12.** (0, 4)   **13.** (−3, 2)
14. (−2, −3)   **15.** (1, −4)   **16.** (5, 0)

17–22.

23. $y = 4x - 7$
   $-7 \overset{?}{=} 4(0) - 7$ Q(0, −7)
   $-7 = -7$
   Q is collinear with M and N.

24. $y = 4x - 7$
   $-5 \overset{?}{=} 4(0.5) - 7$ R(0.5, −5)
   $-5 = -5$
   R is collinear with M and N.

25. $y = 4x - 7$
   $11 \overset{?}{=} 4(-1) - 7$ S(−1, 11)
   $11 \ne -11$
   S is noncollinear with M and N.

26. (−5, 4)   **27.** (0, 4)   **28.** (3, 0)
29. (3, −2)   **30.** (0, −2)   **31.** (−5, 0)

32. Sample points: (0, 5), (−5, 0), (−1, 4); not on line: (0, 0)

33. Sample points: (0, −9), (1, −3), (2, 3); not on line: (0, 0)

34. Sample points: (−3, −1), (−1, 2), (1, 5); not on line: (0, 0)

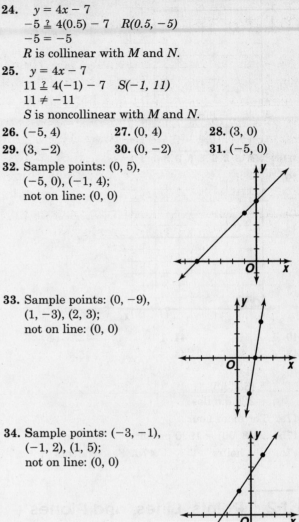

35a. 2; I, IV   **35b.** (2, 0), (6, 0)
35c. Sample answer: (4, −3)
35d. −3   **35e.** 2

36. Plot two points in the plane and draw a line through them. Plot another point not on that line. Then draw all possible lines through any two of the points on the plane. Plot a fourth point not on any of these lines and then draw all possible lines through this point and any other plotted point on the plane. Finally, plot a fifth point not on any of the lines. These five points must be noncollinear.

37. (−3, −4); Substitute the −3 for x and −4 for y in each of the equations to make sure these coordinates satisfy both equations. Since it satisfies both equations, these are the coordinates of a point that lies on the graphs of both equations. In order for the point to lie on two distinct lines, it must be the point they have in common, or their intersection.

38.

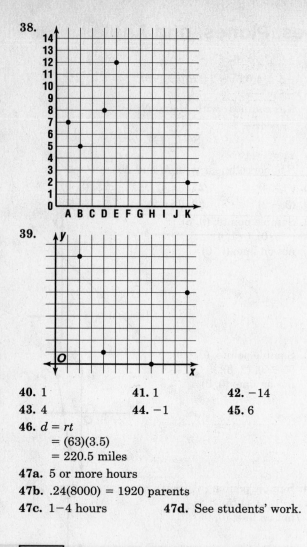

39.

40. 1   **41.** 1   **42.** −14

43. 4   **44.** −1   **45.** 6

46. $d = rt$
  $= (63)(3.5)$
  $= 220.5$ miles

47a. 5 or more hours

47b. .24(8000) = 1920 parents

47c. 1−4 hours   **47d.** See students' work.

1-2 Points, Lines, and Planes

Page 15 Modeling Mathematics

a. For drawing, see part d; no.

b. For drawing, see part d; no.

c. It lies on $\overleftrightarrow{AB}$; for drawing, see part d.

d.

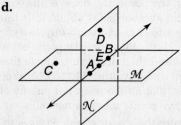

Pages 15–16 Check for Understanding

1. Each wall, floor, and ceiling represents a plane. Where the wall meets the ceiling, floor, or another wall represents a line. Where two walls and the floor or ceiling meet represents a point.

2. point, line, plane

3.

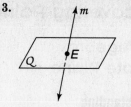

4. Malia; yes: $n(n − 1)(n − 2)$

5. PQR, PRQ, RPQ, RQP, QRP, QPR

6a. If they intersect, they intersect in one point.

6b. If the lines are not parallel, they would eventually intersect.

6c. Yes; parallel lines do not intersect.

7. point   **8.** plane   **9.** line

10. Sample answer: line c

11. Sample answer: plane $\mathcal{A}$

12. Sample answer:

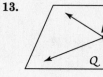

13.

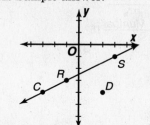

14.

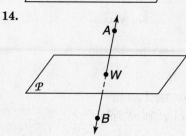

15. $\overleftrightarrow{PR}$ **16.** T **17.** $\overleftrightarrow{PR}$

18. 10: 2 quarters; 1 quarter, 2 dimes, 1 nickels; 1 quarter, 1 dimes, 3 nickels; 1 quarter, 5 nickels; 5 dimes; 4 dimes, 2 nickels; 3 dimes, 4 nickels; 2 dimes, 6 nickels; 1 dimes, 8 nickels; 10 nickels

Pages 16–18 Exercises

19. line   **20.** point   **21.** plane

22. point   **23.** lines   **24.** plane

25. point   **26.** line   **27.** line

28–33. Sample names for figures are given.

28. r **29.** $\overleftrightarrow{BF}$ **30.** F, E

31. $F, C, E,$ or D **32.** BCE **33.** $\mathcal{R}$

34.

35. Sample answer:

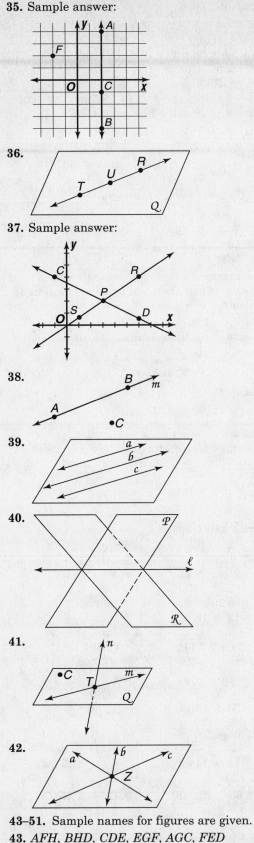

36.

37. Sample answer:

38.

39.

40.

41.

42.

43–51. Sample names for figures are given.

43. *AFH, BHD, CDE, EGF, AGC, FED*

44. *A, F*   **45.** $\overrightarrow{GE}, \overrightarrow{DE}, \overrightarrow{FE}$ **46.** *BHC, EDC*

47. $\overrightarrow{GE}, \overrightarrow{GC}$ **48.** *AGC, $\overleftrightarrow{AF}$*   **49.** *G*

50. lines that cannot be seen from the perspective of the viewer

51. Yes; you can draw $\overleftrightarrow{BG}$ and $\overleftrightarrow{HE}$ to form a plane that fits diagonally through the figure.

52.

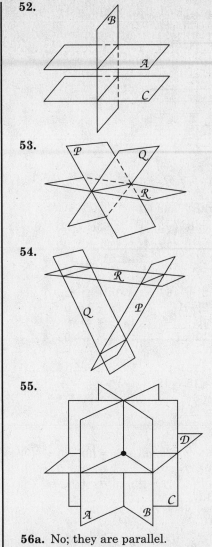

53.

54.

55.

56a. No; they are parallel.

56b. Yes; an example is where the front and side walls meet.

56c. No; there can be all orientations of lines in any plane.

56d. The intersection could be a point or two lines.

57. maximum: 6 points   minimum: 0 points

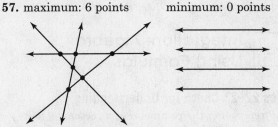

58. There are 16 possible outcomes on the first throw. Let D stand for any face down disk and 1, 2, 3, and 4 represent the number of dots on a face up disk. 1234, 234D, 134D, 124D, 123D, 12DD, 13DD, 14DD, 23DD, 24DD, 34DD, 1DDD, 2DDD, 3DDD, 4DDD, DDDD

59. See students' work.

60. possible observations: a large cube with a small cube cut out; a small cube sitting in the corner of two walls and the floor

61.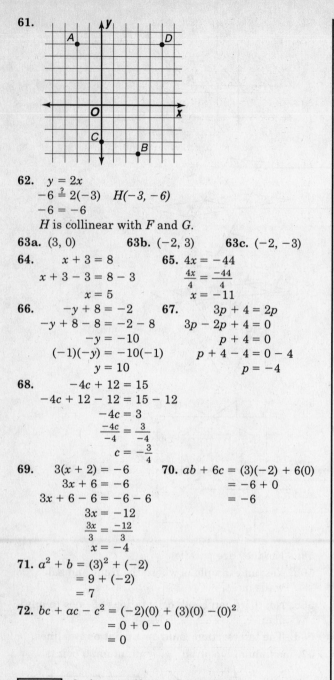

62. $y = 2x$
$-6 \stackrel{?}{=} 2(-3)$ $H(-3, -6)$
$-6 = -6$
H is collinear with F and G.

63a. $(3, 0)$ **63b.** $(-2, 3)$ **63c.** $(-2, -3)$

64. $x + 3 = 8$ **65.** $4x = -44$
$x + 3 - 3 = 8 - 3$ $\frac{4x}{4} = \frac{-44}{4}$
$x = 5$ $x = -11$

66. $-y + 8 = -2$ **67.** $3p + 4 = 2p$
$-y + 8 - 8 = -2 - 8$ $3p - 2p + 4 = 0$
$-y = -10$ $p + 4 = 0$
$(-1)(-y) = -10(-1)$ $p + 4 - 4 = 0 - 4$
$y = 10$ $p = -4$

68. $-4c + 12 = 15$
$-4c + 12 - 12 = 15 - 12$
$-4c = 3$
$\frac{-4c}{-4} = \frac{3}{-4}$
$c = -\frac{3}{4}$

69. $3(x + 2) = -6$ **70.** $ab + 6c = (3)(-2) + 6(0)$
$3x + 6 = -6$ $= -6 + 0$
$3x + 6 - 6 = -6 - 6$ $= -6$
$3x = -12$
$\frac{3x}{3} = \frac{-12}{3}$
$x = -4$

71. $a^2 + b = (3)^2 + (-2)$
$= 9 + (-2)$
$= 7$

72. $bc + ac - c^2 = (-2)(0) + (3)(0) - (0)^2$
$= 0 + 0 - 0$
$= 0$

1-3 Integration: Algebra Using Formulas

Pages 22–23 Check for Understanding

1. P represents the perimeter of a rectangle, w its width, and ℓ its length.

2. In a square all sides have equal length, so ℓ and w can be replaced by s in each formula. $A = \ell w$ becomes $A = s \cdot s$ or s^2. $P = 2\ell + 2w$ becomes $P = 2s + 2s$ or $4s$.

3. Step 1: You explore what the problem is asking.
   Step 2: You plan the solution by determining what strategy you will use to solve the problem.
   Step 3: You solve the problem using the strategy you selected.
   Step 4: You examine the solution to determine if it makes sense in the original problem.

4. See students' work.

5. $P = 2\ell + 2w$ $A = \ell w$
$= 2(4) + 2(10)$ $= (4)(10)$
$= 8 + 20$ or 28 cm $= 40$ cm^2

6. $P = 2\ell + 2w$ $A = \ell w$
$= 2(7) + 2(8.5)$ $= (7)(8.5)$
$= 14 + 17$ or 31 in. $= 59.5$ in^2

7. $A = \ell w$ **8.** $P = 2\ell + 2w$
$= 4(7)$ $= 2(3) + 2(5)$
$= 28$ $= 6 + 10$ or 16

9. $I = prt$ **10.** $d = rt$
$\frac{I}{pr} = t$ $\frac{d}{r} = t$
$t = \frac{42}{350(0.06)}$
$t = 2$

11. $\frac{T - t}{5} = d$
$T - t = 5d$
$T = 5d + t$

12–13. The maximum area of a rectangle with a given perimeter is found by using a square in which $\ell = w = s$.

12. $4s = 24$ $A = s^2$
$s = 6$ mm $= 6^2$ or 36 mm^2

13. $4s = 36$ $A = s^2$
$s = 9$ mi $= 9^2$ or 81 mi^2

14a. $F = \frac{9}{5}C + 32$
$= \frac{9}{5}(18) + 32$
$= 32.4 + 32$ or 64.4
The average temperature in degrees is about 64°.

14b. $\ell = \frac{c}{2.54}$
$= \frac{8.6}{2.54}$ or ≈ 3.4 in.

Pages 23–25 Exercises

15. $P = 2\ell + 2w$ $A = \ell w$
$= 2(3) + 2(10)$ $= 3(10)$
$= 6 + 20$ or 26 m $= 30$ m^2

16. $P = 2\ell + 2w$ $A = \ell w$
$= 2(3) + 2(6)$ $= 3(6)$
$= 6 + 12$ or 18 in. $= 18$ in^2

17. $P = 2\ell + 2w$ $A = \ell w$
$= 2(2.5) + 2(2.5)$ $= (2.5)(2.5)$
$= 10$ cm $= 6.25$ cm^2

18. $P = 2\ell + 2w$ $A = \ell w$
$= 2(1) + 2(12)$ $= 1(12)$
$= 2 + 24$ or 26 yd $= 12$ yd^2

19. $P = 2\ell + 2w$ $A = \ell w$
$= 2\left(1\frac{1}{2}\right) + 2\left(5\frac{1}{2}\right)$ $= \left(1\frac{1}{2}\right)\left(5\frac{1}{2}\right)$
$= 3 + 11$ or 14 mi $= 8\frac{1}{4}$ or 8.25 mi^2

20. $P = 2\ell + 2w$ $A = \ell w$
$= 2(1.65) + 2(1.65)$ $= (1.65)(1.65)$
$= 3.30 + 3.30$ $= 2.7225$ cm^2
$= 6.60$ cm

21. $P = 2\ell + 2w$ **22.** $P = 2\ell + 2w$
$= 2(7) + 2(3)$ $= 2(4.5) + 2(1.5)$
$= 14 + 6$ or 20 $= 9 + 3$ or 12

23. $A = \ell w$ **24.** $A = \ell w$
$= (8)(4)$ or 32 $= (2.2)(1.1)$ or 2.42

25. $A = \ell w$
$36 = 6\ell$
$\frac{36}{6} = \ell$
$6 = \ell$

26. $A = \ell w$
$30 = 12w$
$\frac{30}{12} = w$
$2.5 = w$

27. $A = \ell w$
$34 = 2\ell$
$\frac{34}{2} = \ell$
$17 = \ell$

28. $A = \ell w$
$3\frac{1}{2} = \frac{1}{2}\ell$
$\frac{3\frac{1}{2}}{\frac{1}{2}} = \ell$
$7 = \ell$

29. $P = 2\ell + 2w$
$84 = 2(12) + 2w$
$84 = 24 + 2w$
$60 = 2w$
$\frac{60}{2} = w$
$30 = w$

30. $P = 2\ell + 2w$
$13 = 2\ell + 2(2.5)$
$13 = 2\ell + 5$
$8 = 2\ell$
$\frac{8}{2} = \ell$
$4 = \ell$

31–36. The maximum area of a rectangle with a given perimeter is found by using a square.

31. $4s = 28$ $A = s^2$
$s = 7$ in. $= 7^2$ or 49 in^2

32. $4s = 44$ $A = s^2$
$s = 11$ cm $= 11^2$ or 121 cm^2

33. $4s = 32$ $A = s^2$
$s = 8$ ft $= 8^2$ or 64 ft^2

34. $4s = 26$ $A = s^2$
$s = 6.5$ m $= (6.5)^2$ or 42.25 m^2

35. $4s = 15$ $A = s^2$
$s = 3\frac{3}{4}$ yd $= \left(3\frac{3}{4}\right)^2$ or $14\frac{1}{16}$ yd^2

36. $4s = 5$ $A = s^2$
$s = 1.25$ mm $= (1.25)^2$ or 1.5625 mm^2

37. $A = \frac{1}{2}bh$
$= \frac{1}{2}(10)(12)$
$= 60$ units^2

38. $C = \frac{5}{9}(F - 32)$
$= \frac{5}{9}(212 - 32)$
$= \frac{5}{9}(180)$ or $100°$C

39. $V = \ell wh$
$= (3.5)(4)(1.25)$ or 17.5 units^3

40. $P = 24$ inches; make a table of possible lengths and widths that yield an area of 36 in^2. The least perimeter is a square with sides 6 inches long.

41. Let ℓ represent the length of the side opposite the barn and w represent the lengths of the other two sides of the corral. $\ell + 2w = 195$ and we want to maximize $A = \ell w$. Make a table.

w	ℓ	A
5	185	925
25	145	3625
35	125	4375
40	115	4600
45	105	4725
48.75	97.5	4753.125
50	95	4750
55	85	4675

The maximum area is 4753.125 ft^2. It is achieved when the width is 48.75 feet and the length is 97.5 feet. The result may be verified by graphing.

42. $5 \cdot 8 \cdot 1200$ or $48{,}000$ dots

43a. Perimeter of A = $2(30) + 2(60)$ or 180 ft.
Perimeter of B = $4(42.2)$ or 168.8 ft. Perimeter of C = $45 + 57 + 25 + 37 + 20$ or 204 ft.
House B has the least amount of exterior walls.

43b. Area A = $(30)(60) = 1800$ ft^2
Area B = $(42.2)(42.2) \approx 1781$ ft^2
Area C = $20(20) + 57(25) = 1825$ ft^2
House C has the greatest living area.

44. Sample answer: W, X, U, or V

45. Sample answers: $\overleftrightarrow{ST}$, $\overleftrightarrow{SV}$, $\overleftrightarrow{SR}$

46. $\overleftrightarrow{XY}$

47a. $(1, 3)$ **47b.** $(-1, 1)$ **47c.** $(4, -2)$

48.

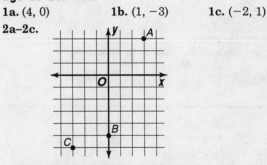

49. $4x(x + 3) + 3x^2 - 5x = 4x^2 + 12x + 3x^2 - 5x$
$= 4x^2 + 3x^2 + 12x - 5x$
$= 7x^2 + 7x$

50. $3x + 4x - 9x + 2 = -2x + 2$

51. $6c + 7d + 2c - 10d = 6c + 2c + 7d - 10d$
$= 8c - 3d$

52. $a^2b + 3a^2b - b + a^2 = 4a^2b - b + a^2$

Page 25 Self Test

1a. $(4, 0)$ **1b.** $(1, -3)$ **1c.** $(-2, 1)$

2a–2c.

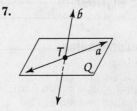

3. $\overleftrightarrow{MN}$, $\overleftrightarrow{NM}$, $\overleftrightarrow{OM}$, $\overleftrightarrow{MO}$, $\overleftrightarrow{ON}$, $\overleftrightarrow{NO}$, line q

4. Yes; they all lie on line AD.

5. No; any three of the points are coplanar, but the fourth does not lie in the same plane as the other three.

6. four: ABC, ACD, BCD, ABD

7.

8.
$$S = 3L - 26$$
$$12\tfrac{1}{2} = 3L - 26$$
$$38\tfrac{1}{2} = 3L$$
$$\frac{38\tfrac{1}{2}}{3} = L$$
$$12\tfrac{5}{6} \text{ in.} = L$$

9.
$$P = 2\ell + 2w$$
$$= 2(22.5) + 2(8)$$
$$= 45 + 16$$
$$= 61 \text{ km}$$

10. The rectangle is a square.
$$4s = 48 \qquad A = s^2$$
$$s = 12 \qquad = 12^2$$
$$= 144 \text{ m}^2$$

1-4A Using Technology Measuring Segments

1. any numbers

2. centimeters or millimeters

3. The calculator shows the measurement of the entire segment containing $\overline{EA}$, not just $\overline{EA}$.

4. It changes with the length of the new segment.

5. Sample answer:

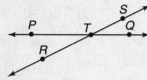

6. Sample answer:

7. Sample answer:

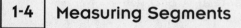

8. Sample answer:

A ———————— B

C ———————— D

9. Sample answer:

2.68 cm
X ———————— Y

10. See students' work.

1-4 Measuring Segments

Pages 32–33 Check for Understanding

1. $XY + YZ = XZ$

2. The measure of the longest side is c, and a and b are the measures of the other two sides. The designation of a and b to a particular side for the Pythagorean Theorem is not important.

---

3. AB is the measure of $\overline{AB}$.

4. E lies between D and F.

5. $AC = |-5 - 3| = |-8| = 8$ units

6. $BD = |-1 - 7| = |-8| = 8$ units

7. $HK = HJ + JK$
$$= 17 + 6 \text{ or } 23$$

8. $MP = |4 - (-4)| = |8| = 8$

9. $NP = \sqrt{(3-5)^2 + (-1-(-4))^2}$
$$= \sqrt{(-2)^2 + (3)^2}$$
$$= \sqrt{4 + 9}$$
$$= \sqrt{13}$$
$$\approx 3.61$$

10. $QR = \sqrt{(0-(-3))^2 + (-1-(-4))^2}$
$$= \sqrt{(-3)^2 + (3)^2}$$
$$= \sqrt{9 + 9}$$
$$= \sqrt{18}$$
$$\approx 4.24$$

11. $NP \angle QR$

12. $(XZ)^2 = (XY)^2 + (ZY)^2$
$$(XZ)^2 = 5^2 + 122$$
$$(XZ)^2 = 25 + 144$$
$$(XZ)^2 = 169$$
$$XZ = \sqrt{169} \text{ or } 13$$

13. $RW + WS = RS$
$$(4n - 3) + (6n + 2) = (7n + 8)$$
$$10n - 1 = 7n + 8$$
$$3n = 9$$
$$n = 3$$
$$WS = 6n + 2$$
$$= 6(3) + 2$$
$$= 18 + 2 \text{ or } 20$$

14. PQ, TU, RS

15a.

416 ft

1128 ft

15b. $x^2 = 416^2 + 1128^2$
$$x^2 = 1{,}445{,}440$$
$$x = \sqrt{1{,}445{,}440} \approx 1202 \text{ feet}$$

Pages 33–35 Exercises

16. $AE = |-9 - 1| = |-10| = 10$

17. $BD = |-6 - (-2)| = |-6 + 2| = |-4| = 4$

18. $EC = |-5 - 1| = |-6| = 6$

19. $EG = |1 - 6| = |-5| = 5$

20. $FC = |-5 - 5| = |-10| = 10$

21. $CA = |-9 - (-5)| = |-9 + 5| = |-4| = 4$

22. $RS + TR = TS$
$$6 + 4.5 = TS$$
$$10.5 = TS$$

23. $SR + RT = ST$
$$3\tfrac{2}{3} + 1\tfrac{2}{3} = ST$$
$$5\tfrac{1}{3} = ST$$

24. $SR + RT = ST$
$$6 + RT = 15$$
$$RT = 9$$

25. $TR + RS = TS$
$$3.4 + RS = 11.75$$
$$RS = 8.35$$

26. $BG = \sqrt{(10 - 5)^2 + [-1 - (-1)]^2}$
$= \sqrt{5^2 + 0^2}$
$= \sqrt{25}$ or 5

27. $HC = \sqrt{[-3 - (-3)]^2 + (-3 - 6)^2}$
$= \sqrt{0^2 + (-9)^2}$
$= \sqrt{81}$ or 9

28. $GH = \sqrt{[10 - (-3)]^2 + (-1 - 6)^2}$
$= \sqrt{13^2 + (-7)^2}$
$= \sqrt{218} \approx 14.76$

29. $EG = \sqrt{(9 - 10)^2 + [-2 - (-1)]^2}$
$= \sqrt{(-1)^2 + (-1)^2}$
$= \sqrt{2} \approx 1.41$

30. $FJ = \sqrt{(0 - 3)^2 + (1 - 5)^2}$
$= \sqrt{(-3)^2 + (-4)^2}$
$= \sqrt{25}$ or 5

31. $JC = \sqrt{[0 - (-3)]^2 + [1 - (-3)]^2}$
$= \sqrt{(-3)^2 + (-4)^2}$
$= \sqrt{25}$ or 5

32. $GB < GF$ **33.** $FJ = JC$ **34.** $AC > AD$

35. $x^2 = 6^2 + 8^2$ **36.** $x^2 = 60^2 + 11^2$
$x^2 = 36 + 64$ $x^2 = 3600 + 121$
$x^2 = 100$ $x^2 = 3721$
$x = \sqrt{100}$ or 10 $x = \sqrt{3721}$ or 61

37. $x^2 = 1^2 + 1^2$
$x^2 = 1 + 1$
$x^2 = 2$
$x = \sqrt{2} \approx 1.414$

38. $TU + UB = TB$ $TU = 2x$
$2x + (3x + 1) = 21$ $= 2(4)$ or 8
$5x + 1 = 21$
$5x = 20$
$x = 4$

39. $TU + UB = TB$ $TU = 4x - 1$
$(4x - 1) + (2x - 1) = 5x$ $= 4(2) - 1$
$6x - 2 = 5x$ $= 8 - 1$ or 7
$x = 2$

40. $TU + UB = TB$ $TU = 1 - x$
$(1 - x) + (4x + 17) = -3x$ $= 1 - (-3)$
$3x + 18 = -3x$ $= 1 + 3$ or 4
$18 = -6x$
$-3 = x$

41.
X   Y

42.
X   Y

43.
X Y

44.
X   Y

45a.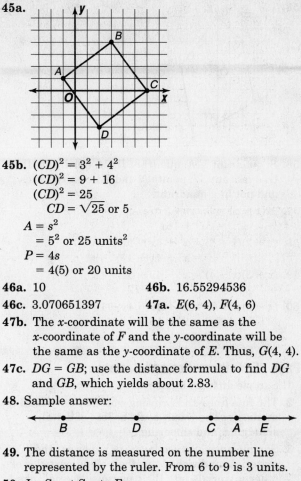

45b. $(CD)^2 = 3^2 + 4^2$
$(CD)^2 = 9 + 16$
$(CD)^2 = 25$
$CD = \sqrt{25}$ or 5
$A = s^2$
$= 5^2$ or 25 units^2
$P = 4s$
$= 4(5)$ or 20 units

46a. 10   **46b.** 16.55294536
46c. 3.070651397   **47a.** $E(6, 4)$, $F(4, 6)$
47b. The x-coordinate will be the same as the x-coordinate of F and the y-coordinate will be the same as the y-coordinate of E. Thus, $G(4, 4)$.
47c. $DG = GB$; use the distance formula to find DG and GB, which yields about 2.83.
48. Sample answer:

B   D   C A E

49. The distance is measured on the number line represented by the ruler. From 6 to 9 is 3 units.
50. JanSport Santa Fe

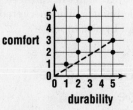

51. $A = \ell w$
$15 = \ell(2.5)$
$\frac{15}{2.5} = \ell$
$6 \text{ cm} = \ell$

52. The rectangle yielding the maximum area is a square.
$P = 4s$
$8 = 4s$
$2 = s$
$A = s^2$
$= 2^2$ or 4 mi^2

53.

54. $\overleftrightarrow{AE}$, $\overleftrightarrow{AD}$, $\overleftrightarrow{AC}$, $\overleftrightarrow{AB}$, $\overleftrightarrow{BC}$, $\overleftrightarrow{BD}$, $\overleftrightarrow{BE}$, $\overleftrightarrow{CD}$, $\overleftrightarrow{CE}$, $\overleftrightarrow{DE}$

55.

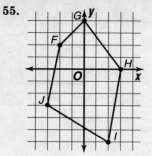

56. S: quadrant I, E: quadrant II, M: quadrant III, G: quadrant IV; points N and T lie on the axes and not in a quadrant.

57. $3x(x + 6) = 3x(x) + 3x(6)$
$\qquad = 3x^2 + 18x$

58. $(x + 2)(x + 2) = x^2 + 2x + 2x + 4$
$\qquad = x^2 + 4x + 4$

59. $(x + 3)(x - 4) = x^2 - 4x + 3x - 12$
$\qquad = x^2 - x - 12$

60. $(x - 4)(x + 4) = x^2 + 4x - 4x - 16$
$\qquad = x^2 - 16$

Page 35 Mathematics and Society

1. Sample answer: by its feel

2. The fine lines and printing would be very hard to duplicate. The result could be loss of detail, smudging, and smearing.

3. Sample answers: use layers of paper or other material sandwiched together; blend particles of other materials into the paper; use special inks that are visible only in ultraviolet or infrared light; using holographic images; use encrypted codes that could be read by a scanner.

1-5 Midpoints and Segment Congruence

Page 36 Modeling Mathematics

a. AC should equal CB.

b. See students' work.

c. Sample answer: The midpoint separates a segment into two segments of equal length.

Pages 40–41 Check for Understanding

1. You can (1) use geometric software to draw a segment and then locate its midpoint automatically; (2) draw a segment on paper and fold the paper so that the endpoints match so that the intersection of the fold and the segment is the midpoint; and (3) use compass and straightedge to construct the segment that bisects the segment. If the segment is graphed on a number line or coordinate plane, there are formulas you can use to find the coordinate(s) of the midpoint.

2. Jadine is correct only if D, E, and F are collinear. Angle DEF is a counterexample.

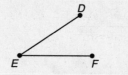

3. Every segment has only one midpoint. However, there are an infinite number of lines, segments, and planes that pass through the point that is the midpoint. So, each segment has an infinite number of bisectors.

4. Since R is the midpoint of $\overline{QS}$, then $QR = RS$. Substitute $8 - x$ for QR and $5x - 10$ for RS and solve the equation. The solution is $x = 3$.

5. Sample answer: Fold the rectangle matching the horizontal sides exactly and fold again, matching the vertical sides exactly.

6. $\dfrac{a + b}{2} = \dfrac{-3 + 2}{2}$
$\qquad = -\dfrac{1}{2}$ or -0.5

The coordinate of the midpoint of $\overline{PQ}$ is -0.5.

7. True; because $SQ = QR = 3$.

8. False; $PS = 2$, $QR = 3$, $2 \neq 3$

9. $\left(\dfrac{x_1 + x_2}{2}, \dfrac{y_1 + y_2}{2} \right) = \left(\dfrac{-2 + 5}{2}, \dfrac{-3 + -1}{2} \right)$
$\qquad = \left(\dfrac{3}{2}, \dfrac{-4}{2} \right)$
$\qquad = (1.5, -2)$

10. $\left(\dfrac{x_1 + x_2}{2}, \dfrac{y_1 + y_2}{2} \right) = \left(\dfrac{-4 + 1}{2}, \dfrac{3 + (-1)}{2} \right)$
$\qquad = \left(\dfrac{-3}{2}, \dfrac{2}{2} \right)$
$\qquad = (-1.5, 1)$

11. See students' work.

12. $\left(\dfrac{x_1 + x_2}{2}, \dfrac{y_1 + y_2}{2} \right) = (2.5)$

$\dfrac{x_1 + x_2}{2} = 2 \qquad\qquad \dfrac{y_1 + y_2}{2} = 5$

$\dfrac{-1 + x_2}{2} = 2 \qquad\qquad \dfrac{8 + y_2}{2} = 5$

$-1 + x_2 = 4 \qquad\qquad 8 + y_2 = 10$

$x_2 = 5 \qquad\qquad\qquad y_2 = 2$

The coordinates of S are $(5, 2)$.

13a. $DE = EB$
$2x + 5 = 13 - 2x$
$\qquad 4x = 8$
$\qquad x = 2$

$DB = DE + EB$
$\qquad = (2x + 5) + (13 - 2x)$
$\qquad = 18$

13b. $AC = 2(EC)$
$x + 3 = 2(3x - 1)$
$x + 3 = 6x - 2$
$\qquad 5 = 5x$
$\qquad 1 = x$

$EA + EC = AC$
$\qquad EA = AC - EC$
$\qquad\quad = x + 3 - (3x - 1)$
$\qquad\quad = -2x + 4$
$\qquad\quad = -2(1) + 4$ or 2

14. By the definition of midpoint, if B is the midpoint of $\overline{DF}$, then $DB = \frac{1}{2}DF$. By the same reason, since E is the midpoint of $\overline{DB}$, then $DE = \frac{1}{2}DB$. Using substitution, $DE = \frac{1}{2}\left(\frac{1}{2}DF\right)$ or $\frac{1}{2}DF$.

Pages 41–43 Exercises

15. $\frac{a+b}{2} = \frac{-5+1}{2} = \frac{-4}{2} = -2$

16. $\frac{a+b}{2} = \frac{-1+5}{2} = \frac{4}{2} = 2$

17. $\frac{a+b}{2} = \frac{-5+(-2)}{2} = \frac{-7}{2} = -3.5$

18. True (because $GI = 6$ and $HJ = 6$)

19. False; sample answer: E is the midpoint of $\overline{HJ}$.

20. False; sample answer: $\overline{AC}$ bisects $\overline{GI}$.

21. True (because $EJ = 3$ and $CI = 3$)

22. True (because $HE = 3$ and $EJ = 3$)

23. True (because $CH = 1$ and $HI = 2$)

24. $\frac{a+b}{2} = \frac{4+(-6)}{2} = \frac{-2}{2} = -1$

The coordinate of W is -1.

25. $-3 = \frac{a+b}{2}$
$-3 = \frac{12+b}{2}$
$-6 = 12 + b$
$-18 = b$
The coordinate of S is -18.

26. $-4 = \frac{a+b}{2}$
$-4 = \frac{2+b}{2}$
$-8 = 2 + b$
$-10 = b$
The coordinate of R is -10.

27. $\left(\frac{x_1+x_2}{2}, \frac{y_1+y_2}{2}\right) = \left(\frac{5+(-1)}{2}, \frac{5+5}{2}\right)$
$= \left(\frac{4}{2}, \frac{10}{2}\right)$
$= (2, 5)$
The coordinates of Y are $(2, 5)$.

28. $\left(\frac{x_1+x_2}{2}, \frac{y_1+y_2}{2}\right) = (-1, 5)$

$\frac{x_1+x_2}{2} = -1$
$\frac{-4+x_2}{2} = -1$
$-4 + x_2 = -2$
$x_2 = 2$

$\frac{y_1+y_2}{2} = 5$
$\frac{3+y_2}{2} = 5$
$3 + y_2 = 10$
$y_2 = 7$

The coordinates of Z are $(2, 7)$.

29. $\left(\frac{x_1+x_2}{2}, \frac{y_1+y_2}{2}\right) = (-2, 2)$

$\frac{x_1+x_2}{2} = -2$
$\frac{2+x_2}{2} = -2$
$2 + x_2 = -4$
$x_2 = -6$

$\frac{y_1+y_2}{2} = 2$
$\frac{8+y_2}{2} = 2$
$8 + y_2 = 4$
$y_2 = -4$

The coordinates of X are $(-6, -4)$.

30. $\left(\frac{x_1+x_2}{2}, \frac{y_1+y_2}{2}\right) = (0, 5.5)$

$\frac{x_1+x_2}{2} = 0$
$\frac{-3+x_2}{2} = 0$
$-3 + x_2 = 0$
$x_2 = 3$

$\frac{y_1+y_2}{2} = 5.5$
$\frac{6+y_2}{2} = 5.5$
$6 + y_2 = 11$
$y_2 = 5$

The coordinates of X are $(3, 5)$.

31. $\left(\frac{x_1+x_2}{2}, \frac{y_1+y_2}{2}\right) = \left(\frac{5}{3}, 3\right)$

$\frac{x_1+x_2}{2} = \frac{5}{3}$
$\frac{\frac{2}{3}+x_2}{2} = \frac{5}{3}$
$\frac{2}{3} + y_2 = \frac{10}{3}$
$x_2 = \frac{8}{3}$

$\frac{y_1+y_2}{2} = 3$
$\frac{-5+y_2}{2} = 3$
$-5 + y_2 = 6$
$y_2 = 11$

The coordinates of Z are $\left(\frac{8}{3}, 11\right)$.

32. $\left(\frac{x_1+x_2}{2}, \frac{y_1+y_2}{2}\right) = \left(\frac{1}{2}, -6\frac{1}{2}\right)$

$\frac{x_1+x_2}{2} = \frac{1}{2}$
$\frac{2+x_2}{2} = \frac{1}{2}$
$2 + x_2 = 1$
$x_2 = -1$

$\frac{y_1+y_2}{2} = -6\frac{1}{2}$
$\frac{-10+y_2}{2} = -6\frac{1}{2}$
$-10 + y_2 = -13$
$y_2 = -3$

The coordinates of Z are $(-1, -3)$.

33. $AB = BC$
$3x + 6 = 2x + 14$
$x = 8$
$AC = AB + BC$
$\quad = 3x + 6 + 2x + 14$
$\quad = 5x + 20$
$\quad = 5(8) + 20$
$\quad = 40 + 20$
$\quad = 60$

34. $AC = CD$
$5x - 8 = 16 - 3x$
$8x = 24$
$x = 3$
$AD = AC + CD$
$\quad = 5x - 8 + 16 - 3x$
$\quad = 2x + 8$
$\quad = 2(3) + 8$
$\quad = 14$

35. $2(AC) = AC$
$2(4x - 3) = 6x - 4$
$8x - 6 = 6x - 4$
$2x = 2$
$x = 1$
$CD = AC$
$\quad = 4x - 3$
$\quad = 4(1) - 3$
$\quad = 4 - 3$
$\quad = 1$

36. $AC = 2(BC)$
$3x - 1 = 2(12 - x)$
$3x - 1 = 24 - 2x$
$5x = 25$
$x = 5$
$AB = BC$
$\quad = 12 - x$
$\quad = 12 - 5$
$\quad = 7$

37. $AD = 4(BC)$
$5x + 2 = 4(7 - 2x)$
$5x + 2 = 28 - 8x$
$13x = 26$
$x = 2$
$CD = 2(BC)$
$\quad = 2(7 - 2x)$
$\quad = 14 - 4x$
$\quad = 14 - 4(2)$
$\quad = 6$

38. $CD = 2(AB)$
$25 + 5x = 2(4x + 17)$
$25 + 5x = 8x + 34$
$-9 = 3x$
$-3 = x$
$BC = AB$
$\quad = 4x + 17$
$\quad = 4(-3) + 17$
$\quad = 5$

39. $AC = \frac{1}{2}\left[\frac{1}{2}\left(\frac{1}{2}AB\right)\right]$
$\quad = \frac{1}{8}AB$

Drawing shown at $\frac{2}{5}$ scale.

40. Let D be the midpoint of $\overline{AB}$.

$D\left(\frac{x_1 + x_2}{2}, \frac{y_1 + y_2}{2}\right) = D\left(\frac{8 + (-4)}{2}, \frac{12 + 0}{2}\right)$

$\qquad\qquad\qquad\quad = D\left(\frac{4}{2}, \frac{12}{2}\right)$

$\qquad\qquad\qquad\quad = D(2, 6)$

C is the midpoint of $\overline{AD}$.

$C\left(\frac{x_1 + x_2}{2}, \frac{y_1 + y_2}{2}\right) = C\left(\frac{8 + 2}{2}, \frac{6 + 12}{2}\right)$

$\qquad\qquad\qquad\quad = C\left(\frac{10}{2}, \frac{18}{2}\right)$

$\qquad\qquad\qquad\quad = C(5, 9)$

41. x change: $\frac{8 - 2}{3} = \frac{6}{3} = 2$

y change: $\frac{-9 - 3}{3} = \frac{-12}{3} = -4$

From P to $R = P(2, 3) \rightarrow R(2 + 2, 3 - 4)$ or $R(4, -1)$

From R to $S = R(4, -1) \rightarrow S(4 + 2, -1 - 4)$ or $S(6, -5)$

42. If E is the midpoint of $\overline{FG}$ and $\overline{HI}$, then $FE = \frac{1}{2}FG$ and $HE = \frac{1}{2}HI$. Since $\overline{FG} \cong \overline{HI}$, then $FG = HI$. If each side is multiplied by $\frac{1}{2}$, the result is $\frac{1}{2}FG = \frac{1}{2}HI$. Substitute values and the result is $FE = HE$.

43.

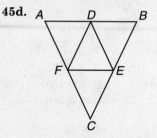

By the Segment Addition Postulate, we know that $SP = SE + EP$ and $SE = ST + TE$. By substituting for SE in the first equation, $SP = ST + TE + EP$.

44a–c. See students' work.

45a–c. See students' work.

45d.

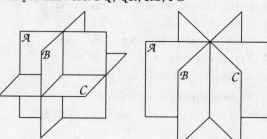

The perimeter of the larger triangle is twice that of the smaller triangle.

45e. The area of the larger triangle is 4 times that of the smaller triangle. Sample answer: If you make four copies of the small triangle, you can fit them on the surface of the large triangle.

46. $\frac{12 - 1.5}{2} = \frac{10.5}{2} = 5.25$ cm

47. $\frac{128 + 184}{2} = \frac{312}{2} = 156 + 3 = 159$

The exit number for the Hays exit is 159.

48. Sample answer:

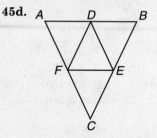

49a. path 1: 8 units; path 2: 8 units;

path 3 $= \sqrt{(-3 - 2)^2 + (-1 - 2)^2}$

$\qquad\quad = \sqrt{(-5)^2 + (-3)^2}$

$\qquad\quad = \sqrt{25 + 9} = \sqrt{34}$

$\qquad\quad \approx 5.83$ units

49b. path 3, because you cannot drive diagonally through city blocks

50. $\sqrt{24^2 + 40^2} = \sqrt{2176} \approx 47$ inches

51a.

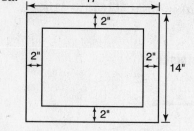

51b. $(14 - 4)(17 - 4) = 10(13)$

$\qquad\qquad\qquad\qquad\quad = 130 \text{ in}^2$

52. Sample answers: $\overrightarrow{PQ}, \overrightarrow{QR}, \overrightarrow{RS}, \overrightarrow{PS}$

53.

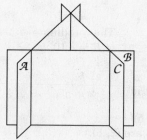

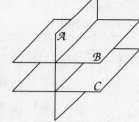

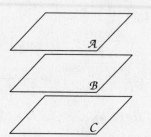

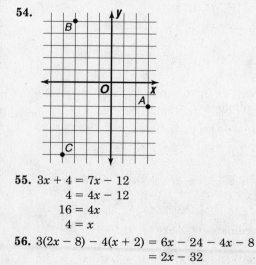

54.

55. $3x + 4 = 7x - 12$

$\qquad\quad 4 = 4x - 12$

$\qquad 16 = 4x$

$\qquad\quad 4 = x$

56. $3(2x - 8) - 4(x + 2) = 6x - 24 - 4x - 8$

$\qquad\qquad\qquad\qquad\qquad\quad = 2x - 32$

Page 49 Check for Understanding

1. two

2. A straight angle is formed by two collinear, not noncollinear, rays.

3. True; all right angles measure 90° and the definition of congruent is that they have the same measure.

4.

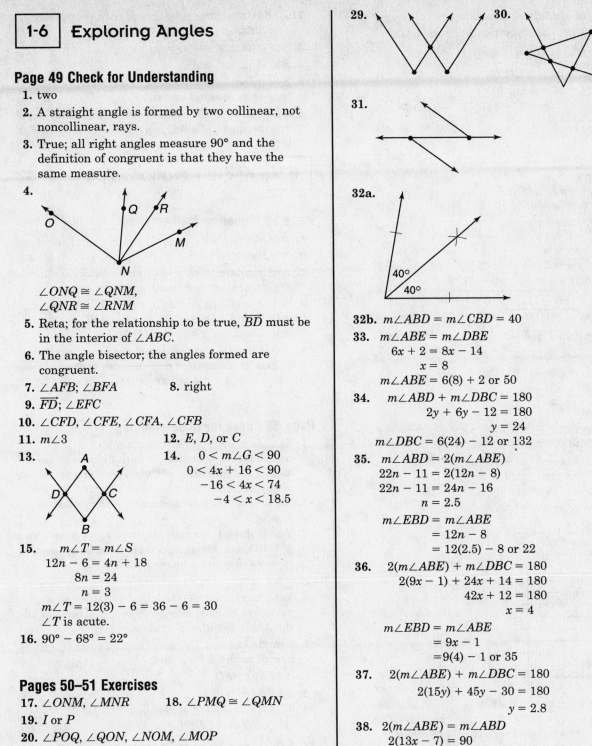

$\angle ONQ \cong \angle QNM$,
$\angle QNR \cong \angle RNM$

5. Reta; for the relationship to be true, $\overleftrightarrow{BD}$ must be in the interior of $\angle ABC$.

6. The angle bisector; the angles formed are congruent.

7. $\angle AFB$; $\angle BFA$ **8.** right

9. $\overrightarrow{FD}$; $\angle EFC$

10. $\angle CFD$, $\angle CFE$, $\angle CFA$, $\angle CFB$

11. $m\angle 3$ **12.** E, D, or C

13.

14. $0 < m\angle G < 90$
$0 < 4x + 16 < 90$
$-16 < 4x < 74$
$-4 < x < 18.5$

15. $m\angle T = m\angle S$
$12n - 6 = 4n + 18$
$8n = 24$
$n = 3$
$m\angle T = 12(3) - 6 = 36 - 6 = 30$
$\angle T$ is acute.

16. $90° - 68° = 22°$

Pages 50–51 Exercises

17. $\angle ONM$, $\angle MNR$ **18.** $\angle PMQ \cong \angle QMN$

19. I or P

20. $\angle POQ$, $\angle QON$, $\angle NOM$, $\angle MOP$

21. obtuse

22. Sample answer: $\overrightarrow{MJ}$ and $\overrightarrow{MN}$

23. $\angle NML$, $\angle NMK$, $\angle NMJ$, $\angle NMP$, $\angle NMO$

24. Sample answer: $\angle LMN$

25. $m\angle PMN = m\angle PMO + m\angle OMN$
$\quad\quad = 55 + 65$ or 120

26. No; more than one angle has P as a vertex, so naming an angle as $\angle P$ would create confusion.

27. $\angle JMQ$ and $\angle NMK$

28. No; while both are rays that contain P and N, $\overrightarrow{PN}$ is a ray whose endpoint is P and $\overrightarrow{NP}$ is a ray whose endpoint is N.

29.   **30.**

31.

32a.

$40°$
$40°$

32b. $m\angle ABD = m\angle CBD = 40$

33. $m\angle ABE = m\angle DBE$
$6x + 2 = 8x - 14$
$x = 8$
$m\angle ABE = 6(8) + 2$ or 50

34. $m\angle ABD + m\angle DBC = 180$
$2y + 6y - 12 = 180$
$y = 24$
$m\angle DBC = 6(24) - 12$ or 132

35. $m\angle ABD = 2(m\angle ABE)$
$22n - 11 = 2(12n - 8)$
$22n - 11 = 24n - 16$
$n = 2.5$
$m\angle EBD = m\angle ABE$
$\quad\quad = 12n - 8$
$\quad\quad = 12(2.5) - 8$ or 22

36. $2(m\angle ABE) + m\angle DBC = 180$
$2(9x - 1) + 24x + 14 = 180$
$42x + 12 = 180$
$x = 4$
$m\angle EBD = m\angle ABE$
$\quad\quad = 9x - 1$
$\quad\quad = 9(4) - 1$ or 35

37. $2(m\angle ABE) + m\angle DBC = 180$
$2(15y) + 45y - 30 = 180$
$y = 2.8$

38. $2(m\angle ABE) = m\angle ABD$
$2(13x - 7) = 90$
$26x - 14 = 90$
$x = 4$

39a. 1, 3, 6, 10, 15

39b. For 4 rays, there are $(4 \cdot 3) \div 2$ or 6 angles.
For 5 rays, there are $(5 \cdot 4) \div 2$ or 10 angles.
For 6 rays, there are $(6 \cdot 5) \div 2$ or 15 angles.

39c. For 7 rays, $(7 \cdot 6) \div 2$ or 21 angles.
For 10 rays, $(10 \cdot 9) \div 2$ or 45 angles.

39d. $a = \frac{n(n-1)}{2}$, for a = number of angles and n = number of noncollinear rays

40. measure of angle of reflection

$= \frac{1}{2}(m\angle IBR) = \frac{1}{2}(78) = 39$

$m\angle IBN = m\angle NBR = 39$

$m\angle IBA = 90 - m\angle IBN$

$m\angle IBA = 90 - 39 \text{ or } 51$

41a. acute   **41b.** $20 - 5 = 15$

42. $\left(\frac{x_1 + x_2}{2}, \frac{y_1 + y_2}{2}\right) = (-4, 2)$

$\frac{5 + x_2}{2} = -4$ $\frac{-3 + y_2}{2} = 2$

$5 + x_2 = -8$ $-3 + y_2 = 4$

$x_2 = -13$ $y_2 = 7$

B has coordinates $(-13, 7)$.

43. $FG + GH = FH$

$8x + 2 + 6 = 16$

$8x = 8$

$x = 1$

$FG = 8(1) + 2 = 10$

44. $PQ = \sqrt{(-3 - 12)^2 + (10 - (-6))^2}$

$= \sqrt{(-15)^2 + (16)^2}$

$= \sqrt{225 + 256}$

$= \sqrt{481} \approx 21.93$

45. $P = 2\ell + 2w$

$27 = 2(8) + 2w$

$27 = 16 + 2w$

$11 = 2w$

$5.5 = w$

The width is 5.5 mm.

46. Sample answer:

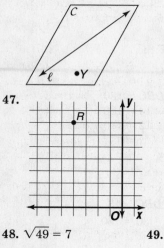

47.

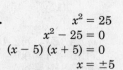

48. $\sqrt{49} = 7$ **49.** $\;\;\;\;\;\;\;\;\;\; x^2 = 25$

$x^2 - 25 = 0$

$(x - 5)(x + 5) = 0$

$x = \pm 5$

---

         12   *Geometry* Chapter 1

2b. The sum of the measures of each pair of angles in a linear pair is 180.

3. See students' work.

4. See students' work.

5. Regardless of the position of the lines, vertical angles have equal measures.

6. Regardless of the position of the lines, the sum of the measures of a linear pair of angles is 180.

1-7   Angle Relationships

Page 54 Modeling Mathematics

a. $\angle ACE \cong \angle DCB$

b. See students' work.

c. $\angle ACE$ and $\angle DCB$; $\angle DCA$ and $\angle BCE$; their measures are equal.

d. $\angle ACE$ and $\angle BCE$; $\angle BCE$ and $\angle DCB$; $\angle DCB$ and $\angle DCA$; $\angle DCA$ and $\angle ACE$; the sum of their measures is 180.

e. Regardless of the position of the lines, vertical angles are congruent and the sum of the measures of a linear pair is 180.

Page 58 Check for Understanding

1. Sample answer: Supplementary and complementary angles are both defined by the sum of the measures of the angles. The measures of supplementary angles have a sum of 180 and the measures of complementary angles have a sum of 90.

2. Yes; if the measures of the two angles have a sum of 180, their non-shared sides must be opposite rays, so they are a linear pair.

3. $n + \ell$

4. Yes, they lie on the same line; no, since no angle measures or markings are given; yes, because of the Angle Addition Postulate.

5. Sample answer: The non-common sides of a linear pair of angles form a line.

6. $\angle AFE$, $\angle BFD$ **7.** $\overline{AD}$

8. $\angle EFA$ or $\angle DFB$

9. $\angle AFB$ and $\angle BFC$, $\angle BFC$ and $\angle CFD$, or $\angle CFD$ and $\angle DFE$

10. $\angle BFA$

11. No, because there are no markings or measures given to indicate that the segments are congruent.

12. $\;\;\;\;\; m\angle N + m\angle M = 90$

$(8x - 6) + (14x + 8) = 90$

$22x = 88$

$x = 4$

$m\angle M = 14x + 8$

$= 14(4) + 8 \text{ or } 64$

1-7A   Using Technology Angle Relationships

Page 52 Exercises

1a. $\angle CBA$ and $\angle DBE$; $\angle CBD$ and $\angle EBA$

1b. The measures of the vertical angles are equal.

2a. $\angle CBD$ and $\angle DBE$; $\angle DBE$ and $\angle EBA$; $\angle EBA$ and $\angle ABC$; $\angle ABC$ and $\angle CBD$

13. Let $x = m\angle S$. Thus, $180 - x$ = measure of its supplement.
$$x = 20 + 4(180 - x)$$
$$= 20 + 720 - 4x$$
$$= 148$$
$$m\angle S = 148$$

14. $180° - 15° = 165°$

Pages 59–60 Exercises

15. $\angle YUW$ and $\angle XUV$ or $\angle YUX$ and $\angle VUW$

16. Yes; they form a linear pair.

17. $\angle TWU$

18. $\angle YUW$ and $\angle XUV$ or $\angle YUX$ and $\angle VUW$

19. No; there are no measures or markings to indicate that right angles are present.

20. $\angle YWT$ and $\angle TWZ$, $\angle YUX$ and $\angle XUV$, $\angle XUV$ and $\angle VUW$, $\angle VUW$ and $\angle WUY$, or $\angle WUY$ and $\angle YUX$

21. congruent, adjacent, supplementary, linear pair

22. Yes; slashes on the segments indicate that they are congruent.

23. No; there is no indication that $\angle SRT$ is a 90° angle.

24. $\angle SPR$ and $\angle RPT$, $\angle RPT$ and $\angle TPQ$, or $\angle SRP$ and $\angle PRT$

25. right

26. Sample answer: $\overline{PT}$ bisects $\angle QPR$, $\overline{QT} \cong \overline{TR}$, $\angle SRQ$ is right, $\overline{PQ} \cong \overline{SR}$.

27a. perpendicular

27b. See students' work.

27c. The angle bisectors are perpendicular, because the angles formed by the two lines measure $45° + 45°$ or $90°$.

28.
$$m\angle A + m\angle B = 90$$
$$(7x + 4) + (4x + 9) = 90$$
$$11x = 77$$
$$x = 7$$
$$m\angle A = 7(7) + 4 = 53$$
$$m\angle B = 4(7) + 9 = 37$$

29. Let x = measure of angle
$180 - x$ = measure of supplement
$$x = 44 + (180 - x)$$
$$2x = 224$$
$$x = 112$$
$$180 - x = 68$$

30. Let x = measure of larger angle
$x - 12$ = measure of smaller angle
$$x + (x - 12) = 90$$
$$x = 51$$
$$x - 12 = 39$$

31.
$$m\angle T + m\angle U = 90$$
$$(16x - 9) + (4x + 3) = 90$$
$$20x = 96$$
$$x = 4.8$$
$$m\angle T = 16(4.8) - 9 = 67.8$$
$$m\angle U = 4(4.8) + 3 = 22.2$$

32.
$$m\angle N + m\angle M = 180$$
$$m\angle N = 4(m\angle M) - 5$$
$$4(m\angle M) - 5 + m\angle M = 180$$
$$m\angle M = 37$$
$$m\angle N = 4(37) - 5 = 143$$

33.
$$m\angle R + m\angle S = 90$$
$$(y - 2) + (2x + 3) = 90$$
$$2x + y = 89$$
$$\underline{3x - y = 91}$$
$$5x \quad\quad = 180$$
$$x = 36$$

$$m\angle R = y - 2$$
$$= 17 - 2 \text{ or } 15$$
$$m\angle S = 2x + 3$$
$$= 2(36) + 3 \text{ or } 75$$

$$m\angle U + m\angle V = 90$$
$$(2x - y) + (x - 1) = 90$$
$$3x - y = 91$$
$$3(36) - y = 91$$
$$y = 17$$
$$m\angle U = 2(36) - 17 \text{ or } 55$$
$$m\angle V = 36 - 1 \text{ or } 35$$

34a.

34b. Given: $\angle ABC$ and $\angle CBD$ form a linear pair; $\angle CBD$ and $\angle DBE$ form a linear pair; $m\angle CBD = 30$

Prove: $\angle ABC \cong \angle DBE$

Sample Paragraph Proof: $\angle ABC$ and $\angle CBD$ form a linear pair, and $\angle CBD$ and $\angle DBE$ form a linear pair. Since the sum of the measures of the angles in a linear pair is 180, $m\angle ABC + m\angle CBD = 180$ and $m\angle CBD + m\angle DBE = 180$. Substitute 30 for $m\angle CBD$. Thus, $m\angle ABC + 30 = 180$ and $30 + m\angle DBE = 180$. By subtracting 30 from each side, $m\angle ABC = 150$ and $m\angle DBE = 150$. Since $\angle ABC$ and $\angle DBE$ have the same measures, they are congruent. That is, $\angle ABC \cong \angle DBE$.

35. Given: $\angle PQR$ and $\angle RQS$ are complementary angles; $m\angle PQR = 45$.

Prove: $\angle PQR \cong \angle RQS$

Sample paragraph proof: Since $\angle PQR$ and $\angle RQS$ are complementary, $m\angle PQR + m\angle RQS = 90$. Susbstitute 45 for $m\angle PQR$ in the equation. This results in $45 + m\angle RQS = 90$. By subtracting 45 from each side, $m\angle PQR = 45$. Since $\angle PQR$ and $\angle QRS$ have the same measure, $\angle PQR \cong \angle QRS$.

36. There is exactly one line through X perpendicular to ℓ. Suppose there were two lines in a plane C perpendicular to line ℓ through X as shown in the figure below.

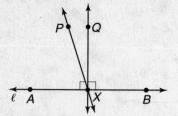

Since $\angle AXP$ and $\angle PXB$ are a linear pair, $m\angle AXP + m\angle PXB = 180$. Also, $m\angle PXB = m\angle PXQ + m\angle QXB$ by Angle Addition Postulate. Thus, $m\angle AXP + m\angle PXQ + m\angle QXB = 180$. But, $m\angle AXP = 90$ and $m\angle QXB = 90$. This means $m\angle PXQ + 180 = 180$, or $m\angle PXQ = 0$, which is not possible. Therefore, there can only be one line perpendicular to the given line through the given point on the line.

37. Sample answer: Complementary is defined as something that completes, and complementary angles complete a right angle. Supplementary is defined as something that supplements or makes an addition, and supplementary angles add up to be a straight angle.

38a. They form a linear pair.

38b.
$$m\angle ABC + m\angle CBD = 180$$
$$110 + m\angle CBD = 180$$
$$m\angle CBD = 70$$

39.
$$m\angle Q = m\angle R$$
$$8x - 17 = 7x - 3$$
$$x = 14$$
$$m\angle Q = 8x - 17$$
$$= 8(14) - 17 \text{ or } 95$$
$\angle Q$ is obtuse.

40.
$$FG = GH$$
$$12x - 11 = 5x + 10$$
$$7x = 21$$
$$x = 3$$

41.
$$5^2 + x^2 = 15^2$$
$$x^2 = 200$$
$$x = \sqrt{200}$$
$$x \approx 14 \text{ ft } 2 \text{ in.}$$

42.
$$A = \ell w$$
$$45 = 18w$$
$$\frac{45}{18} = w$$
$$w = 2.5 \text{ ft}$$

$$P = 2\ell + 2w$$
$$= 2(18) + 2(2.5)$$
$$= 41 \text{ ft}$$

43.

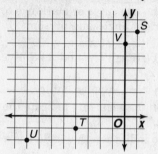

44. $3 \overset{?}{=} -2 + 4$
$3 \neq 2$
W is noncollinear with U and V.

45. $8ab^2 = 2 \cdot 2 \cdot 2 \cdot a \cdot b \cdot b$
$16a^2b = 2 \cdot 2 \cdot 2 \cdot 2 \cdot a \cdot a \cdot b$
$12ab = 2 \cdot 2 \cdot 3 \cdot a \cdot b$
$4ab$ is the greatest common factor.

46. $x^2 - 4x + 4 = (x - 2)^2$

Chapter 1 Highlights

Page 61 Understanding and Using the Vocabulary

1. quadrants
2. obtuse
3. supplementary
4. line
5. line
6. ray
7. origin
8. two congruent segments
9. vertical
10. postulates

Chapter 1 Study Guide and Assessment

Pages 62–64 Skills and Concepts

11–14.

15. Quadrant III
16. no
17. point A
18. Sample answer $\overrightarrow{BA}$, and $\overleftrightarrow{CA}$
19. $d = rt$
$$r = \frac{d}{t}$$
$$= \frac{135}{3} = 45 \text{ mph}$$
20. $P = 2\ell + 2w$
$$45 = 2(17) + 2w$$
$$45 = 34 + 2w$$
$$11 = 2w$$
$$5.5 = w$$
The width is 5.5 in.
21. The greatest area possible for a rectangle with a given perimeter is a square.
$$P = 4s \qquad\qquad A = s^2$$
$$30 = 4s \qquad\qquad = 7.5^2$$
$$7.5 = s \qquad\qquad = 56.25 \text{ cm}^2$$
22. $XT = |2.5 - (-1)| = |3.5| = 3.5$
23. $ZW = |2 - (-1.5)| = |3.5| = 3.5$
24. T, S
25. $HL = \sqrt{(-3-1)^2 + (2-5)^2}$
$$= \sqrt{(-4)^2 + (-3)^2}$$
$$= \sqrt{16 + 9} = \sqrt{25} = 5$$
26. $JH = \sqrt{(-3-7)^2 + (2-0)^2}$
$$= \sqrt{(-10)^2 + (2)^2}$$
$$= \sqrt{100 + 4}$$
$$= \sqrt{104} \approx 10.20$$
27. $KM = \sqrt{[8-(-2)]^2 + (-1-6)^2}$
$$= \sqrt{(10)^2 + (-7)^2}$$
$$= \sqrt{100 + 49}$$
$$= \sqrt{149} \approx 12.21$$

28. $IN = \sqrt{(-4-4)^2 + [-4-(-1)]^2}$
$= \sqrt{(-8)^2 + (-3)^2}$
$= \sqrt{64 + 9}$
$= \sqrt{73} \approx 8.54$

29. $\left(\dfrac{x_1 + x_2}{2}, \dfrac{y_1 + y_2}{2}\right) = \left(\dfrac{4+7}{6}, \dfrac{-1+0}{2}\right)$
$= \left(\dfrac{11}{2}, \dfrac{-1}{2}\right)$
$= (5.5, -0.5)$

30. Sample answer: 1 and 5

31. $2(EF) = EG$
$2(2x + 3) = 6x - 3$
$4x + 6 = 6x - 3$
$9 = 2x$
$x = \dfrac{9}{2}$
$FG = EF$
$FG = 2x + 3$
$= 2\left(\dfrac{9}{2}\right) + 3$ or 12

32. $\overline{PS} \cong \overline{QR}$
$PS = QR$
$|6 - x| = 18$
$6 - x = 18$ or $6 - x = -18$
$x = -12$ $x = 24$
The coordinate of S could be -12 or 24.

33. yes

34. $\overline{UX} \cong \overline{WV}$
$UX = WV$
$4x - 2 = 2x + 8$
$x = 5$
$UX = 4(5) - 2 = 18$

35. $m\angle 3 + m\angle CED = 180$
$32 + m\angle CED = 180$
$m\angle CED = 148$

36. $m\angle 2 + m\angle 4 = m\angle CED$
$(6x - 20) + (3x + 18) = 151$
$9x - 2 = 151$
$9x = 153$
$x = 17$

37. $m\angle 1 + m\angle 4 + m\angle 2 = 180$
$(49 - 2x) + (4x + 12) + 15x = 180$
$61 + 17x = 180$
$17x = 119$
$x = 7$

$m\angle 4 = 4x + 12$
$= 4(7) + 12 = 40$

38. $\angle PTN, \angle NTM$ **39.** $\angle PTN$

40. They are congruent.

41. $m\angle NTP + m\angle PTR = 180$
$m\angle PTR = 2(m\angle NTP)$
$m\angle NTP + 2(m\angle NTP) = 180$
$3(m\angle NTP) = 180$
$m\angle NTP = 60$
$m\angle PTR = 2(m\angle NTP)$
$= 2(60)$ or 120

42. Let x = the measure of the angle.
Thus, $90 - x$ = measure of its complement.
$x = 6(90 - x) - 43$
$x = 540 - 6x - 43$
$7x = 497$
$x = 71$
$90 - x = 19$
The measures of the two angles are 71 and 19.

Page 64 Applications and Problem Solving

43.

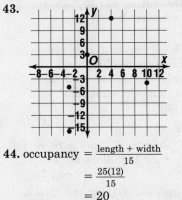

44. occupancy $= \dfrac{\text{length} + \text{width}}{15}$
$= \dfrac{25(12)}{15}$
$= 20$
20 people can safely occupy the sailboat.

45a. As the loft of the club increases, the ball will travel higher in the air and for a shorter distance as long as the balls are struck with the same amount of force.

45b.

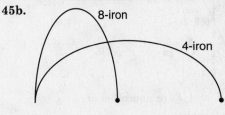

Page 65 Alternative Assessment: Thinking Critically

These points lie on the axes and not in the quadrants. An ordered pair that has 0 as one of its coordinates is on an axis. The axes are not part of any quadrant; they define the quadrant boundaries.

CHAPTER 2 Connecting Reasoning and Proof

 Inductive Reasoning and Conjecturing

Pages 72–73 Check for Understanding

1. A conjecture is a guess, based on limited evidence, about what will always be true.

2. Sample answer: There is no way to draw a straight line through three points lying on the same circle.

3. Sample answer: Skyler looked at only two cases in history where great people did poorly academically. If he had looked at other cases, he could have made different observations.

4. Give a counterexample.

5. See students' work.

6. True; if $m\angle 1 = 70$, then $m\angle 2 = 180 - 70$, or 110, and $m\angle 3 = 180 - 70$, or 110. Since $m\angle 2 = m\angle 3$, then $\angle 2 \cong \angle 3$.

7. If ℓ and m are perpendicular, then they form a right angle.

8. Points A, B, and C are collinear.

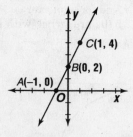

9. Points H, I, and J are noncollinear.

10. false; counterexample:

11. Sample answer: Earth is flat. Earth is the center of the universe.

Pages 73–75 Exercises

12. false; counterexample:

$$\overset{\bullet}{}\ \ \underset{D}{\bullet}\ \ \underset{E}{\bullet}\ \ \underset{F}{\bullet}\ \ \underset{G}{\bullet}\ \ \overset{\bullet}{}$$

13. False; $XZ + YZ = XY$ by the Segment Addition Postulate.

$$\overset{\longleftrightarrow}{\underset{X\ \ \ \ Y\ \ \ \ Z}{\bullet\ \ \ \ \bullet\ \ \ \ \bullet}}$$

14. True; any three noncollinear points can be the vertices of a triangle.

15. Points A, B, and C do not lie on a line.

    $A\bullet$

    $\bullet C$

    $B\bullet$

16. $AB = EF$

17. X, Y, Z, and W are noncollinear.

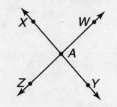

18. $\angle 1$ and $\angle 2$ have a common side and a common vertex.

19. Points R, S, and T are collinear.

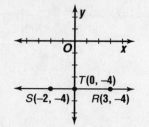

20. $x > 5$

21. $m\angle ABD = m\angle CBD$

22. $\angle A$, $\angle B$, $\angle C$, and $\angle D$ are right angles.

23. false; counterexample:

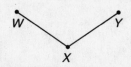

24. True; opposite sides of a rectangle have equal lengths.

25. False; K, L, and M are collinear.

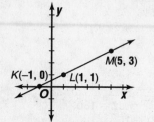

26. False; counterexample: If $x = -2$, then $-x = -(-2) = 2$.

27. $PQRST$ is a pentagon. Sample answer: If no three lines are collinear, each pair of points form segments, which can form a pentagon.

28. $\overline{JK}$, $\overline{KL}$, $\overline{LM}$, $\overline{MN}$, and $\overline{NJ}$ form a quadrilateral. Sample answer: J, K, and L lie on one segment and the other points form three other segments.

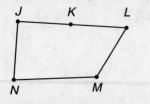

29a. They are congruent.

29b. Sample answer: Use the Angle option on the menu to find the measures of $\angle PQS$ and $\angle QSR$.

29c. See students' work.

30. See students' work.

31. The ball will strike two rails and then continue on a path to the corner of the opposite side of the table at the opposite end.

32. Sample answer: The amount of aluminum cans being recycled is increasing; the amount of recycled cans is leveling off; something happened in 1982 that created an incentive for recycling aluminum or that made recycling of aluminum cans easier. To determine whether each conjecture is true or false, it might help to research the topic of aluminum can recycling.

33. $(3p + 24) + (5p - 4) = 180$
$$8p + 20 = 180$$
$$8p = 160$$
$$p = 20$$
One angle measures $3(20) + 24$ or 84. This is not a right angle so $\overline{DE}$ is not $\perp$ to $\overline{FG}$.

34. $m\angle MOL + m\angle LON = m\angle MON$
$$m\angle MOL = 5(m\angle LON)$$
$$5(m\angle LON) + m\angle LON = 90$$
$$6(m\angle LON) = 90$$
$$m\angle LON = 15$$

35. $\left(\dfrac{x_1 + x_2}{2}, \dfrac{y_1 + y_2}{2}\right) = \left(\dfrac{3 + 17}{2}, \dfrac{5 + 19}{2}\right)$
$$= \left(\dfrac{20}{2}, \dfrac{24}{2}\right)$$
$$= (10, 12)$$

36. $d = \sqrt{(x_2 - x_1)^2 + (y_2 - y_1)^2}$
$$= \sqrt{(5 - 0)^2 + [-3 - (-5)]^2}$$
$$= \sqrt{(5)^2 + (2)^2}$$
$$= \sqrt{25 + 4} = \sqrt{29}$$

37. $P = 2\ell + 2w$
$$44 = 2(x + 6) + 2(2x + 7)$$
$$44 = 2x + 12 + 4x + 14$$
$$44 = 6x + 26$$
$$18 = 6x$$
$$3 = x$$
$$w = x + 6 \text{ or } 9$$
$$\ell = 2x + 7 \text{ or } 13$$

38. thick pepperoni, thick mushroom, thick green pepper, thin pepperoni, thin mushroom, thin green pepper; 6 different pizzas

39. $-\dfrac{1}{4} + \dfrac{2}{5} = -\dfrac{5}{20} + \dfrac{8}{20}$
$$= \dfrac{3}{20}$$

40a. The graph shows the percentage of moviegoers who attend movies in different months of the year.

40b. 11.8% of all moviegoers attend movies in July.

Page 75 Mathematics and Society

1. If a person has lost an arm or leg, the system could scan the remaining limb and, using the computer, create a mirror image of it that could be used to make the replacement limb.

2. Using different angles and perspectives is more accurate than using only one or two views when you are dealing with three-dimensional objects. The locations of the numerous points on the body's surface can be precisely pinpointed by the process of triangulation.

3. See students' work.

2-2 If-Then Statements and Postulates

Page 80 Check for Understanding

1. If-then form makes statements clearer and easier to understand.

2. Sample answer: A conditional statement contains a hypothesis and a conclusion and can be written in if-then form. A sample conditional is, "If it rains tomorrow, then I will not go sailing."

3. Omar and Minaku are correct. It is true that if a figure is a square, then it is a rectangle. However, the converse, if a figure is a rectangle, then it is a square, is not true. Only some rectangles are squares.

4. Sample answer: Both the inverse and the contrapositive of the conditional involve negations of the hypothesis and conclusion. They differ in that the hypothesis of one is the conclusion of the other.

5. See students' work.

6. Hypothesis: you can sell green toothpaste in this country
Conclusion: you can sell opera

7. Hypothesis: three points lie on a line
Conclusion: they are collinear

8. If a fish is a piranha, then it eats other fish.

9. If angles have the same measure, then they are congruent.

10. Three points are noncollinear.

11. Four points are coplanar.

12. Converse: If you are a teenager, then you are 13 years old; false. Counterexample: If you are a teenager, you may be 15 years old.
Inverse: If you are not 13 years old, then you are not a teenager; false. Counterexample: If you are not 13 years old, you may be a 15-year-old teenager.
Contrapositive: If you are not a teenager, then you are not 13 years old; true.

13. Converse: If an angle is a right angle, then it measures 90°; true.
Inverse: If an angle does not measure 90°, then it is not a right angle; true.
Contrapositive: If an angle is not a right angle, then it does not measure 90°; true.

14. False; E is not in $\mathcal{N}$.

15. False; $\overline{BC}$ dies lie in $\mathcal{N}$.

16. true.

17. False; A, B, and D do not lie on the same line.

18a. If people were Maoris, then they were outstanding sculptors.
Converse: If people were outstanding sculptors, then they were Maoris.
Inverse: If people were not Maoris, then they were not outstanding sculptors.
Contrapositive: If people were not outstanding sculptors, then they were not Maoris.

18b. If a building is the Maori treaty house, then it has pillars of carved wood.
Converse: If a building has pillars of carved wood, then it is the Maori treaty house.
Inverse: If a building is not the Maori treaty house, then it does not have pillars of carved wood.
Contrapositive: If a building does not have pillars of carved wood, then it is not the Maori treaty house.

Pages 81–83 Exercises

19. Hypothesis: a man hasn't discovered something that he will die for
Conclusion: he isn't fit to live

20. Hypothesis: you don't know where you are going
Conclusion: you will probably end up somewhere else

21. Hypothesis: we would have new knowledge
Conclusion: we must get a whole world of new questions

22. Hypothesis: you are an NBA basketball player
Conclusion: you are at least 5′2″ tall

23. Hypothesis: $3x - 5 = -11$
Conclusion: $x = -2$

24. Hypothesis: you are an adult
Conclusion: you are at least 21 years old

25. If people are happy, then they rarely correct their faults.

26. If a person is a champion, then he is afraid of losing.

27. If angles are adjacent, then they have a common vertex.

28. If triangles are equiangular, then they are equilateral.

29. If angles have measures between 90 and 180, then they are obtuse.

30. If two lines are perpendicular, then they form right angles.

31. A book is not a mirror.

32. Right angles are acute angles.

33. Rectangles are squares.

34. A cardinal is a dog.

35. You do not live in Dallas.

36. Converse: If a figure is a quadrilateral, then it is a square; false. Counterexample: A trapezoid is a quadrilateral, but not a square.
Inverse: If a figure is not a square, then it is not a quadrilateral; false. Counterexample: A figure may be a parallelogram.
Contrapositive: If a figure is not a quadrilateral, then it is not a square; true.

37. Converse: If there are three points that are noncollinear, then they are not on the same line; true.
Inverse: If there are three points on the same line, then they are collinear; true.
Contrapositive: If there are three points that are collinear, then they are on the same line; true.

38. Converse: If a ray forms two angles that are congruent, then the ray bisects an angle; true.
Inverse: If a ray does not bisect an angle, then the two angles formed are not congruent; true.
Contrapositive: If a ray does not form two angles that are congruent, then the ray does not bisect an angle; true.

39. Converse: If an angle has a measure less than 90, then it is acute; true.
Inverse: If an angle is not acute, then it does not have a measure less than 90; true.
Contrapositive: If an angle does not have a measure less than 90, then it is not acute; true.

40. Converse: If two angles are congruent, then they are vertical; false. Counterexample:

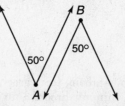

Inverse: If two angles are not vertical, then they are not congruent; false. See counterexample above.
Contrapositive: If two angles are not congruent, then they are not vertical; true.

41. Converse: If you don't live in Illinois, then you don't live in Chicago; true.
Inverse: If you live in Chicago, then you live in Illinois; true.
Contrapositive: If you live in Illinois, then you live in Chicago; false. Counterexample: you may live in another city in Illinois.

42. true   **43.** true

44. False; X lies in $\mathcal{M}$ and Z in $\mathcal{N}$.

45. true   **46.** one

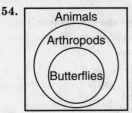

47. three   **48.** six

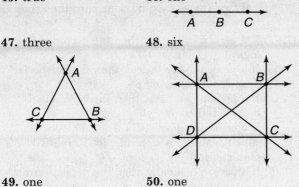

49. one   **50.** one

51a. doubles   **51b.** quadruples

51c. is multiplied by 8

52. If two angles are adjacent, then they are not both acute. This is the original conditional.

53a. The Hatter is right; Alice exchanged the hypothesis and conclusion.

53b. The statements are converses of each other.

54.

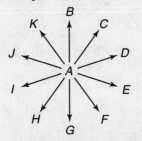

55a. If you try Casa Fiesta, then you're looking for a fast, easy way to add some fun to your family's menu.

55b. They are a fast, easy way to add fun to your family's menu.

55c. No; the conclusion is implied.

56. Sample answer: 10 collisions

57. Sample answer: $\angle C \cong \angle D$

58. False; collinear points cannot be the vertices of a triangle.

59. Sample answer: $RSTU$ has four congruent sides.

60.
$$m\angle AND + m\angle NOR = 90$$
$$4(m\angle NOR) + m\angle NOR = 90$$
$$5(m\angle NOR) = 90$$
$$m\angle NOR = 18$$
$$m\angle AND = 4(m\angle NOR)$$
$$= 4(18) \text{ or } 72$$

61. acute

62. $\left(\dfrac{x_1 + x_2}{2}, \dfrac{y_1 + y_2}{2}\right) = \left(\dfrac{4 + (-3)}{2}, \dfrac{8 + 0}{2}\right)$
$$= \left(\dfrac{1}{2}, 4\right)$$

63. $\ell = 1.5w$
$$A = \ell w$$
$$= 1.5w(w)$$
$$= 1.5w^2$$

$$60 < \quad A \quad < 300$$
$$60 < 1.5w^2 < 300$$
$$40 < \quad w^2 \quad < 200$$
$$40 < \quad w \quad < 200$$
$$6.3 < \quad w \quad < 14.1$$

Make a list of whole number widths between 6.3 and 14 whose coordinating length is also a whole number: 12 in. by 8 in., 15 in. by 10 in., 18 in. by 12 in., 21 in. by 14 in.

64. A square has the maximum area
$$4s = 44 \qquad\qquad A = s^2$$
$$s = 11 \qquad\qquad = 11^2 \text{ or } 121 \ m^2$$

65. $y = x + 5$
$$-4 \overset{?}{=} -1 + 5$$
$$-4 \neq 4$$

T is noncollinear with R and S.

66. $15 + 3n$ **67.** false
$$32 - 5 \overset{?}{=} 6$$
$$9 - 5 \overset{?}{=} 6$$
$$4 \neq 6$$

2-2B Using Technology Testing Conditional Statements

Page 84 Exercises

1. The result is the same, $x < -3$.

2. See students' work.

3. True

4. False; if $4x + 19 \leq -8 + 7x$, then $x \geq 9$.

5. False; if $12 - 3x > 23 - 14x$, then $x > 1$.

2-3 Deductive Reasoning

Page 85 Modeling Mathematics

$\angle ABE \cong \angle DBC$

$\angle ABD \cong \angle EBC$

Sample answer: The angles opposite each other are congruent.

Pages 87–89 Check for Understanding

1. Transitive Prop. (=)

2a. I should choose Tint-and-Trim Hair Salon.

2b. Sample answer: Dogs have four legs. Kitty has four legs. Therefore, Kitty is a dog.

3. See students' work.

4. Nina's reasoning is correct. Marlene's conclusion that she will necessarily make the team is invalid because the fact that she is practicing more on the weekends satisfies the conclusion of the conditional rather than the hypothesis.

5. See students' work.
6. yes; detachment
7. yes; syllogism
8. Invalid: congruent angles are not necessarily vertical angles.
9. Patricia Gorman should get 8 hours of sleep each day; detachment.
10. no conclusion
11. If the measure of an angle is less than 90, then it is not obtuse; syllogism.
12. There is exactly one line that contains points A and B; detachment.
13a. You'll become a true Beatles fan.
13b. no conclusion   13c. no conclusion
13d. You'll love this album.

Pages 89–91 Exercises

14. yes; syllogism   15. yes; detachment
16. Invalid: A, B, C, and D may not form a rectangle.
17. Invalid; angles can be congruent, but not right angles.
18. yes; detachment
19. Invalid; there is nothing to infer that teenagers are customers.
20. yes; syllogism
21. Invalid; this is not the inverse of the first statement.
22. no conclusion
23. Odina lives to eat; detachment.
24. no conclusion
25. If M is the midpoint of $\overline{AB}$, then $\overline{AM} \cong \overline{MB}$; syllogism.
26. $m\angle 2$ is greater than 90; detachment.
27. no conclusion   28. no conclusion
29. Planes $\mathcal{M}$ and $\mathcal{N}$ intersect in a line; detachment.
30. If two angles of a triangle are congruent, then the triangle is isosceles; syllogism.
31. Line t is perpendicular to line q; detachment.
32. Cars are practical; syllogism.
33. $\overline{XY}$ lies in plane p; detachment.
34a. (2) I'm a careful bicycle rider.
     (3) I wear a helmet.
34b. (2) If you wear a helmet, you will have fewer injuries.
     (3) If you're a careful bicycle rider, then you will have fewer injuries.
35a. (2) I like pizza with everything.
     (3) I'll like Jimmy's pizza.
35b. (2) If you like Jimmy's pizza, then you are a pizza connoisseur.
     (3) If you like pizza with everything, then you are a pizza connoisseur.
36a. (2) $\angle A$ and $\angle B$ form a linear pair.
     (3) $\angle A$ and $\angle B$ share a common ray.

36b. (2) If two angles share a common ray, then they are adjacent.
     (3) If two angles form a linear pair, then they are adjacent.
37. (1) If a person is a baby, then the person is not logical. (statement 1)
    (2) If a person is not logical, then the person is despised. (statement 3)
    (3) If a person is a baby, then the person is despised. (Law of Syllogism)
    (4) If a person is despised, then the person cannot manage a crocodile. (contrapositive of statement 2)
    (5) If a person is a baby, then the person cannot manage a crocodile. (Law of Syllogism)
38. (2) An unknown person attempted to give me an item to transport on my flight.
    (3) I did not accept it and notified airline personnel immediately.
39. $9^1 = 9$, $9^2 = 81$, $9^3 = 729$, $9^4 = 6561$; the pattern shows that even powers of 9 end in 1 so 9^{46} has 1 in the ones digit.
40. If the statement you can answer "yes" to these three questions is true, then the conclusion, *you probably qualify for savings of up to 70% on your life insurance* is true.
41. If two lines intersect, then they are perpendicular; false. Counterexample:

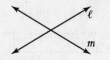

42. If two planes intersect, then they intersect in a line.
43. Sample answer: A, B, C, and D are collinear.

44. $m\angle RUT = m\angle SUV$
    $2z + 54 = 5z - 75$
    $-3z = -129$
    $z = 43$
    $m\angle SUV = 5z - 75$
    $\qquad = 5(43) - 75$ or 140
45. See students' work.
46. $RQ + QS = RS$
    $(6x - 1) + (2x + 4) = 9x - 3$
    $8x + 3 = 9x - 3$
    $-x = -6$
    $x = 6$
    $RS = 9x - 3$
    $\qquad = 9(6) - 3$ or 51
47. $d = \sqrt{(x_2 - x_1)^2 + (y_2 - y_1)^2}$
    $\quad = \sqrt{(4 - 2)^2 + (-1 - 5)^2}$
    $\quad = \sqrt{4 + 36}$
    $\quad = \sqrt{40}$
    $\quad = 2\sqrt{10}$
48. -0.9 49. $\$40 - \$36.78 = \$3.22$

Page 91 Self Test

1. False; counterexample:

2. True; if $m\angle C = 35$, then $m\angle A = 90 - 35$ or 55, and $m\angle B = 90 - 35$ or 55. Since $m\angle A = m\angle B$, then $\angle A \cong \angle B$.

3a. Sample answer: insufficient light or water

3b. Yes; the fungus is killing the plants.

3c. Introduce the fungus to some healthy plants and see if they droop.

4. Hypothesis: you're there before it's over
Conclusion: you're on time

5. If there are clouds, then it is raining.

6. If two lines are not parallel, then they intersect.

7. If a figure does not have four sides, then it is not a square.

8. yes; detachment   9. invalid

10. yes; syllogism

2-4 Integration: Algebra Using Proof in Algebra

Pages 94–96 Check for Understanding

1. given and prove statements and two columns, one of statements, and one of reasons

2. hypothesis; conclusion

3. Sample answer: If $AB = 5$ and $AB + CD = 8$, then $5 + CD = 8$.

4. algebra properties, definitions, postulates, and previously proven theorems

5a. (2) Addition Prop. (=)

5b. (4) Substitution Prop. (=)

5c. (5) Transitive Prop. (=)

5d. (3) Symmetric Prop. (=)

5e. (1) Distributive Prop.

6. Division Prop. (=)

7. Addition Prop. (=)

8. Substitution Prop. (=)

9a. (1) Given

9b. (3) Angle Addition Postulate

9c. (4) or (5) Substitution Prop. (=)

9d. (5) or (4) Substitution Prop. (=)

9e. (2) Subtraction Prop. (=)

10a. Given

10b. Multiplication Prop. (=)

10c. Distributive Prop.

10d. Subtraction Prop. (=)

10e. Division Prop. (=)

11. Given: $k = \dfrac{\Delta \ell}{\ell(T - t)}$

Prove: $T = \dfrac{\Delta \ell}{k\ell} + t$

Proof:

Statements	Reasons
1. $k = \dfrac{\Delta \ell}{\ell(T - t)}$	1. Given
2. $k(T - t) = \dfrac{\Delta \ell}{\ell}$	2. Mult. Prop. (=)
3. $T - t = \dfrac{\Delta \ell}{k\ell}$	3. Div. Prop. (=)
4. $T = \dfrac{\Delta \ell}{k\ell} + t$	4. Add. Prop. (=)

12.

Statements	Reasons
a. $m\angle 1 = m\angle 2$	a. Given
b. $m\angle 3 = m\angle 3$	b. Reflexive Property (=)
c. $m\angle 1 + m\angle 3 = m\angle 2 + m\angle 3$	c. Addition Property (=)
d. $m\angle PXR = m\angle 2 + m\angle 3$ $m\angle SXQ = m\angle 1 + m\angle 3$	d. Angle Addition Postulate
e. $m\angle PXR = m\angle SXQ$	e. Substitution Prop. (=)

Pages 96–99 Exercises

13. Symmetric Prop. (=)

14. Distributive Prop.

15. Division Prop. (=) or Multiplication Prop. (=)

16. Substitution Prop. (=)

17. Division Prop. (=)   18. Reflexive Prop. (=)

19. Transitive Prop. (=)   20. Subtraction Prop. (=)

21. Subtraction Prop. (=)

22a. (1) Given

22b. (4) Multiplication Prop. (=)

22c. (2) Distributive Prop.

22d. (6) Subtraction Prop. (=)

22e. (3) Addition Prop. (=)

22f. (5) Division Prop. (=)

23a. (2) Given

23b. (1) Def. of Supplementary $\angle$s

23c. (3) or (4) Substitution Prop. (=)

23d. (3) or (4) Substitution Prop. (=)

23e. (5) Subtraction Prop. (=)

23f. (6) Def. $\cong$ $\angle$s

24a. Given

24b. Multiplication Prop. (=)

24c. Division Prop. (=) or Multiplication Prop. (=)

25a. Given

25b. Multiplication Prop. (=)

25c. Distributive Prop.   **25d.** Subtraction Prop. (=)

25e. Division Prop. (=)

26a. Given

26b. Segment Addition Postulate

26c. Substitution Prop. (=)

26d. Given

26e. Subtraction Prop. (=)

---

27. Statements

Statements	Reasons
a. $m\angle TUV = 90,$ $m\angle XWV = 90,$ $m\angle 1 = m\angle 3$	**a.** Given
b. $m\angle TUV = m\angle XWV$	**b.** Substitution Prop. (=)
c. $m\angle TUV = m\angle 1 + m\angle 2$ $m\angle XWV = m\angle 3 + m\angle 4$	**c.** Angle Addition Postulate
d. $m\angle 1 + m\angle 2 = m\angle 3 + m\angle 4$	**d.** Substitution Prop. (=)
e. $m\angle 1 + m\angle 2 = m\angle 1 + m\angle 4$	**e.** Substitution Prop. (=)
f. $m\angle 2 = m\angle 4$	**f.** Subtraction Prop. (=)

28. Statements

Statements	Reasons
a. $4 - \frac{1}{2}x = \frac{7}{2} - x$	**a.** Given
b. $2\left(4 - \frac{1}{2}x\right) = 2\left(\frac{7}{2} - x\right)$	**b.** Mult. Prop. (=)
c. $8 - x = 7 - 2x$	**c.** Distributive Property
d. $1 - x = -2x$	**d.** Subtraction Prop. (=)
e. $1 = -x$	**e.** Addition Property (=)
f. $-1 = x$	**f.** Div. Prop. (=) or Mult. Prop. (=)
g. $x = -1$	**g.** Symmetric Prop. (=)

29. Given: $2x + 6 = 3 + \frac{5}{3}x$

Prove: $x = -9$

Proof:

Statements	Reasons
1. $2x + 6 = 3 + \frac{5}{3}x$	**1.** Given
2. $3(2x + 6) = 3\left(3 + \frac{5}{3}x\right)$	**2.** Mult. Prop. (=)
3. $6x + 18 = 9 + 5x$	**3.** Distributive Prop.
4. $x + 18 = 9$	**4.** Subtraction Prop. (=)
5. $x = -9$	**5.** Subtraction Prop. (=)

30. Given: $AC = AB$, $AC = 4x + 1$, $AB = 6x - 13$

Prove: $x = 7$

Proof:

Statements	Reasons
1. $AC = AB$ $AC = 4x + 1$ $AB = 6x - 13$	**1.** Given
2. $4x + 1 = 6x - 13$	**2.** Substitution Prop. (=)
3. $1 = 2x - 13$	**3.** Subtraction Prop. (=)
4. $14 = 2x$	**4.** Addition Prop. (=)
5. $7 = x$	**5.** Division Prop. (=)
6. $x = 7$	**6.** Symmetric Prop. (=)

31. Sample answer: Both properties are transitive; equality relates numbers, congruence relates sets of points.

32. Given: $E_k = h \cdot f + W$

Prove: $f = \dfrac{E_k - W}{h}$

Proof:

Statements	Reasons
1. $E_k = h \cdot f + W$	**1.** Given
2. $E_k - W = h \cdot f$	**2.** Subtraction Prop. (=)
3. $\dfrac{E_k - W}{h} = f$	**3.** Division Prop. (=)
4. $f = \dfrac{E_k - W}{h}$	**4.** Symmetric Prop. (=)

33. Given: $AC = BD$

Prove: $AB = CD$

Proof:

Statements	Reasons
1. $AC = BD$	**1.** Given
2. $AB + BC = AC$ $BC + CD = BD$	**2.** Segment Addition Post.
3. $AB + BC = BC + CD$	**3.** Substitution Prop. (=)
4. $AB = CD$	**4.** Subtraction Prop. (=)

34. no conclusion

35. If $m\angle 1 \neq 27$, then $\angle 1$ is not acute; false, if $m\angle 1 = 32$, then $\angle 1$ is acute.

36. Sample answer: S, P, and T are collinear and X, P, and Y are collinear.

37. Complement does not exist; the measure of the supplement equals $180 - 159$ or 21.

38.
$$RS = ST$$
$$3x + 5 = 9x - 7$$
$$6x = 12$$
$$x = 2$$
$$RT = RS + ST$$
$$= 12x - 2$$
$$= 12(2) - 2 \text{ or } 22$$

39. See students' work.

40. $6 + 3(bc - 4a) + 2bc = 6 + 3bc - 12a + 2bc$
$$= 6 + 5bc - 12a$$

41a. $\dfrac{100 \text{ lb}}{\$300} = \dfrac{390 \text{ lb}}{\$x}$

41b. $300(390) = 100x$
$$x = 1170$$

41c. $23(10)(1170) = \$269,100$

2-5 Verifying Segment Relationships

Pages 102–104 Check For Understanding

1. Sample answer: State the theorem to be proved; list the given information; if possible, draw a diagram to illustrate the given information; state what is to be proved; and develop a system of deductive reasoning.

2. Theorems are statements that are proved through deductive reasoning using definitions, postulates, and undefined terms and other proven theorems.

3. Laws of logic and definitions, postulates, undefined terms and theorems

4. Sample answer: The distance from Atlanta to Montgomery AM is 167 miles; $\overline{AM} \cong \overline{AM}$.

5. Symmetric Prop. of $\cong$ Segments

6. Substitution Prop. (=)

7. Addition Prop. (=)

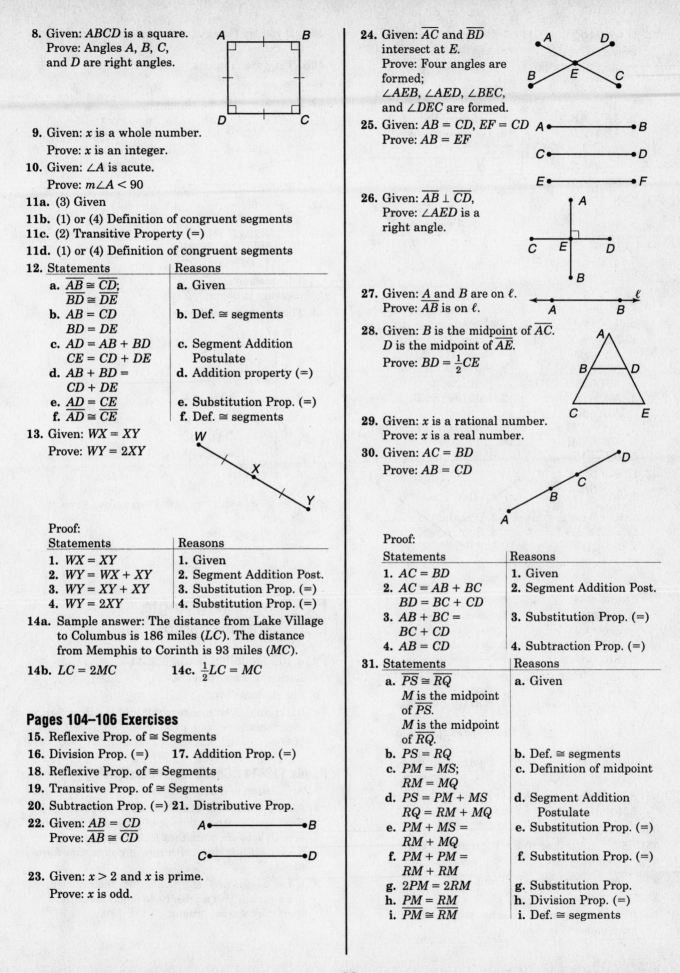

8. Given: *ABCD* is a square.
Prove: Angles *A*, *B*, *C*,
and *D* are right angles.

9. Given: *x* is a whole number.
Prove: *x* is an integer.

10. Given: ∠*A* is acute.
Prove: $m\angle A < 90$

11a. (3) Given
11b. (1) or (4) Definition of congruent segments
11c. (2) Transitive Property (=)
11d. (1) or (4) Definition of congruent segments

12.

Statements	Reasons
a. $\overline{AB} \cong \overline{CD}$; $\overline{BD} \cong \overline{DE}$	**a.** Given
b. $AB = CD$ $BD = DE$	**b.** Def. ≅ segments
c. $AD = AB + BD$ $CE = CD + DE$	**c.** Segment Addition Postulate
d. $AB + BD =$ $CD + DE$	**d.** Addition property (=)
e. $AD = CE$	**e.** Substitution Prop. (=)
f. $\overline{AD} \cong \overline{CE}$	**f.** Def. ≅ segments

13. Given: $WX = XY$
Prove: $WY = 2XY$

Proof:

Statements	Reasons
1. $WX = XY$	1. Given
2. $WY = WX + XY$	2. Segment Addition Post.
3. $WY = XY + XY$	3. Substitution Prop. (=)
4. $WY = 2XY$	4. Substitution Prop. (=)

14a. Sample answer: The distance from Lake Village to Columbus is 186 miles (*LC*). The distance from Memphis to Corinth is 93 miles (*MC*).

14b. $LC = 2MC$ **14c.** $\frac{1}{2}LC = MC$

Pages 104–106 Exercises

15. Reflexive Prop. of ≅ Segments
16. Division Prop. (=)   **17.** Addition Prop. (=)
18. Reflexive Prop. of ≅ Segments
19. Transitive Prop. of ≅ Segments
20. Subtraction Prop. (=) **21.** Distributive Prop.
22. Given: $AB = CD$
Prove: $\overline{AB} \cong \overline{CD}$

23. Given: $x > 2$ and *x* is prime.
Prove: *x* is odd.

24. Given: $\overline{AC}$ and $\overline{BD}$ intersect at *E*.
Prove: Four angles are formed; ∠*AEB*, ∠*AED*, ∠*BEC*, and ∠*DEC* are formed.

25. Given: $AB = CD$, $EF = CD$
Prove: $AB = EF$

26. Given: $\overline{AB} \perp \overline{CD}$,
Prove: ∠*AED* is a right angle.

27. Given: *A* and *B* are on ℓ.
Prove: $\overline{AB}$ is on ℓ.

28. Given: *B* is the midpoint of $\overline{AC}$.
D is the midpoint of $\overline{AE}$.
Prove: $BD = \frac{1}{2}CE$

29. Given: *x* is a rational number.
Prove: *x* is a real number.

30. Given: $AC = BD$
Prove: $AB = CD$

Proof:

Statements	Reasons
1. $AC = BD$	1. Given
2. $AC = AB + BC$ $BD = BC + CD$	2. Segment Addition Post.
3. $AB + BC =$ $BC + CD$	3. Substitution Prop. (=)
4. $AB = CD$	4. Subtraction Prop. (=)

31.

Statements	Reasons
a. $\overline{PS} \cong \overline{RQ}$ *M* is the midpoint of $\overline{PS}$. *M* is the midpoint of $\overline{RQ}$.	**a.** Given
b. $PS = RQ$	**b.** Def. ≅ segments
c. $PM = MS$; $RM = MQ$	**c.** Definition of midpoint
d. $PS = PM + MS$ $RQ = RM + MQ$	**d.** Segment Addition Postulate
e. $PM + MS =$ $RM + MQ$	**e.** Substitution Prop. (=)
f. $PM + PM =$ $RM + RM$	**f.** Substitution Prop. (=)
g. $2PM = 2RM$	**g.** Substitution Prop.
h. $PM = RM$	**h.** Division Prop. (=)
i. $\overline{PM} \cong \overline{RM}$	**i.** Def. ≅ segments

32. Given: $\overline{AB}$
Prove: $\overline{AB} \cong \overline{AB}$

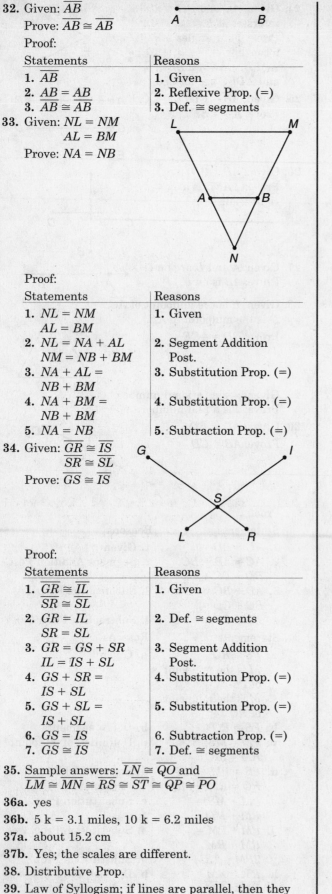

Proof:

Statements	Reasons
1. $\overline{AB}$	1. Given
2. $AB = AB$	2. Reflexive Prop. (=)
3. $\overline{AB} \cong \overline{AB}$	3. Def. $\cong$ segments

33. Given: $NL = NM$
$\quad\quad\quad AL = BM$
Prove: $NA = NB$

Proof:

Statements	Reasons
1. $NL = NM$ $AL = BM$	1. Given
2. $NL = NA + AL$ $NM = NB + BM$	2. Segment Addition Post.
3. $NA + AL =$ $NB + BM$	3. Substitution Prop. (=)
4. $NA + BM =$ $NB + BM$	4. Substitution Prop. (=)
5. $NA = NB$	5. Subtraction Prop. (=)

34. Given: $\overline{GR} \cong \overline{IS}$
$\quad\quad\quad \overline{SR} \cong \overline{SL}$
Prove: $\overline{GS} \cong \overline{IS}$

Proof:

Statements	Reasons
1. $\overline{GR} \cong \overline{IL}$ $\overline{SR} \cong \overline{SL}$	1. Given
2. $GR = IL$ $SR = SL$	2. Def. $\cong$ segments
3. $GR = GS + SR$ $IL = IS + SL$	3. Segment Addition Post.
4. $GS + SR =$ $IS + SL$	4. Substitution Prop. (=)
5. $GS + SL =$ $IS + SL$	5. Substitution Prop. (=)
6. $GS = IS$	6. Subtraction Prop. (=)
7. $\overline{GS} \cong \overline{IS}$	7. Def. $\cong$ segments

35. Sample answers: $\overline{LN} \cong \overline{QO}$ and $\overline{LM} \cong \overline{MN} \cong \overline{RS} \cong \overline{ST} \cong \overline{QP} \cong \overline{PO}$

36a. yes

36b. 5 k = 3.1 miles, 10 k = 6.2 miles

37a. about 15.2 cm

37b. Yes; the scales are different.

38. Distributive Prop.

39. Law of Syllogism; if lines are parallel, then they have no point in common.

40a. If you try Georgia, then you want a fabulous vacation.

40b. They are fabulous.

40c. no

41. $\left(\dfrac{x_1 + x_2}{2}, \dfrac{y_1 + y_2}{2}\right) = (-3, 5)$

$\dfrac{-7 + x_2}{2} = -3 \quad\quad\quad \dfrac{6 + y_2}{2} = 5$

$-7 + x_2 = -6 \quad\quad\quad 6 + y_2 = 10$

$x_2 = 1 \quad\quad\quad\quad\quad y_2 = 4$

The coordinates of H are (1, 4).

42. $\quad 25^2 + 60^2 = x^2$ 　　**43.** $A = \ell w$
$625 + 3600 = x^2$ 　　　　　$= 17(8)$
$\quad\quad 4225 = x^2$ 　　　　　$= 136$
$\quad\sqrt{4225} = x$
$\quad\quad\quad 65 = x$

The missing side measure is 65 cm.

44. The points are collinear.

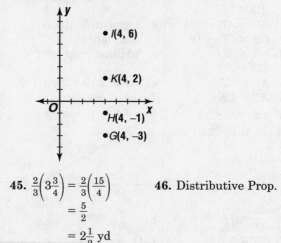

45. $\dfrac{2}{3}\left(3\dfrac{3}{4}\right) = \dfrac{2}{3}\left(\dfrac{15}{4}\right)$ 　　**46.** Distributive Prop.

$\quad\quad = \dfrac{5}{2}$

$\quad\quad = 2\dfrac{1}{2}$ yd

2-6 Verifying Angle Relationships

Page 109 Modeling Mathematics

a. Each angle measures 90°.

b. See students' work.

c. Right angles all measure 90° and are therefore congruent.

Pages 110–111 Check for Understanding

1. An illusion is a misperception.

2. All are transitive. The Transitive Property of Equality is with numbers; of congruent segments is with sets of points that form segments; of congruent angles is with sets of points that form angles.

3. If two angles are congruent, then their measures are equal. If two angles have equal measures, then they are congruent.

4. The next case you try may not be true. Sample answer: 11, 7, 5, and 3 are prime. Therefore, all prime numbers are odd. Since 2 is prime, it is a counterexample.

5a. (2) Given

5b. (3) Definition of complementary $\measuredangle$

5c. (5) Substitution Property (=)

5d. (1) Subtraction Property (=)

5e. (4) Definition of congruent angles

6. Sample answer: All angles of a square are congruent.

7. sometimes   **8.** always

9. sometimes   **10.** always

11. $m\angle 1 + m\angle 2 = 180$
        $(2x - 5) + (x - 4) = 180$
                $3x - 9 = 180$
                    $3x = 189$
                        $x = 63$
    $m\angle 1 = 2x - 5 = 2(63) - 5$ or 121
    $m\angle 2 = x - 4 = 63 - 4$ or 59

12. $m\angle 3 = m\angle 4$
        $228 - 3x = x$
            $228 = 4x$
                $57 = x$
    $m\angle 3 = 228 - 3x = 228 - 3(57) = 57$
    $m\angle 4 = x = 57$

13.

Statements	Reasons
a. $\angle 1$ and $\angle 2$ form a linear pair.	**a.** Given
b. $\overrightarrow{YX}$ and $\overrightarrow{YZ}$ are opposite rays.	**b.** Definition of opposite rays
c. $m\angle XYZ = 180$	**c.** Definition of straight angle
d. $m\angle XYZ = m\angle 1 + m\angle 2$	**d.** Angle Addition Postulate
e. $m\angle 1 + m\angle 2 = 180$	**e.** Substitution Prop. (=)
f. $\angle 1$ and $\angle 2$ are supplementary.	**f.** Def. supp. $\measuredangle$

14. $m\angle 1 + m\angle 2 = 180$
        $55 + m\angle 2 = 180$
                $m\angle 2 = 125$

Pages 111–114 Exercises

15. sometimes   **16.** always

17. always   **18.** sometimes

19. sometimes   **20.** always

21. sometimes   **22.** sometimes

23. never   **24.** always

25. sometimes   **26.** sometimes

27. $m\angle 5 = m\angle 6$
        $x = 6x - 290$
        $-5x = -290$
            $x = 58$
    $m\angle 5 = x = 58$
    $m\angle 6 = 6x - 290 = 6(58) - 290$ or 58

28. $m\angle 7 + m\angle 8 = 180$
        $(2x - 4) + (2x + 4) = 180$
                    $4x = 180$
                    $x = 45$
    $m\angle 7 = 2x - 5 = 2(45) - 4$ or 86
    $m\angle 8 = 2x + 4 = 2(45) + 4$ or 94

29. $m\angle 1 + m\angle 2 = 180$
        $(4x) + (2x - 6) = 180$
                $6x - 6 = 180$
                    $6x = 186$
                    $x = 31$
    $m\angle 1 = 4x = 4(31)$ or 124
    $m\angle 2 = 2x - 6 = 2(31) - 6$ or 56

30. $m\angle 3 = m\angle 4$
        $2x + 7 = x + 30$
            $x = 23$
    $m\angle 3 = 2x + 7 = 2(23) + 7$ or 53
    $m\angle 4 = x + 30 = 23 + 30$ or 53

31. $\angle 5 \cong \angle 6$
        $m\angle 5 = m\angle 6$
        $2x + 2 = x + 32$
            $x = 30$
    $m\angle 5 = 2x + 2 = 2(30) + 2 = 62$
    $m\angle 6 = x + 32 = 30 + 32 = 62$

32. $m\angle 7 + m\angle 8 + m\angle 9 = 180$
        $(x + 20) + (x + 40) + (x + 30) = 180$
                    $3x + 90 = 180$
                        $3x = 90$
                        $x = 30$
    $m\angle 7 = m\angle 10 = 30 + 20 = 50$
    $m\angle 8 = m\angle 11 = 30 + 40 = 70$
    $m\angle 9 = m\angle 12 = 30 + 30 = 60$

33a. $\angle 1$ and $\angle 8$, $\angle 2$ and $\angle 6$, $\angle 3$ and $\angle 5$, $\angle 4$ and $\angle 7$

33b. $\angle AXB$ and $\angle BXE$, $\angle BXC$ and $\angle CXF$, $\angle CXD$ and $\angle DXH$, $\angle DXE$ and $\angle EXG$, $\angle EXF$ and $\angle FXA$, $\angle FXH$ and $\angle HXB$, $\angle HXG$ and $\angle GXC$, $\angle GXA$ and $\angle AXD$

34. Given: $m\angle ABC = m\angle DFE$
            $m\angle 1 = m\angle 4$

Prove: $m\angle 2 = m\angle 3$

Proof:

Statements	Reasons
1. $m\angle ABC = m\angle DFE$ $m\angle 1 = m\angle 4$	**1.** Given
2. $m\angle ABC = m\angle 1 + m\angle 2$ $m\angle DFE = m\angle 3 + m\angle 4$	**2.** Angle Addition Post.
3. $m\angle 1 + m\angle 2 = m\angle 3 + m\angle 4$	**3.** Substitution Prop. (=)
4. $m\angle 4 + m\angle 2 = m\angle 3 + m\angle 4$	**4.** Substitution Prop. (=)
5. $m\angle 2 = m\angle 3$	**5.** Subtraction Prop. (=)

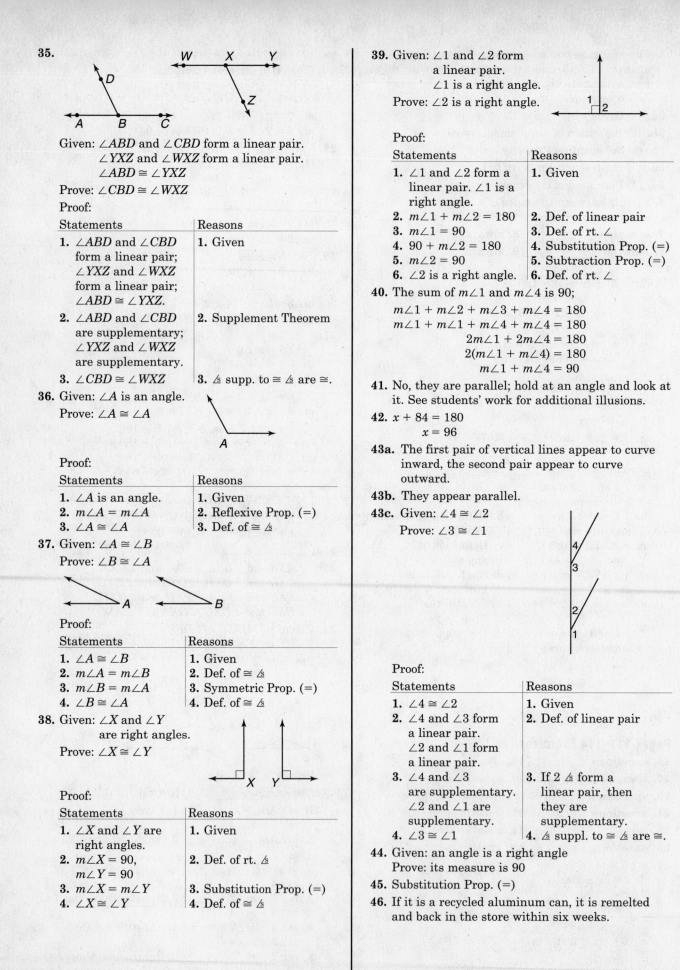

35.

Given: $\angle ABD$ and $\angle CBD$ form a linear pair.
$\angle YXZ$ and $\angle WXZ$ form a linear pair.
$\angle ABD \cong \angle YXZ$

Prove: $\angle CBD \cong \angle WXZ$

Proof:

Statements	Reasons
1. $\angle ABD$ and $\angle CBD$ form a linear pair; $\angle YXZ$ and $\angle WXZ$ form a linear pair; $\angle ABD \cong \angle YXZ$.	1. Given
2. $\angle ABD$ and $\angle CBD$ are supplementary; $\angle YXZ$ and $\angle WXZ$ are supplementary.	2. Supplement Theorem
3. $\angle CBD \cong \angle WXZ$	3. ⦞ supp. to ≅ ⦞ are ≅.

36. Given: $\angle A$ is an angle.
Prove: $\angle A \cong \angle A$

Proof:

Statements	Reasons
1. $\angle A$ is an angle.	1. Given
2. $m\angle A = m\angle A$	2. Reflexive Prop. (=)
3. $\angle A \cong \angle A$	3. Def. of ≅ ⦞

37. Given: $\angle A \cong \angle B$
Prove: $\angle B \cong \angle A$

Proof:

Statements	Reasons
1. $\angle A \cong \angle B$	1. Given
2. $m\angle A = m\angle B$	2. Def. of ≅ ⦞
3. $m\angle B = m\angle A$	3. Symmetric Prop. (=)
4. $\angle B \cong \angle A$	4. Def. of ≅ ⦞

38. Given: $\angle X$ and $\angle Y$ are right angles.
Prove: $\angle X \cong \angle Y$

Proof:

Statements	Reasons
1. $\angle X$ and $\angle Y$ are right angles.	1. Given
2. $m\angle X = 90$, $m\angle Y = 90$	2. Def. of rt. ⦞
3. $m\angle X = m\angle Y$	3. Substitution Prop. (=)
4. $\angle X \cong \angle Y$	4. Def. of ≅ ⦞

39. Given: $\angle 1$ and $\angle 2$ form a linear pair.
$\angle 1$ is a right angle.
Prove: $\angle 2$ is a right angle.

Proof:

Statements	Reasons
1. $\angle 1$ and $\angle 2$ form a linear pair. $\angle 1$ is a right angle.	1. Given
2. $m\angle 1 + m\angle 2 = 180$	2. Def. of linear pair
3. $m\angle 1 = 90$	3. Def. of rt. $\angle$
4. $90 + m\angle 2 = 180$	4. Substitution Prop. (=)
5. $m\angle 2 = 90$	5. Subtraction Prop. (=)
6. $\angle 2$ is a right angle.	6. Def. of rt. $\angle$

40. The sum of $m\angle 1$ and $m\angle 4$ is 90;
$$m\angle 1 + m\angle 2 + m\angle 3 + m\angle 4 = 180$$
$$m\angle 1 + m\angle 1 + m\angle 4 + m\angle 4 = 180$$
$$2m\angle 1 + 2m\angle 4 = 180$$
$$2(m\angle 1 + m\angle 4) = 180$$
$$m\angle 1 + m\angle 4 = 90$$

41. No, they are parallel; hold at an angle and look at it. See students' work for additional illusions.

42. $x + 84 = 180$
$x = 96$

43a. The first pair of vertical lines appear to curve inward, the second pair appear to curve outward.

43b. They appear parallel.

43c. Given: $\angle 4 \cong \angle 2$
Prove: $\angle 3 \cong \angle 1$

Proof:

Statements	Reasons
1. $\angle 4 \cong \angle 2$	1. Given
2. $\angle 4$ and $\angle 3$ form a linear pair. $\angle 2$ and $\angle 1$ form a linear pair.	2. Def. of linear pair
3. $\angle 4$ and $\angle 3$ are supplementary. $\angle 2$ and $\angle 1$ are supplementary.	3. If 2 ⦞ form a linear pair, then they are supplementary.
4. $\angle 3 \cong \angle 1$	4. ⦞ suppl. to ≅ ⦞ are ≅.

44. Given: an angle is a right angle
Prove: its measure is 90

45. Substitution Prop. (=)

46. If it is a recycled aluminum can, it is remelted and back in the store within six weeks.

47. $JK + KL = JL$ **48.** plane
$$3x + (2x - 1) = 24$$
$$5x - 1 = 24$$
$$5x = 25$$
$$x = 5$$
$$JK = 3x$$
$$= 3(5) = 15$$

49. Make a list of whole numbers so that $2w + \ell = 25$ and $\ell w > 70$: 15 ft by 5 ft, 13 ft by 6 ft, 11 ft by 7 ft, 9 ft by 8 ft

50. $6(5) - 1 + 8 \cdot 4 = 30 - 1 + 32$
$$= 61$$

51. Thursday; the largest audience is available.

Chapter 2 Highlights

Page 115 Understanding and Using the Vocabulary

1. (k) hypothesis   **2.** (e) inductive reasoning

3. (b) converse   **4.** (g) Law of Detachment

5. (c) counterexample   **6.** (l) contrapostive

7. (a) conjecture   **8.** (i) negation

9. (h) Law of Syllogism   **10.** (f) inverse

11. (j) proof   **12.** (d) deductive reasoning

Chapter 2 Study Guide and Assessment

Pages 116–118 Skills and Concepts

13. true; definition of midpoint

14. False; if supplementary, $m\angle 1$ could be 50 and $m\angle 2$ could be 130, but they are not congruent.

15. If something is a cloud, then it has a silver lining.

16. If a polygon is a rectangle, then it has four right angles.

17. If a rock is obsidian, then it is a glassy rock produced by a volcano.

18. If two planes intersect, then their intersection is a line.

19. Converse: If a rectangle is a square, then it has four congruent sides.
Inverse: If a rectangle does not have four congruent sides, then it is not a square.
Contrapositive: If a rectangle is not a square, then it does not have four congruent sides.

20. Converse: If three points lie on a straight line, then they are collinear.
Inverse: If three points are noncollinear, then they do not lie on a straight line.
Contrapositive: If three points do not lie on a straight line, then they are noncollinear.

21. Converse: If a month has 31 days, then it is January.
Inverse: If the month is not January, then it does not have 31 days.
Contrapositive: If a month does not have 31 days, then it is not January.

22. Converse: If a point lies on the x-axis, then an ordered pair for the point has 0 as its y-coordinate.
Inverse: If an ordered pair for a point does not have 0 as its y-coordinate, then the point does not lie on the x-axis.
Contrapositive: If a point does not lie on the x-axis, then an ordered pair for the point does not have 0 as its y-coordinate.

23. $\angle A$ and $\angle B$ have measures with a sum of 180; Law of Detachment.

24. no conclusion

25. The sun is in constant motion; Law of Syllogism.

26. Division Prop. (=)   **27.** Reflexive Prop. (=)

28a. Given   **28b.** Addition Prop. (=)

28c. Segment Addition Postulate

28d. Substitution Prop. (=)

29. Subtraction Prop. (=)

30. Symmetric Prop. of $\cong$ Segments

31. Substitution Prop. (=)

32. sometimes   **33.** never

34. always   **35.** never

Page 118 Applications and Problem Solving

36. If you are a hardworking person, then you deserve a great vacation. Hypothesis: you are a hardworking person
Conclusion: You deserve a great vacation
Converse: If you deserve a great vacation, then you are a hardworking person.
Inverse: If you are not a hardworking person, then you do not deserve a great vacation.
Contrapositive: If you do not deserve a great vacation, then you are not a hardworking person.

37. $8 \cdot 7 = 56$ pairs

38. A sponge remains permanently attached to a surface for all of its adult life; Law of Syllogism.

39. Substitution Prop. (=) or Transitive Prop. (=)

40.

Statements	Reasons
1. $t = 35d + 20$	1. Given
2. $t - 20 = 35d$	2. Subtraction Prop. (=)
3. $\frac{t - 20}{35} = d$	3. Division Prop. (=)
4. $d = \frac{t - 20}{35}$	4. Symmetric Prop. (=)

Page 119 Alternative Assessment: Thinking Critically

- no
- An advantage to using symbols would be there would be less writing, statements would be more concise. A disadvantage would be if there were many symbols then memorizing all of them would be like learning another language.

College Entrance Exam Practice, Chapters 1–2

Pages 120–121

1. $5n + 5 = 10$
$$5n = 5$$
$$n = 1$$
$$11 - n = 11 - 1 = 10 \quad \text{(D)}$$

2. $\dfrac{14^{12}}{14^{10}} = 14^{12-10}$
$$= 14^2 \quad \text{(D)}$$

3. $d = \sqrt{(-1-2)^2 + (1-7)^2}$
$$= \sqrt{(-3)^2 + (-6)^2}$$
$$= \sqrt{9 + 36}$$
$$= \sqrt{45} = 3\sqrt{5} \quad \text{(A)}$$

4. $0.08x = 32$
$$\frac{0.08x}{0.08} = \frac{32}{0.08}$$
$$x = 400 \quad \text{(B)}$$

5. $P = 4s$
$$= 4(8)$$
$$= 32 \text{ m} \quad \text{(C)}$$

6. A

7. D

8. $2x + 3 = \frac{1}{2}(10x + 15)$
$$2x + 3 = 2x + 3$$
This is true for any value of x. (D)

9. $30\% = 0.3$
$$0.3(120) = \frac{1}{3}x$$
$$36 = \frac{1}{3}x$$
$$108 = x \quad \text{(C)}$$

10. $y = mx + b$
$$y - b = mx$$
$$\frac{y - b}{m} = x \quad \text{(B)}$$

11. N is one unit to the right and 4 units below M.
$$M(-3 + 1, -4 - 4) = M(-2, -8)$$

12. $(5x - 2)^2 = (5x)^2 - 2(5x)(2) + (-2)^2$
$$= 25x^2 - 20x + 4$$

13. $C = 120(4)$

14. x meters

15. after $9h \to 8$
after $18h \to 8$
after $19h \to 9$
after $24h \to 5$

16. $9x + 5 < 100$
$$9x < 95$$
$$x < 10.6$$
The greatest integer x is 10.

17. $\frac{3}{4}(1600) = 1200$
$$\frac{2}{3}(1200) = 800$$
800 dial phones

18. $AC + CD = 72$
$$BC = AC - AB$$
$$= 60 - 36$$
$$= 14$$
$$CD = 12$$
$$14 > 12 \quad \text{(A)}$$

19. $\dfrac{\frac{1}{3}}{\frac{3}{2}} = 1 \cdot \frac{2}{3} = \frac{2}{3}$
$$\left(\frac{3}{2}\right)^2 = \frac{9}{4}$$
$$\frac{2}{3} < \frac{9}{4} \quad \text{(B)}$$

20. $\frac{3}{4}x = -24$
$$x = -32$$
$$\frac{1}{2}x = \frac{1}{2}(-32)$$
$$= -16$$
$$\frac{3}{2}x = \frac{3}{2}(-32)$$
$$= -48$$
$$-16 > -48 \quad \text{(A)}$$

21. $a^2 + a = (-4)^2 + (-4)$
$$= 16 - 4$$
$$= 12$$
$$12 = 12 \quad \text{(C)}$$

22. $180 - (60 + 50) = 70$
vertical angles are $\cong$.
$$x = 70$$
$$70 > 60 \quad \text{(A)}$$

CHAPTER 3   Using Perpendicular and Parallel Lines

Parallel Lines and Transversals

Page 125 Modeling Mathematics

a. plane *SRZ* and plane *PQY*, plane *SWX* and plane *RZY*, plane *PQR* and plane *XYZ*

b. plane *RQY* in $\overleftrightarrow{QR}$, plane *WSP* in $\overleftrightarrow{PS}$, plane *SRZ* in $\overleftrightarrow{SR}$, plane *PQY* in $\overleftrightarrow{PQ}$

Page 127 Check for Understanding

1. Sample answer: The definition describes parallel lines, because parallel lines are always beside each other and never intersect each other.

2. Both are correct depending on which line is the transversal.

3a. 2 parallel planes $\mathcal{A}$ and $\mathcal{B}$

3b. 2 skew lines ℓ and m in 2 parallel planes

3c. 2 parallel lines c and d and 2 non-parallel transversals a and b

4. Sample answer:

5. intersecting   6. parallel

7. False; a transversal intersects 2 lines in a plane.

8. False; the lines could be skew lines.

9. $\overleftrightarrow{AH}$; alternate interior

10. $\overleftrightarrow{AT}$; consecutive interior

11. plane *ABC* and plane *DEF*

12. $\overleftrightarrow{AC}$ and $\overleftrightarrow{BE}$, $\overleftrightarrow{AC}$ and $\overleftrightarrow{DE}$, $\overleftrightarrow{AC}$ and $\overleftrightarrow{EF}$, $\overleftrightarrow{AB}$ and $\overleftrightarrow{CF}$, $\overleftrightarrow{AB}$ and $\overleftrightarrow{EF}$, $\overleftrightarrow{AB}$ and $\overleftrightarrow{DF}$, $\overleftrightarrow{BC}$ and $\overleftrightarrow{AD}$, $\overleftrightarrow{BC}$ and $\overleftrightarrow{DE}$, $\overleftrightarrow{BC}$ and $\overleftrightarrow{DF}$, $\overleftrightarrow{AD}$ and $\overleftrightarrow{EF}$, $\overleftrightarrow{CF}$ and $\overleftrightarrow{DE}$, $\overleftrightarrow{BE}$ and $\overleftrightarrow{DF}$

13.

14.

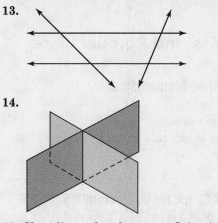

15. Skew lines; the planes are flying in different directions and at different altitudes.

Pages 129–129 Exercises

16. parallel   17. intersecting

18. intersecting   19. parallel

20. skew   21. parallel

22. True; *m* intersects 2 lines *r* and *s* in a plane.

23. False; the angles are not formed by 2 lines and a transversal.

24. True; the angles are exterior angles and on opposite sides of the transversal *s*.

25. True; the angles are in corresponding positions when the transversal *m* intersects *r* and *s*.

26. True; the angles are interior angles and on opposite sides of transversal ℓ.

27. False; the angles are formed by lines ℓ and *m* and transversal *s*.

28. *q*; consecutive interior   29. ℓ; alternate exterior

30. *m*; corresponding   31. ℓ; alternate interior

32. *p*; alternate interior   33. *q*; alternate exterior

34. plane *ADM* and plane *DRM*, plane *ADM* and plane *AEM*, plane *ADM* and plane *ERM*, plane *ADM* and plane *ADR*, plane *DRM* and plane *ERM*, plane *DRM* and plane *AEM*, plane *DRM* and plane *ADR*, plane *ERM* and plane *AEM*, plane *ERM* and plane *ADR*, plane *AEM* and plane *ADR*

35. $\overline{AE}$ and $\overline{DR}$, $\overline{AD}$ and $\overline{ER}$

36. $\overline{AD}$ and $\overline{EM}$, $\overline{AD}$ and $\overline{MR}$, $\overline{AE}$ and $\overline{DM}$, $\overline{AE}$ and $\overline{MR}$, $\overline{ER}$ and $\overline{AM}$, $\overline{ER}$ and $\overline{DM}$, $\overline{DR}$ and $\overline{AM}$, $\overline{DR}$ and $\overline{EM}$

37. none   38. *M*

39. plane *ADR*, plane *DRM*, plane *ERM*, plane *AEM*

40.

41.

42.

43.

44.

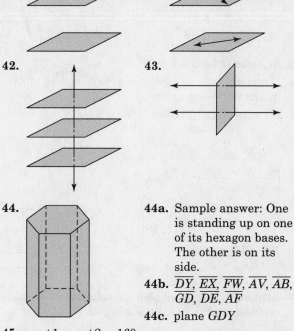

44a. Sample answer: One is standing up on one of its hexagon bases. The other is on its side.

44b. $\overline{DY}$, $\overline{EX}$, $\overline{FW}$, $\overline{AV}$, $\overline{AB}$, $\overline{GD}$, $\overline{DE}$, $\overline{AF}$

44c. plane *GDY*

45a. $m\angle 1 = m\angle 2 = 160$

45b. The measures of alternate interior angles are equal.

46. infinite number; 1

47. Sample answer: parallel circuits in electronics, parallel story lines in literature

48. See students' work.

49.

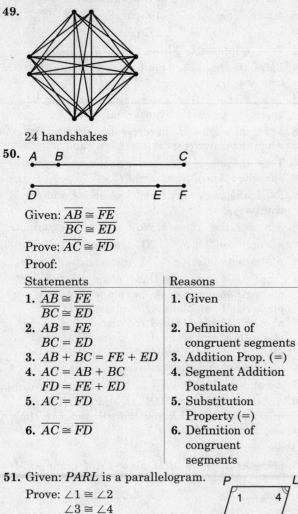

24 handshakes

50.

Given: $\overline{AB} \cong \overline{FE}$
$\overline{BC} \cong \overline{ED}$

Prove: $\overline{AC} \cong \overline{FD}$

Proof:

Statements	Reasons
1. $\overline{AB} \cong \overline{FE}$ $\overline{BC} \cong \overline{ED}$	1. Given
2. $AB = FE$ $BC = ED$	2. Definition of congruent segments
3. $AB + BC = FE + ED$	3. Addition Prop. (=)
4. $AC = AB + BC$ $FD = FE + ED$	4. Segment Addition Postulate
5. $AC = FD$	5. Substitution Property (=)
6. $\overline{AC} \cong \overline{FD}$	6. Definition of congruent segments

51. Given: *PARL* is a parallelogram.
Prove: $\angle 1 \cong \angle 2$
$\angle 3 \cong \angle 4$

52. Symmetric Property (=)

53. If something is a cloud, then it is composed of millions of water droplets.

54. $(9x + 14) + (12x + 19) = 180$
$21x + 33 = 180$
$21x = 147$
$x = 7$

55. $\left(\frac{x_1 + x_2}{2}, \frac{y_1 + y_2}{2}\right) = \left(\frac{7 + 17}{2}, \frac{36 + 0}{2}\right)$
$= \left(\frac{24}{2}, \frac{36}{2}\right)$
$= (12, 18)$

56. $RT + TS = RS$
$RT + 7 = 20$
$RT = 13$

57. Explore the problem; plan the solution; solve the problem; and examine the solution.

58.

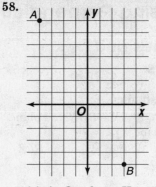

A is in Quadrant II, and *B* is in Quadrant IV.

59. $\frac{2}{5}$

60. 16, because $-16 + 16 = 0$;
16 because $|-16| = -(-16)$ or 16

3-2A **Using Technology
Angles and Parallel Lines**

Page 130 Exercises

1. consecutive interior angles: $\angle CEF$ and $\angle AFE$, $\angle DEF$ and $\angle BFE$
alternate exterior angles: $\angle CEG$ and $\angle BFH$, $\angle DEG$ and $\angle AFH$
alternate interior angles: $\angle CEF$ and $\angle BFE$, $\angle DEF$ and $\angle AFE$
corresponding angles: $\angle CEG$ and $\angle AFE$, $\angle DEG$ and $\angle BFE$, $\angle CEF$ and $\angle AFH$, $\angle DEF$ and $\angle BFH$

2. $\angle GEC \cong \angle DEF \cong \angle EFA \cong \angle HFB$, $\angle GED \cong \angle CEF \cong \angle EFB \cong \angle HFA$

3a. Corresponding angles are congruent.

3b. Alternate interior angles are congruent.

3c. Alternate exterior angles are congruent.

4. yes

5a. The measure of each of the eight angles is 90.

5b. A transversal that is perpendicular to one of two parallel lines is perpendicular to the other.

3-2 **Angles and Parallel Lines**

Page 131 Modeling Mathematics

a. See students' work.

b. The measures are equal.

c. Measures are equal; sum of the measures is 180; measures are equal.

Pages 134–135 Check for Understanding

1. If 2 parallel lines are cut by a transversal, consecutive interior angles are supplementary.

2. Sample answers: Method 1: $m\angle 5 = m\angle 8$ because $\angle 5$ and $\angle 8$ are vertical angles. $m\angle 5 + m\angle 3 = 180$, because if 2 parallel lines are cut by a transversal, the consecutive interior angles are supplementary. Therefore, $130 + m\angle 3 = 180$ and $m\angle 3 = 50$. Method 2: $m\angle 1 = m\angle 8$ because if 2 parallel lines are cut by a transversal, then the alternate exterior angles are congruent. $\angle 1$ and $\angle 3$ are supplementary because $\angle 1$ and $\angle 3$ are a linear pair and if 2 angles form a linear pair, they are supplementary. So, $m\angle 1 + m\angle 3 = 180$ by definition of supplementary. Therefore, $130 + m\angle 3 = 180$ and $m\angle 3 = 50$.

3. The lines are parallel.

4. Corresponding Angles Postulate

5. Since $\overline{SW} \parallel \overline{RK}$ and $\angle 4$ and $\angle 5$ are consecutive interior angles, $m\angle 4 + m\angle 5 = 180$. Substitute 110 for $m\angle 5$ and solve for $m\angle 4$. $m\angle 4 = 70$.

6a. $90°$

6b. Yes; since the measure of the angle is 90, $n \perp \ell$.

7. Alternate Interior Angles Theorem

8. $m\angle 3 = m\angle 1 = 107$

9. $m\angle 5 = m\angle 1 = 107$

10. $m\angle 13 = m\angle 11 = 48$

11. $m\angle 9 = m\angle 11 = 48$

12. $m\angle 15 = m\angle 11 = 48$

13. $m\angle 18 + m\angle 17 = 180$
$121 + m\angle 17 = 180$
$m\angle 17 = 59$

14. $4x - 5 = 3x + 11$
$x = 16$

$(4x - 5) + (3y + 1) = 180$
$4(16) - 5 + 3y + 1 = 180$
$3y + 60 = 180$
$3y = 120$
$y = 40$

15. $6y + (13y - 10) = 180$
$19y - 10 = 180$
$19y = 190$
$y = 10$

$9x + 12 = 13y - 10$
$9x + 12 = 13(10) - 10$
$9x + 12 = 120$
$9x = 108$
$x = 12$

16. 25

Pages 135–137 Exercises

17. Alternate Interior Angles Theorem

18. Alternate Exterior Angles Theorem

19. Corresponding Angles Postulate

20. $m\angle 6 = m\angle 1 = 131$

21. $m\angle 6 + m\angle 7 = 180$
$131 + m\angle 7 = 180$
$m\angle 7 = 49$

22. $m\angle 4 = m\angle 7 = 49$

23. $m\angle 2 = m\angle 4 = 49$

24. $m\angle 5 = m\angle 7 = 49$

25. $m\angle 8 = m\angle 6 = 131$

26. $m\angle 7 = m\angle 1 = 58$

27. $m\angle 5 = m\angle 2 = 47$

28. $m\angle 1 + m\angle 2 + m\angle 6 = 180$
$58 + 47 + m\angle 6 = 180$
$m\angle 6 = 75$

29. $m\angle 4 + m\angle 2 + m\angle 3 = 180$
$m\angle 4 + 47 + 26 = 180$
$m\angle 4 = 107$

30. $m\angle 8 = m\angle 2 + m\angle 3$
$= 47 + 26$
$= 73$

31. $m\angle 11 = m\angle 2 + m\angle 3 \qquad m\angle 10 = m\angle 1$
$m\angle 11 = 47 + 26 \qquad\qquad m\angle 10 = 58$
$m\angle 11 = 73$

$m\angle 10 + m\angle 12 + m\angle 11 = 180$
$58 + m\angle 12 + 73 = 180$
$m\angle 12 = 49$

$m\angle 9 = m\angle 12$
$m\angle 9 = 49$

32. $m\angle 7 = m\angle 8 = 42$

33. $m\angle 5 = m\angle 8 = 42$

34. $m\angle 1 = m\angle 4 = m\angle 7 = 42$

35. $m\angle 4 = m\angle 7 = 42$

36. $m\angle 6 + m\angle 7 + m\angle 8 = 180$
$m\angle 6 + 42 + 42 = 180$
$m\angle 6 = 96$

37. $m\angle 2 + m\angle 1 + m\angle 3 = 180$
$m\angle 2 + 42 + 18 = 180$
$m\angle 2 = 120$

38. $2y + 8 + 142 = 180 \qquad 4x + 6 = 142$
$2y = 30 \qquad\qquad 4x = 136$
$y = 15 \qquad\qquad x = 34$
$z = 142$

39. $x = 90$
$3y - 11 = y + 19$
$2y = 30$
$y = 15$
$4z + 2 + 3y - 11 + x = 180$
$4z + 2 + 3(15) - 11 + 90 = 180$
$4z = 54$
$z = 13.5$

40. $(7x + 9) + (7y - 4) = 180$
$7x + 7y + 5 = 180$
$7x + 7y = 175$
$x + y = 25$
$x = 25 - y$
$(11x - 1) + (2y + 5) = 180$
$11x + 2y + 4 = 180$
$11x + 2y = 176$
$11(25 - y) + 2y = 176 \quad x = 25 - y$
$275 - 11y + 2y = 176$
$275 - 9y = 176$
$-9y = -99$
$y = 11$

$x = 25 - 11$ or 14
$z + (7x + 9) = 180$
$z + 7(14) + 9 = 180$
$z + 107 = 180$
$z = 73$

41. Since $\angle 4$ and $\angle 8$ are alternate exterior angles formed when 2 parallel lines are cut by a transversal, $m\angle 4 = m\angle 8$ or $2x - 25 = x + 26$. Solving this equation, $x = 51$. Therefore, $m\angle 8 = 51 + 26$ or 77. Since $\angle 2$ and $\angle 8$ are vertical angles, $m\angle 2 = m\angle 8$ or $m\angle 2 = 77$.

42. Since $\angle 6$ and $\angle 7$ are consecutive interior angles formed when 2 parallel lines are cut by a transversal, $m\angle 6 + m\angle 7 = 180$ or $2x + 43 + 5x + 11 = 180$. Solving this equation, $x = 18$. Therefore, $m\angle 7 = 5(18) + 11$ or 101. Since $\angle 5$ and $\angle 7$ are corresponding angles formed when 2 parallel lines are cut by a transversal, $m\angle 5 = 101$.

43. 1. Given
  2. Perpendicular lines form 4 right angles.
  3. Definition of right angle
  4. Corresponding Angles Postulate
  5. Definition of congruent angles
  6. Substitution Property (=)
  7. Definition of right angle
  8. Definition of $\perp$ lines

44.

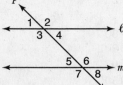

Given: $\ell \parallel m$
Prove: $\angle 3 \cong \angle 6$
  $\angle 4 \cong \angle 5$

Proof:

Statements	Reasons
1. $\ell \parallel m$	1. Given
2. $\angle 3 \cong \angle 2$ $\angle 4 \cong \angle 1$	2. Vertical angles are congruent.
3. $\angle 2 \cong \angle 6$ $\angle 1 \cong \angle 5$	3. Corresponding Angles Postulate
4. $\angle 3 \cong \angle 6$ $\angle 4 \cong \angle 5$	4. Congruence of angles is transitive.

45.

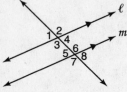

Given: $\ell \parallel m$
Prove: $\angle 3$ and $\angle 5$ are supplementary.
  $\angle 4$ and $\angle 6$ are supplementary.

Proof:

We are given that $\ell \parallel m$. If two parallel lines are cut by a transversal, corresponding angles are congruent So, $\angle 1 \cong \angle 5$ and $\angle 2 \cong \angle 6$ or $m\angle 1 = m\angle 5$ and $m\angle 2 = m\angle 6$. Since $\angle 1$ and $\angle 3$ form a linear pair and $\angle 2$ and $\angle 4$ form a linear pair, $\angle 1$ and $\angle 3$ are supplementary and $\angle 2$ and $\angle 4$ are supplementary. By the definition of supplementary angles, $m\angle 1 + m\angle 3 = 180$ and $m\angle 2 + m\angle 4 = 180$. By the Substitution Property (=), $m\angle 5 + m\angle 3 = 180$ and $m\angle 6 + m\angle 4 = 180$. Therefore, $\angle 3$ and $\angle 5$ are supplementary and $\angle 4$ and $\angle 6$ are supplementary by the definition of supplementary.

46. $x + 27 = 76$ $104 + y = 180$
  $x = 49$ $y = 76$

47.

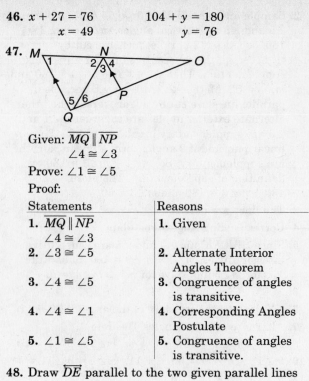

Given: $\overline{MQ} \parallel \overline{NP}$
  $\angle 4 \cong \angle 3$

Prove: $\angle 1 \cong \angle 5$
Proof:

Statements	Reasons
1. $\overline{MQ} \parallel \overline{NP}$ $\angle 4 \cong \angle 3$	1. Given
2. $\angle 3 \cong \angle 5$	2. Alternate Interior Angles Theorem
3. $\angle 4 \cong \angle 5$	3. Congruence of angles is transitive.
4. $\angle 4 \cong \angle 1$	4. Corresponding Angles Postulate
5. $\angle 1 \cong \angle 5$	5. Congruence of angles is transitive.

48. Draw $\overrightarrow{DE}$ parallel to the two given parallel lines

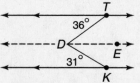

$m\angle TDK = m\angle TDE + m\angle EDK$
    $= 36 + 31$
    $= 67$

49. Since $\overline{AB} \parallel \overline{DC}$, we know $\angle 1 \cong \angle 4$ by the Alternate Interior Angles Theorem. However, $\angle 3$ and $\angle 2$ are not alternate interior angles for a transversal and sides $\overline{AB}$ and $\overline{DC}$. They are alternate interior angles for a transversal and sides $\overline{AD}$ and $\overline{BC}$ which may or may not be parallel.

50. Since $\overline{MN} \parallel \overline{PO}$, we know $\angle 2$ and $\angle 6$ are supplementary by the Consecutive Interior Angles Theorem. However, $\angle 4$ and $\angle 6$ are not consecutive interior angles for a transversal and sides $\overline{MN}$ and $\overline{PO}$. They are consecutive interior angles for a transversal and sides $\overline{MP}$ and $\overline{NO}$ which may or may not be parallel.

51a. Exclude; the transversal was used to show the number of teams not making the playoffs.

51b. Sample answers: to make money, to create excitement during the season

52. The sides of the wallpaper are parallel, so if each new piece is parallel to the last one, they will all be vertical.

53. Yes; If m never intersects n and n never intersects p, then m would never intersect p. Thus, $m \parallel p$.

54.

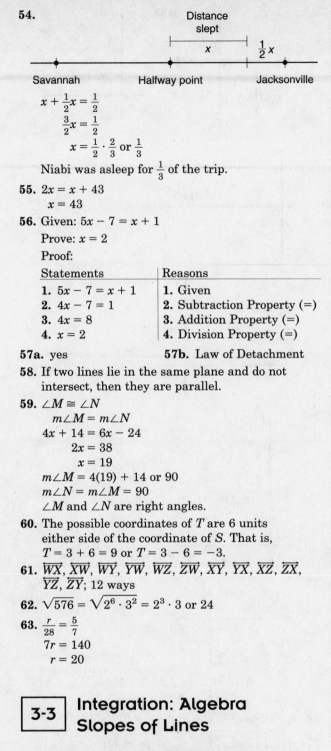

Distance
slept

Savannah   Halfway point   Jacksonville

$x + \frac{1}{2}x = \frac{1}{2}$

$\frac{3}{2}x = \frac{1}{2}$

$x = \frac{1}{2} \cdot \frac{2}{3}$ or $\frac{1}{3}$

Niabi was asleep for $\frac{1}{3}$ of the trip.

55. $2x = x + 43$
$x = 43$

56. Given: $5x - 7 = x + 1$

Prove: $x = 2$

Proof:

Statements	Reasons
1. $5x - 7 = x + 1$	1. Given
2. $4x - 7 = 1$	2. Subtraction Property (=)
3. $4x = 8$	3. Addition Property (=)
4. $x = 2$	4. Division Property (=)

57a. yes   **57b.** Law of Detachment

58. If two lines lie in the same plane and do not intersect, then they are parallel.

59. $\angle M \cong \angle N$
$m\angle M = m\angle N$
$4x + 14 = 6x - 24$
$2x = 38$
$x = 19$
$m\angle M = 4(19) + 14$ or 90
$m\angle N = m\angle M = 90$
$\angle M$ and $\angle N$ are right angles.

60. The possible coordinates of T are 6 units either side of the coordinate of S. That is, $T = 3 + 6 = 9$ or $T = 3 - 6 = -3$.

61. $\overrightarrow{WX}, \overrightarrow{XW}, \overrightarrow{WY}, \overrightarrow{YW}, \overrightarrow{WZ}, \overrightarrow{ZW}, \overrightarrow{XY}, \overrightarrow{YX}, \overrightarrow{XZ}, \overrightarrow{ZX}, \overrightarrow{YZ}, \overrightarrow{ZY}$; 12 ways

62. $\sqrt{576} = \sqrt{2^6 \cdot 3^2} = 2^3 \cdot 3$ or 24

63. $\frac{r}{28} = \frac{5}{7}$
$7r = 140$
$r = 20$

3-3 **Integration: Algebra
Slopes of Lines**

Page 141–142 Check for Understanding

1. A line whose slope is 0 is horizontal and a line whose slope is undefined is vertical.

2. The slope of a vertical line is undefined; yes.

3.   a horizontal line

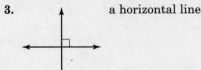

---

4. The resort starts at an elevation of 7900 feet and goes up to an elevation of 11,000 feet. Since $11{,}000 - 7900 = 3100$, the vertical rise is 3100 feet.

5. Find the slope of each line. If the slope is the same, the lines are parallel. If the product of the slopes is -1, the lines are perpendicular. The lines are perpendicular.

6a.

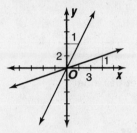

Both lines rise as you move from left to right. A line with a slope of 2 is steeper than a line with a slope of $\frac{1}{3}$.

6b.

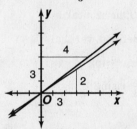

Both lines rise as you move from left to right. Since $\frac{3}{4} = \frac{9}{12}$ and $\frac{2}{3} = \frac{8}{12}$, a line with a slope of $\frac{3}{4}$ is steeper than a line with a slope of $\frac{2}{3}$.

6c.

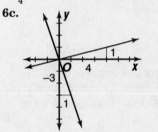

A line with a slope of -3 falls as you move from left to right, while a line with a slope of $\frac{1}{4}$ rises as you move from left to right. A line with a slope of -3 is steeper than a line with a slope of $\frac{1}{4}$.

7. $m = \frac{2 - (-3)}{3 - 4} = \frac{5}{-1} = -5$; falling

8. $m = \frac{6 - (-2)}{-3 - (-3)} = \frac{8}{0}$ undefined; vertical

9. $m = \frac{3 - 0}{4 - 0} = \frac{3}{4}$

10. $m = \frac{5 - 3}{-1 - 4} = \frac{-2}{5}$ slope of line $\perp$ to s: $\frac{5}{2}$

11. $m = \frac{3 - 3}{4 - (-2)} = \frac{0}{6} = 0$ slope of line $\parallel$ to r: 0

12.   **13.**

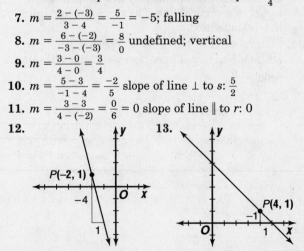

$P(-2, 1)$

$P(4, 1)$

14. No; slope of $\overrightarrow{AB} = \frac{5}{6}$, slope of $\overrightarrow{CD} = \frac{-4}{3}$, and
$\frac{5}{6}\left(-\frac{4}{3}\right) = -\frac{10}{9} \neq -1$.

15. slope of line through $(1, 6)$ and $(7, 2)$ is
$\frac{2-6}{7-1} = -\frac{4}{6} = -\frac{2}{3}$. The slope of line perpendicular
to this line is $\frac{3}{2}$. Use $\frac{3}{2}$ to find x.

$$\frac{6-(-3)}{x-2} = \frac{3}{2}$$
$$18 = 3x - 6$$
$$24 = 3x$$
$$x = 8$$

16. $\frac{33{,}000 - 25}{107} \approx 308.2$ feet per mile

Pages 142–145 Exercises

17. $m = \frac{6-0}{0-4} = -\frac{6}{4} = -\frac{3}{2}$; falling

18. $m = \frac{8-2}{-3-4} = -\frac{6}{7}$; falling

19. $m = \frac{3-3}{6-(-6)} = \frac{0}{12} = 0$; horizontal

20. $m = \frac{1-(-6)}{8-8} = \frac{7}{0}$ undefined; vertical

21. $m = \frac{-3-(-5)}{-2-(-6)} = \frac{2}{4} = \frac{1}{2}$; rising

22. $m = \frac{5-9}{-2-4} = \frac{-4}{-6} = \frac{2}{3}$; rising

23. $m = \frac{2-(-3)}{0-4} = -\frac{5}{4}$
The slope of $\overrightarrow{BD} = -\frac{5}{4}$.

24. $\overrightarrow{CD}$ is horizontal; its slope is 0.

25. $m = \frac{-2-2}{-4-0} = \frac{-4}{-4} = 1$
The slope of $\overrightarrow{AB}$ is 1.

26. $m = \frac{2-0}{4-0} = \frac{2}{4} = \frac{1}{2}$
The slope of $\overrightarrow{EO}$ is $\frac{1}{2}$.

27. $\overrightarrow{DE}$ is vertical and any line parallel to $\overrightarrow{DE}$ is vertical. The slope of vertical lines is undefined.

28. Any line parallel to $\overrightarrow{EO}$ has the same slope as $\overrightarrow{EO}$ or $\frac{1}{2}$.

29. Slope of $\overrightarrow{BD}$ is $-\frac{5}{4}$. The slope of any line perpendicular to $\overrightarrow{BD}$ is $\frac{-1}{-\frac{5}{4}}$ or $\frac{4}{5}$.

30. $\overrightarrow{CD}$ is a horizontal line. Any line perpendicular to $\overrightarrow{CD}$ is a vertical line. The slope of a vertical line is undefined.

31. $\overrightarrow{DE}$ is a vertical line. Any line perpendicular to $\overrightarrow{DE}$ is a horizontal line. Horizontal lines have a slope of 0.

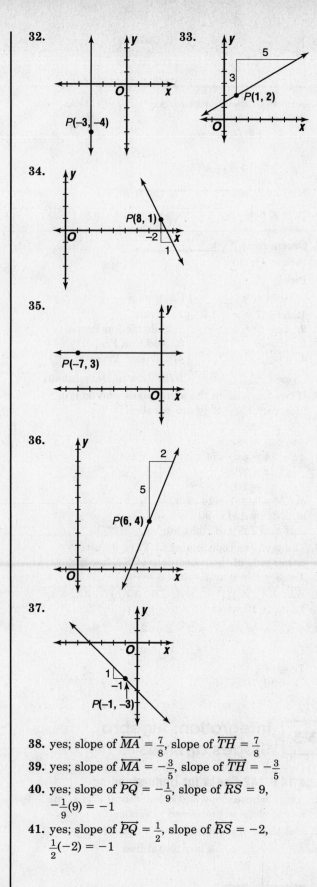

38. yes; slope of $\overrightarrow{MA} = \frac{7}{8}$, slope of $\overrightarrow{TH} = \frac{7}{8}$

39. yes; slope of $\overrightarrow{MA} = -\frac{3}{5}$, slope of $\overrightarrow{TH} = -\frac{3}{5}$

40. yes; slope of $\overrightarrow{PQ} = -\frac{1}{9}$, slope of $\overrightarrow{RS} = 9$,
$-\frac{1}{9}(9) = -1$

41. yes; slope of $\overrightarrow{PQ} = \frac{1}{2}$, slope of $\overrightarrow{RS} = -2$,
$\frac{1}{2}(-2) = -1$

42. $m = \frac{y_2 - y_1}{x_2 - x_1}$

$\frac{4}{5} = \frac{-6 - 2}{-4 - x}$

$4(-4 - x) = 5(-8)$

$-16 - 4x = -40$

$-4x = -24$

$x = 6$

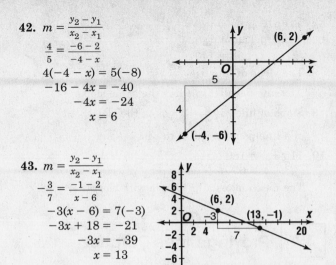

43. $m = \frac{y_2 - y_1}{x_2 - x_1}$

$-\frac{3}{7} = \frac{-1 - 2}{x - 6}$

$-3(x - 6) = 7(-3)$

$-3x + 18 = -21$

$-3x = -39$

$x = 13$

44. The slope of the line through (4, 8) and (2, −1)

is $\frac{-1 - 8}{2 - 4}$ or $\frac{9}{2}$. The slope of the line perpendicular

to this line is $-\frac{2}{9}$.

$m = \frac{y_2 - y_1}{x_2 - x_1}$

$-\frac{2}{9} = \frac{5 - 2}{-4 - x}$

$-2(-4 - x) = 9(3)$

$8 + 2x = 27$

$2x = 19$

$x = 9.5$

45a. slope of $\overline{PQ} = -1$

slope of $\overline{RS} = -1$

slope of $\overline{QR} = 1$

slope of $\overline{PS} = 1$

Since the opposite sides have the same slope, they are parallel.

45b. $-1(1) = -1$ and $1(-1) = -1$

Since the slopes of adjacent sides are opposite reciprocals, they are perpendicular.

45c. $PQ = \sqrt{(5 - 1)^2 + (2 - 6)^2} = \sqrt{32}$

$QR = \sqrt{(1 - (-3)^2 + (6 - 2)^2} = \sqrt{32}$

$RS = \sqrt{(-3 - 1)^2 + (2 - (-2))^2} = \sqrt{32}$

$PS = \sqrt{(5 - 1)^2 + (2 - (-2))^2} = \sqrt{32}$

Since the opposite sides have the same length, they are congruent.

45d. square

46. Suppose $\overline{EH} \parallel \overline{GF}$ and $\overline{HF} \parallel \overline{GE}$. Slopes of $\overline{EH}$

and $\overline{GF} = \frac{-6 - 5}{1 - (-2)}$

or $\frac{-11}{3}$.

Slopes of $\overline{HF}$ and $\overline{GE}$

$= \frac{5 - 3}{-2 - 2}$ or $\frac{-1}{2}$.

Use slopes to draw segments from F and E.

They meet at $H(5, -8)$.

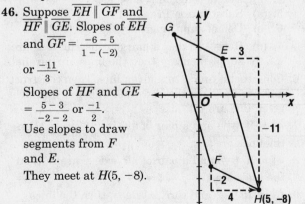

Suppose $\overline{GE} \parallel \overline{FH}$ and $\overline{EF} \parallel \overline{FG}$. Slopes of $\overline{GE}$ and $\overline{FH} = \frac{-1}{2}$

Slopes of $\overline{EF}$ and $\overline{FG} =$

$\frac{-6 - 3}{1 - 2} = \frac{9}{1}$

Use slopes to draw segments from G and F.

They meet at $H(-3, -4)$.

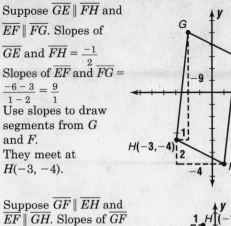

Suppose $\overline{GF} \parallel \overline{EH}$ and $\overline{EF} \parallel \overline{GH}$. Slopes of $\overline{GF}$ and $\overline{EH} = \frac{-11}{3}$. Slopes of $\overline{EF}$ and $\overline{GH} = \frac{9}{1}$. Use slopes to draw segments from G and E. They meet at $H(-1, 14)$.

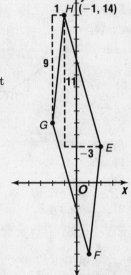

47a. $-\frac{5}{6}$ **b.** $-\frac{5}{2}$ **c.** $\frac{5}{2}$ **d.** $-\frac{3}{4}$

48. slope of line containing (−3, 6) and (1, 2)

$= \frac{6 - 2}{-3 - 1} = \frac{4}{-4} = -1$ slope of line containing

(−3, 6) and (3, 0) $= \frac{6 - 0}{-3 - 3} = \frac{6}{-6} = -1$

Both lines contain the point (−3, 6) and have the same slope, so the lines are the same.

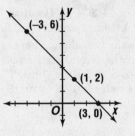

49. $m = \frac{7}{11} = 0.64$ **50.** See students' work.

yes; $0.64 < 0.88$

51a. $\frac{30}{45(12)} = \frac{1}{18}$ **51b.** $\frac{45 \text{ feet}}{30 \text{ inches}} = 1.5$ feet

52a. $\frac{34}{3} \approx 11.3$ million more packages shipped each year

52b. The rate of change equals the slope of a line that relates software sales over time.

52c. $\dfrac{x - 39}{2001 - 1995} = \dfrac{34}{3}$

$3(x - 39) = 321$

$3x - 117 = 204$

$3x = 321$

$x = 107$ million packages

53. $(4x + 7) + (7x - 3) = 180$

$11x = 176$

$x = 16$

$4x + 7 = 6y + 5$

$4(16) + 7 = 6y + 5$

$71 = 6y + 5$

$11 = y$

54a. parallel **54b.** skew

54c. intersecting **54d.** parallel

54e. intersecting

55.

Given: $\angle 1 \cong \angle 2$

Prove: $\angle 1 \cong \angle 3$

Proof:

Statements	Reasons
1. $\angle 1 \cong \angle 2$	1. Given
2. $\angle 2 \cong \angle 3$	2. Vertical $\angle$s are $\cong$.
3. $\angle 1 \cong \angle 3$	3. Congruence of angles is transitive.

56a. Subtraction Property (=)

56b. Congruence of segments is symmetric.

56c. Multiplication Property (=)

57.

$A = 2\pi r^2 + 2\pi rh$	Given
$A - 2\pi r^2 = 2\pi rh$	Subtraction Property (=)
$\dfrac{A - 2\pi r^2}{2\pi r} = h$	Division Property (=)

58. Yes; Law of Detachment

59. Sample answer: $\left(\dfrac{1}{2}\right)^2 = \dfrac{1}{4}, \dfrac{1}{2} > \dfrac{1}{4}$

60. Yes; since $2x + 28 = 5x - 14$, $x = 14$. Because $m\angle 1 = 2(14)$ or 28, $m\angle 1 = m\angle 2$ and $\angle 1 \cong \angle 2$.

61. There is 1 choice (6) for the first digit. There are 2 choices (0 or 1) for the second digit and 9 choices (1, 2, 3, 4, 5, 6, 7, 8, 9) for the third. The number of possible area codes is $1 \cdot 2 \cdot 9$ or 18 area codes.

62. Quadrant III

63. $4x^2 - 3x = 4(-2)^2 - 3(-2)$

$= 4(4) + 6$

$= 22$

64. $4n + 23 = 3 - 6n$

$10n = -20$

$n = -2$

Page 145 Self Test

1. $\overline{AE}, \overline{BD}$ **2.** $\overline{DE}, \overline{BD}, \overline{DF}$

3. plane ABC and plane EDF

4. $m\angle 4 = m\angle 1 = 98$ **5.** $m\angle 8 = m\angle 2 = 40$

6. $m\angle 9 + m\angle 8 = 180$ **7.** $m = \dfrac{3 - 2}{-1 - 2} = -\dfrac{1}{3}$

$m\angle 9 + 40 = 180$

$m\angle 9 = 140$

8. The slope of line b is $\dfrac{2 - (-1)}{2 - 4}$ or $-\dfrac{3}{2}$.

Any line parallel to b has the same slope.

9. Slope of line c is $\dfrac{2 - (-1)}{2 - (-2)}$ or $\dfrac{3}{4}$; the slope of a line perpendicular to c is $\dfrac{-4}{3}$.

10. $115 + x = 180$

$x = 65$

The pipe makes a 65° angle with the other pipe.

3-4   Proving Lines Parallel

Page 146 Modeling Mathematics

a. corresponding

b. Lines ℓ and m appear to be parallel.

c. $(0, 3); \dfrac{5 - 3}{4 - 0} = \dfrac{2}{4} = \dfrac{1}{2}$ **d.** $\dfrac{1 - 0}{2 - 0} = \dfrac{1}{2}$

e. Yes, the slopes are the same and $\ell \parallel m$.

Pages 149–150 Check for Understanding

1. If two lines in a plane are cut by a transversal, the lines are $\parallel$ if one of the following is true.

(1) Corresponding angles are $\cong$.

(2) Alternate exterior angles are $\cong$.

(3) Consecutive interior angles are supplementary.

(4) Alternate interior angles are $\cong$.

(5) Both lines are $\perp$ to the transversal.

2. No more or no less than; such a drawing does not exist.

3. Jasmine; since $127 + 51 = 178$ and $62 + 120 = 182$, the consecutive interior $\angle$s are not supplementary.

4. Sample answers: railroad tracks and yard lines on a football field; If a line is drawn across the tracks and a pair of alternate interior angles are $\cong$, the tracks are $\parallel$. If the yard lines are $\perp$ to one of the sidelines, the lines are $\parallel$.

5. 1. (b) Given

2. (f) Consecutive Interior Angles Theorem

3. (c) Def. of supplementary

4. (g) Def. of congruent angles

5. (a) Substitution Prop. (=)

6. (e) Def. of supplementary $\angle$s

7. (d) If $\overleftrightarrow{}$ so that a pair of consecutive $\angle$s are supplementary then the lines are parallel.

6. Construct a line $\perp$ to a given line. Then construct another line $\perp$ to the new line. This line and the given line are $\parallel$.

7. $a \parallel b$: If $\overleftrightarrow{}$ and a pair of alt. int. $\angle$s are $\cong$, then the lines are $\parallel$.

8. $a \parallel b$: If $\overleftrightarrow{}$ and a pair of alt. ext. $\angle$s are $\cong$, then the lines are $\parallel$.

9. $\ell \parallel m$: If $\overleftrightarrow{}$ and corr. $\angle$s are $\cong$, then the lines are $\parallel$.

10. $8x + 4 = 9x - 11$
$-x = -15$
$x = 15$

11. $(6x - 2) + 140 = 180$
$6x + 138 = 180$
$6x = 42$
$x = 7$

12. $q \parallel p$; In a plane if 2 lines are $\perp$ to the same line, then they are $\parallel$.

13. 1. Given
2. Vertical $\angle$s are $\cong$.
3. Transitive Prop. $\cong$ $\angle$s
4. If $\overleftrightarrow{}$ and corr. $\angle$s are $\cong$, then the lines are $\parallel$.

14. If $\overleftrightarrow{}$ and corr. $\angle$s are $\cong$, then the lines are $\parallel$.

Pages 150–153 Exercises

15. $\overline{EC} \parallel \overline{HF}$; If $\overleftrightarrow{}$ and corr. $\angle$s are $\cong$, then the lines are $\parallel$.

16. $\overline{EC} \parallel \overline{HF}$; If $\overleftrightarrow{}$ and a pair of alt. int. $\angle$s are $\cong$, then the lines are $\parallel$.

17. $\overline{JK} \parallel \overline{BL}$; If $\overleftrightarrow{}$ and a pair of consecutive int. $\angle$s are supplementary, then the lines are $\parallel$.

18. $\overline{EC} \parallel \overline{FH}$; In a plane, if 2 lines are $\perp$ to the same line, then they are $\parallel$.

19. $p \parallel q$; If $\overleftrightarrow{}$ and a pair of alt. ext. $\angle$s are $\cong$, then the lines are $\parallel$.

20. $\ell \parallel m$; If $\overleftrightarrow{}$ and corr. $\angle$s are $\cong$, then the lines are $\parallel$.

21. $p \parallel q$; If $\overleftrightarrow{}$ and a pair of consecutive int. $\angle$s are supplementary, then the lines are $\parallel$.

22. $\ell \parallel m$; If $\overleftrightarrow{}$ and a pair of alt. int. $\angle$s are $\cong$, then the lines are $\parallel$.

23. $\ell \parallel m$; If $\overleftrightarrow{}$ and a pair of consecutive int. $\angle$s are supplementary, then the lines are $\parallel$.

24. Slope of $\ell = \frac{4}{3}$, slope of $m = \frac{4}{3}$; see students' work.

25. $7x - 1 = 90$
$7x = 91$
$x = 13$

26. $(9x - 5) + (7x + 3) = 180$
$16x - 2 = 180$
$16x = 182$
$x = 11.375$

27. $14x + 9 = 5x + 90$
$9x = 81$
$x = 9$

28. $(4x + 9) + (19x + 10) = 180$
$23x + 19 = 180$
$23x = 161$
$x = 7$
$(3y + 8) + (4x + 9) = 180$
$3y + 4(7) + 17 = 180$
$3y + 45 = 180$
$3y = 135$
$y = 45$

29. $5x = 19y - 7$
$\frac{5x + 7}{19} = y$
$4x - 7 = 11y$
$4x - 7 = 11\left(\frac{5x + 7}{19}\right)$
$19(4x - 7) = 11(5x + 7)$
$76x - 133 = 55x + 77$
$21x = 210$
$x = 10$
$\frac{5(10) + 7}{19} = y$
$3 = y$

30. $\overline{EF} \parallel \overline{HG}$; If $\overleftrightarrow{}$ and a pair of alt. int. $\angle$s are $\cong$, then the lines are $\parallel$.

31. $\ell \parallel m$; If $\overleftrightarrow{}$ and a pair of consecutive int. $\angle$s are supplementary, then the lines are $\parallel$.

32. $\overline{AE} \parallel \overline{BD}$; In a plane, if 2 lines are to the same line, then they are $\parallel$. $\overline{AK} \parallel \overline{LB}$; If $\overleftrightarrow{}$ and a pair of alternate interior $\angle$s are $\cong$, then the lines are $\parallel$.

33.

Statements	Reasons
1. $\angle 1$ and $\angle 2$ are supplementary.	1. Given
2. $\angle 2$ and $\angle 3$ form a linear pair.	2. Definition of linear pair
3. $\angle 2$ and $\angle 3$ are supplementary.	3. If 2 angles form a linear pair, they are supplementary.
4. $\angle 1 \cong \angle 3$	4. 2 $\angle$s supplementary to the same $\angle$ are $\cong$.
5. $\ell \cong m$	5. If $\overleftrightarrow{}$ and corr. $\angle$s are $\cong$, then the lines are $\parallel$.

34. Given: $\ell \perp t$
$m \perp t$
Prove: $\ell \parallel m$

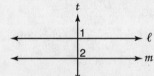

Proof:
We are given $\ell \perp t$ and $m \perp t$. Since $\perp$ lines form right angles, $\angle 1$ and $\angle 2$ are right angles. $\angle 1 \cong \angle 2$ since right angles are $\cong$ to each other. If 2 lines in a plane are cut by a transversal so that corresponding $\angle$s are $\cong$, then the lines are $\parallel$. Therefore, $\ell \parallel m$.

35. Given: $\angle 2 \cong \angle 1$
$\angle 1 \cong \angle 3$
Prove: $\overline{ST} \parallel \overline{YZ}$

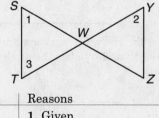

Proof:

Statements	Reasons
1. $\angle 2 \cong \angle 1$ $\angle 1 \cong \angle 3$	1. Given
2. $\angle 2 \cong \angle 3$	2. Congruence of $\angle$s is transitive.
3. $\overline{ST} \parallel \overline{YZ}$	3. If $\overleftrightarrow{}$ and a pair of alt. int. $\angle$s are $\cong$, then the lines are $\parallel$.

36. Given: $\overline{JO} \parallel \overline{KN}$
$\angle 1 \cong \angle 2$
$\angle 3 \cong \angle 4$
Prove: $\overline{KO} \parallel \overline{AN}$

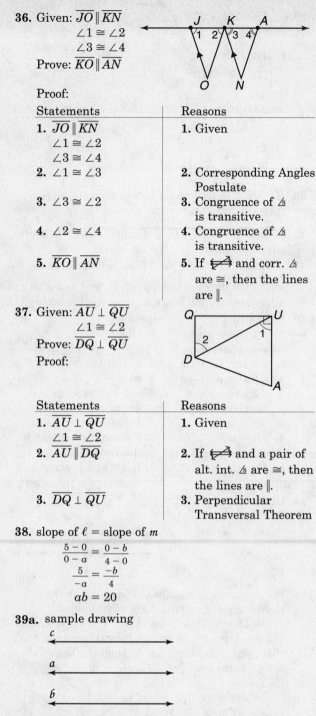

Proof:

Statements	Reasons
1. $\overline{JO} \parallel \overline{KN}$ $\angle 1 \cong \angle 2$ $\angle 3 \cong \angle 4$	1. Given
2. $\angle 1 \cong \angle 3$	2. Corresponding Angles Postulate
3. $\angle 3 \cong \angle 2$	3. Congruence of ∡ is transitive.
4. $\angle 2 \cong \angle 4$	4. Congruence of ∡ is transitive.
5. $\overline{KO} \parallel \overline{AN}$	5. If ⇆ and corr. ∡ are ≅, then the lines are ∥.

37. Given: $\overline{AU} \perp \overline{QU}$
$\angle 1 \cong \angle 2$
Prove: $\overline{DQ} \perp \overline{QU}$
Proof:

Statements	Reasons
1. $\overline{AU} \perp \overline{QU}$ $\angle 1 \cong \angle 2$	1. Given
2. $\overline{AU} \parallel \overline{DQ}$	2. If ⇆ and a pair of alt. int. ∡ are ≅, then the lines are ∥.
3. $\overline{DQ} \perp \overline{QU}$	3. Perpendicular Transversal Theorem

38. slope of ℓ = slope of m
$$\frac{5-0}{0-a} = \frac{0-b}{4-0}$$
$$\frac{5}{-a} = \frac{-b}{4}$$
$$ab = 20$$

39a. sample drawing

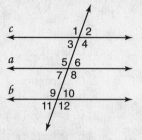

39b. Draw a transversal intersecting all three lines and number the angles formed.

Sample plan for proof: Use corr. ∡ to show $\angle 6 \cong \angle 10$ and $\angle 2 \cong \angle 6$. Then $\angle 2 \cong \angle 10$, which is enough to show that $b \parallel c$.

40. Sample answer:

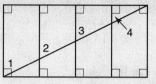

$m\angle 1 = m\angle 2 = m\angle 3 = m\angle 4$; all vertical lines should make right angles with the bottom board; all vertical lines should make right angles with the top board.

41. yes

42. See students' work.

43. $m = \frac{3-(-1)}{-2-(-7)} = \frac{4}{5}$; rising

44. False; the alternate interior angles are congruent and the consecutive interior angles are supplementary.

45. Intersecting; they all meet at the hub.

46.
$$m\angle 1 + m\angle 2 = 180$$
$$(2x+15) + (8x-5) = 180$$
$$10x + 10 = 180$$
$$10x = 170$$
$$x = 17$$

$m\angle 1 = 2x + 15$
$\quad\quad = 2(17) + 15$ or 49

$m\angle 2 = 8x - 5$
$\quad\quad = 8(17) - 5$ or 131

47. Lines p and m never meet; Law of Detachment.

48. $s + 159 = 180$
$\quad\quad s = 21$

49. $\left(\frac{x_1 + x_2}{2}, \frac{y_1 + y_2}{2}\right) = \left(\frac{8 + (-4)}{2}, \frac{11 + 7}{2}\right)$
$\quad\quad\quad\quad\quad = \left(\frac{4}{2}, \frac{18}{2}\right)$
$\quad\quad\quad\quad\quad = (2, 9)$

50. $18 - 37 - 12$, $18 - 12 - 37$, $37 - 12 - 18$, $37 - 18 - 12$, $12 - 18 - 37$, $12 - 37 - 18$; 6 combinations

51. $(2x - 3y)(8x + y)$

52. $f = \frac{WV^2}{gR}$

$R \cdot f = \frac{WV^2}{g}$

$R = \frac{WV^2}{fg}$

3-5 Parallels and Distance

Page 154 Modeling Mathematics

a. See students' work.

b. They seem to be perpendicular.

c. The shortest segment from a line to a point is perpendicular to the line.

Pages 157–158 Check for Understanding

1. Both definitions define parallel as being equidistant. You could measure the perpendicular distance between the rows of dancers to see if they are everywhere equidistant.

2. In both equations, the coefficient of the x term is 2. The coefficient is the slope of the lines.

3. Sample answer: You are camping and need to find the shortest path to the river to get water.

4. You can show that 2 lines in a plane are parallel by comparing the slopes, by using a transversal and angle relationships, and by measuring to see if the lines are everywhere equidistant. To compare slopes, you need to know the vertical and horizontal change. To use transversals and angle relationships, you need a transversal. You can always measure the distance between the lines.

5. Pick any point on one line. Construct a perpendicular segment from the point to the other line.

6.

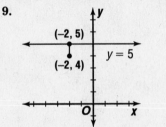

7.

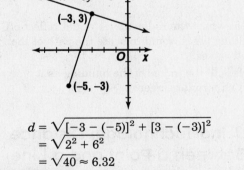

8. Yes; the lines are everywhere equidistant.

9.

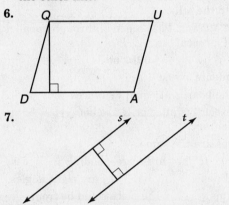

$d = \sqrt{[-2-(-2)]^2 + (5-4)^2} = \sqrt{1}$ or 1

10.

$d = \sqrt{[-3-(-5)]^2 + [3-(-3)]^2}$
$= \sqrt{2^2 + 6^2}$
$= \sqrt{40} \approx 6.32$

11. $\overline{PS}$ **12.** $\overline{RS}$

13. It is everywhere equidistant.

14. **15.**

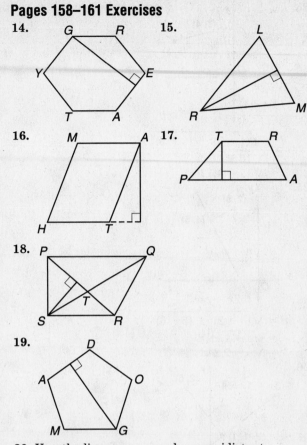

16. **17.**

18.

19.

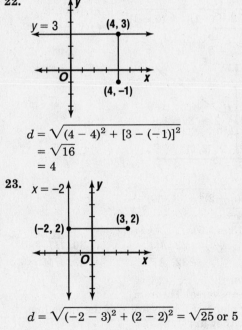

20. Yes; the lines are everywhere equidistant.

21. Yes; the lines are everywhere equidistant.

22.

$d = \sqrt{(4-4)^2 + [3-(-1)]^2}$
$= \sqrt{16}$
$= 4$

23.

$d = \sqrt{(-2-3)^2 + (2-2)^2} = \sqrt{25}$ or 5

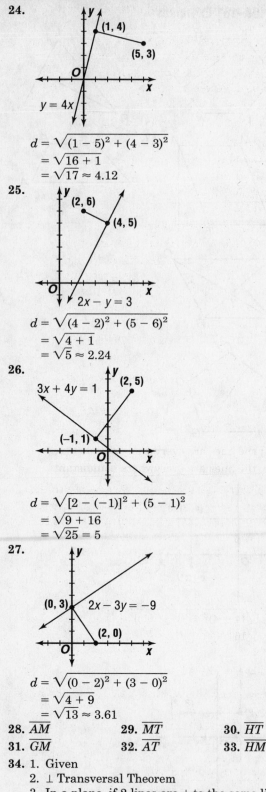

24.

$d = \sqrt{(1-5)^2 + (4-3)^2}$
$= \sqrt{16 + 1}$
$= \sqrt{17} \approx 4.12$

25.

$d = \sqrt{(4-2)^2 + (5-6)^2}$
$= \sqrt{4 + 1}$
$= \sqrt{5} \approx 2.24$

26.

$d = \sqrt{[2-(-1)]^2 + (5-1)^2}$
$= \sqrt{9 + 16}$
$= \sqrt{25} = 5$

27.

$d = \sqrt{(0-2)^2 + (3-0)^2}$
$= \sqrt{4 + 9}$
$= \sqrt{13} \approx 3.61$

28. $\overline{AM}$ **29.** $\overline{MT}$ **30.** $\overline{HT}$

31. $\overline{GM}$ **32.** $\overline{AT}$ **33.** $\overline{HM}$

34. 1. Given
2. ⊥ Transversal Theorem
3. In a plane, if 2 lines are ⊥ to the same line, then they are ∥.

35. Each line has a slope of 1. The slope of the line ⊥ is −1. From (0, 3) go down 1 unit and right 1 unit. Draw the line perpendicular to the two lines. The line seems to interesect the lower line at (3.5, −0.5).
$d = \sqrt{(0 - 3 \cdot 5)^2 + [3 - (-0 \cdot 5)^2}$
$= \sqrt{2.25 + 12.25}$
$= \sqrt{24.5} \approx 4.95$

36. Find the length of a perpendicular segment from plane *ABC* to plane *EFG*.

37. $d = \dfrac{|3.2 + 4.5 - 1|}{\sqrt{3^2 + 4^2}} = 5$

Yes; both equal 5.

38a. Yes; $\ell \perp Q$. If a line is ⊥ to one of 2 ∥ planes, it is ⊥ to the other.

38b. Sample answer: Pass a pencil through parallel sides of a cereal box.

39a. yes   **39b.** no

39c. See students' work.

40. Attach the boards at equal distances.

41. $p \nparallel q$; consecutive interior ⦞ are not supplementary.

42. The slopes are the same.

43. $m\angle 2 = m\angle 4$; They are corresponding ⦞.

44. parallel lines   **45.** They are right angles.

46. Sample answer: No; the piece could be from another puzzle.

47.

48. $68 \div (-17) = -4$ **49.** $0.9a = 7.29$
$a = 8.1$

Page 161 Mathematics & Society

1. Radar waves can be reflected or absorbed by an object.
2. Angles at which the radar waves would reflect off the building (This would indicate the path of the reflected waves.)
3. This refers to the image of the building as it appears on a radar screen.

3-5B ## Using Technology: Distance Between a Point and a Line

Page 162 Excercises

1. 1.41   **2.** 5.39   **3.** 3.16   **4.** 7.21

Integration: Non-Euclidean Geometry; Spherical Geometry

Page 164 Modeling Mathematics

a.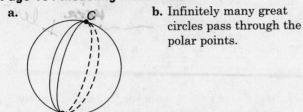

b. Infinitely many great circles pass through the polar points.

Page 167 Check for Understanding

1. Two polar points have many great circles passing through them.

2a. spherical   2b. plane Euclidean

3. Since 24,900 − 6120 = 18,780, it is shorter to go through Castellón de la Plana.

4a. Circle *r* does not divide the sphere into 2 equal halves.

4b. No; unless ℓ is the equator and *P* is a pole, only one great circle can be drawn through *P* and perpendicular to ℓ.

5. true

6. False; in spherical geometry, perpendicular lines form 8 right angles.

7. 41°N, 29°E   8. Dubai, Saudi Arabia

9. The great circle is finite.

10. A curved path on the great circle passing through 2 points is the shortest distance between the 2 points.

11a. See students' work.

11b. See students' work.

Pages 168–169 Excercises

12. False; in spherical geometry, if 3 points are collinear, any point can be between the other 2 points.

13. False; in spherical geometry, a line has finite length.

14. False; in spherical geometry, there are no parallel lines.

15. True

16. False; in spherical geometry, there are no parallel lines.

17. True

18. 29°N, 95°W   19. 30°N, 85°W

20. 27°S, 28°E   21. 19°N, 99°W

22. New Orleans, Louisiana

23. Reno, Nevada   24. Perth, Australia

25. There exist no parallel lines.

26. Two distinct great circles intersect in exactly 2 points.

27. A pair of perpendicular great circles divides the sphere into 4 finite congruent regions.

28. A pair of perpendicular great circles intersects twice and creates 8 right angles.

29. There exists no parallel lines.

30. There are 2 distances between 2 points.

31.   1 perpendicular

32a. half the length of the great circle

32b. one-fourth the length of the great circle

33.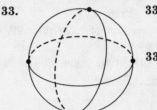

33a. They are each perpendicular to each other.

33b. They lie at the intersection of the other 2 circles.

34a. 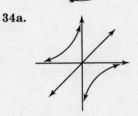   34b. hyperbolic geometry

35a. In a plane, if 2 lines are perpendicular to the same line, then they are parallel.

35b. Yes; 2 intersecting great circles can both be perpendicular to another great circle.

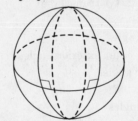

36a. 40°N

36b. Sample answers: Madrid, Spain, and Beijing, China

36c. Yes; distance from the equator affects the closeness of the sun.

37. Sample answer: The spaceship will eventually return to its starting point.

38. $d = \sqrt{(6-6)^2 + (-2-7)^2}$
    $= \sqrt{81} = 9$

39. The 2 lines must be perpendicular to the transversal.

40. $m = \frac{0-(-2)}{3-8} = -\frac{2}{5}$

41.

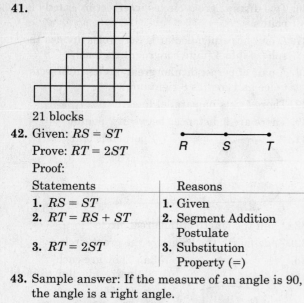

21 blocks

42. Given: $RS = ST$

Prove: $RT = 2ST$

Proof:

Statements	Reasons
1. $RS = ST$	1. Given
2. $RT = RS + ST$	2. Segment Addition Postulate
3. $RT = 2ST$	3. Substitution Property (=)

43. Sample answer: If the measure of an angle is 90, the angle is a right angle.

Hypothesis: if the measure of an angle is 90
Conclusion: the angle is a right angle

44. $AB = \sqrt{(-1-6)^2 + [4-(-20)]^2}$

$= \sqrt{(-7)^2 + (24)^2}$

$= \sqrt{625}$ or 25

45. Commutative Property (+)

46. $-8 - m = 13$

$-m = 21$

$m = -21$

Chapter 3 Highlights

Page 171 Understanding and Using the Vocabulary

1. (f) interior angles   2. (l) transversal
3. (d) corresponding angles
4. (a) alternate exterior angles
5. (g) parallel lines   6. (e) exterior angles
7. (c) consecutive interior angles
8. (h) parallel postulate
9. (b) alternate interior angles
10. (i) skew lines   11. (j) slope

Chapter 3 Study Guide and Assessment

Pages 172–174 Skills and Concepts

12. t and n 13. t and m
14. t and n with transversal ℓ
15. Sample answer: ℓ and n
16. t and m
17. $\angle 3 \cong \angle 5$, $\angle 3 \cong \angle 6$, $\angle 1 \cong \angle 4$, $\angle 5 = \angle 6$,
    $\angle GAB \cong \angle 10$, $\angle GAB \cong \angle ABH$, $\angle FAE \cong \angle 9$
18. $\angle 3 \cong \angle 8$, $\angle 1 \cong \angle 7$, $\angle 5 \cong \angle 6$
19. $\angle 3$, $\angle 8$ 20. $\angle 10$, $\angle ABH$
21. $m = \frac{4-(-2)}{0-(-1)} = \frac{6}{1} = 6$; rising

22. $m = \frac{0-(-6)}{2-2} = \frac{6}{0}$ undefined; vertical
23. $m = \frac{2-4}{11-5} = -\frac{2}{6} = \frac{-1}{3}$; falling
24. $m = \frac{-5-(-7)}{-1-3} = \frac{2}{-4} = -\frac{1}{2}$; falling
25. $m = \frac{7-(-2)}{-3-4} = -\frac{9}{7}$; $m = \frac{7}{9}$
26. $m = \frac{6-6}{0-3} = \frac{0}{-3} = 0$; undefined slope
27. $m = \frac{-2-(-3)}{7-1} = \frac{1}{6}$; $m = -6$
28. $m = \frac{-2-4}{9-(-1)} = \frac{-6}{10} = \frac{-3}{5}$; $m = \frac{5}{3}$
29. $\overline{AD} \parallel \overline{EF}$; $\angle 1 \cong \angle 4$ since vertical angles are congruent. So, $\angle 4$ and $\angle 2$ are supplementary. The lines are parallel because consecutive interior angles are supplementary.
30. $\overline{DE} \parallel \overline{CF}$; alt. int. $\angle$s are $\cong$.
31. $\overline{AD} \parallel \overline{EF}$; corr. $\angle$s are $\cong$.
32. $\overline{PS}$ 33. $\overline{RQ}$
34. $\overline{RQ}$ or $\overline{MP}$ 35. $\overline{PQ}$ or $\overline{MR}$
36. If three points are collinear, any of the points can be between the other 2 points.
37. The intersection of 2 great circles creates 8 angles.
38. There exists no parallel lines.
39. The shortest path between two points is an arc on the great circle passing through the points.
40. There is at least one great circle passing through two points.

Page 174 Applications and Problem Solving

41.

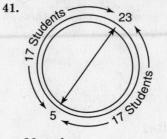

36 students

42a.   2 ft

24 ft

42b. $\frac{2}{24} = \frac{1}{12}$

43. $\frac{455-195}{4} = \frac{260}{4} = 65$ mph

44a. $\frac{6000-6100}{1} = -100$ deer per year

44b. $6000 - 100(10) = 5000$ deer

44c. Decline; since the slope is negative the line will fall as you move from left to right.

Page 175 Alternative Assessment

- no
- no

CHAPTER 4 Identifying Congruent Triangles

| 4-1 | Classifying Triangles |

Page 181 Modeling Mathematics
a. See students' work.
b. See students' work.

Pages 183–184 Check for Understanding
1a. obtuse   **1b.** right
1c. acute, equiangular   **1d.** acute

2. A scalene triangle has no two sides congruent. An isosceles triangle has at least two sides congruent. An equilateral triangle has all three sides congruent.

3. Both are correct. If the triangle is classified according to its sides, it is an isosceles triangle. If it is classified according to its angles, it is a right triangle.

4.
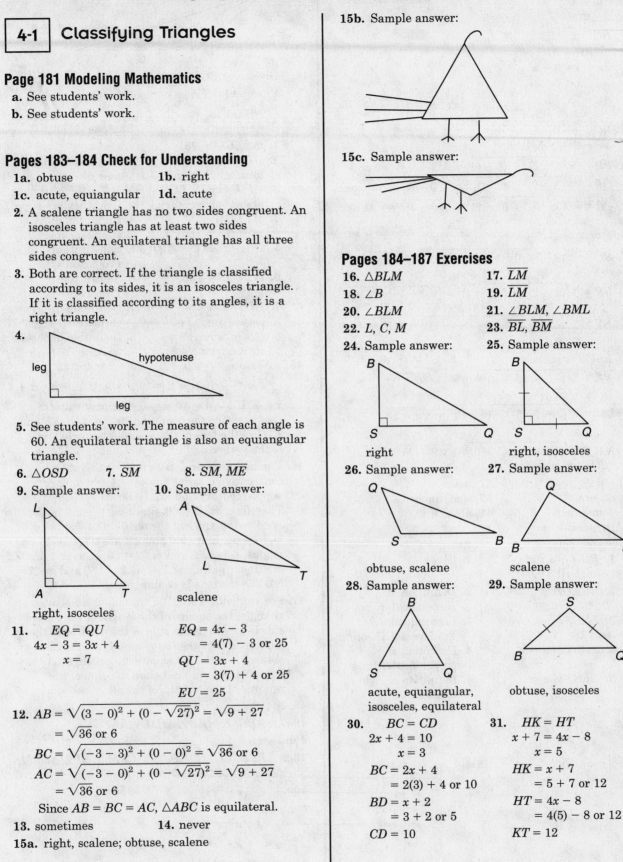

5. See students' work. The measure of each angle is 60. An equilateral triangle is also an equiangular triangle.

6. $\triangle OSD$ **7.** $\overline{SM}$ **8.** $\overline{SM}, \overline{ME}$
9. Sample answer: **10.** Sample answer:

right, isosceles   scalene

11.
$$EQ = QU$$
$$4x - 3 = 3x + 4$$
$$x = 7$$

$$EQ = 4x - 3$$
$$= 4(7) - 3 \text{ or } 25$$
$$QU = 3x + 4$$
$$= 3(7) + 4 \text{ or } 25$$
$$EU = 25$$

12. $AB = \sqrt{(3-0)^2 + (0-\sqrt{27})^2} = \sqrt{9+27}$
$\qquad = \sqrt{36} \text{ or } 6$
$BC = \sqrt{(-3-3)^2 + (0-0)^2} = \sqrt{36} \text{ or } 6$
$AC = \sqrt{(-3-0)^2 + (0-\sqrt{27})^2} = \sqrt{9+27}$
$\qquad = \sqrt{36} \text{ or } 6$
Since $AB = BC = AC$, $\triangle ABC$ is equilateral.

13. sometimes   **14.** never
15a. right, scalene; obtuse, scalene

15b. Sample answer:

15c. Sample answer:

Pages 184–187 Exercises
16. $\triangle BLM$ **17.** $\overline{LM}$
18. $\angle B$ **19.** $\overline{LM}$
20. $\angle BLM$ **21.** $\angle BLM, \angle BML$
22. L, C, M **23.** $\overline{BL}, \overline{BM}$
24. Sample answer: **25.** Sample answer:

right   right, isosceles

26. Sample answer: **27.** Sample answer:

obtuse, scalene   scalene

28. Sample answer: **29.** Sample answer:

acute, equiangular,   obtuse, isosceles
isosceles, equilateral

30.
$$BC = CD$$
$$2x + 4 = 10$$
$$x = 3$$
$$BC = 2x + 4$$
$$= 2(3) + 4 \text{ or } 10$$
$$BD = x + 2$$
$$= 3 + 2 \text{ or } 5$$
$$CD = 10$$

31.
$$HK = HT$$
$$x + 7 = 4x - 8$$
$$x = 5$$
$$HK = x + 7$$
$$= 5 + 7 \text{ or } 12$$
$$HT = 4x - 8$$
$$= 4(5) - 8 \text{ or } 12$$
$$KT = 12$$

32. Let x = the number.
$AC = 2x - 5$
$AB = 3 + x$
$BC = x - 1$
$AC = AB$
$2x - 5 = 3 + x$
$x = 8$

$AC = 2x - 5$ $\qquad$ $AB = 3 + x$
$\quad = 2(8) - 5$ or 11 $\qquad = 3 + 8$ or 11

$BC = x - 1$
$\quad = 8 - 1$ or 7

33. $PQ = \sqrt{(3-0)^2 + (6-6)^2} = \sqrt{9+0} = \sqrt{9}$ or 3
$QR = \sqrt{(3-3)^2 + (0-6)^2} = \sqrt{0+36} = \sqrt{36}$ or 6
$PR = \sqrt{(3-0)^2 + (0-6)^2} = \sqrt{9+36} = \sqrt{45}$ or $3\sqrt{5}$
$\triangle PQR$ is scalene.

34. $SU = \sqrt{(2-(-3))^2 + (1-(-1))^2} = \sqrt{25+4}$
$\quad = \sqrt{29}$
$UV = \sqrt{(2-2)^2 + (-3-1)^2} = \sqrt{0+16} = \sqrt{16}$
$\quad = 4$
$SV = \sqrt{(2-(-3))^2 + (-3-(-1))^2} = \sqrt{25+4}$
$\quad = \sqrt{29}$
$\triangle SUV$ is isosceles.

35. $KL = \sqrt{(-2-4)^2 + (0-0)^2} = \sqrt{36+0}$
$\quad = \sqrt{36}$ or 6
$LM = \sqrt{(1-(-2))^2 + (5-0)^2} = \sqrt{9+25}$
$\quad$ or $\sqrt{34}$
$KM = \sqrt{(1-4)^2 + (5-0)^2} = \sqrt{9+25}$ or $\sqrt{34}$
$\triangle KLM$ is isosceles.

36. always $\qquad$ **37.** never
38. never $\qquad$ **39.** sometimes
40. sometimes $\qquad$ **41.** always
42. right, scalene

43.

Statements	Reasons
1. RGH is a right angle. $TS \parallel HG$	1. Given
2. $\overline{RG} \perp \overline{GH}$	2. Definition of perpendicular
3. $\overline{RS} \perp \overline{ST}$	3. Perpendicular Transversal Theorem
4. $\angle RST$ is a rt $\angle$.	4. Definition of perpendicular lines
5. $\triangle RST$ is a rt. $\triangle$	5. Definition of right triangle.

44.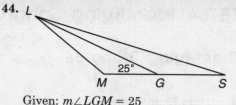

Given: $m\angle LGM = 25$
Prove: $\triangle LGS$ is an obtuse triangle.
Proof:

Statements	Reasons
1. $m\angle LGM = 25$	1. Given
2. $\angle LGM$ and $\angle LGS$ form a linear pair.	2. Definition of linear pair
3. $\angle LGM$ and $\angle LGS$ are supplementary.	3. If 2 $\angle$ form a linear pair, they are supp.
4. $m\angle LGM + m\angle LGS = 180$	4. Definition of supplementary
5. $25 + m\angle LGS = 180$	5. Substitution Property (=)
6. $m\angle LGS = 155$	6. Subtraction Property (=)
7. $\angle LGS$ is an obtuse angle.	7. Definition of obtuse angle
8. $\triangle LGS$ is an obtuse triangle.	8. Definition of obtuse triangle

45. $\angle E$; since $23 < 2x + 2 + 10 + x + 4 < 32$, $\frac{7}{3} < x < \frac{16}{3}$. If $2x + 2 = 10$, $x = 4$. If $2x + 2 = x + 4$, $x = 2$. If $x + 4 = 10$, $x = 6$. The only value of x that satisfies the conditions is $x = 4$, so $\overline{EF}$ and $\overline{ED}$ are the legs of the isosceles triangle and $\angle E$ is the vertex.

46. Equiangular; since $m \parallel n$ and $\angle 1$ and $\angle 5$ are consecutive interior angles, $\angle 1$ and $\angle 5$ are supplementary and $m\angle 1 + m\angle 5 = 180$. Therefore, $m\angle 5 = 60$. Since $m\angle 6 + m\angle 5 + m\angle 4 = 180$ and $m\angle 4 = m\angle 6$, $m\angle 4 = 60$ and $m\angle 6 = 60$. Since $\angle 6$ and $\angle 3$ are corresponding angles, $\angle 3 \cong \angle 6$ and $m\angle 3 = 60$. Since $\angle 1$ and $\angle 2$ are linear pairs, $m\angle 1 + m\angle 2 = 180$ and $m\angle 2 = 60$. The triangle is equiangular.

47. See students' work. If a triangle is an acute triangle, the square of the length of the longest side is less than the sum of the squares of the lengths of the other two sides. If a triangle is an obtuse triangle, the square of the length of the longest side is greater than the sum of the squares of the lengths of the other two sides.

48. 6; 18
49a. $\triangle ABC, \triangle ADG, \triangle AHM, \triangle ANS$
49b. none
49c. $\triangle BED, \triangle CFG, \triangle BJH, \triangle CKM, \triangle DIH, \triangle GLM, \triangle BPN, \triangle CQS, \triangle DON, \triangle GRS$
50a. $\quad \bullet$ $\qquad\qquad$ **50b.** 36
$\qquad\qquad \bullet \quad \bullet$
$\qquad\qquad \bullet \quad \bullet \quad \bullet$
$\qquad\qquad \bullet \quad \bullet \quad \bullet \quad \bullet$
51. infinite number

52.

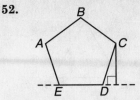

53. (1) If two lines in a plane are cut by a transversal so that corresponding angles are congruent, then the lines are parallel.

(2) If two lines in a plane are cut by a transversal so that a pair of alternate interior angles is congruent, then the lines are parallel.

(3) If two lines in a plane are cut by a transversal so that a pair of consecutive interior angles is supplementary, then the lines are parallel.

(4) If two lines in a plane are cut by a transversal so that a pair of alternate exterior angles is congruent, then the lines are parallel.

(5) In a plane, if two lines are perpendicular to the same line, then they are parallel.

54. $m = \dfrac{2 - (-6)}{r - 4} = \dfrac{-8}{3}$

$\dfrac{8}{r - 4} = \dfrac{-8}{3}$

$8(3) = (r - 4)(-8)$

$24 = -8r + 32$

$-8 = -8r$

$1 = r$

55. Sample answer: the line formed by the intersection of the floor and a wall of a room and the line formed by two walls on the opposite side of the room

56. Congruence of angles is reflexive.

57. Transitive Property of Equality; Sample answer: The Law of Syllogism says if $p \to q$ and $q \to r$, then $p \to r$.
The Transitive Property of Equality says if $p = q$ and $q = r$, then $p = r$.

58. hypothesis: you want a pizza;
conclusion: go to Pizza Haven

59. Let x = measure of angle. Thus, $180 - x$ is the measure of its supplement.

$x = \dfrac{1}{3}(180 - x)$

$3x = 180 - x$

$4x = 180$

$x = 45$

60. $d = \sqrt{(x_2 - x_1)^2 + (y_2 - y_1)^2}$

$5 = \sqrt{(a - 5)^2 + (10 - 6)^2}$

$25 = (a - 5)^2 + (4)^2$

$25 = a^2 - 10a + 25 + 16$

$0 = a^2 - 10 + 16$

$0 = (a - 8)(a - 2)$

$a - 8 = 0 \quad$ or $\quad a - 2 = 0$

$a = 8 \qquad\qquad a = 2$

61. $-6 = 5u + 9$

$-15 = 5u$

$-3 = u$

62. $27 - 40 = x \cdot 10$

$1080 = 10x$

$108 = x$

4-2A Angles of Triangles

Page 188 Modeling Mathematics

1a. See students' work. **1b.** See students' work.

2a. See students' work. **2b.** See students' work.

3. The sum of the measures of a triangle is 180.

4. The measure of an exterior angle is equal to the sum of the measures of the two remote interior angles.

4-2 Measuring Angles in Triangles

Pages 192–193 Check for Understanding

1. Subtract the sum of the measures of the two angles from 180.

2. The exterior angles at a vertex are the two angles that are not the angle of the triangle or the vertical angle to that angle.

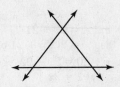

3. The sum of the measures of two obtuse angles is greater than 180. This contradicts the Angle Sum Theorem.

4. Sample answer: 40 and 50; the acute angles of a right triangle are complementary.

5. See students' work.

5a. The sum of the measures of the acute angles of a right triangle is 90.

5b. confirm

6. $38 + 44 + x = 180$ **7.** $x = 49 + 90$
$82 + x = 180$ $x = 139$
$x = 98$

8. $m\angle HKI + m\angle 1 = 120$ **9.** $m\angle 2 = m\angle HKI$
$54 + m\angle 1 = 120$ $m\angle 2 = 54$
$m\angle 1 = 66$

10. $m\angle 2 + m\angle IKJ + m\angle 3 = 180$
$54 + 36 + m\angle 3 = 180$
$m\angle 3 = 90$

11a. $90 + x = x + 2x$ **11b.** $m\angle A = 2x$
$90 + x = 3x$ $= 2(45)$ or 90
$x = 45$

11c. Since $m\angle A = 90$, $\triangle ABC$ is a right triangle.

12. Yes; the two right angles would be at the same vertex.

13. $m\angle S + m\angle R + m\angle A = 180$
$109 + 41 + m\angle A = 180$
$m\angle A = 30$

Pages 193–195 Exercises

14. $x + 52 + 35 = 180$ **15.** $x + 57 + 32 = 180$
$x = 93$ $x = 91$

---

16. $x + 40 + 25 = 180$
$x = 115$

17. $x + 40 = 155$
$x = 115$

18. $x + 42 = 100$
$x = 58$

19. $x + x + 30 = 180$
$2x = 150$
$x = 75$

20. $m\angle 1 + 104 = 180$
$m\angle 1 = 76$

21. $m\angle 2 + 36 = 104$
$m\angle 2 = 68$

22. $m\angle 3 = m\angle 1 = 76$

23. $m\angle 4 = 40$

24. $m\angle 3 + m\angle 4 + m\angle 5 = 180$
$76 + 40 + m\angle 5 = 180$
$m\angle 5 = 64$

25. $m\angle ABC = 90$
$m\angle 5 + m\angle 6 = 90$
$64 + m\angle 6 = 90$
$m\angle 6 = 26$

26. $m\angle 7 + 40 = 180$
$m\angle 7 = 140$

27. $m\angle 6 + m\angle 7 + m\angle 8 = 180$
$26 + 140 + m\angle 8 = 180$
$m\angle 8 = 14$

28. $x + (2x + 21) + 90 = 180$
$3x + 111 = 180$
$3x = 69$
$x = 23$

$m\angle A = 2x + 21$
$= 2(23) + 21$ or 67

29. $x + 80 = 3x - 22$
$102 = 2x$
$51 = x$
$m\angle A = x = 51$

30. $x + 2x + (x - 20) = 180$
$4x - 20 = 180$
$4x = 200$
$x = 50$
$m\angle A = x - 20$
$= 50 - 20$ or 30

31. Scalene; none of the angles are congruent so none of the sides are congruent.

32a. Let $x = m\angle B$, $m\angle A = x + 16$, and $m\angle C = x + 29$.
$(x + 16) + x + (x + 29) = 180$

32b. $x + 16 + x + x + 29 = 180$
$3x + 45 = 180$
$3x = 135$
$x = 45$

$m\angle B = x = 45$
$m\angle A = x + 16 = 45 + 16$ or 61
$m\angle C = x + 29 = 45 + 29$ or 74

33.

$\angle RUW \cong \angle VSR$
Given

↓

$\angle URW \cong \angle VRS$
Congruence of $\angle$s is reflexive.

↓

$\angle V \cong \angle W$
Third Angle Theorem

34. 135; the third angle of the triangle measures 65°. The largest exterior angle of the triangle measures $65 + 70 = 135$.

35. Given: $\triangle RED$ is equiangular.
Prove: $m\angle R = m\angle E = m\angle D = 60$

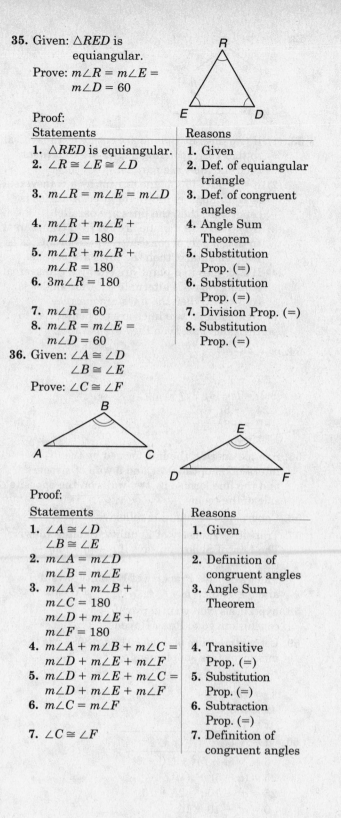

Proof:

Statements	Reasons
1. $\triangle RED$ is equiangular.	1. Given
2. $\angle R \cong \angle E \cong \angle D$	2. Def. of equiangular triangle
3. $m\angle R = m\angle E = m\angle D$	3. Def. of congruent angles
4. $m\angle R + m\angle E + m\angle D = 180$	4. Angle Sum Theorem
5. $m\angle R + m\angle R + m\angle R = 180$	5. Substitution Prop. (=)
6. $3m\angle R = 180$	6. Substitution Prop. (=)
7. $m\angle R = 60$	7. Division Prop. (=)
8. $m\angle R = m\angle E = m\angle D = 60$	8. Substitution Prop. (=)

36. Given: $\angle A \cong \angle D$
$\angle B \cong \angle E$
Prove: $\angle C \cong \angle F$

Proof:

Statements	Reasons
1. $\angle A \cong \angle D$ $\angle B \cong \angle E$	1. Given
2. $m\angle A = m\angle D$ $m\angle B = m\angle E$	2. Definition of congruent angles
3. $m\angle A + m\angle B + m\angle C = 180$ $m\angle D + m\angle E + m\angle F = 180$	3. Angle Sum Theorem
4. $m\angle A + m\angle B + m\angle C = m\angle D + m\angle E + m\angle F$	4. Transitive Prop. (=)
5. $m\angle D + m\angle E + m\angle C = m\angle D + m\angle E + m\angle F$	5. Substitution Prop. (=)
6. $m\angle C = m\angle F$	6. Subtraction Prop. (=)
7. $\angle C \cong \angle F$	7. Definition of congruent angles

37. Given: $\triangle RST$
$\angle R$ is a right angle.

Prove: $\angle S$ and $\angle T$ are complementary.

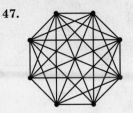

Proof:

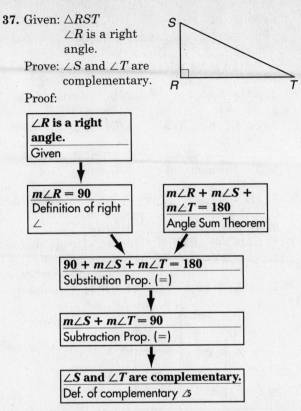

$\angle R$ is a right angle.
Given

↓

$m\angle R = 90$
Definition of right $\angle$

$m\angle R + m\angle S + m\angle T = 180$
Angle Sum Theorem

↓

$90 + m\angle S + m\angle T = 180$
Substitution Prop. (=)

↓

$m\angle S + m\angle T = 90$
Subtraction Prop. (=)

↓

$\angle S$ and $\angle T$ are complementary.
Def. of complementary $\angle$s

38. In $\triangle MNO$, $\angle M$ is a right angle. $m\angle M + m\angle N + m\angle O = 180$. $m\angle M = 90$, so $m\angle N + m\angle O = 90$. If $\angle N$ were a right angle, then $m\angle O = 0$. But that is impossible, so there cannot be two right angles in a triangle. In $\triangle PQR$, $\angle P$ is obtuse. So $m\angle P > 90$. $m\angle P + m\angle Q + m\angle R = 180$. It must be that $m\angle Q + m\angle R < 90$. So, $\angle Q$ and $\angle R$ must be acute.

39. 360

40a. See students' work. **40b.** See students' work.

41a. No; two of the angles are right angles, so the sum of their measures is 180.

41b. The sum of the measures is greater than 180 and less than or equal to 360. The sum of the measures of two angles is 180. The measure of the third angle is greater than 0 and less than or equal to 180.

41c. If the measure of the angle at the pole is less than 90, the triangle is an acute triangle.

41d. If the measure of the angle at the pole is greater than 90, the triangle is an obtuse triangle.

41e. If the measure of the angle at the pole is 90, the triangle is a right triangle.

42. $m\angle L + 27 = 93$
$m\angle L = 66$

43. $25 + 25 + m\angle R = 180$
$m\angle R = 130$

44. Since one angle's measure > 90, the triangle is obtuse.

45. No; if they are parallel, $m\angle 1 = m\angle 5$.

46. $\dfrac{184,000 - 156,000}{1990 - 1980} = \dfrac{28,000}{10}$ or 2800 people per year

47.

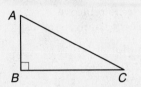

28 games

48. Given: $\angle B$ is a right angle.

Prove: $\angle A$ and $\angle C$ are complementary.

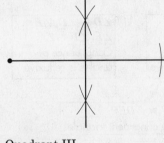

49a. Yes; Derrick will receive an A.
49b. Law of Detachment
50.

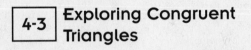

51. Quadrant III
52. $\dfrac{6}{t} = \dfrac{2}{7}$
$42 = 2t$
$21 = t$

53a. 52% of 500 = 0.52(500) or 260 women
53b. 79% of 500 = 0.79(500) or 395 women

4-3	**Exploring Congruent Triangles**

Pages 199–200 Check for Understanding

1. Sample figures:

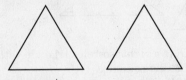

congruent

2. A triangle is congruent to itself.

3. $\angle B \leftrightarrow \angle E$, $\angle C \leftrightarrow \angle F$, $\angle D \leftrightarrow \angle G$

4. The perimeter would remain the same. A congruence transformation preserves size and shape.

5. See students' work.

6. 1, 8, 3, 4; 2, 5, 6, 7

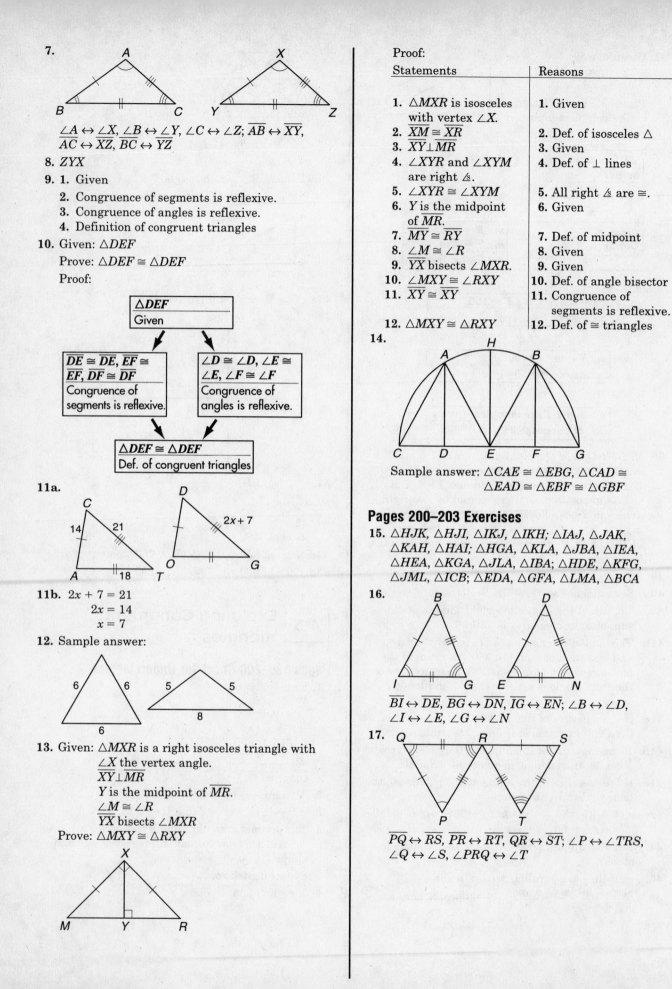

7. $\angle A \leftrightarrow \angle X, \angle B \leftrightarrow \angle Y, \angle C \leftrightarrow \angle Z; \overline{AB} \leftrightarrow \overline{XY},$
$\overline{AC} \leftrightarrow \overline{XZ}, \overline{BC} \leftrightarrow \overline{YZ}$

8. ZYX

9. 1. Given
2. Congruence of segments is reflexive.
3. Congruence of angles is reflexive.
4. Definition of congruent triangles

10. Given: $\triangle DEF$
Prove: $\triangle DEF \cong \triangle DEF$
Proof:

$\boxed{\begin{array}{c} \triangle DEF \\ \text{Given} \end{array}}$

$\boxed{\begin{array}{c} \overline{DE} \cong \overline{DE}, \overline{EF} \cong \\ \overline{EF}, \overline{DF} \cong \overline{DF} \\ \text{Congruence of} \\ \text{segments is reflexive.} \end{array}}$ $\boxed{\begin{array}{c} \angle D \cong \angle D, \angle E \cong \\ \angle E, \angle F \cong \angle F \\ \text{Congruence of} \\ \text{angles is reflexive.} \end{array}}$

$\boxed{\begin{array}{c} \triangle DEF \cong \triangle DEF \\ \text{Def. of congruent triangles} \end{array}}$

11a.

11b. $2x + 7 = 21$
$2x = 14$
$x = 7$

12. Sample answer:

13. Given: $\triangle MXR$ is a right isosceles triangle with
$\angle X$ the vertex angle.
$\overline{XY} \perp \overline{MR}$
Y is the midpoint of $\overline{MR}$.
$\angle M \cong \angle R$
$\overline{YX}$ bisects $\angle MXR$
Prove: $\triangle MXY \cong \triangle RXY$

Proof:

Statements	Reasons
1. $\triangle MXR$ is isosceles with vertex $\angle X$.	1. Given
2. $\overline{XM} \cong \overline{XR}$	2. Def. of isosceles $\triangle$
3. $\overline{XY} \perp \overline{MR}$	3. Given
4. $\angle XYR$ and $\angle XYM$ are right $\angle$s.	4. Def. of $\perp$ lines
5. $\angle XYR \cong \angle XYM$	5. All right $\angle$s are $\cong$.
6. Y is the midpoint of $\overline{MR}$.	6. Given
7. $\overline{MY} \cong \overline{RY}$	7. Def. of midpoint
8. $\angle M \cong \angle R$	8. Given
9. $\overline{YX}$ bisects $\angle MXR$.	9. Given
10. $\angle MXY \cong \angle RXY$	10. Def. of angle bisector
11. $\overline{XY} \cong \overline{XY}$	11. Congruence of segments is reflexive.
12. $\triangle MXY \cong \triangle RXY$	12. Def. of $\cong$ triangles

14.

Sample answer: $\triangle CAE \cong \triangle EBG, \triangle CAD \cong$
$\triangle EAD \cong \triangle EBF \cong \triangle GBF$

Pages 200–203 Exercises

15. $\triangle HJK, \triangle HJI, \triangle IKJ, \triangle IKH; \triangle IAJ, \triangle JAK,$
$\triangle KAH, \triangle HAI; \triangle HGA, \triangle KLA, \triangle JBA, \triangle IEA,$
$\triangle HEA, \triangle KGA, \triangle JLA, \triangle IBA; \triangle HDE, \triangle KFG,$
$\triangle JML, \triangle ICB; \triangle EDA, \triangle GFA, \triangle LMA, \triangle BCA$

16.

$\overline{BI} \leftrightarrow \overline{DE}, \overline{BG} \leftrightarrow \overline{DN}, \overline{IG} \leftrightarrow \overline{EN}; \angle B \leftrightarrow \angle D,$
$\angle I \leftrightarrow \angle E, \angle G \leftrightarrow \angle N$

17.

$\overline{PQ} \leftrightarrow \overline{RS}, \overline{PR} \leftrightarrow \overline{RT}, \overline{QR} \leftrightarrow \overline{ST}; \angle P \leftrightarrow \angle TRS,$
$\angle Q \leftrightarrow \angle S, \angle PRQ \leftrightarrow \angle T$

18.

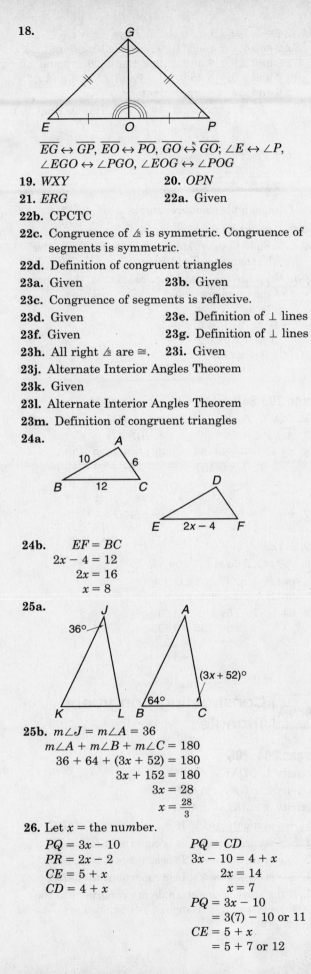

$\overline{EG} \leftrightarrow \overline{GP}$, $\overline{EO} \leftrightarrow \overline{PO}$, $\overline{GO} \leftrightarrow \overline{GO}$; $\angle E \leftrightarrow \angle P$, $\angle EGO \leftrightarrow \angle PGO$, $\angle EOG \leftrightarrow \angle POG$

19. *WXY*
20. *OPN*
21. *ERG*
22a. Given
22b. CPCTC
22c. Congruence of ⩟ is symmetric. Congruence of segments is symmetric.
22d. Definition of congruent triangles
23a. Given
23b. Given
23c. Congruence of segments is reflexive.
23d. Given
23e. Definition of ⊥ lines
23f. Given
23g. Definition of ⊥ lines
23h. All right ⩟ are ≅.
23i. Given
23j. Alternate Interior Angles Theorem
23k. Given
23l. Alternate Interior Angles Theorem
23m. Definition of congruent triangles
24a.

24b.
$EF = BC$
$2x - 4 = 12$
$2x = 16$
$x = 8$

25a.

25b. $m\angle J = m\angle A = 36$
$m\angle A + m\angle B + m\angle C = 180$
$36 + 64 + (3x + 52) = 180$
$3x + 152 = 180$
$3x = 28$
$x = \dfrac{28}{3}$

26. Let x = the number.
$PQ = 3x - 10$
$PR = 2x - 2$
$CE = 5 + x$
$CD = 4 + x$

$PQ = CD$
$3x - 10 = 4 + x$
$2x = 14$
$x = 7$
$PQ = 3x - 10$
$\quad = 3(7) - 10 \text{ or } 11$
$CE = 5 + x$
$\quad = 5 + 7 \text{ or } 12$

27. Sample answer:

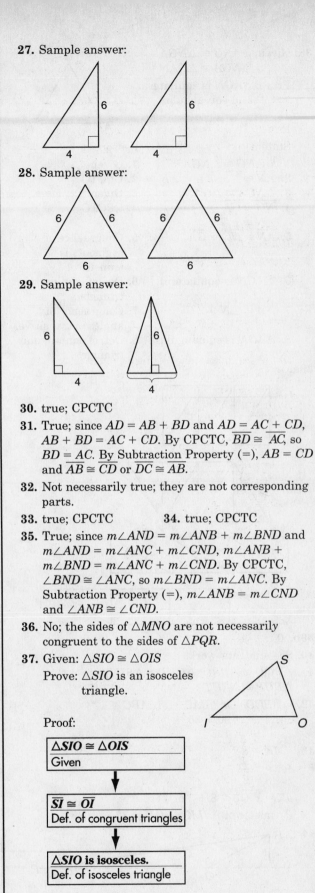

28. Sample answer:

29. Sample answer:

30. true; CPCTC

31. True; since $AD = AB + BD$ and $AD = AC + CD$, $AB + BD = AC + CD$. By CPCTC, $\overline{BD} \cong \overline{AC}$, so $BD = AC$. By Subtraction Property (=), $AB = CD$ and $\overline{AB} \cong \overline{CD}$ or $\overline{DC} \cong \overline{AB}$.

32. Not necessarily true; they are not corresponding parts.

33. true; CPCTC
34. true; CPCTC

35. True; since $m\angle AND = m\angle ANB + m\angle BND$ and $m\angle AND = m\angle ANC + m\angle CND$, $m\angle ANB + m\angle BND = m\angle ANC + m\angle CND$. By CPCTC, $\angle BND \cong \angle ANC$, so $m\angle BND = m\angle ANC$. By Subtraction Property (=), $m\angle ANB = m\angle CND$ and $\angle ANB \cong \angle CND$.

36. No; the sides of $\triangle MNO$ are not necessarily congruent to the sides of $\triangle PQR$.

37. Given: $\triangle SIO \cong \triangle OIS$
Prove: $\triangle SIO$ is an isosceles triangle.

Proof:

$\triangle SIO \cong \triangle OIS$
Given

↓

$\overline{SI} \cong \overline{OI}$
Def. of congruent triangles

↓

$\triangle SIO$ is isosceles.
Def. of isosceles triangle

38. Given: $\triangle ANG \cong \triangle NGA$
$\triangle NGA \cong \triangle GAN$

Prove: $\triangle AGN$ is equilateral
and equiangular.

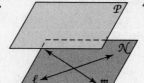

Proof:

Statements	Reasons
1. $\triangle ANG \cong \triangle NGA$	1. Given
2. $\overline{AN} \cong \overline{NG}$, $\angle A \cong \angle N$	2. CPCTC
3. $\triangle NGA \cong \triangle GAN$	3. Given
4. $\overline{NG} \cong \overline{GA}$ $\angle N \cong \angle G$	4. CPCTC
5. $\overline{AN} \cong \overline{NG} \cong \overline{GA}$	5. Congruence of segments is transitive.
6. $\triangle AGN$ is equilateral.	6. Def. of equilateral triangle
7. $\angle A \cong \angle N \cong \angle G$	7. Congruence of angles is transitive.
8. $\triangle AGN$ is equiangular.	8. Def. of equiangular triangle

39a. 4

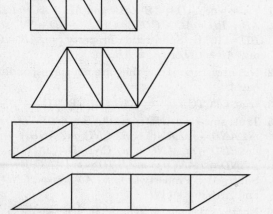

39b. 0

40. See students' work.

41. $\triangle RQU \cong \triangle RSU$; $\triangle QUP \cong \triangle SUT$; $\triangle RUP \cong \triangle RUT$

42. $m\angle BCD = m\angle BAC + m\angle ABC$
$= 90 + 35$
$= 125$

43. $JK = KJ$
$x + 3 = 2x - 5$
$8 = x$
$JK = x + 3 = 8 + 3$ or 11
Perimeter of $\triangle JLK = 3(11) = 33$

44.

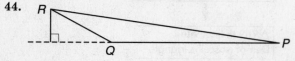

45. $\angle 1 \cong \angle 7 \cong \angle 9$, $\angle 10 \cong \angle 8$, $\angle 3 \cong \angle 5 \cong \angle 6$, $\angle 2 \cong \angle 4$; $\angle 1$ and $\angle 10$, $\angle 7$ and $\angle 10$, $\angle 7$ and $\angle 8$, $\angle 8$ and $\angle 9$, $\angle 9$ and $\angle 10$, $\angle 1$ and $\angle 8$, $\angle 2$ and $\angle 6$, $\angle 2$ and $\angle 5$, $\angle 5$ and $\angle 4$, $\angle 4$ and $\angle 3$, $\angle 3$ and $\angle 2$, $\angle 6$ and $\angle 4$ are supplementary.

46.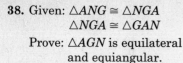

47. Substitution Prop. (=)

48. false; sample counterexample: $a = -2$, $-2 < -\frac{1}{2}$

49. a straight angle

50a. Sample answer: More countries belong to the U.N. than the World Bank.

50b. No; since the data is not connected, the average of the numbers would have no meaning.

51. $-10 < 3x - 1 \le 5$
$-9 < \quad 3x \quad \le 6$
$-3 < \quad x \quad \le 2$
$\{x \mid -3 < x \le 2\}$

Page 203 Self Test

1. $\triangle DBC$, $\triangle ABD$
2. $\triangle ABD$
3. $\overline{AD}$, $\overline{AC}$
4. $\overline{BD}$, $\overline{AD}$

5. $42 + 31 + x = 180$
$73 + x = 107$
$x = 107$

6. $x + x + 78 = 180$
$2x + 78 = 180$
$2x = 102$
$x = 51$

7. $x = 35 + 90$
$x = 125$

8. $\triangle EAD$

9. $\triangle YZX$

10. $\angle B \cong \angle R$ so $m\angle B = m\angle R$.
$m\angle B + m\angle C + m\angle D = 180$
$m\angle R + m\angle C + m\angle D = 180$
$64 + 57 + (5x + 4) = 180$
$5x + 125 = 180$
$5x = 55$
$x = 11$

4-4A Constructing Congruent Triangles

Pages 204–205

Activity 1: $\triangle DEF \cong \triangle ABC$
Activity 2: $\triangle GHI \cong \triangle ABC$
Activity 3: $\triangle JKL \cong \triangle ABC$

1. See students' work. It is congruent to $\triangle ABC$.
2. See students' work. It is congruent to $\triangle ABC$.
3. See students' work. It is congruent to $\triangle ABC$.
4. See students' work. It is congruent to $\triangle ABC$.
5. If the sides of one triangle are congruent to the sides of another triangle, the triangles are congruent.

6. If two sides and the included angle of one triangle are congruent to two sides and the included angle of another triangle, the triangles are congruent.

7. If two angles and the included side of one triangle are congruent to two angles and the included side of another triangle, the triangles are congruent.

8. If the angles of one triangle are congruent to the angles of another triangle, the triangles have the same shape, but not necessarily the same size.

4-4 **Proving Triangles Congruent**

Pages 208–209 Check for Understanding

1. See students' work; right triangle.

2. You can first prove the triangles congruent, then use the definition of congruent triangles to prove the corresponding parts are congruent.

3. Mirna is correct. The SAS postulate requires 2 sides and an included angle.

4. $\triangle TUS$ is a rotation of $\triangle VRS$.

5. SSS

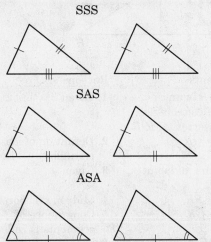

SAS

ASA

All are used to prove triangles congruent and require 3 parts congruent to 3 parts. One requires 3 sides, one 2 sides and an angle, and one 2 angles and a side.

6. ASA   **7.** SSS

8. $AC = \sqrt{(0-0)^2 + (0-4)^2} = \sqrt{16}$ or 4

$CM = \sqrt{(3-0)^2 + (0-0)^2} = \sqrt{9}$ or 3

$AM = \sqrt{(3-0)^2 + (0-4)^2} = \sqrt{25}$ or 5

$SC = \sqrt{(0-(-4))^2 + (0-0)^2} = \sqrt{16}$ or 4

$CR = \sqrt{(0-0)^2 + (-4-0)^2} = \sqrt{16}$ or 4

$SR = \sqrt{(0-(-4))^2 + (-4-0)^2} = \sqrt{32}$ or $4\sqrt{2}$

No; $\overline{AC} \cong \overline{SC}$, but the other sides are not congruent.

9. 1. Given

   2. Definition of segment bisector

   3. Given

   4. Alternate Interior Angles Theorem

   5. Vertical angles are $\cong$.

   6. ASA

10. Given: $\overline{OM}$ bisects $\angle LMN$. $\overline{LM} \cong \overline{NM}$
Prove: $\triangle MOL \cong \triangle MON$

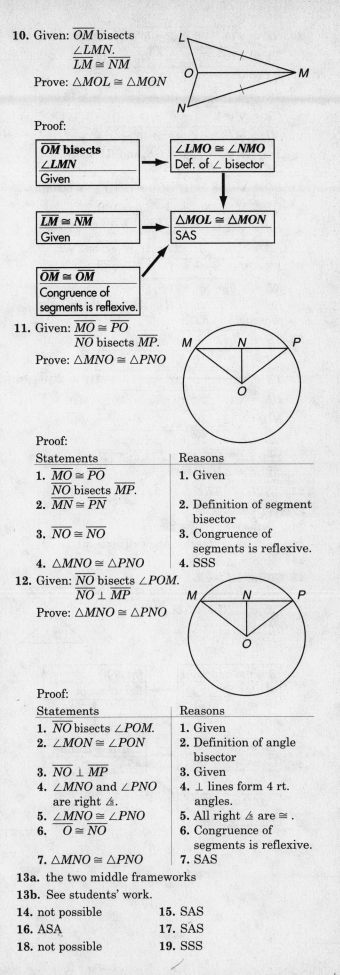

Proof:

| $\overline{OM}$ bisects $\angle LMN$ Given | $\rightarrow$ | $\angle LMO \cong \angle NMO$ Def. of $\angle$ bisector |

| $\overline{LM} \cong \overline{NM}$ Given | $\rightarrow$ | $\triangle MOL \cong \triangle MON$ SAS |

| $\overline{OM} \cong \overline{OM}$ Congruence of segments is reflexive. |

11. Given: $\overline{MO} \cong \overline{PO}$ $\overline{NO}$ bisects $\overline{MP}$.
Prove: $\triangle MNO \cong \triangle PNO$

Proof:

Statements	Reasons
1. $\overline{MO} \cong \overline{PO}$ $\overline{NO}$ bisects $\overline{MP}$.	1. Given
2. $\overline{MN} \cong \overline{PN}$	2. Definition of segment bisector
3. $\overline{NO} \cong \overline{NO}$	3. Congruence of segments is reflexive.
4. $\triangle MNO \cong \triangle PNO$	4. SSS

12. Given: $\overline{NO}$ bisects $\angle POM$. $\overline{NO} \perp \overline{MP}$
Prove: $\triangle MNO \cong \triangle PNO$

Proof:

Statements	Reasons
1. $\overline{NO}$ bisects $\angle POM$.	1. Given
2. $\angle MON \cong \angle PON$	2. Definition of angle bisector
3. $\overline{NO} \perp \overline{MP}$	3. Given
4. $\angle MNO$ and $\angle PNO$ are right $\angle$s.	4. $\perp$ lines form 4 rt. angles.
5. $\angle MNO \cong \angle PNO$	5. All right $\angle$s are $\cong$.
6. $\overline{O} \cong \overline{NO}$	6. Congruence of segments is reflexive.
7. $\triangle MNO \cong \triangle PNO$	7. SAS

13a. the two middle frameworks

13b. See students' work.

14. not possible   **15.** SAS

16. ASA   **17.** SAS

18. not possible   **19.** SSS

20. $RT = \sqrt{(5-2)^2 + (2-5)^2} = \sqrt{18}$ or $3\sqrt{2}$

$TY = \sqrt{(1-5)^2 + (1-2)^2} = \sqrt{17}$

$RY = \sqrt{(1-2)^2 + (1-5)^2} = \sqrt{17}$

$MG = \sqrt{(-7-(-4))^2 + (1-4)^2} = \sqrt{18}$ or $3\sqrt{2}$

$GE = \sqrt{(-3-(-7))^2 + (0-1)^2} = \sqrt{17}$

$ME = \sqrt{(-3-(-4))^2 + (0-4)^2} = \sqrt{17}$

Yes; $\overline{RT} \cong \overline{MG}$, $\overline{TY} \cong \overline{GE}$, and $\overline{RY} \cong \overline{ME}$, so $\triangle RTY \cong \triangle MGE$ by SSS.

21. $PQ = \sqrt{(0-(-1))^2 + (6-(-1))^2} = \sqrt{50}$ or $5\sqrt{2}$

$QR = \sqrt{(2-0)^2 + (3-6)^2} = \sqrt{13}$

$PR = \sqrt{(2-(-1))^2 + (3-(-1))^2} = \sqrt{25}$ or 5

$XY = \sqrt{(5-3)^2 + (3-1)^2} = \sqrt{8}$ or $2\sqrt{2}$

$YZ = \sqrt{(8-5)^2 + (1-3)^2} = \sqrt{13}$

$XZ = \sqrt{(8-3)^2 + (1-1)^2} = \sqrt{25}$ or 5

No; $\overline{QR} \cong \overline{YZ}$ and $\overline{PR} \cong \overline{YZ}$, but $\overline{PQ}$ is not congruent to $\overline{XY}$.

22. $TS = \sqrt{(-2-(-1))^2 + (-2-(-1))^2} = \sqrt{2}$

$SR = \sqrt{(-5-(-2))^2 + (-1-(-2))^2} = \sqrt{10}$

$TR = \sqrt{(-5-(-1))^2 + (-1-(-1))^2} = \sqrt{16}$ or 4

$HN = \sqrt{(3-2)^2 + (-2-(-1))^2} = \sqrt{2}$

$ND = \sqrt{(2-3)^2 + (-5-(-2))^2} = \sqrt{10}$

$HD = \sqrt{(2-2)^2 + (-5-(-1))^2} = \sqrt{16}$ or 4

Yes; $\overline{TS} \cong \overline{HN}$, $\overline{SR} \cong \overline{ND}$, and $\overline{TR} \cong \overline{HD}$, so $\triangle TSR \cong \triangle HND$ by SSS.

23. $\angle SRU \cong \angle TRU$ **24a.** Given

24b. Given

24c. Reflexive Prop. $\cong$ Segments

24d. Alternate Interior Angles Theorem

24e. SAS

25. Given: $\angle J \cong \angle L$
B is the midpoint of $\overline{JL}$.
Prove: $\triangle JHB \cong \triangle LCB$

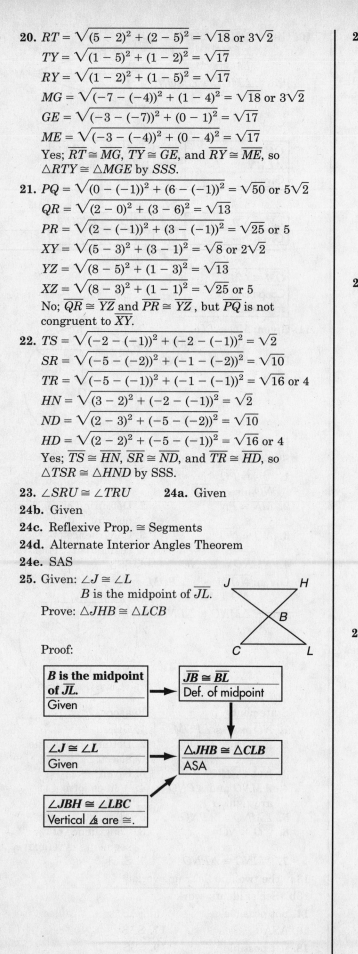

Proof:

26. Given: $\overline{JL}$ bisects $\overline{HC}$.
$\overline{HC}$ Bisects $\overline{JL}$.
Prove: $\triangle JHB \cong \triangle LCB$

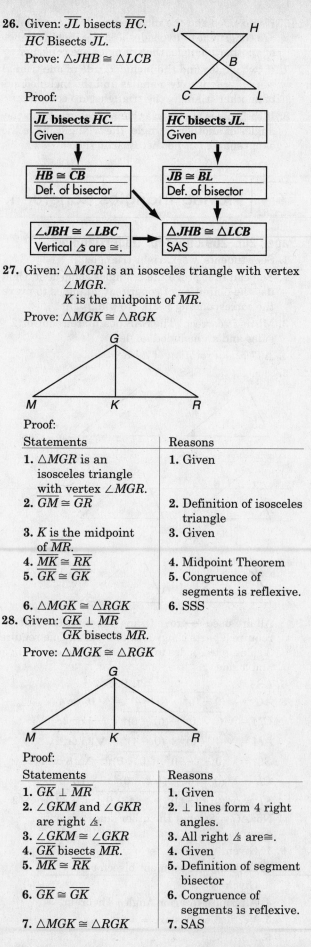

Proof:

27. Given: $\triangle MGR$ is an isosceles triangle with vertex $\angle MGR$.
K is the midpoint of $\overline{MR}$.
Prove: $\triangle MGK \cong \triangle RGK$

Proof:

Statements	Reasons
1. $\triangle MGR$ is an isosceles triangle with vertex $\angle MGR$.	1. Given
2. $\overline{GM} \cong \overline{GR}$	2. Definition of isosceles triangle
3. K is the midpoint of $\overline{MR}$.	3. Given
4. $\overline{MK} \cong \overline{RK}$	4. Midpoint Theorem
5. $\overline{GK} \cong \overline{GK}$	5. Congruence of segments is reflexive.
6. $\triangle MGK \cong \triangle RGK$	6. SSS

28. Given: $\overline{GK} \perp \overline{MR}$
$\overline{GK}$ bisects $\overline{MR}$.
Prove: $\triangle MGK \cong \triangle RGK$

Proof:

Statements	Reasons
1. $\overline{GK} \perp \overline{MR}$	1. Given
2. $\angle GKM$ and $\angle GKR$ are right $\angle$s.	2. $\perp$ lines form 4 right angles.
3. $\angle GKM \cong \angle GKR$	3. All right $\angle$s are $\cong$.
4. $\overline{GK}$ bisects $\overline{MR}$.	4. Given
5. $\overline{MK} \cong \overline{RK}$	5. Definition of segment bisector
6. $\overline{GK} \cong \overline{GK}$	6. Congruence of segments is reflexive.
7. $\triangle MGK \cong \triangle RGK$	7. SAS

29. Given: $\overline{RL} \parallel \overline{DC}$
$\overline{LC} \parallel \overline{RD}$
Prove: $\angle R \cong \angle C$

Proof:

Statements	Reasons
1. $\overline{RL} \parallel \overline{DC}$	1. Given
2. $\angle 1 \cong \angle 3$	2. Alternate Interior Angles Theorem
3. $\overline{LC} \parallel \overline{RD}$	3. Given
4. $\angle 2 \cong \angle 4$	4. Alternate Interior Angles Theorem
5. $\overline{LD} \cong \overline{DL}$	5. Congruence of segments is reflexive.
6. $\triangle RLD \cong \triangle CDL$	6. ASA
7. $\angle R \cong \angle C$	7. CPCTC

30. Given: $\angle 4 \cong \angle 2$
$\overline{DR} \cong \overline{LC}$
Prove: $\overline{RL} \cong \overline{CD}$

Proof:

Statements	Reasons
1. $\angle 4 \cong \angle 2$ $\overline{DR} \cong \overline{LC}$	1. Given
2. $\overline{LD} \cong \overline{DL}$	2. Congruence of segments is reflexive.
3. $\triangle RLD \cong \triangle CDL$	3. SAS
4. $\overline{RL} \cong \overline{CD}$	4. CPCTC

31. Given: $\angle 1 \cong \angle 2$
$\angle 3 \cong \angle 4$
$\overline{LA} \cong \overline{RU}$
Prove: $\triangle WLU \cong \triangle WRA$

Proof:

Statements	Reasons
1. $\angle 1 \cong \angle 2$ $\angle 3 \cong \angle 4$ $\overline{LA} \cong \overline{RU}$	1. Given
2. $LA = RU$	2. Definition of congruent segments
3. $LU = LA + AU$ $RA = RU + AU$	3. Segment Addition Postulate
4. $RA = LA + AU$	4. Substitution Prop. (=)
5. $LU = RA$	5. Substitution Prop. (=)
6. $\overline{LU} \cong \overline{RA}$	6. Def. of congruent segments
7. $\triangle WLU \cong \triangle WRA$	7. ASA

32. Given: $\angle LWU \cong \angle RWA$
$\angle 3 \cong \angle 4$
$\overline{LW} \cong \overline{RW}$
Prove: $\triangle LWA \cong \triangle RWU$

Proof:

Statements	Reasons
1. $\angle LWU \cong \angle RWA$	1. Given
2. $m\angle LWU = m\angle RWA$	2. Def. of congruent angles
3. $m\angle LWU = m\angle 5 + m\angle 6$ $m\angle RWA = m\angle 7 + m\angle 6$	3. Angle Addition Postulate
4. $m\angle 5 + m\angle 6 = m\angle 7 + m\angle 6$	4. Substitution Prop. (=)
5. $m\angle 5 = m\angle 7$	5. Subtraction Prop. (=)
6. $\angle 5 \cong \angle 7$	6. Def. of congruent angles
7. $\angle 3 \cong \angle 4$ $\overline{LW} \cong \overline{RW}$	7. Given
8. $\triangle LWA \cong \triangle RWU$	8. ASA

33. Given: $\angle 5 \cong \angle 7$
$\angle 3 \cong \angle 4$
$\overline{LW} \cong \overline{RW}$
Prove: $\overline{LU} \cong \overline{RA}$

Proof:

Statements	Reasons
1. $\angle 5 \cong \angle 7$	1. Given
2. $m\angle 5 = m\angle 7$	2. Def. of congruent $\angle$
3. $m\angle LWU = m\angle 5 + m\angle 6$ $m\angle RWA = m\angle 7 + m\angle 6$	3. Angle Addition Postulate
4. $m\angle RWA = m\angle 5 + m\angle 6$	4. Substitution Prop. (=)
5. $m\angle LWU = m\angle RWA$	5. Substitution Prop. (=)
6. $\angle LWU \cong \angle RWA$	6. Def. of congruent $\angle$
7. $\angle 3 \cong \angle 4$ $\overline{LW} \cong \overline{RW}$	7. Given
8. $\triangle LWU \cong \triangle RWA$	8. ASA
9. $\overline{LU} \cong \overline{RA}$	9. CPCTC

34. Given: $\overline{LU} \cong \overline{RA}$
$\angle 3 \cong \angle 4$
$\overline{LW} \cong \overline{RW}$
Prove: $\overline{AW} \cong \overline{UW}$

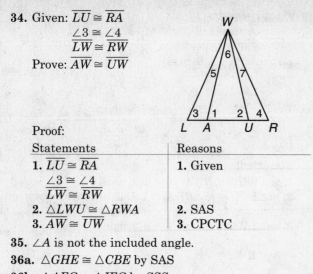

Proof:

Statements	Reasons
1. $\overline{LU} \cong \overline{RA}$ $\angle 3 \cong \angle 4$ $\overline{LW} \cong \overline{RW}$	**1.** Given
2. $\triangle LWU \cong \triangle RWA$	**2.** SAS
3. $\overline{AW} \cong \overline{UW}$	**3.** CPCTC

35. $\angle A$ is not the included angle.

36a. $\triangle GHE \cong \triangle CBE$ by SAS

36b. $\triangle AEG \cong \triangle IEG$ by SSS

36c. $\triangle ACI \cong \triangle CAG$ by SAS

37. Since Jamal is perpendicular to the ground, two right triangles are formed and the two right angles are congruent. The angles of sight are the same and his height is the same, so the triangles are congruent by ASA. By CPCTC, the distances are the same and the method is valid.

38a.

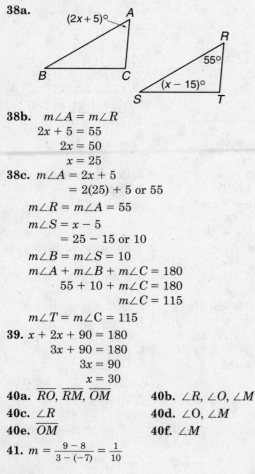

38b. $m\angle A = m\angle R$
$2x + 5 = 55$
$2x = 50$
$x = 25$

38c. $m\angle A = 2x + 5$
$= 2(25) + 5$ or 55
$m\angle R = m\angle A = 55$
$m\angle S = x - 5$
$= 25 - 15$ or 10
$m\angle B = m\angle S = 10$
$m\angle A + m\angle B + m\angle C = 180$
$55 + 10 + m\angle C = 180$
$m\angle C = 115$
$m\angle T = m\angle C = 115$

39. $x + 2x + 90 = 180$
$3x + 90 = 180$
$3x = 90$
$x = 30$

40a. $\overline{RO}, \overline{RM}, \overline{OM}$ **40b.** $\angle R, \angle O, \angle M$

40c. $\angle R$ **40d.** $\angle O, \angle M$

40e. $\overline{OM}$ **40f.** $\angle M$

41. $m = \dfrac{9 - 8}{3 - (-7)} = \dfrac{1}{10}$

42. Converse: If an angle is acute, then its measure is 60; false; sample counterexample: An acute angle could measure 20.

Inverse: If the measure of an angle is not 60, then the angle is not acute; false; sample counterexample: An angle that measures 20 is acute.

Contrapositive: If an angle is not acute, then its measure is not 60; true.

43. Sample answer: The plants need more sunlight to live. Place them somewhere with more sun and see if they survive.

44a. no   **44b.** W **44c.** $\overline{VU}$

45.

$d = rt$ $d = rt$
$d = 55t$ $d = 45t$

Miriam H David

150 miles

Let $t =$ the number of hours.
$55t + 45t = 150$
$100t = 150$
$t = 1.5$ hours

46. $3c - 12d = 6$
$\dfrac{3c - 12d}{3} = \dfrac{6}{3}$
$c - 4d = 2$

$c - 4d = 2$ is equivalent to $c = 4d + 2$, so there are infinitely many solutions.

Page 213 Mathematics and Society

1. same shapes; reflect light in same direction

2. Near the South Pole; these displays are caused by light that is refracted and reflected from ice crystals, and these crystals would be much more plentiful near the South Pole. (However, these sights do occur at all latitudes, even at the equator, because of the coldness of the air at high altitudes.)

3. The crystal with one side that remains horizontal; the stable orientation of crystals like these permits patterns to form, but a randomly tumbling crystal would cause light to be scattered in all directions, rather than being focused or concentrated in a specific area.

4-5 More Congruent Triangles

Page 214 Modeling Mathematics

Activity: It is congruent to $\triangle ABC$.

a. See students' work. It is congruent to $\triangle ABC$.

b. If 2 angles and a nonincluded side of a triangle are congruent to the corresponding angles and side of another triangle, the triangles are congruent.

Pages 216–218 Check for Understanding

1. In AAS the side is not included, but in ASA the side is included.

2. Both refer to three parts of a triangle. AAS requires 2 angles and a nonincluded side. SSA requires 2 sides and a nonincluded angle. AAS is a triangle congruence theorem, but SSA is not.

3. It is often helpful to use a congruence transformation to draw the two triangles separately when writing a proof involving overlapping triangles.

4.   CPCTC

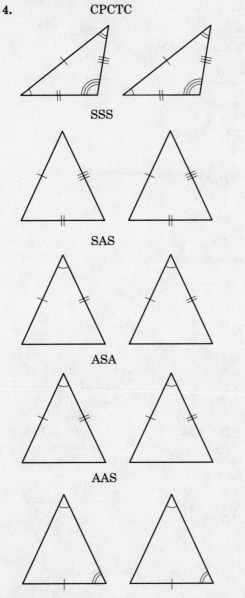

SSS

SAS

ASA

AAS

5a. See students' work.   5b. See students' work.

5c. no

5d. No; more than one triangle can be formed with 2 sides and a nonincluded angle congruent.

6. $\overline{DC}$

7. Sample answer: $\angle 1$ and $\angle 5$

8. VCE; ASA

9. Yes; since $\angle 7 \cong \angle 11$, $\overline{AD} \parallel \overline{EV}$. Then $\angle 6 \cong \angle 10$, by the Alternate Interior Angles Theorem. Then you have two sides and the included angle congruent.

10.

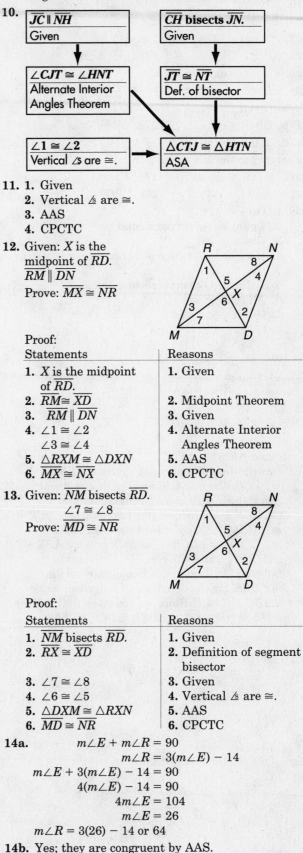

11. 1. Given
    2. Vertical $\angle$s are $\cong$.
    3. AAS
    4. CPCTC

12. Given: X is the midpoint of $\overline{RD}$.
    $\overline{RM} \parallel \overline{DN}$
    Prove: $\overline{MX} \cong \overline{NR}$

Proof:

Statements	Reasons
1. X is the midpoint of $\overline{RD}$.	1. Given
2. $\overline{RM} \cong \overline{XD}$	2. Midpoint Theorem
3. $\overline{RM} \parallel \overline{DN}$	3. Given
4. $\angle 1 \cong \angle 2$ $\angle 3 \cong \angle 4$	4. Alternate Interior Angles Theorem
5. $\triangle RXM \cong \triangle DXN$	5. AAS
6. $\overline{MX} \cong \overline{NX}$	6. CPCTC

13. Given: $\overline{NM}$ bisects $\overline{RD}$.
    $\angle 7 \cong \angle 8$
    Prove: $\overline{MD} \cong \overline{NR}$

Proof:

Statements	Reasons
1. $\overline{NM}$ bisects $\overline{RD}$.	1. Given
2. $\overline{RX} \cong \overline{XD}$	2. Definition of segment bisector
3. $\angle 7 \cong \angle 8$	3. Given
4. $\angle 6 \cong \angle 5$	4. Vertical $\angle$s are $\cong$.
5. $\triangle DXM \cong \triangle RXN$	5. AAS
6. $\overline{MD} \cong \overline{NR}$	6. CPCTC

14a.
$$m\angle E + m\angle R = 90$$
$$m\angle R = 3(m\angle E) - 14$$
$$m\angle E + 3(m\angle E) - 14 = 90$$
$$4(m\angle E) - 14 = 90$$
$$4m\angle E = 104$$
$$m\angle E = 26$$
$$m\angle R = 3(26) - 14 \text{ or } 64$$

14b. Yes; they are congruent by AAS.

15. $\overline{FD}$

16. $\overline{DS}$

17. $\overline{DR}$ or $\overline{RS}$

18. $\overline{DT}$ or $\overline{CT}$

19. $\angle 10$ and $\angle 11$

20. $\angle 3$ and $\angle 6$

21. $\angle 1$ and $\angle 4$ or $\angle 2$ and $\angle 4$

22. $\angle 7$ and $\angle 12$ or $\angle 7$ and $\angle 8$

23. *SRD*; AAS

24. *RDS*; ASA

25. $\overline{FD} \cong \overline{CD}$ and $\overline{DR} \cong \overline{DT}$

26. $\angle 5 \cong \angle 7$ or $\angle 6 \cong \angle 8$

27a. Given

27b. Given

27c. Given

27d. $\perp$ lines form 4 rt. $\angle$s

27e. $\perp$ lines form 4 rt. $\angle$s.

27f. All rt. $\angle$s are $\cong$.

27g. Given

27h. AAS

27i. CPCTC

28. 1. Given
   2. Definition of perpendicular lines
   3. Given
   4. If a line is $\perp$ to one of 2 ∥ lines, then it is $\perp$ to the other.
   5. Definition of perpendicular lines
   6. All right $\angle$s are $\cong$.
   7. Given
   8. Given
   9. AAS
   10. CPCTC

29. Given: $\angle A \cong \angle D$
$\angle EBC \cong \angle ECB$
$\overline{AE} \cong \overline{DE}$

Prove: $\triangle ABE \cong \triangle DCE$

Proof:
Since $\angle EBC \cong \angle ECB$, by definition of congruent angles $m\angle EBC = m\angle ECB$. Since $\angle ABE$ and $\angle EBC$ are linear pairs, the angles are supplementary and $m\angle ABE + m\angle EBC = 180$. Likewise, $m\angle DCE + m\angle ECB = 180$. By substitution, $m\angle ABE + m\angle EBC = m\angle DCE + m\angle ECB$ and $m\angle ABE + m\angle ECB = m\angle DCE + m\angle ECB$. Using the Subtraction Property of Equality, $m\angle ABE = m\angle DCE$. By the definition of congruent angles, $\angle ABE \cong \angle DCE$. Since we are given that $\angle A \cong \angle D$ and $\overline{AE} \cong \overline{DE}$, $\triangle ABE \cong \triangle DCE$ by AAS.

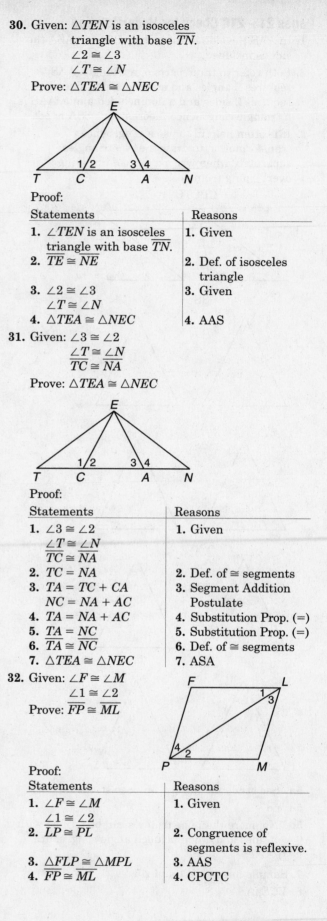

30. Given: $\triangle TEN$ is an isosceles triangle with base $\overline{TN}$.
$\angle 2 \cong \angle 3$
$\angle T \cong \angle N$
Prove: $\triangle TEA \cong \triangle NEC$

Proof:

Statements	Reasons
1. $\angle TEN$ is an isosceles triangle with base $\overline{TN}$.	1. Given
2. $\overline{TE} \cong \overline{NE}$	2. Def. of isosceles triangle
3. $\angle 2 \cong \angle 3$ $\angle T \cong \angle N$	3. Given
4. $\triangle TEA \cong \triangle NEC$	4. AAS

31. Given: $\angle 3 \cong \angle 2$
$\angle T \cong \angle N$
$\overline{TC} \cong \overline{NA}$
Prove: $\triangle TEA \cong \triangle NEC$

Proof:

Statements	Reasons
1. $\angle 3 \cong \angle 2$ $\angle T \cong \angle N$ $\overline{TC} \cong \overline{NA}$	1. Given
2. $TC = NA$	2. Def. of $\cong$ segments
3. $TA = TC + CA$ $NC = NA + AC$	3. Segment Addition Postulate
4. $TA = NA + AC$	4. Substitution Prop. (=)
5. $TA = NC$	5. Substitution Prop. (=)
6. $\overline{TA} \cong \overline{NC}$	6. Def. of $\cong$ segments
7. $\triangle TEA \cong \triangle NEC$	7. ASA

32. Given: $\angle F \cong \angle M$
$\angle 1 \cong \angle 2$
Prove: $\overline{FP} \cong \overline{ML}$

Proof:

Statements	Reasons
1. $\angle F \cong \angle M$ $\angle 1 \cong \angle 2$	1. Given
2. $\overline{LP} \cong \overline{PL}$	2. Congruence of segments is reflexive.
3. $\triangle FLP \cong \triangle MPL$	3. AAS
4. $\overline{FP} \cong \overline{ML}$	4. CPCTC

33. Given: $\overline{FP} \parallel \overline{ML}$
$\overline{FL} \parallel \overline{MP}$
Prove: $\overline{PM} \cong \overline{LF}$

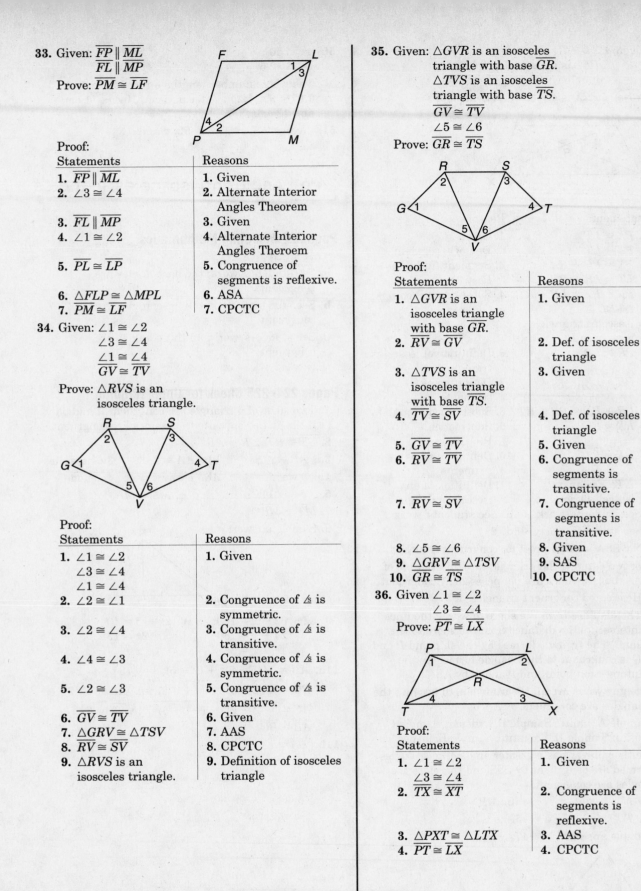

Proof:

Statements	Reasons
1. $\overline{FP} \parallel \overline{ML}$	1. Given
2. $\angle 3 \cong \angle 4$	2. Alternate Interior Angles Theorem
3. $\overline{FL} \parallel \overline{MP}$	3. Given
4. $\angle 1 \cong \angle 2$	4. Alternate Interior Angles Theroem
5. $\overline{PL} \cong \overline{LP}$	5. Congruence of segments is reflexive.
6. $\triangle FLP \cong \triangle MPL$	6. ASA
7. $\overline{PM} \cong \overline{LF}$	7. CPCTC

34. Given: $\angle 1 \cong \angle 2$
$\angle 3 \cong \angle 4$
$\angle 1 \cong \angle 4$
$\overline{GV} \cong \overline{TV}$

Prove: $\triangle RVS$ is an isosceles triangle.

Proof:

Statements	Reasons
1. $\angle 1 \cong \angle 2$ $\angle 3 \cong \angle 4$ $\angle 1 \cong \angle 4$	1. Given
2. $\angle 2 \cong \angle 1$	2. Congruence of $\angle$s is symmetric.
3. $\angle 2 \cong \angle 4$	3. Congruence of $\angle$s is transitive.
4. $\angle 4 \cong \angle 3$	4. Congruence of $\angle$s is symmetric.
5. $\angle 2 \cong \angle 3$	5. Congruence of $\angle$s is transitive.
6. $\overline{GV} \cong \overline{TV}$	6. Given
7. $\triangle GRV \cong \triangle TSV$	7. AAS
8. $\overline{RV} \cong \overline{SV}$	8. CPCTC
9. $\triangle RVS$ is an isosceles triangle.	9. Definition of isosceles triangle

35. Given: $\triangle GVR$ is an isosceles triangle with base $\overline{GR}$.
$\triangle TVS$ is an isosceles triangle with base $\overline{TS}$.
$\overline{GV} \cong \overline{TV}$
$\angle 5 \cong \angle 6$
Prove: $\overline{GR} \cong \overline{TS}$

Proof:

Statements	Reasons
1. $\triangle GVR$ is an isosceles triangle with base $\overline{GR}$.	1. Given
2. $\overline{RV} \cong \overline{GV}$	2. Def. of isosceles triangle
3. $\triangle TVS$ is an isosceles triangle with base $\overline{TS}$.	3. Given
4. $\overline{TV} \cong \overline{SV}$	4. Def. of isosceles triangle
5. $\overline{GV} \cong \overline{TV}$	5. Given
6. $\overline{RV} \cong \overline{TV}$	6. Congruence of segments is transitive.
7. $\overline{RV} \cong \overline{SV}$	7. Congruence of segments is transitive.
8. $\angle 5 \cong \angle 6$	8. Given
9. $\triangle GRV \cong \triangle TSV$	9. SAS
10. $\overline{GR} \cong \overline{TS}$	10. CPCTC

36. Given $\angle 1 \cong \angle 2$
$\angle 3 \cong \angle 4$
Prove: $\overline{PT} \cong \overline{LX}$

Proof:

Statements	Reasons
1. $\angle 1 \cong \angle 2$ $\angle 3 \cong \angle 4$	1. Given
2. $\overline{TX} \cong \overline{XT}$	2. Congruence of segments is reflexive.
3. $\triangle PXT \cong \triangle LTX$	3. AAS
4. $\overline{PT} \cong \overline{LX}$	4. CPCTC

37. Given: $\overline{PX} \cong \overline{LT}$

$\triangle PRL$ is an isosceles triangle with base $\overline{PL}$.

Prove: $\triangle TRX$ is an isosceles triangle.

Proof:

Statements	Reasons
1. $\overline{PX} \cong \overline{LT}$	1. Given
2. $PX = LT$	2. Def. of $\cong$ segments
3. $PX = PR + RX$ $LT = LR + RT$	3. Segment Addition Postulate
4. $PR + RX = LR + RT$	4. Substitution Prop. (=)
5. $\triangle PRL$ is an isosceles triangle with base $\overline{PL}$.	5. Given
6. $\overline{PR} \cong \overline{LR}$	6. Definition of isosceles triangle
7. $PR = LR$	7. Definition of $\cong$ segments
8. $PR + RX = PR + RT$	8. Substitution Prop. (=)
9. $RX = RT$	9. Subtraction Prop. (=)
10. $\overline{RX} \cong \overline{RT}$	10. Definition of $\cong$ segments
11. $\triangle TRX$ is an isosceles triangle.	11. Definition of an isosceles triangle.

38a. See students' work. **38b.** See students' work.

38c. See students' work. **38d.** 2; 1

38e. No; SSA is not a proof for congruent triangles.

39. No; two equiangular triangles are an example of AAA, but the sides are not necessarily congruent.

40a. He created congruent triangles.

40b. The distance from the shore to where the lines intersect is the distance from the shore to the ship. The triangle formed by the ship and P and Q is congruent to the triangle formed by the intersection point and P and Q by ASA.

41. The guy wires are all the same length because the triangles are congruent by AAS.

42. Sample A, halite; Sample B, feldspar; Sample C, biotite; Sample D, hematite; Sample E, jasper

43. Neither player has a greater angle. The triangles formed are congruent by SSS and therefore the angles are congruent.

44a. $\angle N$ **44b.** $\overline{MP}$

44c. $\angle T$ **45.** no

46. Sample answer: **47.** $-\frac{1}{9}$

48. $m\angle B = 90 - 34 = 56$ **49.** a straight angle
$m\angle C = m\angle A = 34$

50. $4s < 50$ $s^2 > 50$
    $s < 12.5$ $s > 7.07$

The whole number lengths for s such that $7.07 < s < 12.5$ are 8 cm, 9 cm, 10 cm, 11 cm, and 12 cm.

51. inverse; 18   **52.** c and d

4-6 Analyzing Isosceles Triangles

Page 222 Modeling Mathematics

• $\angle A \cong \angle B$

a. See students' work; the base angles are congruent.

b. See students' work; the base angles are congruent.

c. See students' work; all three angles are congruent.

Pages 224–225 Check for Understanding

1. Two sides of a triangle are congruent if and only if the angles opposite those sides are congruent.

2. $\overline{ST} \cong \overline{RT}$, $\angle R \cong \angle S$

3a. $\overline{AB} \cong \overline{A'B}$ **3b.** $\angle A \cong \angle A'$ **3c.** isosceles

4a. 3 ways   **4b.** 1 way   **4c.** none

5. $\angle 5 \cong \angle 11$ **6.** $\overline{ML} \cong \overline{MN}$

7. $\overline{MT} \cong \overline{MR}$

8. Sample answer:

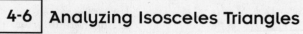

9. $62 + 62 + x = 180$ **10.** $2x - 5 = 10$
    $124 + x = 180$ $2x = 15$
         $x = 56$ $x = 7.5$

11a. $AB = \sqrt{(5 - 2)^2 + (2 - 5)^2} = \sqrt{18}$ or $3\sqrt{2}$

$BC = \sqrt{(2 - 5)^2 + (-1 - 2)^2} = \sqrt{18}$ or $3\sqrt{2}$

$AC = \sqrt{(2 - 2)^2 + (-1 - 5)^2} = \sqrt{36}$ or 6

$\overline{AB} \cong \overline{BC}$

11b. $\angle A \cong \angle C$

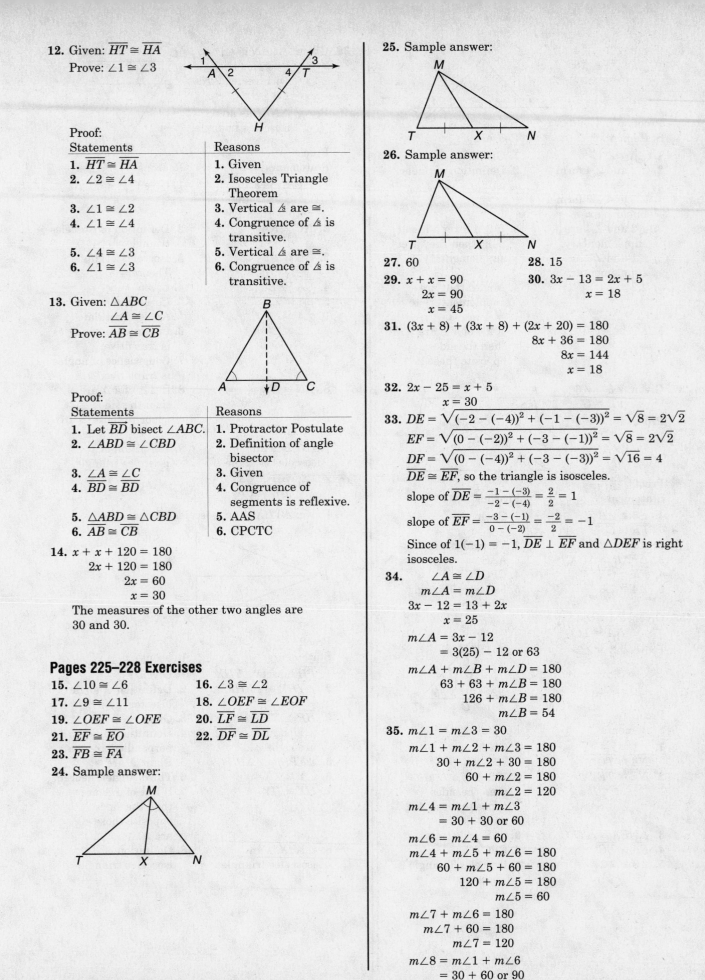

12. Given: $\overline{HT} \cong \overline{HA}$

Prove: $\angle 1 \cong \angle 3$

Proof:

Statements	Reasons
1. $\overline{HT} \cong \overline{HA}$	1. Given
2. $\angle 2 \cong \angle 4$	2. Isosceles Triangle Theorem
3. $\angle 1 \cong \angle 2$	3. Vertical $\angle$ are $\cong$.
4. $\angle 1 \cong \angle 4$	4. Congruence of $\angle$ is transitive.
5. $\angle 4 \cong \angle 3$	5. Vertical $\angle$ are $\cong$.
6. $\angle 1 \cong \angle 3$	6. Congruence of $\angle$ is transitive.

13. Given: $\triangle ABC$

$\angle A \cong \angle C$

Prove: $\overline{AB} \cong \overline{CB}$

Proof:

Statements	Reasons
1. Let $\overline{BD}$ bisect $\angle ABC$.	1. Protractor Postulate
2. $\angle ABD \cong \angle CBD$	2. Definition of angle bisector
3. $\angle A \cong \angle C$	3. Given
4. $\overline{BD} \cong \overline{BD}$	4. Congruence of segments is reflexive.
5. $\triangle ABD \cong \triangle CBD$	5. AAS
6. $\overline{AB} \cong \overline{CB}$	6. CPCTC

14. $x + x + 120 = 180$

$2x + 120 = 180$

$2x = 60$

$x = 30$

The measures of the other two angles are 30 and 30.

Pages 225–228 Exercises

15. $\angle 10 \cong \angle 6$

16. $\angle 3 \cong \angle 2$

17. $\angle 9 \cong \angle 11$

18. $\angle OEF \cong \angle EOF$

19. $\angle OEF \cong \angle OFE$

20. $\overline{LF} \cong \overline{LD}$

21. $\overline{EF} \cong \overline{EO}$

22. $\overline{DF} \cong \overline{DL}$

23. $\overline{FB} \cong \overline{FA}$

24. Sample answer:

25. Sample answer:

26. Sample answer:

27. 60

28. 15

29. $x + x = 90$

$2x = 90$

$x = 45$

30. $3x - 13 = 2x + 5$

$x = 18$

31. $(3x + 8) + (3x + 8) + (2x + 20) = 180$

$8x + 36 = 180$

$8x = 144$

$x = 18$

32. $2x - 25 = x + 5$

$x = 30$

33. $DE = \sqrt{(-2 - (-4))^2 + (-1 - (-3))^2} = \sqrt{8} = 2\sqrt{2}$

$EF = \sqrt{(0 - (-2))^2 + (-3 - (-1))^2} = \sqrt{8} = 2\sqrt{2}$

$DF = \sqrt{(0 - (-4))^2 + (-3 - (-3))^2} = \sqrt{16} = 4$

$\overline{DE} \cong \overline{EF}$, so the triangle is isosceles.

slope of $\overline{DE} = \frac{-1 - (-3)}{-2 - (-4)} = \frac{2}{2} = 1$

slope of $\overline{EF} = \frac{-3 - (-1)}{0 - (-2)} = \frac{-2}{2} = -1$

Since of $1(-1) = -1$, $\overline{DE} \perp \overline{EF}$ and $\triangle DEF$ is right isosceles.

34. $\angle A \cong \angle D$

$m\angle A = m\angle D$

$3x - 12 = 13 + 2x$

$x = 25$

$m\angle A = 3x - 12$

$= 3(25) - 12$ or 63

$m\angle A + m\angle B + m\angle D = 180$

$63 + 63 + m\angle B = 180$

$126 + m\angle B = 180$

$m\angle B = 54$

35. $m\angle 1 = m\angle 3 = 30$

$m\angle 1 + m\angle 2 + m\angle 3 = 180$

$30 + m\angle 2 + 30 = 180$

$60 + m\angle 2 = 180$

$m\angle 2 = 120$

$m\angle 4 = m\angle 1 + m\angle 3$

$= 30 + 30$ or 60

$m\angle 6 = m\angle 4 = 60$

$m\angle 4 + m\angle 5 + m\angle 6 = 180$

$60 + m\angle 5 + 60 = 180$

$120 + m\angle 5 = 180$

$m\angle 5 = 60$

$m\angle 7 + m\angle 6 = 180$

$m\angle 7 + 60 = 180$

$m\angle 7 = 120$

$m\angle 8 = m\angle 1 + m\angle 6$

$= 30 + 60$ or 90

 Geometry Chapter 4

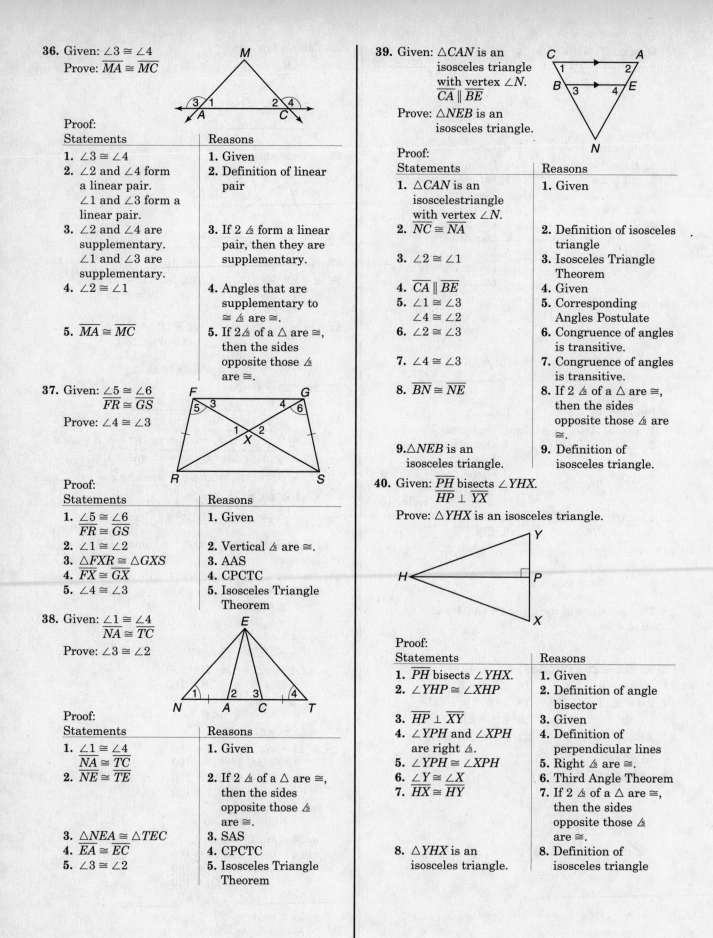

36. Given: $\angle 3 \cong \angle 4$
Prove: $\overline{MA} \cong \overline{MC}$

Proof:

Statements	Reasons
1. $\angle 3 \cong \angle 4$	1. Given
2. $\angle 2$ and $\angle 4$ form a linear pair. $\angle 1$ and $\angle 3$ form a linear pair.	2. Definition of linear pair
3. $\angle 2$ and $\angle 4$ are supplementary. $\angle 1$ and $\angle 3$ are supplementary.	3. If 2 $\angle$s form a linear pair, then they are supplementary.
4. $\angle 2 \cong \angle 1$	4. Angles that are supplementary to $\cong$ $\angle$s are $\cong$.
5. $\overline{MA} \cong \overline{MC}$	5. If 2 $\angle$s of a $\triangle$ are $\cong$, then the sides opposite those $\angle$s are $\cong$.

37. Given: $\angle 5 \cong \angle 6$
$\overline{FR} \cong \overline{GS}$
Prove: $\angle 4 \cong \angle 3$

Proof:

Statements	Reasons
1. $\angle 5 \cong \angle 6$ $\overline{FR} \cong \overline{GS}$	1. Given
2. $\angle 1 \cong \angle 2$	2. Vertical $\angle$s are $\cong$.
3. $\triangle FXR \cong \triangle GXS$	3. AAS
4. $\overline{FX} \cong \overline{GX}$	4. CPCTC
5. $\angle 4 \cong \angle 3$	5. Isosceles Triangle Theorem

38. Given: $\angle 1 \cong \angle 4$
$\overline{NA} \cong \overline{TC}$
Prove: $\angle 3 \cong \angle 2$

Proof:

Statements	Reasons
1. $\angle 1 \cong \angle 4$ $\overline{NA} \cong \overline{TC}$	1. Given
2. $\overline{NE} \cong \overline{TE}$	2. If 2 $\angle$s of a $\triangle$ are $\cong$, then the sides opposite those $\angle$s are $\cong$.
3. $\triangle NEA \cong \triangle TEC$	3. SAS
4. $\overline{EA} \cong \overline{EC}$	4. CPCTC
5. $\angle 3 \cong \angle 2$	5. Isosceles Triangle Theorem

39. Given: $\triangle CAN$ is an isosceles triangle with vertex $\angle N$.
$\overline{CA} \parallel \overline{BE}$
Prove: $\triangle NEB$ is an isosceles triangle.

Proof:

Statements	Reasons
1. $\triangle CAN$ is an isosceles triangle with vertex $\angle N$.	1. Given
2. $\overline{NC} \cong \overline{NA}$	2. Definition of isosceles triangle
3. $\angle 2 \cong \angle 1$	3. Isosceles Triangle Theorem
4. $\overline{CA} \parallel \overline{BE}$	4. Given
5. $\angle 1 \cong \angle 3$ $\angle 4 \cong \angle 2$	5. Corresponding Angles Postulate
6. $\angle 2 \cong \angle 3$	6. Congruence of angles is transitive.
7. $\angle 4 \cong \angle 3$	7. Congruence of angles is transitive.
8. $\overline{BN} \cong \overline{NE}$	8. If 2 $\angle$s of a $\triangle$ are $\cong$, then the sides opposite those $\angle$s are $\cong$.
9. $\triangle NEB$ is an isosceles triangle.	9. Definition of isosceles triangle.

40. Given: $\overline{PH}$ bisects $\angle YHX$.
$\overline{HP} \perp \overline{YX}$
Prove: $\triangle YHX$ is an isosceles triangle.

Proof:

Statements	Reasons
1. $\overline{PH}$ bisects $\angle YHX$.	1. Given
2. $\angle YHP \cong \angle XHP$	2. Definition of angle bisector
3. $\overline{HP} \perp \overline{XY}$	3. Given
4. $\angle YPH$ and $\angle XPH$ are right $\angle$s.	4. Definition of perpendicular lines
5. $\angle YPH \cong \angle XPH$	5. Right $\angle$s are $\cong$.
6. $\angle Y \cong \angle X$	6. Third Angle Theorem
7. $\overline{HX} \cong \overline{HY}$	7. If 2 $\angle$s of a $\triangle$ are $\cong$, then the sides opposite those $\angle$s are $\cong$.
8. $\triangle YHX$ is an isosceles triangle.	8. Definition of isosceles triangle

41. Given: $\triangle IOE$ is an isosceles triangle with base $\overline{OE}$.
$\overline{AO}$ bisects $\angle IOE$.
$\overline{AE}$ bisects $\angle IEO$.

Prove: $\triangle EAO$ is an isosceles triangle.

Proof:

Statements	Reasons
1. $\overline{AO}$ bisects $\angle IOE$. $\overline{AE}$ bisects $\angle IEO$.	1. Given
2. $\angle 1 \cong \angle 2$ $\angle 3 \cong \angle 4$	2. Definition of angle bisector
3. $m\angle 1 = m\angle 2$ $m\angle 3 = m\angle 4$	3. Definition of congruent angles
4. $m\angle IOE = m\angle 1 + m\angle 2$ $m\angle IEO = m\angle 3 + m\angle 4$	4. Angle Addition Postulate
5. $m\angle IOE = 2m\angle 2$ $m\angle IEO = 2m\angle 4$	5. Substitution Property (=)
6. $\triangle IOE$ is an isosceles triangle with base $\overline{OE}$.	6. Given
7. $\overline{IE} \cong \overline{IO}$	7. Definition of isosceles triangle
8. $\angle IOE \cong \angle IEO$	8. Isosceles Triangle Theorem
9. $m\angle IOE = m\angle IEO$	9. Definition of congruent $\angle$s
10. $2m\angle 2 = 2m\angle 4$	10. Substitution Property (=)
11. $m\angle 2 = m\angle 4$	11. Division Prop. (=)
12. $\angle 2 \cong \angle 4$	12. Definition of $\cong \angle$s
13. $\overline{AE} \cong \overline{AO}$	13. If 2 $\angle$s of a $\triangle$ are $\cong$, then the sides opposite those $\angle$s are $\cong$.
14. $\triangle AEO$ is an isosceles triangle.	14. Definition of isosceles triangle

42. Given: $\triangle ABC$ is an equilateral triangle.

Prove: $\triangle ABC$ is an equiangular triangle.

Proof:

Statements	Reasons
1. $\triangle ABC$ is an equilateral triangle.	1. Given
2. $\overline{AB} \cong \overline{AC} \cong \overline{BC}$	2. Definition of equilateral
3. $\angle A \cong \angle B \cong \angle C$	3. Isosceles Triangle Theorem
4. $\triangle ABC$ is an equiangular triangle.	4. Definition of equiangular

Given: $\triangle ABC$ is an equiangular triangle.

Prove: $\triangle ABC$ is an equilateral triangle.

Proof:

Statements	Reasons
1. $\triangle ABC$ is an equiangular triangle.	1. Given
2. $\angle A \cong \angle B \cong \angle C$	2. Definition of equiangular
3. $\overline{AB} \cong \overline{AC} \cong \overline{BC}$	3. If two $\angle$s of a $\triangle$ are $\cong$, then the sides opposite those $\angle$s are $\cong$.
4. $\triangle ABC$ is an equilateral triangle.	4. Definition of equilateral

43. Given: $\triangle MNO$ is an equilateral triangle.

Prove: $m\angle M = m\angle N = m\angle O = 60$

Proof:

Statements	Reasons
1. $\triangle MNO$ is an equilateral triangle.	1. Given
2. $\overline{MN} \cong \overline{MO} \cong \overline{NO}$	2. Definition of equilateral
3. $\angle M \cong \angle N \cong \angle O$	3. Isosceles Triangle Theorem
4. $m\angle M = m\angle N = m\angle O$	4. Definition of $\cong \angle$s
5. $m\angle M + m\angle N + m\angle O = 180$	5. Angle Sum Theorem
6. $3m\angle M = 180$	6. Substitution Prop. (=)
7. $m\angle M = 60$	7. Division Prop. (=)
8. $m\angle M = m\angle N = m\angle O = 60$	8. Substitution Prop. (=)

44a. 77, 77   **44b.** 30, 30

44c. 51, 51   **44d.** 39.5, 39.5

45.

45a. $\triangle DEB \cong \triangle FEC$; since E is the midpoint of $\overline{BC}$, $\overline{BE} \cong \overline{CE}$. Since $\overline{AC} \cong \overline{AB}$, $\angle B \cong \angle C$. Since D is the midpoint of $\overline{AB}$, F is the midpoint of $\overline{AC}$, and $\overline{AB} \cong \overline{AC}$; $\overline{AD} \cong \overline{AF}$. Therefore, $\triangle DEB \cong \triangle FEC$ by SAS.

45b. $\triangle ABC$, $\triangle ADF$, $\triangle DEF$; We are given $\triangle ABC$ is an isosceles triangle. Since D is the midpoint of $\overline{AB}$, F is the midpoint of $\overline{AC}$, and $\overline{AB} \cong \overline{AC}$; $\overline{AD} \cong \overline{AF}$ and $\triangle ADF$ is an isosceles triangle. Since $\triangle DEB \cong \triangle FEC$, $\overline{DE} \cong \overline{FE}$ and $\triangle DEF$ is an isosceles triangle.

46a. Sample answer:

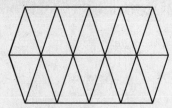

46b. Sample answer:

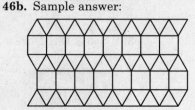

46c. Sample answer:

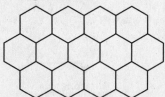

47. Point M; if the surface is level then it is horizontal. The plumb line will be vertical so it is perpendicular to the surface. A perpendicular dropped from the vertex angle of an isosceles triangle will pass through the midpoint of the base.

48. Let L represent the lighthouse. By the Exterior Angle Theorem, $2x = x + m\angle L$ and $x = m\angle L$. Since the two angles are congruent, the sides opposite the lighthouse and the side opposite the angle labeled $x°$ are congruent. Therefore, the distance traveled by the ship equals its distance from the lighthouse.

49. SSA means 2 sides and a nonincluded angle are congruent to the corresponding sides and angle. It cannot be used as a proof for congruent triangles. SAS means 2 sides and the included angle are congruent to 2 sides and the included angle. It can be used as a proof for congruent triangles.

50. Amy, Sept.; Kiana, Aug.; Timothy, Feb.; Pablo, Jan.

51. $\angle C \leftrightarrow \angle P$, $\angle D \leftrightarrow \angle Q$, $\angle E \leftrightarrow \angle R$, $\overline{CD} \leftrightarrow \overline{PQ}$, $\overline{DE} \leftrightarrow \overline{QR}$, $\overline{CE} \leftrightarrow \overline{PR}$

52. $54 + 79 = 133$

53. $6x - 6 = x + 9$
$\quad\quad 5x = 15$
$\quad\quad\ x = 3$
$6x - 6 = 6(3) - 6$ or 12 units

54. $m = \dfrac{-1 - (-3)}{6 - 7} = -2$

55. Given: $\overline{AB} \cong \overline{EF}$
$\qquad\quad \overline{EF} \cong \overline{JK}$
$\qquad\quad \overline{BC} \cong \overline{HJ}$
Prove: $\overline{AC} \cong \overline{HK}$

A ─── B ──────────── C
D ──────── E ── F ──── G
H ───────────────── J ── K

Proof:

Statements	Reasons
1. $\overline{AB} \cong \overline{EF}$ $\overline{EF} \cong \overline{JK}$	1. Given
2. $\overline{AB} \cong \overline{JK}$	2. Congruence of segments is transitive.
3. $AB = JK$	3. Def. of $\cong$ segments
4. $\overline{BC} \cong \overline{HJ}$	4. Given
5. $BC = HJ$	5. Congruence of segments is transitive.
6. $AB + BC = JK + HJ$	6. Addition Prop. (=)
7. $AC = AB + BC$ $HK = JK + HJ$	7. Segment Addition Postulate
8. $AC = HK$	8. Substitution Prop. (=)
9. $\overline{AC} \cong \overline{HK}$	9. Def. of $\cong$ segments

56. If a number is a whole number, then it is an integer.

57. $DC = \sqrt{[7 - (-3)]^2 + (4 - 8)^2}$
$\quad\quad = \sqrt{10^2 + (-4)^2}$
$\quad\quad = \sqrt{116}$
$\quad\quad = 2\sqrt{29} \approx 10.77$

$\left(\dfrac{x_1 + x_2}{2}, \dfrac{y_1 + y_2}{2}\right) = \left(\dfrac{7 + (-3)}{2}, \dfrac{4 + 8}{2}\right)$
$\qquad\qquad\qquad = \left(\dfrac{4}{2}, \dfrac{12}{2}\right) = (2, 6)$

58. $D = \{7, 4, -19, 5\}$
$\quad\ R = \{-2, 0, -1, 5\}$

59. x-intercept: Let $y = 0$. y-intercept: Let $x = 0$.
$\quad 9x - 2(0) = 18$ $\qquad\qquad 9(0) - 2y = 18$
$\qquad\quad\ \ 9x = 18$ $\qquad\qquad\qquad -2y = 18$
$\qquad\qquad\ x = 2$ $\qquad\qquad\qquad\quad\ y = -9$

Chapter 4 Highlights

Page 229 Understanding and Using the Vocabulary

1. true
2. false; hypotenuse
3. false; base angles
4. true
5. false; nonincluded
6. true
7. true
8. false; three
9. false; flow proof
10. false; equilateral triangle
11. true
12. true
13. false; base
14. false; corollary
15. true

Chapter 4 Study Guide and Assessment

Pages 230–232 Skills and Concepts

16. $\triangle RSV$ **17.** $\triangle SUV$, $\triangle STU$

18. $\triangle RSV$, $\triangle SWV$, $\triangle TWU$

19. $\triangle SWT$, $\triangle VWU$

20. $\triangle SWV$, $\triangle SWT$, $\triangle TWU$, $\triangle UWV$

21. $\overline{SV}$ **22.** $\angle RSV$

23. $m\angle 1 = 90$

24. $m\angle 2 + m\angle 5 = 90$ **25.** $m\angle 3 + 115 = 180$
$m\angle 2 + 40 = 90$ $m\angle 3 = 65$
$m\angle 2 = 50$

26. $m\angle 4 + m\angle 3 + 40 = 180$
$m\angle 4 + 65 + 40 = 180$
$m\angle 4 = 75$

27. $m\angle 5 = m\angle KRL$ **28.** 120
$m\angle 5 = 40$

29. $x = r + 65$ **30.** $w + 120 = 180$
$120 = r + 65$ $w = 60$
$55 = r$

31. $y + 65 = 90$ **32.** $x + y + z = 180$
$y = 25$ $120 + 25 + z = 180$
$z = 35$

33. $s = r = 55$ **34.** $v = w = 60$

35. $v + s + t = 180$
$60 + 55 + t = 180$
$t = 65$

36. $\angle O$ **37.** $\overline{RT}$

38. $\overline{NM}$ **39.** $\angle ONM$

40. $\overline{OM}$ **41.** $\angle STR$

42. Given: $\overline{EF} \cong \overline{GH}$
$\overline{EH} \cong \overline{GF}$
Prove: $\triangle EFH \cong \triangle GHF$

Proof:

$\overline{EF} \cong \overline{GH}$
Given

$\overline{EH} \cong \overline{GF}$
Given

$\triangle EFH \cong \triangle GHF$
SSS

$\overline{HF} \cong \overline{FH}$
Congruence of segments is reflexive.

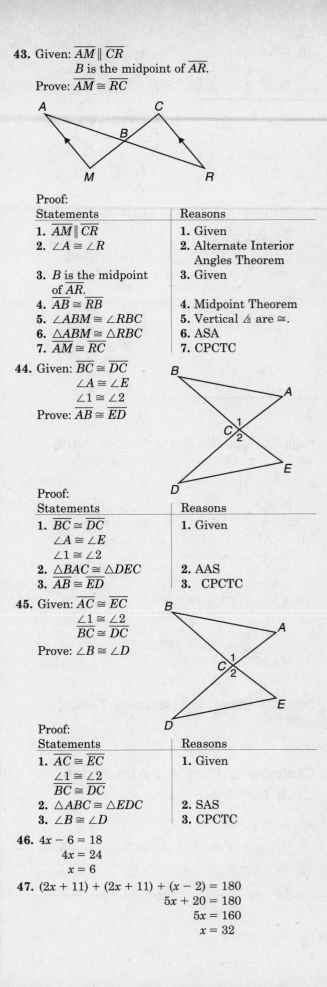

43. Given: $\overline{AM} \parallel \overline{CR}$
B is the midpoint of $\overline{AR}$.
Prove: $\overline{AM} \cong \overline{RC}$

Proof:

Statements	Reasons
1. $\overline{AM} \parallel \overline{CR}$	1. Given
2. $\angle A \cong \angle R$	2. Alternate Interior Angles Theorem
3. B is the midpoint of $\overline{AR}$.	3. Given
4. $\overline{AB} \cong \overline{RB}$	4. Midpoint Theorem
5. $\angle ABM \cong \angle RBC$	5. Vertical $\angle$ are $\cong$.
6. $\triangle ABM \cong \triangle RBC$	6. ASA
7. $\overline{AM} \cong \overline{RC}$	7. CPCTC

44. Given: $\overline{BC} \cong \overline{DC}$
$\angle A \cong \angle E$
$\angle 1 \cong \angle 2$
Prove: $\overline{AB} \cong \overline{ED}$

Proof:

Statements	Reasons
1. $\overline{BC} \cong \overline{DC}$ $\angle A \cong \angle E$ $\angle 1 \cong \angle 2$	1. Given
2. $\triangle BAC \cong \triangle DEC$	2. AAS
3. $\overline{AB} \cong \overline{ED}$	3. CPCTC

45. Given: $\overline{AC} \cong \overline{EC}$
$\angle 1 \cong \angle 2$
$\overline{BC} \cong \overline{DC}$
Prove: $\angle B \cong \angle D$

Proof:

Statements	Reasons
1. $\overline{AC} \cong \overline{EC}$ $\angle 1 \cong \angle 2$ $\overline{BC} \cong \overline{DC}$	1. Given
2. $\triangle ABC \cong \triangle EDC$	2. SAS
3. $\angle B \cong \angle D$	3. CPCTC

46. $4x - 6 = 18$
$4x = 24$
$x = 6$

47. $(2x + 11) + (2x + 11) + (x - 2) = 180$
$5x + 20 = 180$
$5x = 160$
$x = 32$

48. Given: $\angle 2 \cong \angle 1$
$\angle 4 \cong \angle 3$
Prove: $\overline{AM} \cong \overline{AO}$

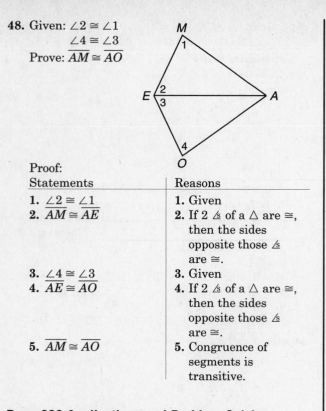

Proof:

Statements	Reasons
1. $\angle 2 \cong \angle 1$	1. Given
2. $\overline{AM} \cong \overline{AE}$	2. If 2 $\angle$s of a $\triangle$ are $\cong$, then the sides opposite those $\angle$s are $\cong$.
3. $\angle 4 \cong \angle 3$	3. Given
4. $\overline{AE} \cong \overline{AO}$	4. If 2 $\angle$s of a $\triangle$ are $\cong$, then the sides opposite those $\angle$s are $\cong$.
5. $\overline{AM} \cong \overline{AO}$	5. Congruence of segments is transitive.

Page 232 Applications and Problem Solving

49. Let x = measure of the acute angle.
$x + 54 = 90$
$x = 36$

50. Sample 1, mercury; Sample 2, gallium; Sample 3, lithium; Sample 4, calcium

51. $m\angle ABC + m\angle ACB + m\angle BAC + m\angle CAD + m\angle ADC + m\angle ACD = 360$
$m\angle ABC = m\angle ACB = m\angle ACD = m\angle ADC$
Let $x = m\angle ABC$
$x + x + 90 + x + x = 360$
$4x + 90 = 360$
$4x = 270$
$x = 67.5$
$m\angle BCD = 2x = 135$

Page 233 Alternative Assessment: Thinking Critically

• yes

College Entrance Exam Practice, Chapters 1–4

Pages 234–235

1. $\frac{-2 - 4}{3 - (-6)} = \frac{-6}{9} = \frac{-2}{3}$ (B) **2.** (C)

3. $\frac{360}{2} = 180 = a + b + c$ (C)

4. (C)

5. $0.08 = \frac{8}{x}$
$.08x = 8$
$x = 100$ (B)

6. (A)

7.

$m\angle AFC = 40 + 80$ or 120
$m\angle AFC + 30 + x = 180$
$120 + 30 + x = 180$
$x = 30$ (D)

8. I. Vertical angles are $\cong$.
II. Vertical angles are $\cong$.
III. Alt. Ext. angles are supp.
IV. Ext. angles same side of transversal are supp.
V. $m\angle 7 = m\angle 6 + m\angle 8$ (B)

9. $5x - y = 10$
$-y = -5x + 10$
$y = 5x + 10$
Slope of parallel line is 5.

10. $4(5)(6) = 2(10 + x)$
$120 = 20 + 2x$
$x = 50$

11. $\frac{x}{2} + \frac{x}{3} + \frac{x}{6} = kx$ **12.** $10x - 4 = 8$
$\frac{3x}{6} + \frac{2x}{6} + \frac{x}{6} = kx$ $10x = 12$
$x = kx$ $x = 1.2$
$k = 1$ $10x - 5 = 10(1.2) - 5$
$= 12 - 5$ or 7

13. $AB:CD = 1:1 = 1$

14. $\frac{x^2 y}{(x - 2)^2} = \frac{1^2(-1)}{[1 - (-2)]^2} = \frac{-1}{(3)^2} = \frac{-1}{9}$

15. $\angle 1 \cong \angle 2$ *Vertical angles*
$\angle 2 \cong \angle 4$ *Alternate interior $\angle$s*
$\angle 1 \cong \angle 2 \cong 4$
$\angle 1, \angle 2, \angle 4$

16. 70% of $36.50 = \$25.55$ (A)

17. $3x^2$ $(3x)^2 = 9x^2$ (B)

18. $\frac{3}{5} = \frac{x}{20}$ $\frac{4}{8} = \frac{y}{2y}$
$5x = 60$ $8y = 96$
$x = 12$ $y = 12$ (C)

19. $2(9 + 6) - 4(10 \div 2)$ $2 \times 9 + 6 - 4 \times 10 \div 2$
$= 2(15) - 4 (5)$ $= 18 + 6 - 40 \div 2$
$= 30 - 20$ $= 24 - 20$
$= 10$ $= 4$ (A)

20. $x = 180 - 89$ Vertical angles are $\cong$.
$x = 91$ $y = 89$ (A)

CHAPTER 5 Applying Congruent Triangles

Page 238 Modeling Mathematics

Sample answer: Both the perpendicular bisector and the altitude are perpendicular to the side of the triangle. They are parallel to each other. The perpendicular bisector and the median intersect at the midpoint of the side.

Pages 241–242 Check for Understanding

1. Both the perpendicular bisector and the altitude are perpendicular to a side of the triangle. However, a perpendicular bisector passes through the midpoint of the side to which it is perpendicular. A perpendicular bisector does not necessarily pass through a vertex of the triangle. An altitude passes through the vertex of the triangle opposite the side to which the altitude is perpendicular. An altitude does not necessarily pass through the midpoint of the side to which it is perpendicular. One of of the perpendicular bisectors in an isosceles triangle is also an altitude.

2. Altitudes may occur outside of a triangle.

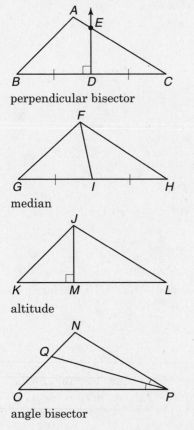

perpendicular bisector

median

altitude

angle bisector

3. The altitude and the angle bisector to the vertex of the vertex angle of an isosceles triangle are the same segment.

4. a right triangle

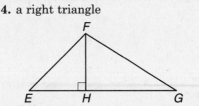

5. The altitude and the perpendicular bisector are parallel. See students' justifications.

6.

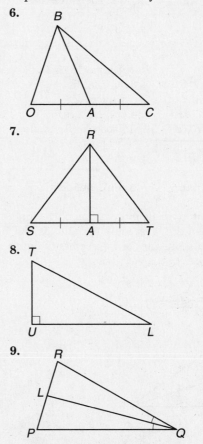

7.

8.

9.

Sample answers given for Exercises 10–14.

10. $\overline{SM} \perp \overline{RE}$.

11. N is the midpoint of $\overline{SE}$; $\overline{RN}$ is a median of $\triangle RES$.

12. $\overline{SM} \perp \overline{RE}$; $\overline{RM} \cong \overline{ME}$; $\overline{SM}$ is the perpendicular bisector of $\overline{RE}$.

13. $\overline{NR}$ bisects $\angle SRE$.

14. $\overline{EL}$ is an altitude of $\angle RES$.

15a. $T\left(\dfrac{x_1 + x_2}{2}, \dfrac{y_1 + y_2}{2}\right) = T\left(\dfrac{5 + 9}{2}, \dfrac{11 + (-1)}{2}\right)$
$= T\left(\dfrac{14}{2}, \dfrac{10}{2}\right) = T(7, 5)$

15b. $m = \dfrac{5 - (-9)}{7 - (-3)} = \dfrac{14}{10}$ or $\dfrac{7}{5}$

15c. No; because $\dfrac{7}{5} \cdot -3 \neq -1$.

15d. No, $AT \approx 17.2$ and $AB \approx 21.5$

$AT = \sqrt{(-3-7)^2 + (-9-5)^2} =$
$\sqrt{100 + 196} = \sqrt{296} \approx 17.2$

$AB = \sqrt{(-3-5)^2 + (-9-11)^2} =$
$\sqrt{64 + 400} = \sqrt{464} \approx 21.5$

16. Given: $\overline{EG} \cong \overline{EH}$
$\overline{ER}$ is an
altitude of
$\triangle EGH$.

Prove: $\overline{ER}$ is a
median of
$\triangle EGH$.

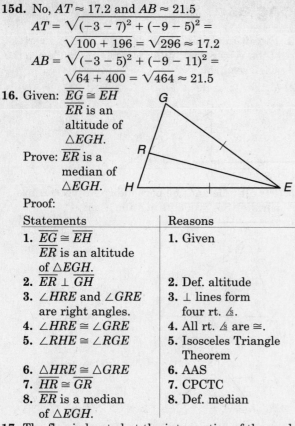

Proof:

Statements	Reasons
1. $\overline{EG} \cong \overline{EH}$ $\overline{ER}$ is an altitude of $\triangle EGH$.	1. Given
2. $\overline{ER} \perp \overline{GH}$	2. Def. altitude
3. $\angle HRE$ and $\angle GRE$ are right angles.	3. $\perp$ lines form four rt. $\angle$s.
4. $\angle HRE \cong \angle GRE$	4. All rt. $\angle$s are $\cong$.
5. $\angle RHE \cong \angle RGE$	5. Isosceles Triangle Theorem
6. $\triangle HRE \cong \triangle GRE$	6. AAS
7. $\overline{HR} \cong \overline{GR}$	7. CPCTC
8. $\overline{ER}$ is a median of $\triangle EGH$.	8. Def. median

17. The flag is located at the intersection of the angle bisector between the West and Shore Roads and the perpendicular bisector of the segment joining the lookout tower to the entrance.

Pages 242–244 Excercises

18.

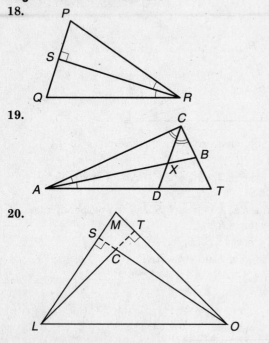

19.

20.

21.

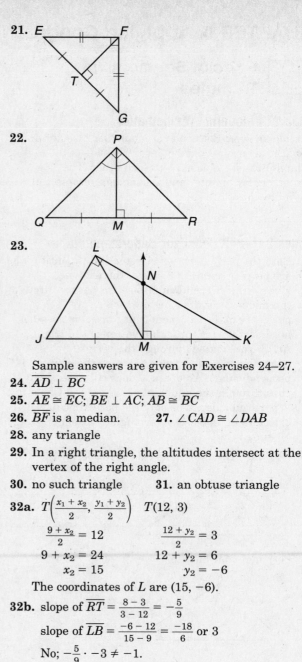

22.

23.

Sample answers are given for Exercises 24–27.

24. $\overline{AD} \perp \overline{BC}$

25. $\overline{AE} \cong \overline{EC}$; $\overline{BE} \perp \overline{AC}$; $\overline{AB} \cong \overline{BC}$

26. $\overline{BF}$ is a median.   **27.** $\angle CAD \cong \angle DAB$

28. any triangle

29. In a right triangle, the altitudes intersect at the vertex of the right angle.

30. no such triangle   **31.** an obtuse triangle

32a. $T\left(\frac{x_1 + x_2}{2}, \frac{y_1 + y_2}{2}\right)$ $T(12, 3)$

$\frac{9 + x_2}{2} = 12$ $\frac{12 + y_2}{2} = 3$

$9 + x_2 = 24$ $12 + y_2 = 6$

$x_2 = 15$ $y_2 = -6$

The coordinates of L are $(15, -6)$.

32b. slope of $\overline{RT} = \frac{8-3}{3-12} = -\frac{5}{9}$

slope of $\overline{LB} = \frac{-6-12}{15-9} = \frac{-18}{6}$ or 3

No; $-\frac{5}{9} \cdot -3 \neq -1$.

32c. $\left(\frac{x_1 + x_2}{2}, \frac{y_1 + y_2}{2}\right) = \left(\frac{3+9}{2}, \frac{8+12}{2}\right)$

$= \left(\frac{12}{2}, \frac{20}{2}\right)$

$= (6, 10)$

C is the midpoint of $\overline{RB}$ so $\overline{SC}$ is a bisector of $\overline{RB}$.

slope of $\overline{RB} = \frac{12-8}{9-3} = \frac{4}{6}$ or $\frac{2}{3}$

slope of $\overline{SC} = \frac{13-10}{4-6} = -\frac{3}{2}$

Since $\frac{2}{3}\left(-\frac{3}{2}\right) = -1$, $\overline{SC} \perp \overline{RB}$.

Thus, $\overline{SC}$ is a perpendicular bisector of $\overline{RB}$.

33a. $m\angle RST = 90$

$2x + 10 = 90$

$2x = 80$

$x = 40$

33b. $m\angle RTA = m\angle ATE$

$4y - 17 = 3y - 4$

$y = 13$

$m\angle RTA = 4y - 17$

$= 4(13) - 17$

$= 35$

33c. $RY = YT$
$2z - 1 = 4z - 11$
$-2z = -10$
$z = 5$
$RY = 2z - 1$
$= 2(5) - 1$ or 9
$TY = 4z - 11$
$= 4(5) - 11$ or 9
$RT = RY + YT$
$RT = 9 + 9$ or 18

34. Given: $\overline{CD}$ is an angle bisector. $\overline{CD}$ is an altitude.

Prove: $\triangle ABC$ is isosceles.

Proof:

Statements	Reasons
1. $\overline{CD}$ is an angle bisector. $\overline{CD}$ is an altitude.	1. Given
2. $\angle ACD \cong \angle BCD$	2. Def. bisector
3. $\overline{CD} \perp \overline{AB}$	3. Def. altitude
4. $\angle CDA$ and $\angle CDB$ are right angles.	4. $\perp$ lines form four rt. $\angle$s.
5. $\angle CDA \cong \angle CDB$	5. All rt. $\angle$s are $\cong$.
6. $\overline{CD} \cong \overline{CD}$	6. Congruence of segments is reflexive.
7. $\angle ACD \cong \angle BCD$	7. ASA
8. $\overline{AC} \cong \overline{BC}$	8. CPCTC
9. $\triangle ACB$ is isosceles.	9. Def. isosceles $\triangle$

35. Given: $\overline{UW}$ is the perpendicular bisector of $\overline{XZ}$.

Prove: For any point V on $\overline{UW}$, $VX = VZ$.

Proof:

Statements	Reasons
1. $\overline{UW}$ is the $\perp$ bisector of $\overline{XZ}$.	1. Given
2. W is the midpoint of $\overline{XZ}$.	2. Def. $\perp$ bisector
3. $\overline{XW} \cong \overline{WZ}$	3. Def. midpoint
4. $\overline{UW} \perp \overline{XZ}$	4. Def. $\perp$ bisector
5. $\angle XWV, \angle ZWV$ are right $\angle$s.	5. $\perp$ lines form four rt. $\angle$s.
6. $\angle XWV \cong \angle ZWV$	6. All rt. $\angle$s are $\cong$.
7. $\overline{VW} \cong \overline{VW}$	7. Congruence of segments is reflexive.
8. $\triangle XWV \cong \triangle ZWV$	8. SAS
9. $\overline{VX} \cong \overline{VZ}$	9. CPCTC
10. $VX = VZ$	10. Def. $\cong$ segments

36. Given: $\overline{CA} \cong \overline{CB}$, $\overline{AD} \cong \overline{BD}$

Prove: C and D are on the perpendicular bisector of $\overline{AB}$.

Proof:

Statements	Reasons
1. $\overline{CA} \cong \overline{CB}$, $\overline{AD} \cong \overline{BD}$	1. Given
2. $\overline{CD} \cong \overline{CD}$	2. Congruence of segments is reflexive.
3. $\triangle ACD \cong \triangle BCD$	3. SSS
4. $\angle ACD \cong \angle BCD$	4. CPCTC
5. $\overline{CE} \cong \overline{CE}$	5. Congruence of segments is reflexive.
6. $\triangle CEA \cong \triangle CEB$	6. SAS
7. $\overline{AE} \cong \overline{BE}$	7. CPCTC
8. E is the midpoint of $\overline{AB}$.	8. Def. midpoint
9. $\angle CEA \cong \angle CEB$	9. CPCTC
10. $\angle CEA$ and $\angle CEB$ form a linear pair.	10. Def. linear pair
11. $\angle CEA$ and $\angle CEB$ are supplementary.	11. Supplement Theorem
12. $m\angle CEA + m\angle CEB = 180$	12. Def. supplementary
13. $m\angle CEA + m\angle CEA = 180$	13. Substitution Prop. (=)
14. $2m\angle CEA = 180$	14. Substitution Prop. (=)
15. $m\angle CEA = 90$	15. Division Prop. (=)
16. $\angle CEA$ and $\angle CEB$ are rt. $\angle$s.	16. Def. rt. $\angle$
17. $\overline{CD} \perp \overline{AB}$	17. Def. $\perp$
18. $\overline{CD}$ is the perpendicular bisector of $\overline{AB}$.	18. Def. $\perp$ bisector
19. C and D are on the perpendicular bisector of $\overline{AB}$.	19. Def. point on a line

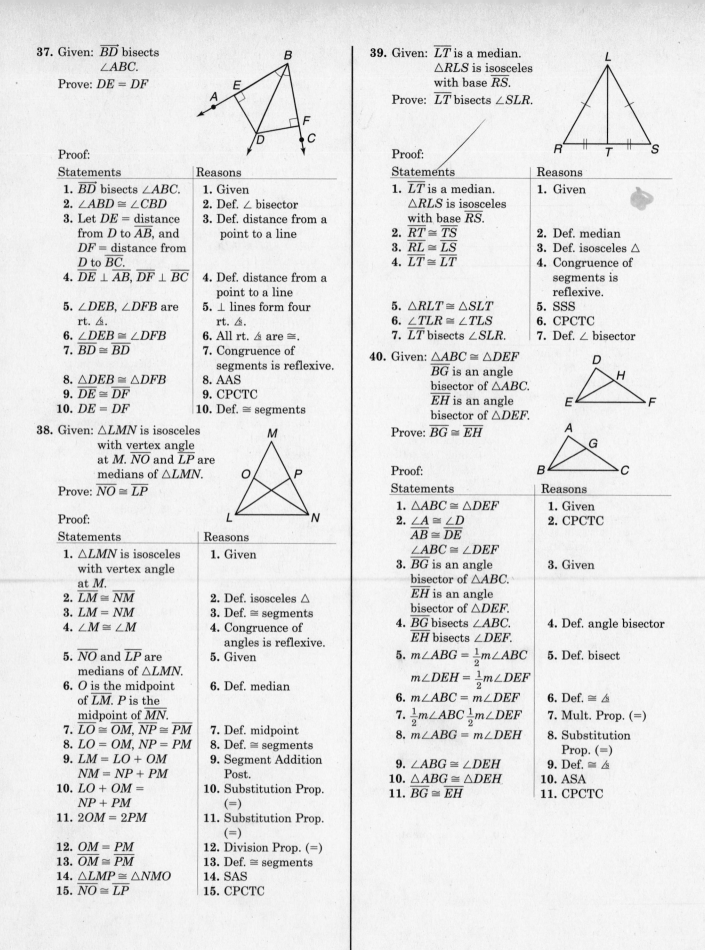

37. Given: $\overrightarrow{BD}$ bisects $\angle ABC$.

Prove: $DE = DF$

Proof:

Statements	Reasons
1. $\overrightarrow{BD}$ bisects $\angle ABC$.	1. Given
2. $\angle ABD \cong \angle CBD$	2. Def. $\angle$ bisector
3. Let $DE =$ distance from D to $\overline{AB}$, and $DF =$ distance from D to $\overline{BC}$.	3. Def. distance from a point to a line
4. $\overline{DE} \perp \overline{AB}$, $\overline{DF} \perp \overline{BC}$	4. Def. distance from a point to a line
5. $\angle DEB$, $\angle DFB$ are rt. $\angle$s.	5. $\perp$ lines form four rt. $\angle$s.
6. $\angle DEB \cong \angle DFB$	6. All rt. $\angle$ are $\cong$.
7. $\overline{BD} \cong \overline{BD}$	7. Congruence of segments is reflexive.
8. $\triangle DEB \cong \triangle DFB$	8. AAS
9. $\overline{DE} \cong \overline{DF}$	9. CPCTC
10. $DE = DF$	10. Def. $\cong$ segments

38. Given: $\triangle LMN$ is isosceles with vertex angle at M. $\overline{NO}$ and $\overline{LP}$ are medians of $\triangle LMN$.

Prove: $\overline{NO} \cong \overline{LP}$

Proof:

Statements	Reasons
1. $\triangle LMN$ is isosceles with vertex angle at M.	1. Given
2. $\overline{LM} \cong \overline{NM}$	2. Def. isosceles $\triangle$
3. $LM = NM$	3. Def. $\cong$ segments
4. $\angle M \cong \angle M$	4. Congruence of angles is reflexive.
5. $\overline{NO}$ and $\overline{LP}$ are medians of $\triangle LMN$.	5. Given
6. O is the midpoint of $\overline{LM}$. P is the midpoint of $\overline{MN}$.	6. Def. median
7. $\overline{LO} \cong \overline{OM}$, $\overline{NP} \cong \overline{PM}$	7. Def. midpoint
8. $LO = OM$, $NP = PM$	8. Def. $\cong$ segments
9. $LM = LO + OM$ $NM = NP + PM$	9. Segment Addition Post.
10. $LO + OM =$ $NP + PM$	10. Substitution Prop. (=)
11. $2OM = 2PM$	11. Substitution Prop. (=)
12. $OM = PM$	12. Division Prop. (=)
13. $\overline{OM} \cong \overline{PM}$	13. Def. $\cong$ segments
14. $\triangle LMP \cong \triangle NMO$	14. SAS
15. $\overline{NO} \cong \overline{LP}$	15. CPCTC

39. Given: $\overline{LT}$ is a median. $\triangle RLS$ is isosceles with base $\overline{RS}$.

Prove: $\overline{LT}$ bisects $\angle SLR$.

Proof:

Statements	Reasons
1. $\overline{LT}$ is a median. $\triangle RLS$ is isosceles with base $\overline{RS}$.	1. Given
2. $\overline{RT} \cong \overline{TS}$	2. Def. median
3. $\overline{RL} \cong \overline{LS}$	3. Def. isosceles $\triangle$
4. $\overline{LT} \cong \overline{LT}$	4. Congruence of segments is reflexive.
5. $\triangle RLT \cong \triangle SLT$	5. SSS
6. $\angle TLR \cong \angle TLS$	6. CPCTC
7. $\overline{LT}$ bisects $\angle SLR$.	7. Def. $\angle$ bisector

40. Given: $\triangle ABC \cong \triangle DEF$
$\overline{BG}$ is an angle bisector of $\triangle ABC$.
$\overline{EH}$ is an angle bisector of $\triangle DEF$.

Prove: $\overline{BG} \cong \overline{EH}$

Proof:

Statements	Reasons
1. $\triangle ABC \cong \triangle DEF$	1. Given
2. $\angle A \cong \angle D$ $\overline{AB} \cong \overline{DE}$ $\angle ABC \cong \angle DEF$	2. CPCTC
3. $\overline{BG}$ is an angle bisector of $\triangle ABC$. $\overline{EH}$ is an angle bisector of $\triangle DEF$.	3. Given
4. $\overline{BG}$ bisects $\angle ABC$. $\overline{EH}$ bisects $\angle DEF$.	4. Def. angle bisector
5. $m\angle ABG = \frac{1}{2}m\angle ABC$ $m\angle DEH = \frac{1}{2}m\angle DEF$	5. Def. bisect
6. $m\angle ABC = m\angle DEF$	6. Def. $\cong$ $\angle$s
7. $\frac{1}{2}m\angle ABC = \frac{1}{2}m\angle DEF$	7. Mult. Prop. (=)
8. $m\angle ABG = m\angle DEH$	8. Substitution Prop. (=)
9. $\angle ABG \cong \angle DEH$	9. Def. $\cong$ $\angle$s
10. $\triangle ABG \cong \triangle DEH$	10. ASA
11. $\overline{BG} \cong \overline{EH}$	11. CPCTC

41. Given: $\triangle ABC \cong \triangle XYZ$
$\overline{AD}$ is a median
of $\triangle ABC$. $\overline{XW}$ is
a median of
$\triangle XYZ$.
Prove: $\overline{AD} \cong \overline{XW}$

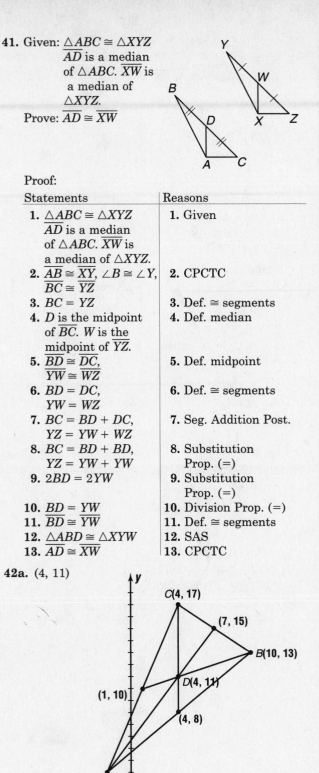

Proof:

Statements	Reasons
1. $\triangle ABC \cong \triangle XYZ$ $\overline{AD}$ is a median of $\triangle ABC$. $\overline{XW}$ is a median of $\triangle XYZ$.	1. Given
2. $\overline{AB} \cong \overline{XY}$, $\angle B \cong \angle Y$, $\overline{BC} \cong \overline{YZ}$	2. CPCTC
3. $BC = YZ$	3. Def. $\cong$ segments
4. D is the midpoint of $\overline{BC}$. W is the midpoint of $\overline{YZ}$.	4. Def. median
5. $\overline{BD} \cong \overline{DC}$, $\overline{YW} \cong \overline{WZ}$	5. Def. midpoint
6. $BD = DC$, $YW = WZ$	6. Def. $\cong$ segments
7. $BC = BD + DC$, $YZ = YW + WZ$	7. Seg. Addition Post.
8. $BC = BD + BD$, $YZ = YW + YW$	8. Substitution Prop. (=)
9. $2BD = 2YW$	9. Substitution Prop. (=)
10. $BD = YW$	10. Division Prop. (=)
11. $\overline{BD} \cong \overline{YW}$	11. Def. $\cong$ segments
12. $\triangle ABD \cong \triangle XYW$	12. SAS
13. $\overline{AD} \cong \overline{XW}$	13. CPCTC

42a. $(4, 11)$

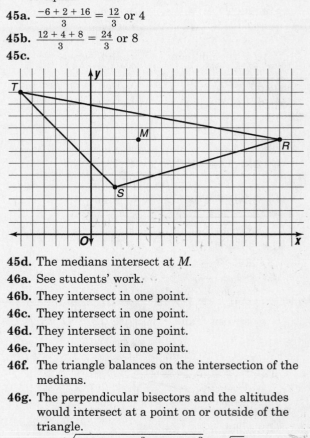

42b. The distance from A to D is
$\sqrt{(4-4)^2 + (11-8)^2} = \sqrt{9}$ or 3.
The distance from the midpoint of $\overline{AB}$ to C
is $\sqrt{(4-4)^2 + (17-9)^2} = \sqrt{81}$ or 9.
3 is one-third of 9.

43. See students' work. Acute triangle: all segments meet inside the triangle; right triangle: altitudes meet at the vertex of the right angle, other segments meeting inside the triangle: obtuse triangle: altitudes meet outside the triangle, other segments meet inside.

44. The altitude will be the same for both triangles and the bases will be congruent, so the areas will be equal.

45a. $\frac{-6 + 2 + 16}{3} = \frac{12}{3}$ or 4

45b. $\frac{12 + 4 + 8}{3} = \frac{24}{3}$ or 8

45c.

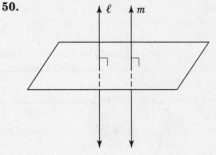

45d. The medians intersect at M.

46a. See students' work.

46b. They intersect in one point.

46c. They intersect in one point.

46d. They intersect in one point.

46e. They intersect in one point.

46f. The triangle balances on the intersection of the medians.

46g. The perpendicular bisectors and the altitudes would intersect at a point on or outside of the triangle.

47. $BA = \sqrt{(-1-(-5))^2 + (1-4)^2} = \sqrt{25}$ or 5
$AY = \sqrt{(-5-3)^2 + (4-4)^2} = \sqrt{64}$ or 8
$BY = \sqrt{(-1-3)^2 + (1-4)^2} = \sqrt{25}$ or 5
$BA = BY$, $\triangle BAY$ is isosceles.

48. Raul: pet store; Molesha: fast food; Jennifer: day camp

49. slope of $\overline{PQ} = \frac{-2-0}{3-0} = -\frac{2}{3}$

slope of $\overline{RS} = \frac{-7-(-3)}{1-(-5)} = \frac{-4}{6}$ or $-\frac{2}{3}$

Yes; both have slope of $-\frac{2}{3}$.

50.

51.

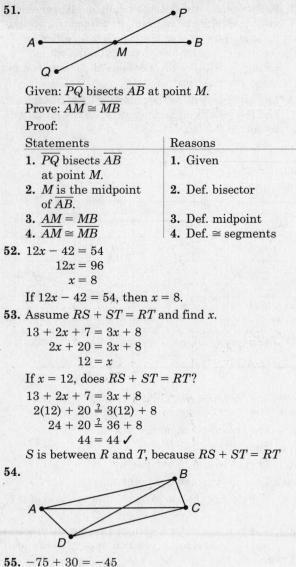

Given: $\overline{PQ}$ bisects $\overline{AB}$ at point M.
Prove: $\overline{AM} \cong \overline{MB}$
Proof:

Statements	Reasons
1. $\overline{PQ}$ bisects $\overline{AB}$ at point M.	1. Given
2. M is the midpoint of $\overline{AB}$.	2. Def. bisector
3. $AM = MB$	3. Def. midpoint
4. $\overline{AM} \cong \overline{MB}$	4. Def. $\cong$ segments

52. $12x - 42 = 54$
$\qquad 12x = 96$
$\qquad\quad x = 8$
If $12x - 42 = 54$, then $x = 8$.

53. Assume $RS + ST = RT$ and find x.
$13 + 2x + 7 = 3x + 8$
$\quad 2x + 20 = 3x + 8$
$\qquad\quad 12 = x$
If $x = 12$, does $RS + ST = RT$?
$13 + 2x + 7 = 3x + 8$
$2(12) + 20 \stackrel{?}{=} 3(12) + 8$
$\quad 24 + 20 \stackrel{?}{=} 36 + 8$
$\qquad\quad 44 = 44 \checkmark$
S is between R and T, because $RS + ST = RT$

54.

55. $-75 + 30 = -45$
She was at a depth of 45 meters.

56. $12r - (-10r) = 12r + 10r$
$\qquad\qquad\qquad\quad = 22r$

5-2 Right Triangles

Pages 248–249 Check for Understanding

1. Right triangles always have one part, a right angle, in common.

2. LL is the same as SAS since the congruent right angles are between the congruent sides, the legs. LA is the same as ASA or AAS since the leg may be included between the right angle and the acute angle or it may be nonincluded. HA is the same as AAS.

3. The leg may be included between the right angle and the acute angle or it may be nonincluded.

4. Jeannie is correct. LL is the same as SAS because the hypotenuse is not given as congruent, but the right angle is.

5. See students' work.

6. $\angle B$ and $\angle D$ are right angles.

7. $\overline{ST} \cong \overline{TU}$

8. $\overline{LN} \cong \overline{QR}$ or $\overline{NM} \cong \overline{RP}$

9. $2x + 10 = 5x - 8$
$\quad -3x = -18$
$\qquad x = 6$

10. $x + 7 = 3x - 5$
$\quad -2x = -12$
$\qquad x = 6$

11. $4x - 26 = 10$
$\quad 4x = 36$
$\qquad x = 9$

12. Given: $\angle RLT$ and $\angle SLT$ are right angles.
$\qquad \angle LTR \cong \angle LTS$
Prove: $\overline{LR} \cong \overline{LS}$
Proof:

Statements	Reasons
1. $\angle RLT$ and $\angle SLT$ are right angles. $\angle LTR \cong \angle LTS$	1. Given
2. $\triangle RLT$ and $\triangle SLT$ are right triangles.	2. Def. rt. $\triangle$
3. $\overline{LT} \cong \overline{LT}$	3. Congruence of segments is reflexive.
4. $\triangle RLT \cong \triangle SLT$	4. LA
5. $\overline{R} \cong \overline{LS}$	5. CPCTC

13. yes, LL

Pages 249–251 Exercises

14. $\overline{UX} \cong \overline{XW}$

15. $\overline{JT} \cong \overline{MR}$ and $\angle J \cong \angle M$ or $\overline{JT} \cong \overline{MR}$ and $\angle T \cong \angle R$

16. $\overline{AD} \cong \overline{CD}$ or $\overline{AB} \cong \overline{CB}$

17. $\overline{MN} \cong \overline{OP}$

18. no extra information needed

19. $\overline{VX} \cong \overline{XY}$ or $\overline{WX} \cong \overline{XZ}$

20. $AB = XZ$
$2x + 6 = 20$
$\quad 2x = 14$
$\qquad x = 7$

21. $BC = YZ$
$15x + 2 = 4x + 13$
$\quad 11x = 11$
$\qquad x = 1$

22. $m\angle A = m\angle X$
$11x - 3 = 9x + 9$
$\quad 2x = 12$
$\qquad x = 6$

23. $AC = XZ$
$28 = 9x + 1$
$27 = 9x$
$\quad 3 = x$

24. Given: $\overline{NO} \perp \overline{MN}$
$\overline{NO} \perp \overline{OP}$
$\angle M \cong \angle P$

Prove: $\overline{MO} \cong \overline{NP}$

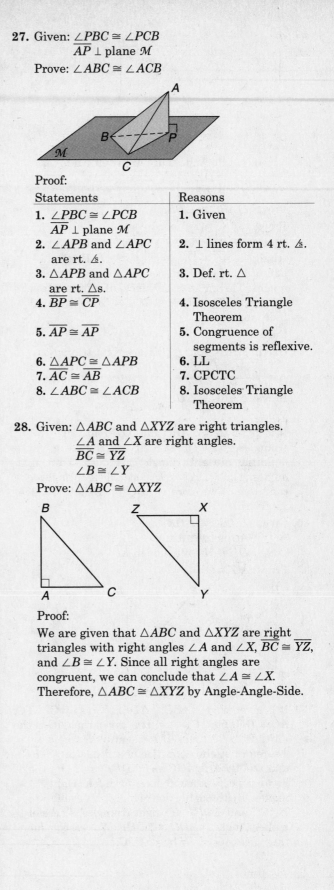

Proof:

Statements	Reasons
1. $\overline{NO} \perp \overline{MN}$ $\overline{NO} \perp \overline{OP}$ $\angle M \cong \angle P$	1. Given
2. $\angle MNO$ and $\angle NOP$ are rt. $\angle$s.	2. $\perp$ lines form 4 rt. $\angle$s.
3. $\triangle MNO$ and $\triangle NOP$ are rt. $\triangle$s.	3. Def. rt. $\triangle$
4. $\overline{NO} \cong \overline{NO}$	4. Congruence of segments is reflexive.
5. $\triangle MNO \cong \triangle NOP$	5. LA
6. $\overline{MO} \cong \overline{NP}$	6. CPCTC

25. Given: $\angle M$ and $\angle P$ are right angles.
$\overline{MN} \parallel \overline{OP}$

Prove: $\overline{MN} \cong \overline{OP}$

Proof:

Statements	Reasons
1. $\angle M$ and $\angle P$ are right angles. $\overline{MN} \parallel \overline{OP}$	1. Given
2. $\triangle MNO$ and $\triangle PON$ are rt. $\triangle$s.	2. Def. rt. $\triangle$
3. $\angle MNO \cong \angle PON$	3. Alternate Interior Angles Theorem
4. $\overline{NO} \cong \overline{NO}$	4. Congruence of segments is reflexive.
5. $\triangle MNO \cong \triangle PON$	5. HA
6. $\overline{MN} \cong \overline{OP}$	6. CPCTC

26. Given: $\overline{AP} \perp$ plane $\mathcal{M}$
$\overline{AB} \cong \overline{AC}$

Prove: $\triangle BPC$ is isosceles.

Proof:

Statements	Reasons
1. $\overline{AP} \perp$ plane $\mathcal{M}$ $\overline{AB} \cong \overline{AC}$	1. Given
2. $\angle APB$ and $\angle APC$ are rt. $\angle$s.	2. $\perp$ lines form 4 rt. $\angle$s.
3. $\triangle APB$ and $\triangle APC$ are rt. $\triangle$s.	3. Def. rt. $\triangle$
4. $\overline{AP} \cong \overline{AP}$	4. Congruence of segments is reflexive.
5. $\triangle APB \cong \triangle APC$	5. HL
6. $\overline{PB} \cong \overline{PC}$	6. CPCTC
7. $\triangle BPC$ is isosceles.	7. Def. isosceles $\triangle$

27. Given: $\angle PBC \cong \angle PCB$
$\overline{AP} \perp$ plane $\mathcal{M}$

Prove: $\angle ABC \cong \angle ACB$

Proof:

Statements	Reasons
1. $\angle PBC \cong \angle PCB$ $\overline{AP} \perp$ plane $\mathcal{M}$	1. Given
2. $\angle APB$ and $\angle APC$ are rt. $\angle$s.	2. $\perp$ lines form 4 rt. $\angle$s.
3. $\triangle APB$ and $\triangle APC$ are rt. $\triangle$s.	3. Def. rt. $\triangle$
4. $\overline{BP} \cong \overline{CP}$	4. Isosceles Triangle Theorem
5. $\overline{AP} \cong \overline{AP}$	5. Congruence of segments is reflexive.
6. $\triangle APC \cong \triangle APB$	6. LL
7. $\overline{AC} \cong \overline{AB}$	7. CPCTC
8. $\angle ABC \cong \angle ACB$	8. Isosceles Triangle Theorem

28. Given: $\triangle ABC$ and $\triangle XYZ$ are right triangles.
$\angle A$ and $\angle X$ are right angles.
$\overline{BC} \cong \overline{YZ}$
$\angle B \cong \angle Y$

Prove: $\triangle ABC \cong \triangle XYZ$

Proof:

We are given that $\triangle ABC$ and $\triangle XYZ$ are right triangles with right angles $\angle A$ and $\angle X$, $\overline{BC} \cong \overline{YZ}$, and $\angle B \cong \angle Y$. Since all right angles are congruent, we can conclude that $\angle A \cong \angle X$. Therefore, $\triangle ABC \cong \triangle XYZ$ by Angle-Angle-Side.

29.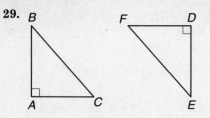

Case 1:

Given: △ABC and △DEF are right triangles.
  $\overline{AC} \cong \overline{DF}$
  $\angle C \cong \angle F$

Prove: △ABC ≅ △DEF

Proof:

It is given that △ABC and △DEF are right triangles, $\overline{AC} \cong \overline{DF}$, and $\angle C \cong \angle F$. By the definition of right triangle, $\angle A$ and $\angle D$ are right angles. Thus, $\angle A \cong \angle D$ since all right angles are congruent. Therefore, △ABC ≅ △DEF by Angle-Side-Angle.

Case 2:

Given: △ABC and △DEF are right triangles.
  $\overline{AC} \cong \overline{DF}$
  $\angle B \cong \angle E$

Prove: △ABC ≅ △DEF

Proof:

It is given that △ABC and △DEF are right triangles, $\overline{AC} \cong \overline{DF}$, and $\angle B \cong \angle E$. By the definition of right triangle, $\angle A$ and $\angle D$ are right angles. Thus, $\angle A \cong \angle D$ since all right angles are congruent. Therefore, △ABC ≅ △DEF by Angle-Angle-Side.

30. Given: △ABC ≅ △DEF
  $\overline{AG}$ is the altitude to $\overline{BC}$.
  $\overline{DH}$ is the altitude to $\overline{EF}$.

Prove: $\overline{AG} \cong \overline{DH}$

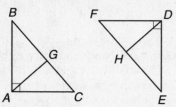

Proof:

It is given that △ABC ≅ △DEF. Thus by CPCTC, $\overline{AC} \cong \overline{DF}$ and $\angle C \cong \angle F$. It is given that $\overline{AG}$ is the altitude to $\overline{BC}$ and $\overline{DH}$ is the altitude to $\overline{EF}$. Therefore by the definition of altitude, $\overline{AG} \perp \overline{BC}$ and $\overline{DH} \perp \overline{EF}$. $\angle AGC$ and $\angle DHF$ are right angles because perpendicular lines form four right angles. By the definition of a right triangle, △AGC and △DHF are right triangles. Therefore by Leg-Angle, △AGC ≅ △DHF. We can conclude then that $\overline{AG} \cong \overline{DH}$ by CPCTC.

31. Given: △LMN is isosceles with base $\overline{LN}$.
  O is the midpoint of $\overline{LM}$.
  P is the midpoint of $\overline{NM}$.
  $\overline{OQ} \perp \overline{LN}, \overline{PR} \perp \overline{LN}$
Prove: $\overline{OQ} \cong \overline{PR}$

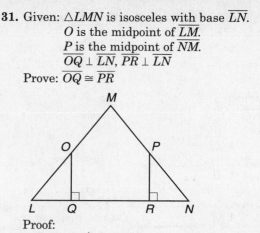

Proof:

It is given that △LMN is isosceles. By the definition of isosceles triangle, $\overline{LM} \cong \overline{NM}$. Thus, $LM = NM$ by the definition of congruent segments. $\angle L \cong \angle N$ because if two sides of a triangle are congruent, then the angles opposite the sides are congruent also. We were given that O is the midpoint of $\overline{LM}$ and P is the midpoint of $\overline{NM}$. The definition of midpoint lets us say that $\overline{LO} \cong \overline{OM}$ and $\overline{NP} \cong \overline{PM}$. Thus by the definition of congruent segments, $LO = OM$ and $NP = PM$. By the Segment Addition Postulate, $LM = LO + OM$ and $NM = NP + PM$. Thus, $LO + OM = NP + PM$ by substitution. Then $2LO = 2NP$ by substitution. By the Division Property of Equality, $LO = NP$. Then $\overline{LO} \cong \overline{NP}$ by the definition of congruent segments. It was given that $\overline{OQ} \perp \overline{LN}$ and $\overline{PR} \perp \overline{LN}$. Then $\angle OQL$ and $\angle PRN$ are right angles since perpendicular lines form four right angles. Then △OQL and △PRN are right triangles by the definition of right triangle. By Hypotenuse-Angle, △OQL △PRN. Therefore, $\overline{OQ} \cong \overline{PR}$ by CPCTC.

32. Given: △RST with obtuse angle S
  $\overline{RS} \cong \overline{UT}$
  $\angle RST$ is supplementary to $\angle UTS$.
  $\overline{BU}$ and $\overline{RA}$ are altitudes to $\overline{ST}$.

Prove: $\overline{RA} \cong \overline{BU}$

Proof:

It is given that RST has obtuse angle S, that $\overline{RS} \cong \overline{UT}$, $\angle RST$ is supplementary to $\angle UTS$, and $\overline{BU}$ and $\overline{RA}$ are altitudes to $\overline{ST}$. By definition, an altitude is perpendicular to the side to which it is drawn. So $\overline{BU} \perp \overline{ST}$ and $\overline{RA} \perp \overline{ST}$. Since perpendicular lines form four right angles, $\angle RAS$ and $\angle UBT$ are right angles. So by the definition of a right triangle, △RAS and △UBT are right triangles. $\angle RSA$ and $\angle RST$ form a linear pair. Since two angles that form a linear pair are supplementary, $\angle RSA$ and $\angle RST$ are supplementary. $\angle RSA \cong \angle UTS$ because if two angles are supplementary to the same angle then they are congruent. By Hypotenuse-Angle, △RSA ≅ △UTB.

33. The corresponding sides are proportional, but not necessarily congruent.

34. Draw auxiliary segments $\overline{XY}$ and $\overline{WZ}$.

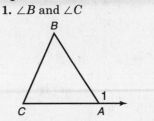

$\angle WBX$ is a right angle because perpendicular lines form four right angles. So $m\angle WBX = 90$. By the Angle Sum Theorem, $m\angle XWB + m\angle BXW + m\angle WBX = 180$. Since $m\angle XWB = m\angle BXW$, $2(m\angle XWB) + 90 = 180$ or $m\angle XWB = 45$. Thus, $m\angle BXW = 45$.

In $\triangle AXZ$, $\angle XAZ$ is a right angle, so $m\angle XAZ = 90$. Since $m\angle ZXA = 45$, $m\angle XZA = 45$. Thus, $\angle XZA \cong \angle ZXA$.

Since $\angle XZA \cong \angle ZXA$, $\overline{AX} \cong \overline{AZ}$, because if two angles of a triangle are congruent, then the sides opposite the angles are congruent. Likewise, since $m\angle AWY = m\angle AYW$, $\angle AWY \cong \angle AYW$ and $\overline{AY} \cong \overline{AW}$.

Triangles AXY and AZW are right triangles. $\triangle AXY \cong \triangle AZW$, by HL. So, $\overline{XY} \cong \overline{ZW}$ by CPCTC. So, if $WZ = 10$, then $XY = 10$.

35. legs: 48 in. and 60 in.; hypotenuse and an angle: 76.8 in. and 51° or 76.8 in. and 39°; leg and an angle: 60 in. and 51°, or 60 in. and 39°, 48 in. and 51°,or 48 in. and 39°; hypotenuse and a leg: 76.8 in. and 60 in. or 76.8 in. and 48 in.

36. All the triangles are right, and they are all congruent by LL.

37.

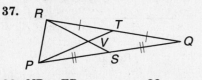

38. $ND = ED$
$19 = 4x - 1$
$20 = 4x$
$5 = x$

39.

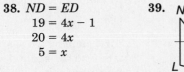

obtuse, isosceles

40. Alt. int. $\angle$s are $\cong$; corr. $\angle$s are $\cong$; alt. ext. $\angle$s are $\cong$; cons. ext. $\angle$s are $\cong$; cons. int. $\angle$s are supplementary; two lines in a plane are parallel to a third line.

41. $\frac{-11 - 9}{6 - 4} = \frac{-20}{2} = -10$

42. Distributive Property and Division Prop. (=)

43. converse: interchange the hypothesis and conclusion
inverse: negate the hypothesis and the conclusion
contrapositive: negate and interchange the hypothesis and conclusion

44. $\frac{3}{20} = \frac{15}{100} = 15\%$

45. {(1938, 50,000), (1939, 40,000), (1938, 5200), (1938, 4200), (1939, 4020)}; D = {1938, 1939}; R = {50,000, 40,000, 5200, 4200, 4020}

5-3 | **Indirect Proof and Inequalities**

Pages 255–256 Check for Understanding

1. $\angle B$ and $\angle C$

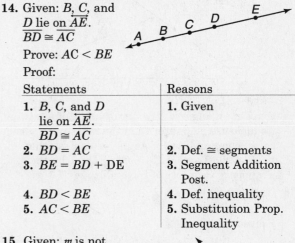

2. The statement is not always true. $10 > -1$ and $-5 > -10$, but -50 is not greater than 10.

3. See students' work.   **4.** See students' work.

5. Lines ℓ and m do not intersect at point X.

6. If the alternate interior angles formed by two lines and a transversal are congruent, the lines are not parallel.

7. Sabrina did not eat the leftover pizza.

8. $\angle 2, \angle 3, \angle 5, \angle 6, \angle 7$

9. $\angle 1, \angle 4, \angle 8$

10. $\angle 8$; by the Transitive Prop. (=); $m\angle 8 > m\angle 4$; $m\angle 4 > m\angle 7$ by the Exterior Angle Inequality Theorem in both cases.

11. Division Prop. ($\neq$)   **12.** Addition Prop. ($\neq$)

13. Transitive Prop. ($\neq$)

14. Given: B, C, and D lie on $\overleftrightarrow{AE}$. $\overline{BD} \cong \overline{AC}$

Prove: $AC < BE$

Proof:

Statements	Reasons
1. B, C, and D lie on $\overleftrightarrow{AE}$. $\overline{BD} \cong \overline{AC}$	1. Given
2. $BD = AC$	2. Def. $\cong$ segments
3. $BE = BD + DE$	3. Segment Addition Post.
4. $BD < BE$	4. Def. inequality
5. $AC < BE$	5. Substitution Prop. Inequality

15. Given: m is not parallel to n.

Prove: $m\angle 3 \neq m\angle 2$

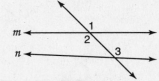

Proof:

Step 1: Assume $m\angle 3 = m\angle 2$.

Step 2: $\angle 3$ and $\angle 2$ are alternate interior angles. If 2 lines are cut by a transversal so that alternate interior angles are congruent, then the lines are parallel. This means that $m \parallel n$. However, that contradicts the given statement.

Step 3: Therefore, since the assumption leads to a contradiction, the assumption must be false. Thus, $m\angle 3 \neq m\angle 2$.

16. Let x = the original price.

$$80\% \text{ or } 0.8x = \text{sales price}$$
$$90\% \, (0.8x) \text{ or } 0.72x = \text{sale price with school discount}$$
$$0.72x + 0.07\,(0.72x) = \$97.05$$
$$0.7704x = \$97.05$$
$$x = \$125.97$$

Pages 256–258 Exercises

17. $\overline{AB}$ is not congruent to $\overline{CD}$.

18. The altitude of an angle in an isosceles triangle is not a median of the triangle.

19. The disk is not defective.

20. The suspect is not guilty.

21. If two altitudes of a triangle are congruent, then the triangle is not isosceles.

22. If two lines are cut by a transversal and corresponding angles are congruent, then the lines are not parallel.

23. $m\angle 7$ **24.** $m\angle 1$

25. Sample answer: $\angle 1$ **26.** $\angle 1, \angle 7, \angle 8$

27. $\angle 2, \angle 3, \angle 4, \angle 5, \angle 6$ **28.** $m\angle 8$

29. Division Prop. ($\neq$) **30.** Transitive Prop. ($\neq$)

31. Comparison Prop. ($\neq$) **32.** Subtraction Prop. ($\neq$)

33. Division Prop. ($\neq$) **34.** Comparison Prop. ($\neq$)

35. Given: $\triangle XYV$, $\triangle XZU$

Prove: $m\angle 7 > m\angle 6$

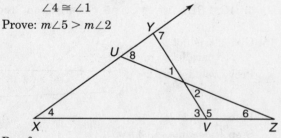

Proof:
Since if an angle is an exterior angle of a triangle its measure is greater than the measure of either corresponding interior angle, we can say that $m\angle 7 > m\angle 8$ and $m\angle 8 > m\angle 6$. Thus, by the Transitive Property of Inequality, $m\angle 7 > m\angle 6$.

36. Given: $\triangle XYV$, $\triangle XZU$

$\angle 4 \cong \angle 1$

Prove: $m\angle 5 > m\angle 2$

Proof:
We are given that $\angle 4 \cong \angle 1$. The definition of congruent angles allows us to say that $m\angle 4 = m\angle 1$. Since if an angle is an exterior angle of a triangle its measure is greater than the measure of either corresponding interior angle, we can say that $m\angle 5 > m\angle 4$. By the Substitution Property of Inequality, $m\angle 5 > m\angle 1$. $\angle 1 \cong \angle 2$ because they are vertical angles. Thus by the definition of congruent angles, $m\angle 1 = m\angle 2$. Then by the Substitution Property of Inequality, $m\angle 5 > m\angle 2$.

37. Given: $\overline{FD} \perp \overline{AB}$
$\overline{GE} \perp \overline{AB}$

Prove: $m\angle 5 > m\angle 2$

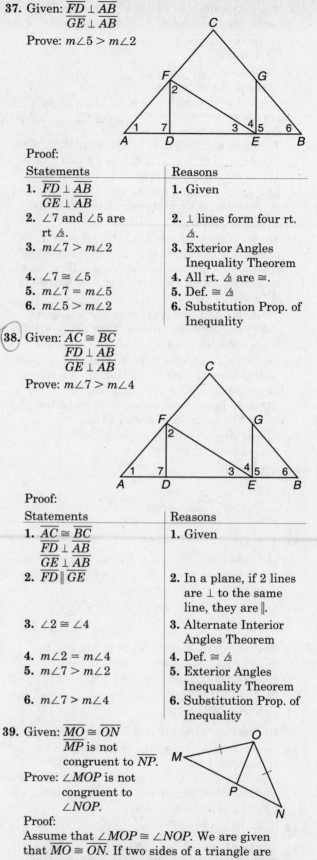

Proof:

Statements	Reasons
1. $\overline{FD} \perp \overline{AB}$ $\overline{GE} \perp \overline{AB}$	**1.** Given
2. $\angle 7$ and $\angle 5$ are rt $\angle$s.	**2.** $\perp$ lines form four rt. $\angle$s.
3. $m\angle 7 > m\angle 2$	**3.** Exterior Angles Inequality Theorem
4. $\angle 7 \cong \angle 5$	**4.** All rt. $\angle$s are $\cong$.
5. $m\angle 7 = m\angle 5$	**5.** Def. $\cong \angle$s
6. $m\angle 5 > m\angle 2$	**6.** Substitution Prop. of Inequality

38. Given: $\overline{AC} \cong \overline{BC}$
$\overline{FD} \perp \overline{AB}$
$\overline{GE} \perp \overline{AB}$

Prove: $m\angle 7 > m\angle 4$

Proof:

Statements	Reasons
1. $\overline{AC} \cong \overline{BC}$ $\overline{FD} \perp \overline{AB}$ $\overline{GE} \perp \overline{AB}$	**1.** Given
2. $\overline{FD} \parallel \overline{GE}$	**2.** In a plane, if 2 lines are $\perp$ to the same line, they are $\parallel$.
3. $\angle 2 \cong \angle 4$	**3.** Alternate Interior Angles Theorem
4. $m\angle 2 = m\angle 4$	**4.** Def. $\cong \angle$s
5. $m\angle 7 > m\angle 2$	**5.** Exterior Angles Inequality Theorem
6. $m\angle 7 > m\angle 4$	**6.** Substitution Prop. of Inequality

39. Given: $\overline{MO} \cong \overline{ON}$
$\overline{MP}$ is not congruent to $\overline{NP}$.

Prove: $\angle MOP$ is not congruent to $\angle NOP$.

Proof:
Assume that $\angle MOP \cong \angle NOP$. We are given that $\overline{MO} \cong \overline{ON}$. If two sides of a triangle are congruent, then the angles opposite the sides are congruent also. Thus, $\angle M \cong \angle N$. Therefore, $\triangle MOP \cong \triangle NOP$ by ASA. We can then conclude that $\overline{MP} \cong \overline{NP}$ by CPCTC. But this contradicts the given information. Therefore, the assumption is incorrect and $\angle MOP$ is not congruent to $\angle NOP$.

40. Given: $\triangle ABC$
$\angle 6$ is acute.
Prove: $\angle 1$ and $\angle 4$
are obtuse.

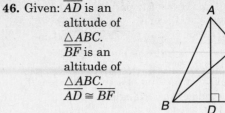

Proof:

Assume that $\angle 4$ is acute. $\angle 5$ and $\angle 6$, and $\angle 3$ and $\angle 4$ are linear pairs. Thus, $\angle 5$ and $\angle 6$, and $\angle 3$ and $\angle 4$ are supplementary. By the definition of supplementary angles, $m\angle 5 + m\angle 6 = 180$, and $m\angle 3 + m\angle 4 = 180$. By the given and the assumption, $\angle 4$ and $\angle 6$ are acute. Then by the definition of acute, $m\angle 4 < 90$ and $m\angle 6 < 90$. The definition of inequality allows us to say that for some x and y where x and y are both greater than 0, $m\angle 4 + x = 90$ and $m\angle 6 + y = 90$. Then by the Subtraction Property of Equality, $m\angle 4 = 90 - x$ and $m\angle 6 = 90 - y$. Substitute so $m\angle 3 + (90 - x) = 180$ and $m\angle 5 + (90 - y) = 180$. Then $m\angle 3 = 90 + x$ and $m\angle 5 = 90 + y$. So by the definition of inequality, $m\angle 3 > 90$ and $m\angle 5 > 90$. By the definition of obtuse, $\angle 3$ and $\angle 5$ are obtuse. However, a triangle cannot have more than one obtuse angle. Therefore the assumption must be incorrect. A similar argument could prove that $\angle 1$ cannot be acute if $\angle 6$ is acute. Therefore, a triangle can have only one acute exterior angle.

41. Given: $\triangle XYZ$
$m\angle X \neq$
$m\angle Y \neq m\angle Z$
Prove: $XY \neq YZ \neq XZ$
Proof:

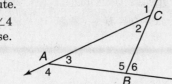

Assume that $XY = YZ$. Then because of the Isosceles Triangle Theorem, $\angle Z \cong \angle X$. Then by the definition of congruent angles, $m\angle Z = m\angle X$. However, we are given that $m\angle X \neq m\angle Y \neq m\angle Z$. Therefore the assumption is incorrect and $XY \neq YZ$. A similar argument could prove that $YZ \neq XZ$ and $XY \neq XZ$. Thus, if a triangle has no two angles congruent, then it has no two sides congruent.

42. October

43. The door on the left. If the sign on the door on the right were true, then both signs would be true. But one sign is false, so the sign on the door on the right must be false.

44. By assuming it was each of them, the police would find a contradiction from their past that would eliminate all but the actual murderer.

45. Yes. If you assume the client was at the scene of the crime, it is contradicted by his presence at the meeting in New York City. Thus, the assumption he was present at the crime is wrong.

46. Given: $\overline{AD}$ is an altitude of $\triangle ABC$. $\overline{BF}$ is an altitude of $\triangle ABC$. $\overline{AD} \cong \overline{BF}$

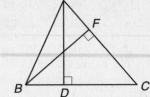

Prove: $\triangle ABC$ is isosceles.
Proof:

Statements	Reasons
1. $\overline{AD}$ is an altitude of $\triangle ABC$. $\overline{BF}$ is an altitude of $\triangle ABC$. $\overline{AD} \cong \overline{BF}$	1. Given
2. $\overline{AD} \perp \overline{BC}$ $\overline{BF} \perp \overline{AC}$	2. Def. altitude
3. $\angle ADB$ is a right angle. $\angle BFA$ is a right angle.	3. $\perp$ lines form four rt. $\angle$s.
4. $\triangle ADB$ is a right triangle. $\triangle BFA$ is a right triangle.	4. Def. rt. $\triangle$
5. $\overline{AB} \cong \overline{BA}$	5. Congruence of segments is reflexive.
6. $\triangle ADB \cong \triangle BFA$	6. HL
7. $\angle FAB \cong \angle DBA$	7. CPCTC
8. $\overline{BC} \cong \overline{AC}$	8. Isosceles Triangle Theorem
9. $\triangle ABC$ is isosceles.	9. Def. isosceles $\triangle$

47.

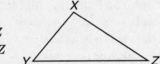

48. $\angle 1 \cong \angle 2$, $\overline{KM} \neq \overline{LM}$

49.

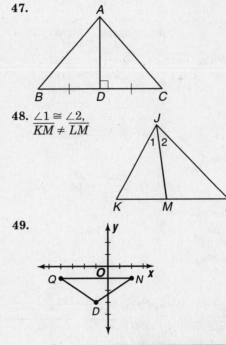

$NQ = \sqrt{(2 - (-4))^2 + (-1 - (-1))^2} = \sqrt{36}$ or 6
$QD = \sqrt{(-4 - (-1))^2 + (-1 - (-3))^2} = \sqrt{13}$
$ND = \sqrt{(2 - (-1))^2 + (-1 - (-3))^2} = \sqrt{13}$

Since $QD = ND$, NQD is isosceles. $\angle D$ is obtuse so $\triangle NQD$ is obtuse.

50. $2 = \frac{r - 3}{5 - 2}$

$2 = \frac{r - 3}{3}$

$6 = r - 3$

$r = 9$

51. parallel planes

52. If a segment is a median of a triangle, then it bisects one side of the triangle.

53.

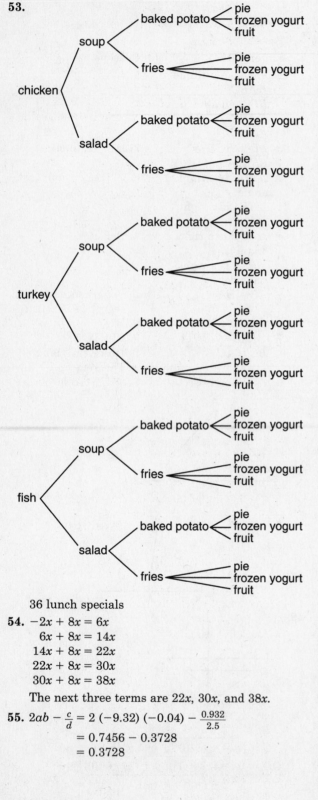

36 lunch specials

54. $-2x + 8x = 6x$

$6x + 8x = 14x$

$14x + 8x = 22x$

$22x + 8x = 30x$

$30x + 8x = 38x$

The next three terms are $22x$, $30x$, and $38x$.

55. $2ab - \frac{c}{d} = 2\,(-9.32)\,(-0.04) - \frac{0.932}{2.5}$

$= 0.7456 - 0.3728$

$= 0.3728$

1. $BD = CD$

$4x + 9 = 7x - 6$

$-3x = -15$

$x = 5$

2. $\overline{AD} \perp \overline{BC}$

$m\angle ADC = 90$

$2y - 6 = 90$

$2y = 96$

$y = 48$

3. yes; by LL or SAS

4. $\overline{AB} \cong \overline{AC}$

5. Given: $\overleftrightarrow{AB}$ and $\overleftrightarrow{PQ}$ are skew.

Prove: $\overleftrightarrow{AP}$ and $\overleftrightarrow{BQ}$ are skew.

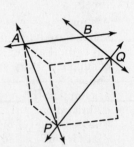

Proof:

Assume that $\overleftrightarrow{AP}$ and $\overleftrightarrow{BQ}$ are not skew. Then either $\overleftrightarrow{AP} \parallel \overleftrightarrow{BQ}$ or $\overleftrightarrow{AP}$ and $\overleftrightarrow{BQ}$ intersect. In either case, A, B, P, and Q are coplanar. It is given that $\overleftrightarrow{AB}$ and $\overleftrightarrow{PQ}$ are skew, so $\overleftrightarrow{AB}$ and $\overleftrightarrow{PQ}$ do not lie in the same plane, and A and B are not coplanar with P and Q. This is a contradiction. Therefore, $\overleftrightarrow{AP}$ and $\overleftrightarrow{BQ}$ must be skew.

5-4 Inequalities for Sides and Angles of a Triangle

Page 259 Modeling Mathematics

a. It is the greatest measure.

b. It is the least measure.

c. See students' work.

d. Sample answer: The measures of the angles opposite the sides are in the same order as the lengths of the respective sides.

Pages 262–263 Check for Understanding

1. See students' drawings. The 40° angle is opposite 5 cm side, 60° angle is opposite the 6.7 cm side, and the 80° angle is opposite the 7.7 cm side.

2. No; the difference between the y-intercepts will not be the distance along a perpendicular between the two lines unless the lines are horizontal. If the lines are not horizontal, this method finds a distance longer than the distance between the lines.

3. In an obtuse triangle, there is one obtuse angle and it must be the largest angle of the triangle. The longest side must be opposite the largest angle.

4a. $\angle Z \cong \angle Y$

4b. $XZ > XY$

4c. $m\angle Z < m\angle Y$

5. The distance is an altitude of $\triangle ABC$.

6. $CB > CD$

$m\angle CDB > m\angle CBD$

7. yes; $AB > AD$

$m\angle ADB > m\angle DBA$

8. $m\angle CDB > m\angle CBD$

$m\angle ADB > m\angle DBA$

$m\angle CDB + m\angle ADB > m\angle CBD + m\angle DBA$

$m\angle CDA > m\angle CBA$

9. $m\angle RTU = 30$, $m\angle TUR = 70$, $m\angle TRU = 80$
$RU < TR < TU$
$\overline{TU}$ is the longest side.

10. Since $m\angle TUS = 110$, it is the largest angle of the triangle. So, $\overline{TS}$ must be the longest side.

11. If $\overline{TU}$ is an angle bisector, $m\angle RTU = m\angle UTS = 30$. Thus, $m\angle RTS = 60$ and $m\angle TSR = 40$. Since $m\angle TRU = 80$, $m\angle TSR < m\angle RTS = 60 < m\angle TRU = 80$ and $TR < RS < TS$. So, $\overline{TS}$ is the longest side of $\triangle RST$.

12.
$$m\angle A + m\angle B + m\angle C = 180$$
$$(3x + 20) + (2x + 37) + (4x + 15) = 180$$
$$9x + 72 = 180$$
$$9x = 108$$
$$x = 12$$

$m\angle A = 3x + 20 = 3(12) + 20$ or 56
$m\angle B = 2x + 37 = 2(12) + 37$ or 61
$m\angle C = 4x + 15 = 4(12) + 15$ or 63
Since $m\angle A < m\angle B < m\angle C$, $BC < AC < AB$.

13. Given: $\angle B$ is a right angle. $\overline{BD}$ is an altitude.

Prove: $BD < AB$ and $BD < BC$

Proof:
We are given that $\overline{BD}$ is an altitude. Therefore by the definition of altitude, $\overline{BD} \perp \overline{AC}$. Then since perpendicular lines form four right angles, $\angle ADB$ and $\angle CDB$ are right angles. Then $\triangle ADB$ and $\triangle CDB$ are right triangles by the definition of right triangle. $\angle BAD$ and $\angle DBA$, and $\angle BCD$ and $\angle DBC$ are complementary since acute angles of right triangles are complementary. By the definition of complementary angles, $m\angle BAD + m\angle DBA = 90$ and $m\angle BCD + m\angle DBC = 90$. The definition of inequality allows us to say that $m\angle BAD < 90$ and $m\angle BCD < 90$. $m\angle ADB = 90$ and $m\angle CDB = 90$ by the definition of a right angle. Thus by substitution, $m\angle BAD < m\angle ADB$ and $m\angle BCD < m\angle CDB$. Therefore in $\triangle ABD$, $BD < AB$; and in $\triangle BCD$, $BD < BC$.

14. The prediction will be the least accurate for plane C, which goes about 413 mph and costs \$1800 per hour to operate. The line predicts about \$2250 per hour.

Pages 263–265 Exercises

15. $LM < MN < LN$
$\angle N$ is opposite $\overline{LM}$, so $\angle N$ has the least measure.

16. $MO > OT > MT$
$\angle T$ is opposite $\overline{MO}$, so $\angle T$ has the greatest measure.

17. $m\angle LMN > m\angle L > m\angle N$
$m\angle T > m\angle OMT > m\angle O$
Since $m\angle LMN = m\angle OMT$, $\angle T$ has the greatest measure in the two triangles.

18. $XZ > YZ > XY$, so $m\angle XYZ > m\angle YXZ > m\angle Z$. $\angle Z$ has the least measure and $\angle XYZ$ has the greatest measure.

19. $WX < WY < XY$
$\angle WYX$ is opposite $\overline{WX}$, so $\angle WYX$ has the least measure.

20. $\angle Z$, $\angle YXZ$, $\angle XYZ$, $\angle WYX$, $\angle WXY$, $\angle W$ or $\angle Z$, $\angle YXZ$, $\angle WYX$, $\angle XYZ$, $\angle WXY$, $\angle W$

21. $m\angle EDC = 75$, so $\angle EDC$ has the greatest measure. $\overline{CE}$ is opposite $\angle EDC$ so $\overline{CE}$ is the longest segment in $\triangle CED$.

22. $\triangle ABE$ is a right triangle. The longest side is the hypotenuse, $\overline{BE}$.

23. $\overline{BE}$; In $\triangle ECD$, $\overline{EC}$ is longest. In $\triangle BEC$, $BE > EC$ and $\overline{BE}$ is longest. In $\triangle ABE$, $\overline{BE}$ is longest. Thus, $\overline{BE}$ is the longest segment.

24. In $\triangle CDE$, $EC > CD > ED$. In $\triangle EBC$, $EC = BC$ and $BE > EC$. Thus, $\overline{ED}$ is the shortest segment in $BCDE$.

25. No, the segments do not all have the correct relative lengths.

26.
$$m\angle A + m\angle B + m\angle C = 180$$
$$(9x + 29) + (93 - 5x) + (10x + 2) = 180$$
$$14x + 124 = 180$$
$$14x = 56$$
$$x = 4$$

$m\angle A = 9x + 29 = 9(4) + 29$ or 65
$m\angle B = 93 - 5x = 93 - 5(4)$ or 73
$m\angle C = 10x + 2 = 10(4) + 2$ or 42
$m\angle C < m\angle A < m\angle B$
$AB < BC < AC$

27.
$$m\angle A + m\angle B + m\angle C = 180$$
$$(9x - 4) + (4x - 16) + (68 - 2x) = 180$$
$$11x + 48 = 180$$
$$11x = 132$$
$$x = 12$$

$m\angle A = 9x - 4 = 9(12) - 4$ or 104
$m\angle B = 4x - 16 = 4(12) - 16$ or 32
$m\angle C = 68 - 2x = 68 - 2(12) = 44$
$m\angle B < m\angle C < m\angle A$
$AC < AB < BC$

28.
$$m\angle A + m\angle B + m\angle C = 180$$
$$(12x - 9) + (62 - 3x) + (16x + 2) = 180$$
$$25x + 55 = 180$$
$$25x = 125$$
$$x = 5$$

$m\angle A = 12x - 9 = 12(5) - 9$ or 51
$m\angle B = 62 - 3x = 62 - 3(5)$ or 47
$m\angle C = 16x + 2 = 16(5) + 2$ or 82
$m\angle B < m\angle A < m\angle C$
$AC < BC < AB$

29. Given: $\overrightarrow{RQ}$ bisects $\angle SRT$.
Prove: $m\angle SQR > m\angle SRQ$

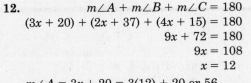

Proof:

Statements	Reasons
1. $\overrightarrow{RQ}$ bisects $\angle SRT$.	1. Given
2. $\angle SRQ \cong \angle QRT$	2. Def. $\angle$ bisector
3. $m\angle SRQ = m\angle QRT$	3. Def. $\cong \angle$s
4. $m\angle SQR > m\angle QRT$	4. Exterior Angles Inequality Theorem
5. $m\angle SQR > m\angle SRQ$	5. Substitution Prop. (=)

Geometry Chapter 5

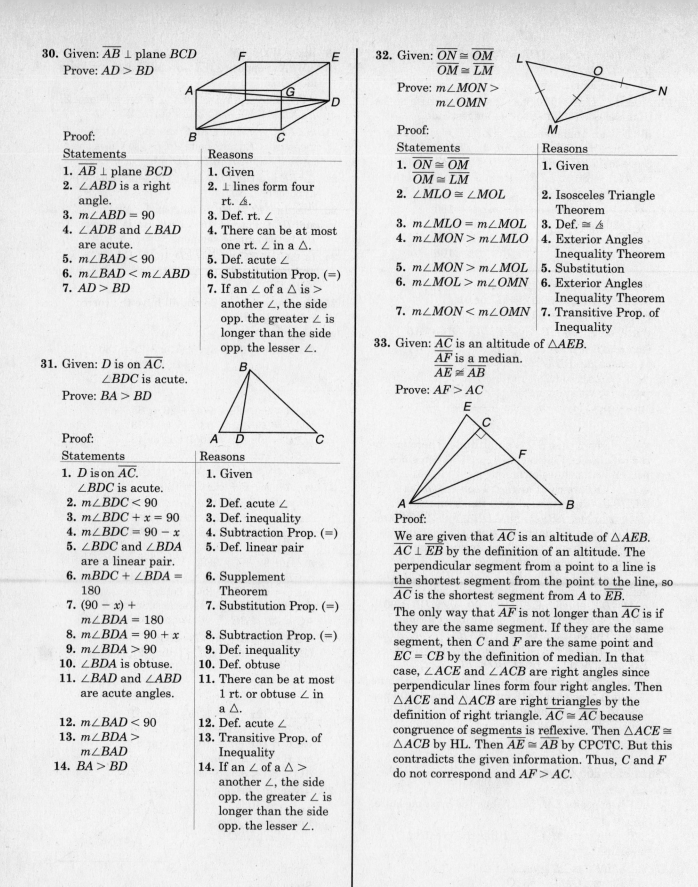

30. Given: $\overline{AB} \perp$ plane BCD

Prove: $AD > BD$

Proof:

Statements	Reasons
1. $\overline{AB} \perp$ plane BCD	1. Given
2. $\angle ABD$ is a right angle.	2. $\perp$ lines form four rt. $\angle$s.
3. $m\angle ABD = 90$	3. Def. rt. $\angle$
4. $\angle ADB$ and $\angle BAD$ are acute.	4. There can be at most one rt. $\angle$ in a $\triangle$.
5. $m\angle BAD < 90$	5. Def. acute $\angle$
6. $m\angle BAD < m\angle ABD$	6. Substitution Prop. (=)
7. $AD > BD$	7. If an $\angle$ of a $\triangle$ is $>$ another $\angle$, the side opp. the greater $\angle$ is longer than the side opp. the lesser $\angle$.

31. Given: D is on $\overline{AC}$.

$\angle BDC$ is acute.

Prove: $BA > BD$

Proof:

Statements	Reasons
1. D is on $\overline{AC}$. $\angle BDC$ is acute.	1. Given
2. $m\angle BDC < 90$	2. Def. acute $\angle$
3. $m\angle BDC + x = 90$	3. Def. inequality
4. $m\angle BDC = 90 - x$	4. Subtraction Prop. (=)
5. $\angle BDC$ and $\angle BDA$ are a linear pair.	5. Def. linear pair
6. $m BDC + \angle BDA = 180$	6. Supplement Theorem
7. $(90 - x) + m\angle BDA = 180$	7. Substitution Prop. (=)
8. $m\angle BDA = 90 + x$	8. Subtraction Prop. (=)
9. $m\angle BDA > 90$	9. Def. inequality
10. $\angle BDA$ is obtuse.	10. Def. obtuse
11. $\angle BAD$ and $\angle ABD$ are acute angles.	11. There can be at most 1 rt. or obtuse $\angle$ in a $\triangle$.
12. $m\angle BAD < 90$	12. Def. acute $\angle$
13. $m\angle BDA > m\angle BAD$	13. Transitive Prop. of Inequality
14. $BA > BD$	14. If an $\angle$ of a $\triangle$ > another $\angle$, the side opp. the greater $\angle$ is longer than the side opp. the lesser $\angle$.

32. Given: $\overline{ON} \cong \overline{OM}$

$\overline{OM} \cong \overline{LM}$

Prove: $m\angle MON > m\angle OMN$

Proof:

Statements	Reasons
1. $\overline{ON} \cong \overline{OM}$ $\overline{OM} \cong \overline{LM}$	1. Given
2. $\angle MLO \cong \angle MOL$	2. Isosceles Triangle Theorem
3. $m\angle MLO = m\angle MOL$	3. Def. $\cong \angle$s
4. $m\angle MON > m\angle MLO$	4. Exterior Angles Inequality Theorem
5. $m\angle MON > m\angle MOL$	5. Substitution
6. $m\angle MOL > m\angle OMN$	6. Exterior Angles Inequality Theorem
7. $m\angle MON < m\angle OMN$	7. Transitive Prop. of Inequality

33. Given: $\overline{AC}$ is an altitude of $\triangle AEB$.

$\overline{AF}$ is a median.

$\overline{AE} \cong \overline{AB}$

Prove: $AF > AC$

Proof:

We are given that $\overline{AC}$ is an altitude of $\triangle AEB$. $\overline{AC} \perp \overline{EB}$ by the definition of an altitude. The perpendicular segment from a point to a line is the shortest segment from the point to the line, so $\overline{AC}$ is the shortest segment from A to $\overline{EB}$.

The only way that $\overline{AF}$ is not longer than $\overline{AC}$ is if they are the same segment. If they are the same segment, then C and F are the same point and $EC = CB$ by the definition of median. In that case, $\angle ACE$ and $\angle ACB$ are right angles since perpendicular lines form four right angles. Then $\triangle ACE$ and $\triangle ACB$ are right triangles by the definition of right triangle. $\overline{AC} \cong \overline{AC}$ because congruence of segments is reflexive. Then $\triangle ACE \cong \triangle ACB$ by HL. Then $\overline{AE} \cong \overline{AB}$ by CPCTC. But this contradicts the given information. Thus, C and F do not correspond and $AF > AC$.

34.

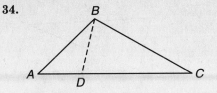

Given: $m\angle A > m\angle ABC$

Prove: $BC > AC$

Proof:

Assume $BC \not> AC$. By the Comparison Property, $BC = AC$ or $BC < AC$.

Case 1: If $BC = AC$, then $\angle ABC \cong \angle A$ by the Isosceles Triangle Theorem (If two sides of a triangle are congruent, then the angles opposite those sides are congruent.) But, $\angle ABC \cong \angle A$ contradicts the given statement that $m\angle A > m\angle ABC$. So, $BC \neq AC$.

Case 2: If $BC < AC$, then there must be a point D between A and C so that $\overline{DC} \cong \overline{BC}$. Draw the auxiliary segment $\overline{BD}$. Since $DC = BC$, by the Isosceles Triangle Theorem $\angle BDC \cong \angle DBC$. Now $\angle BDC$ is an exterior angle of $\triangle BAD$, and by the Exterior Angles Inequality Theorem (the measure of an exterior angle of a triangle is greater than the measure of either corresponding remote interior angle) $m\angle BDC > m\angle A$. By the Angle Addition Postulate, $m\angle ABC = m\angle ABD + m\angle DBC$. Then by the definition of inequality, $m\angle ABC > m\angle DBC$. By Substitution and the Transitive Property of Inequality, $m\angle ABC > m\angle A$. But this contradicts the given statement that $m\angle A > m\angle ABC$. In both cases, a contradiction was found, and hence our assumption must have been false. Therefore, $BC > AC$.

35. Given: $\overline{PQ} \perp$ plane $\mathcal{M}$

Prove: $\overline{PQ}$ is the shortest segment from P to plane $\mathcal{M}$.

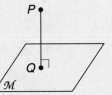

Proof:

By definition, $\overline{PQ}$ is perpendicular to plane $\mathcal{M}$ if it is perpendicular to every line in $\mathcal{M}$ that intersects it. But since the perpendicular segment from a point to a line is the shortest segment from the point to the line, that perpendicular segment is the shortest segment from the point to each of these lines. Therefore, $\overline{PQ}$ is the shortest segment from P to $\mathcal{M}$.

36. slope of $\overline{AB} = \frac{9 - (-11)}{9 - (-1)} = 2$

slope of $\overline{CD} = -\frac{1}{2}$

Find the equation for $\overline{AB}$.

$y = mx + b$
$9 = 2(9) + b$
$-9 = b$
$y = 2x - 9$

Find the equation for $\overline{CD}$.

$y = mx + b$
$2 = -\frac{1}{2}(-2) + b$
$1 = b$
$y = -\frac{1}{2}x + 1$

Find point where $\overline{CD}$ intersects $\overline{AB}$.

$2x - 9 = -\frac{1}{2}x + 1$
$4x - 18 = -x + 2$
$5x = 20$
$x = 4$
$y = 2x - 9$
$\quad = 2(4) - 9 \text{ or } -1$

Coordinates of D are $(4, -1)$.

37a.

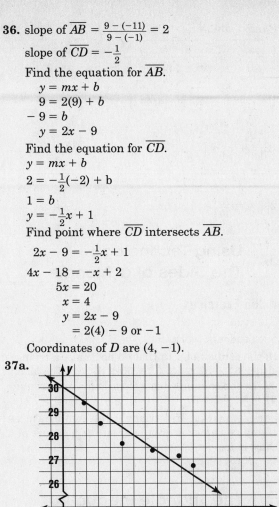

37b. The equation is the best predictor for Henry Rono's record in 1978. It is the worst predictor for Ron Clarke's record in 1965.

38. Since $m\angle B > m\angle A$, the side opposite $\angle B$ should be longer. Attach the longer bar at end A.

39. Work backward and make a chart.

	Songan	Lucy	Tamoko
last hand	8	8	8
second hand	4	4	16
first hand	2	14	8
beginning points	13	7	4
	lost 5 points	gained 1 point	gained 4 points

Songan lost the most points

40. No; the sides may not be congruent.

41. See students' work.

42. Yes; the triangles are congruent by SAS.

43. False; the hypotenuse must be longer than the other two sides. counterexample:

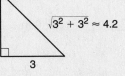

44. $\overline{AX}$ is an altitude of $\triangle ABC$; Law of Detachment.

45. Sample answers:

x	$2x - 6$	(x, y)
0	-6	$(0, -6)$
2	-2	$(2, -2)$
4	2	$(4, 2)$

46. $\frac{1}{3} + \frac{5}{x} = \frac{1}{x}$

$3x\left(\frac{1}{3} + \frac{5}{x}\right) = \left(\frac{1}{x}\right)3x$

$x + 15 = 3$

$x = -12$

47. $230\% = \frac{230}{100} = 2.30$ or 2.3

 5-5A   ## Using Technology
The Sides of a Triangle

Page 266 Exercises

1. See students' work.

2. See students' work.

3. In the column of sets that do not make a triangle, either $51 + 52 \leq 53$, $52 + 53 \leq 51$, or $51 + 53 \leq 52$. In the column of sets that do make a triangle, $51 + 52 > 53$, $52 + 53 > 51$, and $51 + 53 > 52$.

4. Sample answer: In a triangle, the sum measures of any two sides is greater than the measure of a third side.

5-5   ## The Triangle Inequality

Pages 269–270 Check for Understanding

1. See students' work.

2. The base must be less than 42 cm long.

3. Brittany is correct. $5 + 8$ is not greater than 13. But $5 + 13 > 13$.

4. $1 + 2 \not> 3$ no
$2 + 3 > 1$ yes
$1 + 3 > 2$ yes   no

5. $21 + 32 > 18$ yes
$21 + 18 > 32$ yes
$32 + 18 > 21$ yes

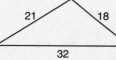

6. $11 + 6 > 2$ yes
$6 + 2 \not> 11$ no
$11 + 2 > 6$ yes   no

7. $21 + 27 > t$ $21 + t > 27$ $27 + t > 21$
$\qquad 48 > t$ $\qquad t > 6$ $\qquad t > -6$
$6 < t < 48$; 6 and 48

8. $5 + 11 > t$ $11 + t > 5$ $5 + t > 11$
$\qquad 16 > t$ $\qquad t > -6$ $\qquad t > 6$
$6 < t < 16$; 6 and 16

9. $30 + 30 > t$ $30 + t > 30$
$\qquad 60 > t$ $\qquad t > 0$
$0 < t < 60$; 0 and 60

10. Never true; $AD + AB > DB$.

11. Always true; $DB < 7$ and $BC < 2 + DB$.

12. Given: $\overline{PO} \cong \overline{OM}$
Prove: $PO + MN > ON$

Proof:

Statements	Reasons
1. $\overline{PO} \cong \overline{OM}$	1. Given
2. $PO = OM$	2. Def. $\cong$ segments
3. $OM + MN > ON$	3. Triangle Inequality Theorem
4. $PO + MN > ON$	4. Substitution Prop. (=)

13. $OR = \sqrt{(1 - (-2))^2 + (1 - 5)^2} = \sqrt{9 + 16} = 5$
$RS = \sqrt{(-2 - (-5))^2 + (5 - (-4))^2}$
$\quad = \sqrt{9 + 81} = \sqrt{90}$
$QS = \sqrt{(1 - (-5))^2 + (1 - (-4))^2}$
$\quad = \sqrt{36 + 25} = \sqrt{61}$
Yes; the measures of the sides are 5, $\sqrt{61}$, and $\sqrt{90}$ and the Triangle Inequality Theorem applies.

14. yes;

15. yes;

16. $5 + 10 = 15$; no

17. yes:

18. $301 + 8 \not> 310$; no   **19.** yes;

20. $12 + 2.2 \not> 14.3$; no   **21.** $10 + 150 \not> 200$; no

22. $84 + 7 \not> 115$; no

23. $18 - 15 < x < 15 + 18$
$\quad 3 < x < 33$; 3 and 33

24. $23 - 14 < x < 14 + 23$
$\quad 9 < x < 37$; 9 and 37

25. $34 - 22 < x < 34 + 22$
$\quad 12 < x < 56$; 12 and 56

26. $47 - 21 < x < 21 + 47$
$\quad 26 < x < 68$; 26 and 68

27. $88 - 64 < x < 64 + 88$
$\quad 24 < x < 152$; 24 and 152

28. $99 - 2 < x < 99 + 2$
$\quad 97 < x < 101$; 97 and 101

29. $71 - 47 < x < 71 + 47$
$\quad 24 < x < 118$; 24 and 118

30. $118 - 104 < x < 104 + 118$
$\quad 14 < x < 222$; 14 and 222

31. $|a - b| < x < a + b$

$|a - b|$ and $a + b$

32. Always true; $BC < AB + AC$.

33. Sometimes true; $BD + DC < BC$ and $BC + DC > BC$, so $10 < BC < 38$. 12 is one of the acceptable values for BC.

34. Always true; $AB = AC$ and $BC < AB + AC$, $BC < 2AB$, $\frac{1}{2}BC < AB$.

35. Always true; $AB + AC > BC$ and $BC + DC > BD$, so $AB + AC > BD - DC$, then $AB + AC > BD$.

36. Sometimes true; this is true if $\triangle ABC \cong \triangle DBC$.

37. Never true; $\overline{BA}$ is the perpendicular, so it is the shortest distance from B to $\overline{AC}$.

38. $RS = \sqrt{(0 - 3)^2 + (0 - 5)^2} = \sqrt{9 + 25} = \sqrt{34} \approx 5.8$

$ST = \sqrt{(3 - 5)^2 + (5 - 3)^2} = \sqrt{4 + 4} = \sqrt{8} \approx 2.8$

$RT = \sqrt{(0 - 5)^2 + (0 - 3)^2} = \sqrt{25 + 9} = \sqrt{34} \approx 5.8$

Yes; these measures satisfy the Triangle Inequality Theorem.

39. $AB = \sqrt{(2 - (-5))^2 + (3 - (-11))^2} = \sqrt{49 + 196} = \sqrt{245} \approx 15.7$

$AC = \sqrt{(2 - (-8))^2 + (3 - 15)^2} = \sqrt{100 + 144} = \sqrt{244} \approx 15.6$

$BC = \sqrt{(-5 - (-8))^2 + (-11 - 15)^2} = \sqrt{9 + 676} = \sqrt{685} \approx 26.2$

Yes; these measures satisfy the Triangle Inequality Theorem.

40. $JK = \sqrt{(1 - (-3))^2 + (-4 - (-20))^2} = \sqrt{16 + 256} = \sqrt{272} \approx 16.5$

$JL = \sqrt{(1 - 5)^2 + (-4 - 12)^2} = \sqrt{16 + 256} = \sqrt{272} \approx 16.5$

$KL = \sqrt{(-3 - 5)^2 + (-20 - 12)^2} = \sqrt{64 + 1024} = \sqrt{1088} \approx 33.0$

No; these measures do not satisfy the Triangle Inequality Theorem.

41. $DE = \sqrt{(1 - 5)^2 + (4 - (-1))^2} = \sqrt{16 + 25} = \sqrt{41} \approx 6.4$

$EF = \sqrt{(5 - 1)^2 + (-1 - (-4))^2} = \sqrt{16 + 9} = \sqrt{25}$ or 5

$DF = \sqrt{(1 - 1)^2 + (4 - (-4))^2} = \sqrt{64}$ or 8

Yes; these measures satisfy the Triangle Inequality Theorem.

42. Given: $RS = RT$

Prove: $UV + VS > UT$

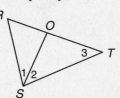

Proof:

Statements	Reasons
1. $RS = RT$	1. Given
2. $UV + VS > US$	2. Triangle Inequality Theorem
3. $US = UR + RS$	3. Segment Addition Post.
4. $UV + VS > UR + RS$	4. Substitution Prop. (=)
5. $UV + VS > UR + RT$	5. Substitution Prop. (=)
6. $UR + RT > UT$	6. Triangle Inequality Theorem
7. $UV + VS > UT$	7. Transitive Prop. of Inequality

43. Given: quadrilateral $ABCD$

Prove: $AD + CD + AB > BC$

Proof:

Statements	Reasons
1. quadrilateral $ABCD$	1. Given
2. Draw $\overline{AC}$.	2. Through any 2 pts. there is 1 line.
3. $AD + CD > AC$ $AB + AC > BC$	3. Triangle Inequality Theorem
4. $AC > BC - AB$	4. Subtraction Prop. of Inequality
5. $AD + CD > BC - AB$	5. Transitive Prop. of Inequality
6. $AD + CD + AB > AC$	6. Addition Prop. of Inequality

44. Given: $\triangle ROS$

Prove: $SO + OR > RS$

Proof:

The Ruler Postulate allows us to construct $\overline{OT}$ so that O is between R and T and $\overline{OS} \cong \overline{OT}$. $OS = OT$ by the definition of congruent segments. If any two sides of a triangle are congruent, then the angles opposite the sides are congruent, so $\angle 2 \cong \angle 3$. $m\angle 2 = m\angle 3$ by the definition of congruent angles. The Angle Addition Postulate allows us to say that $m\angle 1 + m\angle 2 = m\angle RST$. Substituting, we can conclude that $m\angle 1 + m\angle 3 = m\angle RST$. By the definition of inequality, $m\angle 3 < m\angle RST$. If the measures of an angle of a triangle is greater than the measure of another angle, then the side opposite the larger angle is longer than the side opposite the smaller angle, so $RS < RT$. $RT = RO + OT$ by the Segment Addition Postulate. Substitution allows us to say that $RS < RO + OT$. Then by substitution $RS < RO + OS$.

45a. no triangle   **45b.** Triangle exists.
45c. no triangle   **45d.** Triangle exists.
45e. Triangle exists.
46. It is true; $a + b > c$, $a > c - b$ or $c - b < a$.
47a. a is either 15 cm, or 16 cm; z is 14 cm, 15 cm, or 16 cm. The possible triangles that can be made from sides with those measures are (2 cm, 15 cm, 14 cm), (2 cm, 15 cm, 15 cm), (2cm, 15 cm, 16 cm), (2 cm, 16 cm, 15 cm), (2 cm, 16 cm, 16 cm).
47b. 2 of 5 possible triangles are isosceles; $\frac{2}{5}$.
48. She can use the 20 and 24 cm braces.
49.
$$m\angle A + m\angle B + m\angle C = 180$$
$$(4x + 61) + (67 - 3x) + (x + 74) = 180$$
$$2x = -22$$
$$x = -11$$
$m\angle A = 4x + 61 = 4(-11) + 61 = 17$
$m\angle B = 67 - 3x = 67 - 3(-11) = 100$
$m\angle C = x + 74 = (-11) + 74 = 63$
$\angle B$ has the greatest measure so $\overline{AC}$ is the longest side.
50. $\overline{NM}$ is not a median of $\triangle NOP$.
51. no triangle   **52.** $\angle 1 \cong \angle 6$
53. $6x - 6 = x + 9$
$5x = 15$
$x = 3$
$x + 9 = 3 + 9 = 12$ units
54. False; the segment must be perpendicular to the lines to represent the distance.
55. Given: $\ell \parallel m$
       $s \parallel t$
       $t \perp \ell$

Prove: $\angle 3$ is a
       right angle.

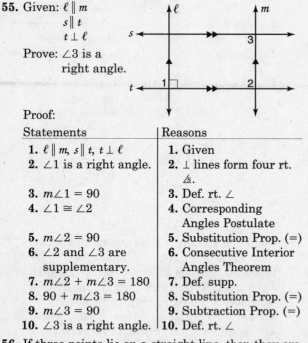

Proof:

Statements	Reasons
1. $\ell \parallel m$, $s \parallel t$, $t \perp \ell$	1. Given
2. $\angle 1$ is a right angle.	2. $\perp$ lines form four rt. $\angle$s.
3. $m\angle 1 = 90$	3. Def. rt. $\angle$
4. $\angle 1 \cong \angle 2$	4. Corresponding Angles Postulate
5. $m\angle 2 = 90$	5. Substitution Prop. (=)
6. $\angle 2$ and $\angle 3$ are supplementary.	6. Consecutive Interior Angles Theorem
7. $m\angle 2 + m\angle 3 = 180$	7. Def. supp.
8. $90 + m\angle 3 = 180$	8. Substitution Prop. (=)
9. $m\angle 3 = 90$	9. Subtraction Prop. (=)
10. $\angle 3$ is a right angle.	10. Def. rt. $\angle$

56. If three points lie on a straight line, then they are collinear. True.
57. $90 - 63 = 27$, $180 - 63 = 117$
58. $\sqrt{28x^4} = \sqrt{2^2 \cdot 7 \cdot x^2 \cdot x^2} = 2 \cdot x \cdot x\sqrt{7}$ or $2x^2\sqrt{7}$

59a. the percentage of classical music listeners who are in different age groups
59b. $0.11(8,000,000) = 880,000$ people

Page 272 Mathematics and Society

1. when to change directions to get its final location
2. 30°
3. Conduct an experiment where there is no sun to see if the animal can still find its way. Also, you could create an artificial sun out of some light source and observe how the animal responds to it.

5-6 Inequalities Involving Two Triangles

Page 273 Modeling Mathematics
a. $m\angle R < m\angle R'$, $PT < P'T'$
b. If $m\angle R$ becomes greater than $m\angle R'$, then $PT > P'T'$. Otherwise the relationship stays the same.
c. $AC > DF$

Pages 275–276 Check for Understanding
1a. the triangle with base of 8 cm
1b. SSS Inequality
2. The SAS Inequality Theorem compares the third side of a triangle for which two sides are congruent and the included angle is different. The SAS Postulate states that two triangles that have two sides and an included angle congruent are congruent.
3. Answers may vary. A sample answer is that as the angle between the edges of a hinge gets larger, the distance between the ends of the sides gets larger.
4a. As the string gets shorter, the angle gets smaller.
4b. SSS Inequality
5. Since $AB = BD$, $BF = BF$, $FD < AF$, $m\angle DBF < m\angle FBA$.
6. Since $AB = 11$ and $FD = 8$, $AB > FD$
7. Since $BD = BD$, $FD = CD$, and $BF > BC$, $m\angle FDB > m\angle BDC$.
8. always true   **9.** sometimes true
10. never true
11. $5x - 14 > 0$ and $5x - 14 < 46$
$x > \frac{14}{5}$ or 2.8 $x < 12$
$2.8 < x$ and $x < 12$

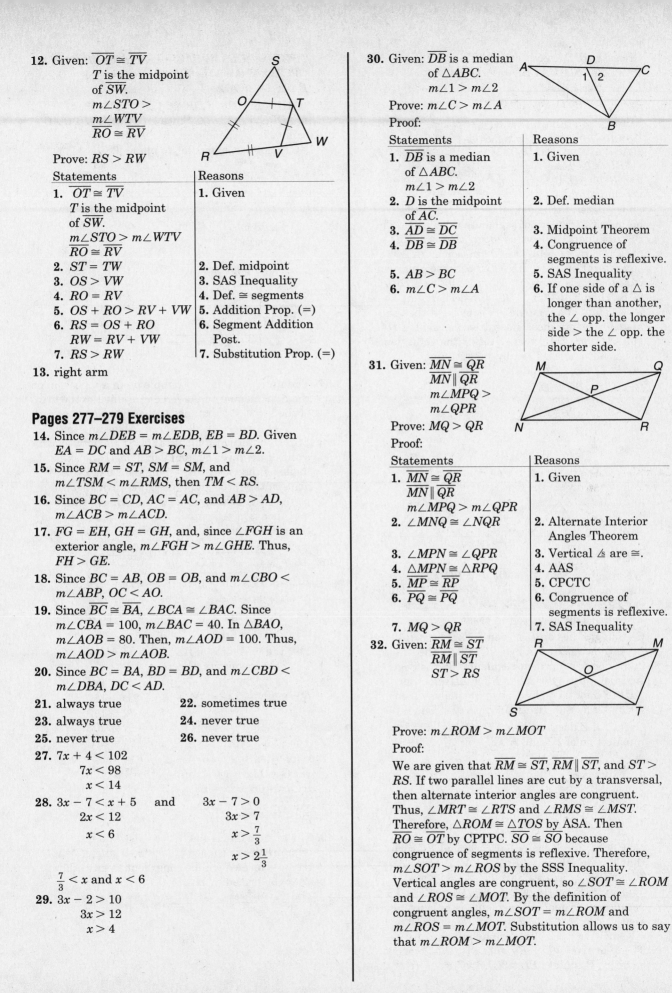

12. Given: $\overline{OT} \cong \overline{TV}$
T is the midpoint of $\overline{SW}$.
$m\angle STO > m\angle WTV$
$\overline{RO} \cong \overline{RV}$

Prove: $RS > RW$

Statements	Reasons
1. $\overline{OT} \cong \overline{TV}$ T is the midpoint of $\overline{SW}$. $m\angle STO > m\angle WTV$ $\overline{RO} \cong \overline{RV}$	1. Given
2. $ST = TW$	2. Def. midpoint
3. $OS > VW$	3. SAS Inequality
4. $RO = RV$	4. Def. $\cong$ segments
5. $OS + RO > RV + VW$	5. Addition Prop. (=)
6. $RS = OS + RO$ $RW = RV + VW$	6. Segment Addition Post.
7. $RS > RW$	7. Substitution Prop. (=)

13. right arm

Pages 277–279 Exercises

14. Since $m\angle DEB = m\angle EDB$, $EB = BD$. Given $EA = DC$ and $AB > BC$, $m\angle 1 > m\angle 2$.

15. Since $RM = ST$, $SM = SM$, and $m\angle TSM < m\angle RMS$, then $TM < RS$.

16. Since $BC = CD$, $AC = AC$, and $AB > AD$, $m\angle ACB > m\angle ACD$.

17. $FG = EH$, $GH = GH$, and, since $\angle FGH$ is an exterior angle, $m\angle FGH > m\angle GHE$. Thus, $FH > GE$.

18. Since $BC = AB$, $OB = OB$, and $m\angle CBO < m\angle ABP$, $OC < AO$.

19. Since $\overline{BC} \cong \overline{BA}$, $\angle BCA \cong \angle BAC$. Since $m\angle CBA = 100$, $m\angle BAC = 40$. In $\triangle BAO$, $m\angle AOB = 80$. Then, $m\angle AOD = 100$. Thus, $m\angle AOD > m\angle AOB$.

20. Since $BC = BA$, $BD = BD$, and $m\angle CBD < m\angle DBA$, $DC < AD$.

21. always true
22. sometimes true
23. always true
24. never true
25. never true
26. never true

27. $7x + 4 < 102$
$\quad 7x < 98$
$\quad\ x < 14$

28. $3x - 7 < x + 5$ and $\quad 3x - 7 > 0$
$\quad 2x < 12 \qquad\qquad\qquad 3x > 7$
$\quad\ x < 6 \qquad\qquad\qquad\ x > \frac{7}{3}$
$\qquad\qquad\qquad\qquad\qquad\quad x > 2\frac{1}{3}$

$\frac{7}{3} < x$ and $x < 6$

29. $3x - 2 > 10$
$\quad 3x > 12$
$\quad\ x > 4$

30. Given: $\overline{DB}$ is a median of $\triangle ABC$.
$m\angle 1 > m\angle 2$

Prove: $m\angle C > m\angle A$

Proof:

Statements	Reasons
1. $\overline{DB}$ is a median of $\triangle ABC$. $m\angle 1 > m\angle 2$	1. Given
2. D is the midpoint of $\overline{AC}$.	2. Def. median
3. $\overline{AD} \cong \overline{DC}$	3. Midpoint Theorem
4. $\overline{DB} \cong \overline{DB}$	4. Congruence of segments is reflexive.
5. $AB > BC$	5. SAS Inequality
6. $m\angle C > m\angle A$	6. If one side of a $\triangle$ is longer than another, the $\angle$ opp. the longer side > the $\angle$ opp. the shorter side.

31. Given: $\overline{MN} \cong \overline{QR}$
$\overline{MN} \parallel \overline{QR}$
$m\angle MPQ > m\angle QPR$

Prove: $MQ > QR$

Proof:

Statements	Reasons
1. $\overline{MN} \cong \overline{QR}$ $\overline{MN} \parallel \overline{QR}$ $m\angle MPQ > m\angle QPR$	1. Given
2. $\angle MNQ \cong \angle NQR$	2. Alternate Interior Angles Theorem
3. $\angle MPN \cong \angle QPR$	3. Vertical $\angle$s are $\cong$.
4. $\triangle MPN \cong \triangle RPQ$	4. AAS
5. $\overline{MP} \cong \overline{RP}$	5. CPCTC
6. $\overline{PQ} \cong \overline{PQ}$	6. Congruence of segments is reflexive.
7. $MQ > QR$	7. SAS Inequality

32. Given: $\overline{RM} \cong \overline{ST}$
$\overline{RM} \parallel \overline{ST}$
$ST > RS$

Prove: $m\angle ROM > m\angle MOT$

Proof:
We are given that $\overline{RM} \cong \overline{ST}$, $\overline{RM} \parallel \overline{ST}$, and $ST > RS$. If two parallel lines are cut by a transversal, then alternate interior angles are congruent. Thus, $\angle MRT \cong \angle RTS$ and $\angle RMS \cong \angle MST$. Therefore, $\triangle ROM \cong \triangle TOS$ by ASA. Then $\overline{RO} \cong \overline{OT}$ by CPTPC. $\overline{SO} \cong \overline{SO}$ because congruence of segments is reflexive. Therefore, $m\angle SOT > m\angle ROS$ by the SSS Inequality. Vertical angles are congruent, so $\angle SOT \cong \angle ROM$ and $\angle ROS \cong \angle MOT$. By the definition of congruent angles, $m\angle SOT = m\angle ROM$ and $m\angle ROS = m\angle MOT$. Substitution allows us to say that $m\angle ROM > m\angle MOT$.

33. Given: $\triangle ABC$ is equilateral.
$\triangle ABD \cong \triangle CBD$
$BD > AD$

Prove: $m\angle BCD > m\angle DAC$
Proof:

It is given that $\triangle ABC$ is equilateral, $\triangle ABD \cong \triangle CBD$, and $BD > AD$. By the definition of an equilateral triangle, $\overline{AC} \cong \overline{BC}$. $\overline{DC} \cong \overline{DC}$ because congruence of segments is reflexive. The SSS Inequality allows us to say that $m\angle BCD > m\angle DCA$. $\overline{BC} \cong \overline{BA}$ by the definition of an equilateral triangle. $\overline{DB} \cong \overline{DB}$ because congruence of segments is reflexive. Thus, $\triangle DBC \cong \triangle DBA$ by SAS. Then by CPCTC, $\overline{DC} \cong \overline{DA}$. Therefore, since if two sides of a triangle are congruent then the angles opposite those sides are congruent, $\angle DAC \cong \angle DCA$. $m\angle DAC = m\angle DCA$ by the definition of congruent angles. Then by substitution, $m\angle BCD > m\angle DAC$.

34. Given: $\triangle ABC$, $\triangle DEF$
$\overline{AC} \cong \overline{DF}$
$\overline{BC} \cong \overline{EF}$
$m\angle F > m\angle C$

Prove: $DE > AB$

Proof:

We are given that $\overline{AC} \cong \overline{DF}$ and $\overline{BC} \cong \overline{EF}$. We also know that $m\angle F > m\angle C$. Now draw auxiliary ray FZ such that $m\angle DFZ = m\angle C$ and that $\overline{ZF} \cong \overline{BC}$. This leads to two cases.

Case 1: If Z lies on $\overline{DE}$, then $\triangle FZD \cong \triangle CBA$ by SAS. Hence $ZD = BA$ by CPCTC and the definition of congruent segments. By the Segment Addition Postulate, $DE = EZ + ZD$ and hence $DE > ZD$ by the definition of inequality, then $DE > AB$ by Substitution Property of Equality.

Case 2: If Z does not lie on $\overline{DE}$, then let the intersection of $\overline{FZ}$ and $\overline{ED}$ be point T.

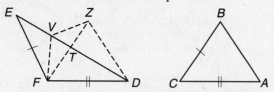

Now draw another auxiliary segment $\overline{FV}$ such that V is on $\overline{DE}$ and $\angle EFV \cong \angle VFZ$. Since $\overline{FZ} \cong \overline{BC}$ and $\overline{BC} \cong \overline{EF}$, we have $\overline{FZ} \cong \overline{EF}$ by the Transitive Property of Equality. Also, $\overline{VF} \cong \overline{VF}$ because congruence of segments is reflexive. Hence, $\triangle EFV \cong \triangle ZFV$ by SAS. Then by CPCTC, $\overline{EV} \cong \overline{ZV}$. In $\triangle VZD$ the Triangle Inequality Theorem gives $VD + EV > ZD$. By the Segment Addition Postulate $ED > ZD$. We also have

$\triangle FZD \cong \triangle CBA$ by SAS, which gives $\overline{ZD} \cong \overline{AB}$ by CPCTC. Making the substitution, we get $ED > BA$ or $DE > AB$.

35. If $AB = BC$, $DB = DB$, and $DC > DA$, then $m\angle DBC > m\angle DBA$. Since $\angle DBC \cong \angle DBA$, $\overline{AC}$ cannot be perpendicular to $\overline{DB}$. $\overline{DB}$ lies in $\mathcal{F}$ so, $\overline{AC}$ is not perpendicular to plane $\mathcal{F}$.

36a. $v = \dfrac{0.78s^{1.67}}{h^{1.17}}$

$= \dfrac{0.78(2.26)^{1.67}}{(1.08)^{1.17}}$

≈ 2.78 m/s

$v = \dfrac{0.78(2.40)^{1.67}}{(1.08)^{1.17}}$

≈ 3.07 m/s

36b.

As the length of the stride increases, the angle formed at the hip increases.

37. The nutcracker is an example of an application of the SAS inequality. As force is applied to the arms of the lever, the distance between the ends of the arms of the lever is decreased. According to the SSS inequality, this makes the angle between the arms of the lever get smaller. This is the same angle as the one in the triangle formed by the arms of the lever and the segment between the points where the nut meets the arms of the lever. As this angle gets smaller, the segment between the points where the nut meets the arms of the lever gets shorter, thereby crushing the nut.

38. $AB = \sqrt{(3-9)^2 + (1-9)^2} = \sqrt{36 + 64} = 10$

$BC = \sqrt{(9-4)^2 + (9-7)^2} = \sqrt{25 + 4} =$
$\sqrt{29} \approx 5.4$

$AC = \sqrt{(3-4)^2 + (1-7)^2} = \sqrt{1 + 36} =$
$\sqrt{37} \approx 6.1$

Yes; the measures of $\overline{AB}$, $\overline{BC}$, and $\overline{AC}$ satisfy the Triangle Inequality Theorem.

39. $m\angle F + m\angle G + m\angle H = 180$
$(6x + 25) + (14x - 18) + (65 - 2x) = 180$
$18x + 72 = 180$
$18x = 108$
$x = 6$

$m\angle F = 6x + 25 = 6(6) + 25 = 61$
$m\angle G = 14x - 18 = 14(6) - 18 = 66$
$m\angle H = 65 - 2x = 65 - 2(6) = 53$

$m\angle H < m\angle F < m\angle G$
$\overline{FG}, \overline{GH}, \overline{FH}$

40. The anchor line is the hypotenuse and the tripping line is the leg of a right triangle. Any triangle formed will be congruent to any other triangle formed by HL.

41. $\left(\dfrac{x_1 + x_2}{2}, \dfrac{y_1 + y_2}{2}\right) = T\left(\dfrac{-2 + 9}{2}, \dfrac{7 + 0}{2}\right)$

$= T\left(\dfrac{7}{2}, \dfrac{7}{2}\right)$

42. $m\angle BNC = m\angle BCN$

$m\angle NBC + m\angle BNC + m\angle BCN = 180$

$34 + 2(m\angle BNC) = 180$

$2(m\angle BNC) = 146$

$m\angle BNC = 73$

$m\angle ANB + m\angle BNC = 180$

$m\angle ANB + 73 = 180$

$m\angle ANB = 107$

43.

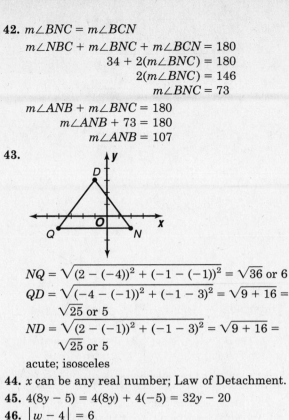

$NQ = \sqrt{(2 - (-4))^2 + (-1 - (-1))^2} = \sqrt{36}$ or 6

$QD = \sqrt{(-4 - (-1))^2 + (-1 - 3)^2} = \sqrt{9 + 16} = \sqrt{25}$ or 5

$ND = \sqrt{(2 - (-1))^2 + (-1 - 3)^2} = \sqrt{9 + 16} = \sqrt{25}$ or 5

acute; isosceles

44. x can be any real number; Law of Detachment.

45. $4(8y - 5) = 4(8y) + 4(-5) = 32y - 20$

46. $|w - 4| = 6$

$w - 4 = 6$ or $w - 4 = -6$

$w = 10$ $w = -2$

$\{-2, 10\}$

Chapter 5 Highlights

Page 281 Understanding and Using the Vocabulary

1. a. Division Property of Inequality
2. e. median
3. b. altitude *and* l. perpendicular bisector
4. f. Leg-Angle Theorem
5. h. Triangle Inequality Theorem
6. j. indirect reasoning
7. m. Transitive Property of Inequality
8. b. altitude
9. k. Hypetenuse-Angle Theorem
10. g. SSS Inequality

Chapter 5 Study Guide and Assessment

Pages 282–284 Skills and Concepts

11. $m\angle ONQ = 2(m\angle QNP)$

$= 2(33)$

$= 66$

$m\angle QNP + m\angle NPQ + m\angle NQP = 180$

$33 + 90 + m\angle NQP = 180$

$m\angle NQP = 57$

$m\angle QNO = m\angle NQO + m\angle NOQ = 180$

$66 + 57 + m\angle NOQ = 180$

$m\angle NOQ = 57$

12. $m\angle 1 + m\angle 2 = 90$

$(3x + 11) + (7x + 9) = 90$

$10x + 20 = 90$

$10x = 70$

$x = 7$

$m\angle 2 = 7x + 9 = 7(7) + 9 = 58$

13. $QS = SN$

$3x - 14 = 2x - 1$

$x = 13$

$m\angle MSQ = 7x + 1 = 7(13) + 1 = 92$

Since $m\angle MSQ \neq 90$, $\overline{MS}$ is not an altitude.

14. $XY = AB$

$3x + 1 = 40$

$3x = 39$

$x = 13$

$m\angle C = m\angle Z$

$3y - 1 = 50$

$3y = 51$

$y = 17$

15. $AC = XZ$

$4x + 3 = 27$

$4x = 24$

$x = 6$

$m\angle A = m\angle X$

$43 = 2y - 9$

$52 = 2y$

$26 = y$

16. $XY = AB$

$42 = 5x - 8$

$50 = 5x$

$10 = x$

$m\angle A = m\angle X$

$m\angle X + m\angle Z = 90$

$m\angle X + 68 = 90$

$m\angle X = 22$

$14y - 6 = 22$

$14y = 28$

$y = 2$

17. $AC = XZ$

$12y + 1 = 10y + 3$

$2y = 2$

$y = 1$

$AB = XY$

$x + 3 = 4x - 3$

$-3x = -6$

$x = 2$

18. Given: $\overline{MJ}$ does not bisect $\angle NML$. $\overline{MN} \cong \overline{ML}$

Prove: $\overline{MJ}$ is not a median of $\triangle NML$.

Proof:

We assume that $\overline{MJ}$ is a median of $\triangle LMN$. By the definition of median, J is the midpoint of $\overline{LN}$, and hence by the definition of midpoint, $\overline{LJ} \cong \overline{JN}$. We are given that $\overline{ML} \cong \overline{MN}$ and we know that $\overline{MJ} \cong \overline{MJ}$ since congruence of segments is reflexive. Therefore, $\triangle MJL \cong \triangle MJN$ by SSS and $\angle LMJ \cong \angle NMJ$ by CPCTC. By the definition of angle bisector, $\overline{MJ}$ bisects $\angle LMN$. But this contradicts our given statement. So, our assumption must be false, and $\overline{MJ}$ is not a median of $\triangle LMN$.

19. Given: $\triangle MJN \cong \triangle MJL$
$\overline{MJ}$ does not
bisect $\angle NML$.
Prove: $\overline{MJ}$ is an altitude
of $\triangle NML$.

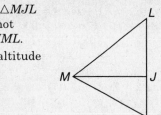

Proof:
We assume that $\overline{MJ}$ is not an altitude of $\triangle LMN$.
This means that $\overline{MJ}$ is not perpendicular to $\overline{LN}$
by the definition of altitude. So, by the definition
of perpendicular, this means $\angle MJN$ is not a right
angle. Therefore, $\angle MJN$ is either acute or obtuse.
Since $\angle MJL$ and $\angle MJN$ form a linear pair, these
two angles are supplementary. Hence, if $\angle MJL$ is
acute, $\angle MJN$ is obtuse (or vice versa), by the
definition of supplementary. In either case,
$\angle MJL \not\cong \angle MJN$. This is a contradiction, and
hence our assumption must be false. Therefore
$\overline{MJ}$ is an altitude of $\triangle LMN$.

20. Since $m\angle 3 + m\angle 5 = m\angle ACB$, $m\angle ACB > m\angle 3$.

21. Sample answer: $\angle 7$

22. $m\angle 11 = m\angle 8 + m\angle 6 + m\angle 5$, so $m\angle 11 > m\angle 6$.

23. $\angle YXB$, $\angle ACB$, $\angle 9$, $\angle 4$, $\angle 11$, $\angle 1$ **24.** $m\angle 1$

25. $\overline{SQ}$ is the shortest segment in $\triangle SQR$. $\overline{SP}$ is the
shortest segment in $\triangle SPQ$, and $SP < SQ$. So, $\overline{SQ}$
is the shortest segment.

26. $m\angle ABC < m\angle BAC < m\angle ACB$
So, $AC < BC < AB$.

27. Given: $FG < FH$
Prove: $m\angle 1 > m\angle 2$

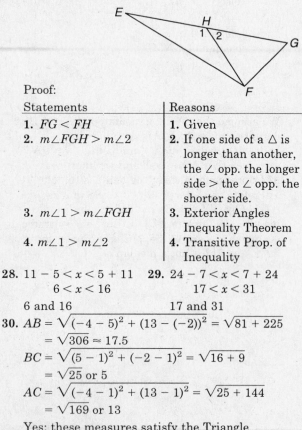

Proof:

Statements	Reasons
1. $FG < FH$	1. Given
2. $m\angle FGH > m\angle 2$	2. If one side of a $\triangle$ is longer than another, the $\angle$ opp. the longer side > the $\angle$ opp. the shorter side.
3. $m\angle 1 > m\angle FGH$	3. Exterior Angles Inequality Theorem
4. $m\angle 1 > m\angle 2$	4. Transitive Prop. of Inequality

28. $11 - 5 < x < 5 + 11$
$\quad\quad 6 < x < 16$
6 and 16

29. $24 - 7 < x < 7 + 24$
$\quad\quad 17 < x < 31$
17 and 31

30. $AB = \sqrt{(-4 - 5)^2 + (13 - (-2))^2} = \sqrt{81 + 225}$
$\quad\quad = \sqrt{306} \approx 17.5$
$BC = \sqrt{(5 - 1)^2 + (-2 - 1)^2} = \sqrt{16 + 9}$
$\quad\quad = \sqrt{25}$ or 5
$AC = \sqrt{(-4 - 1)^2 + (13 - 1)^2} = \sqrt{25 + 144}$
$\quad\quad = \sqrt{169}$ or 13

Yes; these measures satisfy the Triangle
Inequality Theorem.

31. $DE = \sqrt{(-5 - 1)^2 + (2 - (-7))^2} = \sqrt{36 + 81}$
$\quad\quad = \sqrt{117} \approx 10.8$
$EF = \sqrt{(1 - (-3))^2 + (-7 - (-1))^2} = \sqrt{16 + 36}$
$\quad\quad = \sqrt{52} \approx 7.2$
$DF = \sqrt{(-5 - (-3))^2 + (2 - (-1))^2} = \sqrt{4 + 9}$
$\quad\quad = \sqrt{13} \approx 3.6$

No; these measures do not satisfy the Triangle
Inequality Theorem.

32. (2, 3, 4), (3, 4, 5), (2, 4, 5); 3

33. $m\angle ALK < m\angle ALN$ **34.** $m\angle ALK < m\angle NLO$

35. $m\angle OLK > m\angle NLO$ **36.** $m\angle KLO = m\angle ALN$

37. Given: $AD = BC$
Prove: $AC > DB$

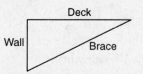

Proof:

Statements	Reasons
1. $AD = BC$	1. Given
2. $\overline{AD} \cong \overline{BC}$	2. Def. $\cong$ segments
3. $\overline{BA} \cong \overline{BA}$	3. Congruence of segments is reflexive.
4. $m\angle CBA > m\angle DAB$	4. Exterior Angles Inequality Theorem
5. $AC > DB$	5. SAS Inequality

Page 284 Applications and Problem Solving

38. The brace represents the hypotenuse of a right
triangle as shown in the diagram below,
assuming that the deck will be attached at a right
angle to the wall. If each brace is attached at the
same distance from the wall, this distance
represents a leg of the triangle. HL says that the
four triangles will be congruent and hence all will
be attached at the same distance on the wall since
that distance represents the other leg of the
triangle.

39. Final Round

(score $\times$ by 3)	1500
(400 + 500) deducted	500
6(200) correct	1400
beginning points	200

40. $4 < y < 9$

Page 285 Alternative Assessment: Thinking Critically

If you can prove a theorem and its negation from
three postulates, then the postulates must
contradict each other. Then one or more of the
postulates should not be assumed to be true.

CHAPTER 6   Exploring Quadrilaterals

6-1A Using Technology
Exploring Parallelograms

Page 290 Exercises

1. Sample answer: The opposite sides are congruent.

2. Sample answer: The opposite angles are congruent. Pairs of consecutive angles are supplementary.

3. Sample answer: Yes, the same relationships hold true.

6-1 Parallelograms

Page 292 Modeling Mathematics

a. They are congruent.   b. They are congruent.

c. They form a linear pair. The consecutive angles are supplementary.

Pages 294–295 Check for Understanding

1. quadrilateral

This is a quadrilateral because it is in a plane, its sides intersect exactly two other sides, one at each endpoint, no two sides with a common endpoint are collinear, and it has exactly four sides.

not a quadrilateral

2. A general quadrilateral is a polygon with four sides. A parallelogram is a special quadrilateral with opposite sides parallel.

3. $\overline{RT}$ and $\overline{SV}$ intersect at $M(4.5, 4.5)$.

$RM = \sqrt{(1 - 4.5)^2 + (1 - 4.5)^2}$ or $\sqrt{24.5}$

$TM = \sqrt{(8 - 4.5)^2 + (8 - 4.5)^2}$ or $\sqrt{24.5}$

$SM = \sqrt{(3 - 4.5)^2 + (6 - 4.5)^2}$ or $\sqrt{4.5}$

$VM = \sqrt{(6 - 4.5)^2 + (3 - 4.5)^2}$ or $\sqrt{4.5}$

Thus since $RM = TM$ and $SM = VM$, the diagonals bisect each other.

4. The opposite sides are parallel, the opposite sides are congruent, the opposite angles are congruent, the consecutive angles are supplementary, and the diagonals bisect each other.

5a. Two pairs of triangles are congruent, $\triangle QRP \cong \triangle STP$ and $\triangle RSP \cong \triangle TQP$.

5b. All red segments are congruent and all blue segments are congruent.

5c. The diagonals bisect each other.

6. $\overline{HF}$; Diagonals of a parallelogram bisect each other.

7. $\overline{DC}$; Opposite sides of a parallelogram are parallel.

8. $\angle DFG$; Opposite angles of a parallelogram are $\cong$.

9. $\overline{GF}$; Opposite sides of a parallelogram are $\cong$.

10. $\angle CDF$ and $\angle CGF$; Consecutive angles of a parallelogram are supplementary.

11. $\triangle HDF$; SSS. Since the diagonals of a parallelogram bisect each other, $\overline{HC} \cong \overline{HF}$ and $\overline{HG} \cong \overline{HD}$ and since the opposite sides of a parallelogram are $\cong$, $\overline{GC} \cong \overline{DF}$.

12. $AB = CD$
$2x + 5 = 21$
$2x = 16$
$x = 8$

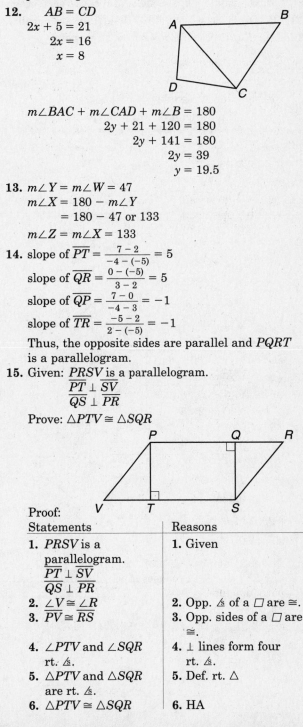

$m\angle BAC + m\angle CAD + m\angle B = 180$
$2y + 21 + 120 = 180$
$2y + 141 = 180$
$2y = 39$
$y = 19.5$

13. $m\angle Y = m\angle W = 47$
$m\angle X = 180 - m\angle Y$
$\qquad = 180 - 47$ or 133
$m\angle Z = m\angle X = 133$

14. slope of $\overline{PT} = \dfrac{7 - 2}{-4 - (-5)} = 5$

slope of $\overline{QR} = \dfrac{0 - (-5)}{3 - 2} = 5$

slope of $\overline{QP} = \dfrac{7 - 0}{-4 - 3} = -1$

slope of $\overline{TR} = \dfrac{-5 - 2}{2 - (-5)} = -1$

Thus, the opposite sides are parallel and $PQRT$ is a parallelogram.

15. Given: $PRSV$ is a parallelogram.
$\overline{PT} \perp \overline{SV}$
$\overline{QS} \perp \overline{PR}$

Prove: $\triangle PTV \cong \triangle SQR$

Proof:

Statements	Reasons
1. $PRSV$ is a parallelogram. $\overline{PT} \perp \overline{SV}$ $\overline{QS} \perp \overline{PR}$	1. Given
2. $\angle V \cong \angle R$	2. Opp. $\angle$s of a $\square$ are $\cong$.
3. $\overline{PV} \cong \overline{RS}$	3. Opp. sides of a $\square$ are $\cong$.
4. $\angle PTV$ and $\angle SQR$ rt. $\angle$s.	4. $\perp$ lines form four rt. $\angle$s.
5. $\triangle PTV$ and $\triangle SQR$ are rt. $\angle$s.	5. Def. rt. $\triangle$
6. $\triangle PTV \cong \triangle SQR$	6. HA

16. Sample answer: Make sure that opposite sides are congruent or make sure that opposite angles are congruent.

Pages 295–297 Exercises

17. $\overline{AR}$; Opposite sides of a parallelogram are parallel.

18. $\overline{SR}$; Diagonals of a parallelogram bisect each other.

19. $\angle MAR$; Opposite angles of a parallelogram are $\cong$.

20. $\overline{AK}$; Diagonals of a parallelogram bisect each other.

21. $\triangle RKM$; SSS. $\overline{MA} \cong \overline{RK}$ and $\overline{RA} \cong \overline{MK}$ because opposite sides of a parallelogram are $\cong$. $\overline{RM} \cong \overline{RM}$ because congruence of segments is reflexive.

22. $\overline{SK}$; Diagonals of a parallelogram bisect each other.

23. $\overline{RK}$; Opposite sides of a parallelogram are parallel.

24. $\angle MAR$ or $\angle RKM$; Consecutive angles of a parallelogram are supplementary.

25. $\triangle SKR$; SAS. Diagonals bisect each other, so $\overline{SA} \cong \overline{SK}$ and $\overline{SM} \cong \overline{SR}$. $\angle ASM \cong \angle KSR$ because they are vertical angles.

26. $\angle KAM$; If parallel lines cut by a transversal, alternate interior angles are congruent.

27. $x = 118$
$y = 180 - x = 180 - 118$ or 62
$z = 118$

28. $x + z + 90 = 180$
$x + 20 + 90 = 180$
$x + 110 = 180$
$x = 70$
$y = 42$
$z = 20$

29. $z + 15 + 112 = 180$
$z + 127 = 180$
$z = 53$
$x = z = 53$
$y = 15$

30. $CM = \sqrt{(2-0)^2 + (0-2)^2} = \sqrt{4+4}$
$\quad = \sqrt{8}$ or $2\sqrt{2}$
$ME = \sqrt{(4-2)^2 + (-2-0)^2} = \sqrt{4+4}$
$\quad = \sqrt{8}$ or $2\sqrt{2}$
$DM = \sqrt{(-2-2)^2 + (-2-0)^2} = \sqrt{16+4}$
$\quad = \sqrt{20}$ or $2\sqrt{5}$
$FM = \sqrt{(6-2)^2 + (2-0)^2} = \sqrt{16+4}$
$\quad = \sqrt{20}$ or $2\sqrt{5}$

31. $CE = \sqrt{(4-0)^2 + (-2-2)^2} = \sqrt{16+16}$
$\quad = \sqrt{32}$ or $4\sqrt{2}$
$DF = \sqrt{(6-(-2))^2 + (2-(-2))^2} = \sqrt{64+16}$
$\quad = \sqrt{80}$ or $4\sqrt{5}$

The diagonals are not congruent.

32. slope of $\overline{CD} = \frac{2-(-2)}{0-(-2)} = \frac{4}{2}$ or 2
slope of $\overline{CF} = \frac{2-2}{6-0} = 0$

Since the slope of $\overline{CD}$ is 2, the slope of $\overline{CF}$ is 0, and $2(0) \neq -1$, the consecutive sides are not perpendicular.

33. Let N be the fourth vertex of the parallelogram. Suppose $\overline{TD} \parallel \overline{KN}$ and $\overline{KD} \parallel \overline{NT}$.

slope of $\overline{TD}$ and $\overline{KN} = \frac{-1-1}{4-(-4)} = -\frac{2}{8}$ or $-\frac{1}{4}$

slope of $\overline{KD}$ and $\overline{NT} = \frac{1-8}{-4-0} = \frac{-7}{-4}$ or $\frac{7}{4}$

equation for $\overline{KN}$: $\frac{y-8}{x-0} = -\frac{1}{4}$
$\quad 4y - 32 = -x$
$\quad x + 4y = 32$

equation for $\overline{NT}$: $\frac{y-(-1)}{x-4} = \frac{7}{4}$
$\quad 4y + 4 = 7x - 28$
$\quad -7x + 4y = -32$
$\quad 7x - 4y = 32$

Find x and y:
$\quad x + 4y = 32 \qquad\qquad x + 4y = 32$
$\quad 7x - 4y = 32 \qquad\qquad 8 + 4y = 32$
$\quad \overline{ 8x = 64} \qquad\qquad 4y = 24$
$\qquad\qquad x = 8 \qquad\qquad\quad y = 6$

Suppose $\overline{TD} \parallel \overline{KN}$ and $\overline{TK} \parallel \overline{DN}$.

slope of $\overline{TK}$ and $\overline{DN} = \frac{-1-8}{4-0} = -\frac{9}{4}$

equation for $\overline{DN}$: $\frac{y-1}{x-(-4)} = -\frac{9}{4}$
$\quad 4y - 4 = -9x - 36$
$\quad 9x + 4y = -32$

equation for $\overline{KN}$: $x + 4y = 32$

Find x and y:
$\quad 9x + 4y = -32 \qquad\quad x + 4y = 32$
$\quad \underline{x + 4y = 32} \qquad\quad -8 + 4y = 32$
$\qquad\quad 8x = -64 \qquad\qquad 4y = 40$
$\qquad\quad x = -8 \qquad\qquad y = 10$

Suppose $\overline{KD} \parallel \overline{NT}$ and $\overline{TK} \parallel \overline{DN}$.
equation for $\overline{NT}$: $7x - 4y = 32$
equation for $\overline{DN}$: $9x + 4y = -32$

Find x and y:
$\quad 7x - 4y = 32 \qquad\quad 9x + 4y = -32$
$\quad \underline{9x + 4y = -32} \qquad\quad 9(0) + 4y = -32$
$\quad 16x = 0 \qquad\quad 4y = -32$
$\qquad x = 0 \qquad\qquad\quad y = -8$

The three possible coordinates of the fourth vertex are $(8, 6)$, $(-8, 10)$, and $(0, -8)$.

34. $\qquad 2NQ = NT$
$2(3a + 18) = 12a$
$\quad 6a + 36 = 12a$
$\quad\quad -6a = -36$
$\qquad\quad a = 6$
$\qquad QC = QM$
$\quad a + 2b = 3b + 1$
$\quad 6 + 2b = 3b + 1$
$\qquad -b = -5$
$\qquad\quad b = 5$
$CM = QC + QM$
$\quad = a + 2b + 3b + 1$
$\quad = 6 + 2(5) + 3(5) + 1$
$\quad = 32$

35. $m\angle BPQ = m\angle SRD = 13$
$m\angle APS + m\angle SPQ + m\angle BPQ = 180$
$\quad\quad m\angle APS + 48 + 13 = 180$
$\quad\quad\quad\quad m\angle APS = 19$

88

36. Given: *SRWV* and *TVXY* are parallelograms.
Prove: $\angle Y \cong \angle R$

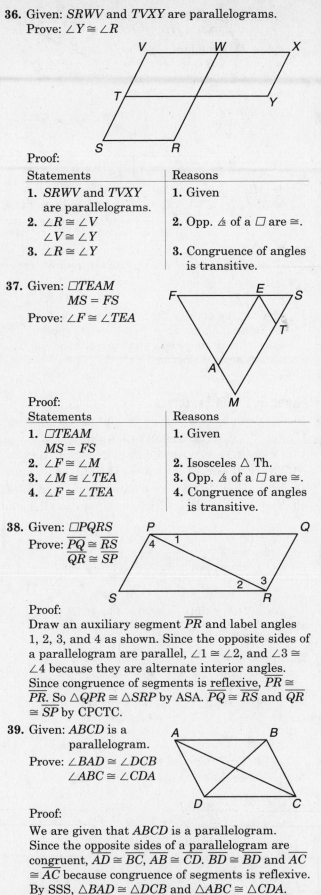

Proof:

Statements	Reasons
1. *SRWV* and *TVXY* are parallelograms.	1. Given
2. $\angle R \cong \angle V$ $\angle V \cong \angle Y$	2. Opp. ∠s of a ▱ are ≅.
3. $\angle R \cong \angle Y$	3. Congruence of angles is transitive.

37. Given: ▱*TEAM*
$MS = FS$
Prove: $\angle F \cong \angle TEA$

Proof:

Statements	Reasons
1. ▱*TEAM* $MS = FS$	1. Given
2. $\angle F \cong \angle M$	2. Isosceles △ Th.
3. $\angle M \cong \angle TEA$	3. Opp. ∠s of a ▱ are ≅.
4. $\angle F \cong \angle TEA$	4. Congruence of angles is transitive.

38. Given: ▱*PQRS*
Prove: $\overline{PQ} \cong \overline{RS}$
$\overline{QR} \cong \overline{SP}$

Proof:
Draw an auxiliary segment $\overline{PR}$ and label angles 1, 2, 3, and 4 as shown. Since the opposite sides of a parallelogram are parallel, $\angle 1 \cong \angle 2$, and $\angle 3 \cong \angle 4$ because they are alternate interior angles. Since congruence of segments is reflexive, $\overline{PR} \cong \overline{PR}$. So $\triangle QPR \cong \triangle SRP$ by ASA. $\overline{PQ} \cong \overline{RS}$ and $\overline{QR} \cong \overline{SP}$ by CPCTC.

39. Given: *ABCD* is a parallelogram.
Prove: $\angle BAD \cong \angle DCB$
$\angle ABC \cong \angle CDA$

Proof:
We are given that *ABCD* is a parallelogram. Since the opposite sides of a parallelogram are congruent, $\overline{AD} \cong \overline{BC}$, $\overline{AB} \cong \overline{CD}$. $\overline{BD} \cong \overline{BD}$ and $\overline{AC} \cong \overline{AC}$ because congruence of segments is reflexive. By SSS, $\triangle BAD \cong \triangle DCB$ and $\triangle ABC \cong \triangle CDA$. Therefore, we can conclude that $\angle BAD \cong \angle DCB$ and $\angle ABC \cong \angle CDA$ by CPCTC.

40. Given: *EAST* is a parallelogram.
Prove: $\overline{ES}$ bisects $\overline{AT}$.
$\overline{AT}$ bisects $\overline{ES}$.

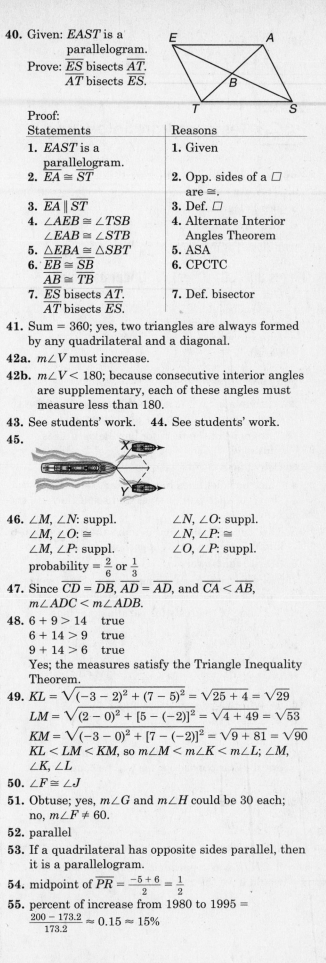

Proof:

Statements	Reasons
1. *EAST* is a parallelogram.	1. Given
2. $\overline{EA} \cong \overline{ST}$	2. Opp. sides of a ▱ are ≅.
3. $\overline{EA} \parallel \overline{ST}$	3. Def. ▱
4. $\angle AEB \cong \angle TSB$ $\angle EAB \cong \angle STB$	4. Alternate Interior Angles Theorem
5. $\triangle EBA \cong \triangle SBT$	5. ASA
6. $\overline{EB} \cong \overline{SB}$ $\overline{AB} \cong \overline{TB}$	6. CPCTC
7. $\overline{ES}$ bisects $\overline{AT}$. $\overline{AT}$ bisects $\overline{ES}$.	7. Def. bisector

41. Sum = 360; yes, two triangles are always formed by any quadrilateral and a diagonal.

42a. $m\angle V$ must increase.

42b. $m\angle V < 180$; because consecutive interior angles are supplementary, each of these angles must measure less than 180.

43. See students' work.   **44.** See students' work.

45.

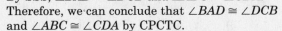

46. $\angle M, \angle N$: suppl. $\angle N, \angle O$: suppl.
$\angle M, \angle O$: ≅ $\angle N, \angle P$: ≅
$\angle M, \angle P$: suppl. $\angle O, \angle P$: suppl.
probability $= \frac{2}{6}$ or $\frac{1}{3}$

47. Since $\overline{CD} = \overline{DB}$, $\overline{AD} = \overline{AD}$, and $\overline{CA} < \overline{AB}$, $m\angle ADC < m\angle ADB$.

48. $6 + 9 > 14$ true
$6 + 14 > 9$ true
$9 + 14 > 6$ true
Yes; the measures satisfy the Triangle Inequality Theorem.

49. $KL = \sqrt{(-3-2)^2 + (7-5)^2} = \sqrt{25+4} = \sqrt{29}$
$LM = \sqrt{(2-0)^2 + [5-(-2)]^2} = \sqrt{4+49} = \sqrt{53}$
$KM = \sqrt{(-3-0)^2 + [7-(-2)]^2} = \sqrt{9+81} = \sqrt{90}$
$KL < LM < KM$, so $m\angle M < m\angle K < m\angle L$; $\angle M$, $\angle K$, $\angle L$

50. $\angle F \cong \angle J$

51. Obtuse; yes, $m\angle G$ and $m\angle H$ could be 30 each; no, $m\angle F \neq 60$.

52. parallel

53. If a quadrilateral has opposite sides parallel, then it is a parallelogram.

54. midpoint of $\overline{PR} = \frac{-5+6}{2} = \frac{1}{2}$

55. percent of increase from 1980 to 1995 = $\frac{200 - 173.2}{173.2} \approx 0.15 \approx 15\%$

56. $\frac{d-4}{3} = 5$

$d - 4 = 15$

$d = 19$

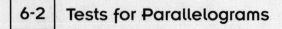
Page 298 Modeling Mathematics

a. They are parallel.

b. parallelograms

c. They are congruent.

d. Opposite sides are congruent.

Pages 300–301 Check for Understanding

1. One pair of congruent angles does not guarantee that the opposite sides will be parallel.

2a. The quadrilateral is a parallelogram because the opposite pairs of angles are congruent.

2b. No; none of the tests for parallelograms is fulfilled.

3. Celina; one pair of sides could be parallel.

4. Since parallel lines have the same slope, find the slopes of each pair of sides and see if they are the same.

5. Theorems 6-1, 6-2, and 6-4 and theorems 6-5, 6-6, and 6-7 are converses of each other.

6. See students' work.

7. Yes; the triangles are congruent by SAS, so both pairs of opposite sides are congruent.

8. No; none of the tests for parallelograms is fulfilled.

9. $6x = 4x + 8$ $\qquad$ $y^2 = y$

$\quad 2x = 8$ $\qquad\qquad$ $y^2 - y = 0$

$\quad\ x = 4$ $\qquad\qquad$ $y(y - 1) = 0$

$\qquad\qquad\qquad\qquad\quad$ $y = 1$

10. $2x + 8 = 120$ $\qquad$ $120 + 5y = 180$

$\quad\ 2x = 112$ $\qquad\qquad$ $5y = 60$

$\qquad x = 56$ $\qquad\qquad$ $y = 12$

11. False; the diagonals being congruent does not ensure that opposite sides will be congruent or parallel.

12. slope of $\overline{GH} = \frac{8-4}{-2-4} = \frac{4}{-6} = -\frac{2}{3}$

slope of $\overline{JK} = \frac{-3-(-7)}{6-(-1)} = \frac{4}{7}$.

No; the slope of $\overline{GH} = \frac{-2}{3}$ and the slope of $\overline{JK} = \frac{4}{7}$.

If $GHJK$ was a parallelogram, these segments would have the same slope.

13. Given: $\overline{HD} \cong \overline{DN}$

$\angle DHM \cong \angle DNT$

Prove: Quadrilateral $MNTH$ is a parallelogram.

Proof:

Statements	Reasons
1. $\overline{HD} \cong \overline{DN}$ $\angle DHM \cong \angle DNT$	1. Given
2. $\angle MDH \cong \angle TDN$	2. Vert. $\angle$s are $\cong$.
3. $\triangle MDH \cong \triangle TDN$	3. ASA
4. $\overline{MH} \cong \overline{TN}$	4. CPCTC
5. $\overline{MH} \parallel \overline{NT}$	5. If $\leftrightarrow$ and alt. int. $\angle$s are $\cong$, then the lines are $\parallel$.
6. $MNTH$ is a parallelogram.	6. If one pair of opp. sides of a quad. are both $\parallel$ and $\cong$, then the quad. is a $\square$.

14. The lengths of the sides of each part of the gate are non-changing. Thus, both pairs of opposite sides remain congruent and the quadrilateral is always a parallelogram.

Pages 301–304 Exercises

15. Yes; both pairs of opposite angles are congruent.

16. Yes; the diagonals bisect each other.

17. Yes; both pairs of opposite angles are congruent.

18. Yes; both pairs of opposite angles are congruent.

19. No; none of the tests for parallelograms is fulfilled.

20. Yes; one pair of opposite sides is both parallel and congruent.

21. $3x + 17 = 2y$ $\qquad$ $3x + 17 = 2y$

$\quad 4x - y = 4$ $\qquad\quad$ $3x + 17 = 2(4x - 4)$

$\qquad\ y = 4x - 4$ $\qquad$ $3x + 17 = 8x - 8$

$\qquad\qquad\qquad\qquad\qquad$ $-5x = -25$

$\qquad\qquad\qquad\qquad\qquad\quad\ x = 5$

$y = 4x - 4 = 4(5) - 4 = 20 - 4$ or 16

22. $4x = 76$ $\qquad\qquad$ $12y = 96$

$\quad x = 19$ $\qquad\qquad\ y = 8$

23. $6x - 2 = 64$ $\qquad$ $5y = 2y + 36$

$\quad\ 6x = 66$ $\qquad\qquad$ $3y = 36$

$\qquad x = 11$ $\qquad\qquad$ $y = 12$

24. $\quad\ 4x = y + 2$ $\qquad\qquad$ $2y = 7x$

$4x - 2 = y$ $\qquad\qquad$ $2(4x - 2) = 7x$

$\qquad\qquad\qquad\qquad\qquad$ $8x - 4 = 7x$

$\qquad\qquad\qquad\qquad\qquad\qquad\ x = 4$

$y = 4(4) - 2 = 16 - 2$ or 14

25. $\frac{1}{2}x = 2y - 15$ $\qquad$ $x = 4y - 30$

$\quad\ x = 4y - 30$ $\qquad\qquad$ $= 4(23.5) - 30$

$\qquad\qquad\qquad\qquad\qquad\quad$ $= 64$

$2y + 12 = x - 5$

$2y + 12 = 4y - 30 - 5$

$\quad -2y = -47$

$\qquad\ y = 23.5$

26. $\qquad x^2 = x + 6$ $\qquad\qquad$ $y^2 = 49$

$\quad x^2 - x - 6 = 0$ $\qquad\qquad$ $y^2 - 49 = 0$

$(x - 3)(x + 2) = 0$ $\qquad$ $(y - 7)(y + 7) = 0$

$\qquad\quad x = 3$ or -2 $\qquad\qquad$ $y = 7$ or -7

27. false, counterexample:

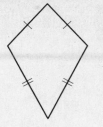

28. True; if all four sides are congruent, then both pairs of opposite sides are congruent and the quadrilateral is a parallelogram.

29. false, counterexample:

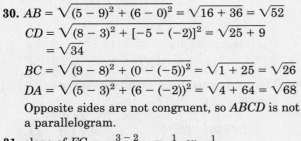

30. $AB = \sqrt{(5-9)^2 + (6-0)^2} = \sqrt{16+36} = \sqrt{52}$

$CD = \sqrt{(8-3)^2 + [-5-(-2)]^2} = \sqrt{25+9}$
$\quad = \sqrt{34}$

$BC = \sqrt{(9-8)^2 + (0-(-5))^2} = \sqrt{1+25} = \sqrt{26}$

$DA = \sqrt{(5-3)^2 + (6-(-2))^2} = \sqrt{4+64} = \sqrt{68}$

Opposite sides are not congruent, so $ABCD$ is not a parallelogram.

31. slope of $FG = \frac{3-2}{-7-(-3)} = \frac{1}{-4}$ or $-\frac{1}{4}$

slope of $HJ = \frac{-4-(-3)}{0-(-4)} = -\frac{1}{4}$

$FG = \sqrt{[-7-(-3)]^2 + (3-2)^2} = \sqrt{16+1}$
$\quad = \sqrt{17}$

$HJ = \sqrt{[0-(-4)]^2 + [-4-(-3)]^2} = \sqrt{16+1}$
$\quad = \sqrt{17}$

One pair of opposite sides is both parallel and congruent, $FGHJ$ is a parallelogram.

32. midpoint of $\overline{KM} = \left(\frac{-1+6}{2}, \frac{9+2}{2}\right) = \left(\frac{5}{2}, \frac{11}{2}\right)$ or
$\quad (2.5, 5.5)$

midpoint of $\overline{LN} = \left(\frac{3+2}{2}, \frac{8+3}{2}\right) = \left(\frac{5}{2}, \frac{11}{2}\right)$ or
$\quad (2.5, 5.5)$

Since the diagonals bisect each other, $KLMN$ is a parallelogram.

33.

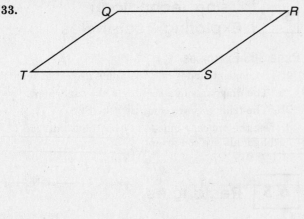

34. Given: $\overline{TV} \cong \overline{YX}$
$\quad\quad\quad \overline{TY} \cong \overline{VX}$

Prove: $TVXY$ is a parallelogram.

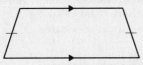

Proof:

We are given that $\overline{TV} \cong \overline{YX}$ and $\overline{TY} \cong \overline{VX}$. Since the congruence of segments is reflexive, $\overline{YV} \cong \overline{YV}$. Thus, $\triangle TVY \cong \triangle XYV$ by SSS. We can conclude that $\angle 1 \cong \angle 2$ and $\angle 3 \cong \angle 4$ by CPCTC. If two lines are cut by a transversal and alternate interior angles are congruent, then the lines are parallel. Therefore, $\overline{TY} \parallel \overline{XV}$ and $\overline{TV} \parallel \overline{YX}$. Thus, $TVXY$ is a parallelogram by the definition of a parallelogram.

35. Given: $\overline{BD}$ bisects $\overline{AC}$.
$\quad\quad\quad \overline{AC}$ bisects $\overline{BD}$.

Prove: $ABCD$ is a parallelogram.

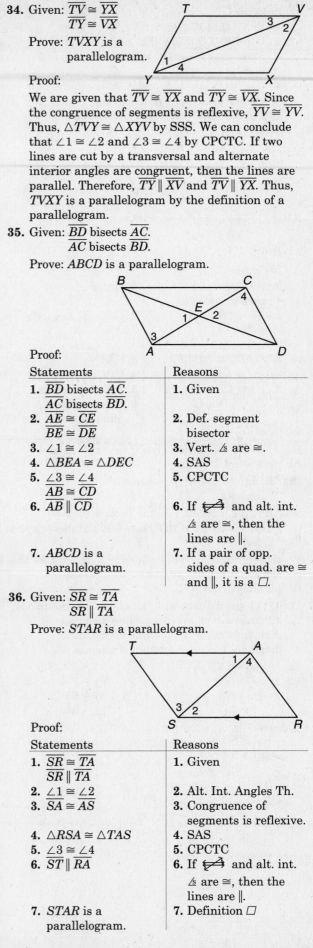

Proof:

Statements	Reasons
1. $\overline{BD}$ bisects $\overline{AC}$. $\overline{AC}$ bisects $\overline{BD}$.	1. Given
2. $\overline{AE} \cong \overline{CE}$ $\overline{BE} \cong \overline{DE}$	2. Def. segment bisector
3. $\angle 1 \cong \angle 2$	3. Vert. $\angle$s are $\cong$.
4. $\triangle BEA \cong \triangle DEC$	4. SAS
5. $\angle 3 \cong \angle 4$ $\overline{AB} \cong \overline{CD}$	5. CPCTC
6. $\overline{AB} \parallel \overline{CD}$	6. If $\overleftrightarrow{}$ and alt. int. $\angle$s are $\cong$, then the lines are $\parallel$.
7. $ABCD$ is a parallelogram.	7. If a pair of opp. sides of a quad. are $\cong$ and $\parallel$, it is a $\square$.

36. Given: $\overline{SR} \cong \overline{TA}$
$\quad\quad\quad \overline{SR} \parallel \overline{TA}$

Prove: $STAR$ is a parallelogram.

Proof:

Statements	Reasons
1. $\overline{SR} \cong \overline{TA}$ $\overline{SR} \parallel \overline{TA}$	1. Given
2. $\angle 1 \cong \angle 2$	2. Alt. Int. Angles Th.
3. $\overline{SA} \cong \overline{AS}$	3. Congruence of segments is reflexive.
4. $\triangle RSA \cong \triangle TAS$	4. SAS
5. $\angle 3 \cong \angle 4$	5. CPCTC
6. $\overline{ST} \parallel \overline{RA}$	6. If $\overleftrightarrow{}$ and alt. int. $\angle$s are $\cong$, then the lines are $\parallel$.
7. $STAR$ is a parallelogram.	7. Definition $\square$

37. Subgoals:
1. Prove that $\triangle ABC \cong \triangle DEF$.
2. Use CPCTC to say that $\overline{AC} \cong \overline{FD}$.
3. State that $\overline{FA} \cong \overline{DC}$ by the definition of a regular hexagon.
4. Use both pair of opposite sides congruent to show $FDCA$ is a parallelogram.

Given: $ABCDEF$ is a regular hexagon.

Prove: $FDCA$ is a $\square$.

Proof:

Statements	Reasons
1. $ABCDEF$ is a regular hexagon.	1. Given
2. $\overline{AB} \cong \overline{DE}$ $\overline{BC} \cong \overline{EF}$ $\angle E \cong \angle B$	2. Def. reg. hexagon
3. $\triangle ABC \cong \triangle DEF$	3. SAS
4. $\overline{AC} \cong \overline{DF}$	4. CPCTC
5. $\overline{FA} \cong \overline{CD}$	5. Def. reg. hexagon
6. $FDCA$ is a $\square$.	6. If opp. sides of a quad. are $\cong$, it is a $\square$.

38a. no

38b. No; the conclusion should be $\angle 1 \cong \angle 3$ and $\angle 2 \cong \angle 4$.

39a. Sample answer: Measure each pair of opposite segments.

39b. Sample answer: Yes; the pattern yields quadrilaterals with guaranteed parallel opposite sides.

40. Both pairs of opposite sides are congruent, so the sides and arms of the ruler always form a parallelogram.

41. 42: 11 red diamonds, 11 single outline diamonds; 12 diamonds made of 2 outline diamonds, 6 diamonds made of 3 outline diamonds, 2 diamonds made of 4 outline diamonds

42.
$$AB = CD \qquad\qquad AD = BC$$
$$2x + 5 = y + 1 \qquad y + 5 = 3x - 4$$
$$2x + 4 = y \qquad (2x + 4) + 5 = 3x - 4$$
$$2x + 9 = 3x - 4$$
$$13 = x$$

$$2x + 5 = y + 1$$
$$2(13) + 5 = y + 1$$
$$30 = y$$
$$AB = 2x + 5 = 2(13) + 5 \text{ or } 31$$
$$CD = y + 1 = 30 + 1 \text{ or } 31$$
$$AD = y + 5 = 30 + 5 \text{ or } 35$$
$$BC = 3x - 4 = 3(13) - 4 \text{ or } 35$$

43.
$$(3x + 2) + (8x + 10) > 5x + 8$$
$$11x + 12 > 5x + 8$$
$$6x > -4$$
$$x > -\frac{2}{3}$$
$$(8x + 10) + (5x + 8) > 3x + 2$$
$$13x + 18 > 3x + 2$$
$$10x > -16$$
$$x > -\frac{8}{5}$$
$$(3x + 2) + (5x + 8) > 8x + 10$$
$$8x + 10 > 8x + 10$$
$$0 > 0$$

no solution

Since there is no solution for one part of the Triangle Inequality, there is no value for x that creates a triangle with these measures.

44. Let x = original price.
$$(x - 0.20x)(1.06) = 190.80$$
$$0.848x = 190.80$$
$$x = 225.00$$

The original price was \$225.

45. $\overline{TA}$ **46.** slope of $\overline{AB} = \frac{8 - 0}{-4 - 3}$ or $-\frac{8}{7}$

47. The quadrilateral is a parallelogram; see students' work.

48.
$$m\angle B = m\angle L \qquad\qquad m\angle B = 7x + 29$$
$$7x + 29 = 9x - 1 \qquad\qquad = 7(15) + 29$$
$$2x = 30 \qquad\qquad = 105 + 29 \text{ or } 134$$
$$x = 15$$
$\angle B$ is obtuse.

49a. 36%   **49b.** $0.52(25,465,000) = 13,241,800$

50. Let x = number of pounds of coffee at \$6/lb.
$$6x + 10(7.25) = 7(x + 10)$$
$$6x + 72.5 = 7x + 70$$
$$x = 2.5 \text{ lb}$$

Page 304 Mathematics and Society

1. No; it's not a four-sided polygon.
2. The building could eventually collapse.
3. The concrete building; it would not flex and stretch as much as a steel one.

6-3A Using Technology Exploring Rectangles

Page 305 Exercises

1. The opposite sides of a rectangle are congruent.
2a. The diagonals of a rectangle are congruent.
2b. The triangles are congruent by SSS.
3. Yes; the opposite sides are congruent and the diagonals are congruent.

6-3 Rectangles

Pages 309–310 Check for Understanding

1. All rectangles are parallelograms, but not all parallelograms are rectangles.

2. Sample answer:

3. Sample answer: Kalere is correct. If the diagonals bisect each other, then the quadrilateral is a parallelogram. If the diagonals of a parallelogram are congruent, then it is a rectangle.

4. Answers will vary. See students' work.

5. $MO = NP$
$2x - 8 = 23$
$2x = 31$
$x = 15.5$

6. $CN = CO$ **7.** $MO = 2(PC)$
$x^2 + 1 = 3x + 11$ $4x - 13 = 2(x + 7)$
$x^2 - 3x - 10 = 0$ $4x - 13 = 2x + 14$
$(x - 5)(x + 2) = 0$ $2x = 27$
$x = 5$ or $x = -2$ $x = 13.5$

8. False; if a quadrilateral has opposite sides that are congruent, then it is a parallelogram, but it may not be a rectangle.

9. slope of $\overline{AB} = \frac{8 - 1}{4 - (-3)} = \frac{7}{7} = 1$

slope of $\overline{BC} = \frac{8 - 5}{4 - 7} = \frac{3}{-3} = -1$

slope of $\overline{CD} = \frac{5 - (-2)}{7 - 0} = \frac{7}{7} = 1$

slope of $\overline{DA} = \frac{-2 - 1}{0 - (-3)} = \frac{-3}{3} = -1$

Since $\overline{AB} \parallel \overline{CD}$, $\overline{BC} \parallel \overline{DA}$, and $\overline{BC} \perp \overline{AB}$, $ABCD$ is a rectangle.

10. $m\angle 1 + m\angle 2 = 90$ $m\angle 5 = m\angle 1 = 70$
$70 + m\angle 2 = 90$ $m\angle 6 = m\angle 2 = 20$
$m\angle 2 = 20$

11. $m\angle 6 + m\angle 7 + m\angle 9 = 180$
$2(m\angle 6) + 128 = 180$
$m\angle 6 = 26$

$m\angle 6 = m\angle 7 = 26$
$m\angle 7 + m\angle 8 = 90$
$26 + m\angle 8 = 90$
$m\angle 8 = 64$

12. $m\angle 1 = m\angle 5 = 36$
$m\angle 1 + m\angle 2 = 90$
$36 + m\angle 2 = 90$
$m\angle 2 = 54$
$m\angle 3 = m\angle 2 = 54$

13. Left; when stakes F and G are moved left an appropriate distance, $\overline{MK}$ lengthens and its midpoint will coincide with the midpoint of $\overline{JL}$, which becomes shorter after the move.

14. Given: $ABCD$ is a rectangle with diagonals $\overline{AC}$ and $\overline{BD}$.
Prove: $\overline{AC} \cong \overline{BD}$

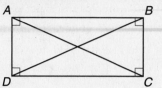

Proof:

Statements	Reasons
1. $ABCD$ is a rectangle with diagonals $\overline{AC}$ and $\overline{BD}$.	1. Given
2. $\overline{DC} \cong \overline{DC}$	2. Congruence of segments is reflexive.
3. $\overline{AD} \cong \overline{BC}$	3. Opp. sides of a $\square$ are $\cong$.
4. $\angle ADC$ and $\angle BCD$ are rt $\angle$s.	4. Def. rectangle
5. $\angle ADC \cong \angle BCD$	5. All rt. $\angle$s are $\cong$.
6. $\triangle ADC \cong \triangle BCD$	6. SAS
7. $\overline{AC} \cong \overline{BD}$	7. CPCTC

Pages 310–312 Exercises

15. $DU = 2(QP)$
$26 = 2(2x + 7)$
$26 = 4x + 14$
$12 = 4x$
$3 = x$

16. $m\angle 2 = m\angle 3$
$52 = 16x - 12$
$64 = 16x$
$4 = x$

17. $m\angle 2 = m\angle 3 = 2x + 4$
$m\angle 4 = m\angle 2 + m\angle 3$
$6x - 16 = 2x + 4 + 2x + 4$
$2x = 24$
$x = 12$

18. $DP = QP$
$4x + 1 = x + 13$
$3x = 12$
$x = 4$

19. $m\angle 3 + m\angle 6 = 90$
$(70 - 4x) + (18x - 8) = 90$
$14x + 72 = 90$
$14x = 28$
$x = 2$

20. True; all rectangles are parallelograms.

21. false; counterexample:

22. True; consider parallelogram $ABCD$. Since opposite angles of a parallelogram are congruent, if $\angle A$ of $\square ABCD$ is right, then $\angle C$ is right. Since consecutive angles of a parallelogram are supplementary, then if $\angle A$ is right, then $\angle B$ and $\angle D$ are right. Thus, if one angle of a parallelogram is right then all angles are right. Therefore, $\square ABCD$ is a rectangle.

23. True; the sum of the measures of the angles of a quadrilateral is 360. If all four angles are congruent, then the measure of each angle is $\frac{360}{4}$ or 90. Thus, all four angles are right and the definition of a rectangle is a quadrilateral with four right angles.

24. $QS = 2(QC)$
$10 = 2(2x + 1)$
$10 = 4x + 2$
$-4x = -8$
$x = 2$

25. $m\angle TQC = m\angle QTC = 70$
$m\angle QCR = m\angle TQC + m\angle QTC$
$m\angle QCR = 70 + 70$ or 140
$m\angle QZR = m\angle QCR = 140$

26. $m\angle RTS = m\angle CTS = m\angle CST$
$m\angle RCS = m\angle CTS + m\angle CST$
$35 = 2(m\angle RTS)$
$17.5 = m\angle RTS$

27. $RT = 2(QC)$
$3x^2 = 2(5x + 4)$
$3x^2 = 10x + 8$
$3x^2 - 10x - 8 = 0$
$(3x + 2)(x - 4) = 0$
$x = \frac{-2}{3}$ or $x = 4$

28. $RZ = QC, QC = CS$ $2Q = RC, RC = CS$
$RZ = CS$ $RQ = CS$
$6x = 14 - x$ $3x + 2y = 14 - x$
$7x = 14$ $3(2) + 2y = 14 - 2$
$x = 2$ $2y = 6$
                               $y = 3$

29. $m\angle QRT + m\angle TRS = 90$
$2(m\angle QRT) = 90$
$m\angle QRT = 45$
$m\angle RQC = m\angle QRT = 45$
$m\angle TCQ = m\angle CQR + m\angle CRQ$
$= 45 + 45$ or 90

30. $m\angle 2 = m\angle 3$
$m\angle 1 + m\angle 2 + m\angle 3 = 180$
$30 + 2(m\angle 2) = 180$
$2(m\angle 2) = 150$
$m\angle 2 = 75$

31. $m\angle 6 + m\angle 4 = 90$ **32.** $m\angle 2 = m\angle 3$
$57 + m\angle 4 = 90$ $m\angle 8 = m\angle 2 + m\angle 3$
$m\angle 4 = 33$ $133 = 2(m\angle 2)$
                                        $66.5 = m\angle 2$

33. $m\angle 5 = m\angle 4 = 16$
$m\angle 4 + m\angle 3 = 90$
$16 + m\angle 3 = 90$
$m\angle 3 = 74$

34. slope of $\overline{PS} = \frac{-1 - 1}{9 - (-6)} = \frac{-2}{15}$
slope of $\overline{QR} = \frac{5 - 5}{9 - (-6)} = 0$
No; $\overline{PS}$ and $\overline{QR}$ are not parallel.

35. No; $\overline{PQ}, \overline{QR}, \overline{RS},$ and $\overline{SP}$ do not form a quadrilateral.

36. slope of $\overline{PQ} = \frac{-3 - 8}{-4 - (-5)} = \frac{-11}{1}$ or -11
slope of $\overline{RS} = \frac{9 - (-2)}{6 - 7} = \frac{11}{-1}$ or -11
slope of $\overline{PS} = \frac{-3 - (-2)}{-4 - 7} = \frac{-1}{-11}$ or $\frac{1}{11}$
slope of $\overline{QR} = \frac{8 - 9}{-5 - 6} = \frac{-1}{-11}$ or $\frac{1}{11}$
Yes; opposite sides parallel and consecutive sides are perpendicular.

37.

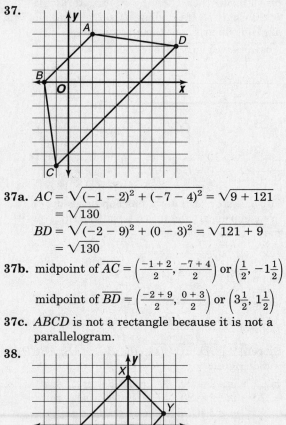

37a. $AC = \sqrt{(-1 - 2)^2 + (-7 - 4)^2} = \sqrt{9 + 121}$
$= \sqrt{130}$
$BD = \sqrt{(-2 - 9)^2 + (0 - 3)^2} = \sqrt{121 + 9}$
$= \sqrt{130}$

37b. midpoint of $\overline{AC} = \left(\frac{-1 + 2}{2}, \frac{-7 + 4}{2}\right)$ or $\left(\frac{1}{2}, -1\frac{1}{2}\right)$
midpoint of $\overline{BD} = \left(\frac{-2 + 9}{2}, \frac{0 + 3}{2}\right)$ or $\left(3\frac{1}{2}, 1\frac{1}{2}\right)$

37c. $ABCD$ is not a rectangle because it is not a parallelogram.

38.

38a. Sample answer: Test the slopes of opposite pairs of sides to see that they are parallel and test a pair of consecutive sides to see that they are perpendicular; test the diagonals to see that they are congruent and bisect each other.

38b. slope of $\overline{WX} = \frac{-3 - 4}{-7 - 0} = \frac{-7}{-7}$ or 1
slope of $\overline{ZY} = \frac{-7 - 1}{-4 - 3} = \frac{-8}{-7}$ or $\frac{8}{7}$
No; opposite sides are not parallel.

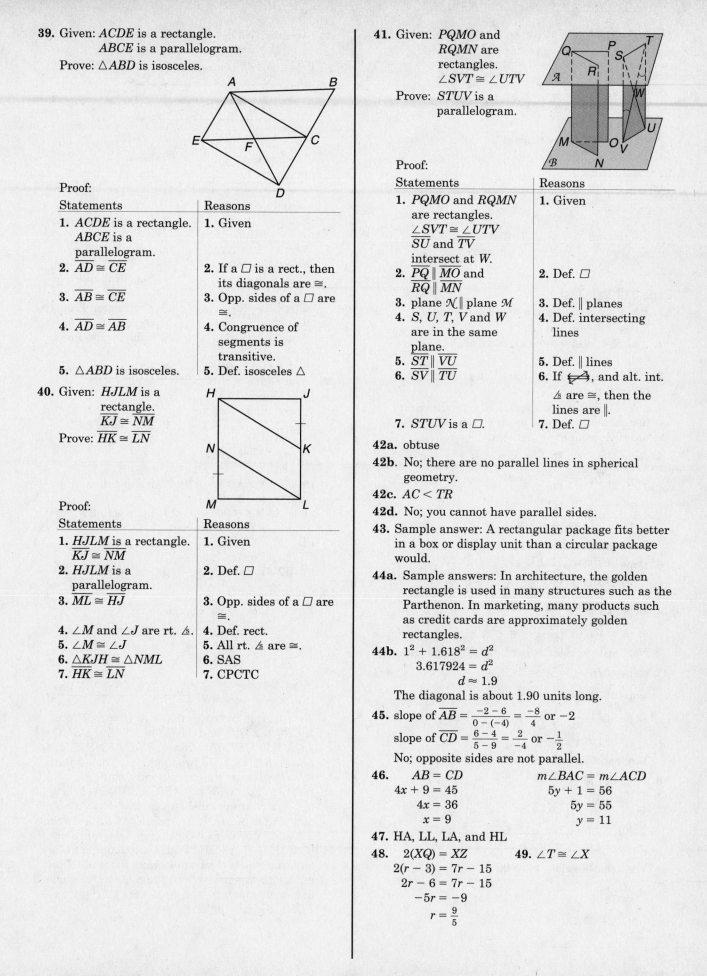

39. Given: $ACDE$ is a rectangle.
$ABCE$ is a parallelogram.
Prove: $\triangle ABD$ is isosceles.

Proof:

Statements	Reasons
1. $ACDE$ is a rectangle. $ABCE$ is a parallelogram.	1. Given
2. $\overline{AD} \cong \overline{CE}$	2. If a $\square$ is a rect., then its diagonals are $\cong$.
3. $\overline{AB} \cong \overline{CE}$	3. Opp. sides of a $\square$ are $\cong$.
4. $\overline{AD} \cong \overline{AB}$	4. Congruence of segments is transitive.
5. $\triangle ABD$ is isosceles.	5. Def. isosceles $\triangle$

40. Given: $HJLM$ is a rectangle.
$\overline{KJ} \cong \overline{NM}$
Prove: $\overline{HK} \cong \overline{LN}$

Proof:

Statements	Reasons
1. $HJLM$ is a rectangle. $\overline{KJ} \cong \overline{NM}$	1. Given
2. $HJLM$ is a parallelogram.	2. Def. $\square$
3. $\overline{ML} \cong \overline{HJ}$	3. Opp. sides of a $\square$ are $\cong$.
4. $\angle M$ and $\angle J$ are rt. $\angle$s.	4. Def. rect.
5. $\angle M \cong \angle J$	5. All rt. $\angle$s are $\cong$.
6. $\triangle KJH \cong \triangle NML$	6. SAS
7. $\overline{HK} \cong \overline{LN}$	7. CPCTC

41. Given: $PQMO$ and $RQMN$ are rectangles.
$\angle SVT \cong \angle UTV$
Prove: $STUV$ is a parallelogram.

Proof:

Statements	Reasons
1. $PQMO$ and $RQMN$ are rectangles. $\angle SVT \cong \angle UTV$ $\overline{SU}$ and $\overline{TV}$ intersect at W.	1. Given
2. $\overline{PQ} \parallel \overline{MO}$ and $\overline{RQ} \parallel \overline{MN}$	2. Def. $\square$
3. plane $\mathcal{N} \parallel$ plane $\mathcal{M}$	3. Def. $\parallel$ planes
4. S, U, T, V and W are in the same plane.	4. Def. intersecting lines
5. $\overline{ST} \parallel \overline{VU}$	5. Def. $\parallel$ lines
6. $\overline{SV} \parallel \overline{TU}$	6. If $\leftrightarrow$, and alt. int. $\angle$s are $\cong$, then the lines are $\parallel$.
7. $STUV$ is a $\square$.	7. Def. $\square$

42a. obtuse

42b. No; there are no parallel lines in spherical geometry.

42c. $AC < TR$

42d. No; you cannot have parallel sides.

43. Sample answer: A rectangular package fits better in a box or display unit than a circular package would.

44a. Sample answers: In architecture, the golden rectangle is used in many structures such as the Parthenon. In marketing, many products such as credit cards are approximately golden rectangles.

44b. $1^2 + 1.618^2 = d^2$
$3.617924 = d^2$
$d \approx 1.9$
The diagonal is about 1.90 units long.

45. slope of $\overline{AB} = \frac{-2 - 6}{0 - (-4)} = \frac{-8}{4}$ or -2
slope of $\overline{CD} = \frac{6 - 4}{5 - 9} = \frac{2}{-4}$ or $-\frac{1}{2}$
No; opposite sides are not parallel.

46.

$AB = CD$	$m\angle BAC = m\angle ACD$
$4x + 9 = 45$	$5y + 1 = 56$
$4x = 36$	$5y = 55$
$x = 9$	$y = 11$

47. HA, LL, LA, and HL

48. $2(XQ) = XZ$
$2(r - 3) = 7r - 15$
$2r - 6 = 7r - 15$
$-5r = -9$
$r = \frac{9}{5}$

49. $\angle T \cong \angle X$

50. $(7x - 8) + (3x + 3) + (18x - 11) = 180$
$$28x - 16 = 180$$
$$28x = 196$$
$$x = 7$$

$7x - 8 = 7(7) - 8 = 41$
$3x + 3 = 3(7) + 3 = 24$
$18x - 11 = 18(7) - 11 = 115$
obtuse; one obtuse angle

51. Transitive Property (=)

52. $180 - 167 = 13$

53. $-6 = 5u + 9$
$-15 = 5u$
$-3 = u$

54. $\frac{x_1}{y_1} = \frac{x_2}{y_2}$
$\frac{13}{1.3} = \frac{x_2}{8}$
$104 = 1.3x_2$
$80 = x_2$

Page 312 Self Test

1. $\overline{PN}$; opposite sides of a parallelogram are parallel by definition.

2. $\angle LPN$; opposite angles of a parallelogram are congruent.

3. $\overline{LP}$; opposite sides of a parallelogram are congruent.

4. $\triangle NPQ$; SSS with diagonals of a parallelogram bisect each other and opposite sides of a parallelogram are congruent.

5. slope of $\overline{AB} = \frac{-5 - 0}{2 - 9} = \frac{5}{7}$

slope of $\overline{DC} = \frac{0 - (-5)}{13 - 6} = \frac{5}{7}$

slope of $\overline{BC} = \frac{-5 - (-5)}{2 - 6} = 0$

slope of $\overline{AD} = \frac{0 - 0}{13 - 9} = 0$

Yes: opposite sides do not have the same slope.

6. slope of $\overline{EF} = \frac{-1 - 1}{-1 - 1} = 1$

slope of $\overline{GH} = \frac{-6 - 0}{6 - (-6)} = \frac{-6}{12}$ or $\frac{-1}{2}$

slope of $\overline{FG} = \frac{-6 - 1}{6 - 1} = \frac{-7}{5}$

slope of $\overline{EH} = \frac{-1 - 0}{-1 - (-6)} = \frac{-1}{5}$

No; opposite sides do not have the same slope.

7. slope of $\overline{HI} = \frac{-5 - 0}{0 - 5} = 1$

slope of $\overline{JK} = \frac{0 - 5}{-5 - 0} = 1$

slope of $\overline{IJ} = \frac{-5 - 0}{0 - (-5)} = -1$

slope of $\overline{HK} = \frac{0 - 5}{5 - 0} = -1$

Yes; opposite sides have the same slope.

8. slope of $\overline{LM} = \frac{-1 - 5}{-2 - 2} = \frac{-6}{-4} = \frac{3}{2}$

slope of $\overline{NP} = \frac{13 - 7}{-10 - (-14)} = \frac{6}{4} = \frac{3}{2}$

slope of $\overline{MN} = \frac{5 - 13}{2 - (-10)} = \frac{-8}{12} = \frac{-2}{3}$

slope of $\overline{LP} = \frac{-1 - 7}{-2 - (-14)} = \frac{-8}{12} = \frac{-2}{3}$

Yes; opposite sides have the same slope.

9. Given: $\square WXZY$
$\angle 1$ and $\angle 2$ are complementary.
Prove: $WXZY$ is a rectangle.

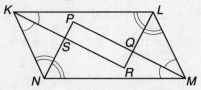

Proof:

Statements	Reasons
1. $WXZY$ $\angle 1$ and $\angle 2$ are complementary.	1. Given
2. $m\angle 1 + m\angle 2 = 90$	2. Def. complementary $\angle$s
3. $m\angle 1 + m\angle 2 + m\angle X = 180$	3. Angle Sum Theorem
4. $90 + m\angle X = 180$	4. Substitution Prop. (=)
5. $m\angle X = 90$	5. Subtraction Prop. (=)
6. $\angle X \cong \angle Y$	6. Opp. $\angle$s of a $\square$ are $\cong$.
7. $m\angle Y = 90$	7. Substitution Prop. (=)
8. $\angle X$ and $\angle XWY$ are supp. $\angle X$ and $\angle XZY$ are supp.	8. Consec. $\angle$s of a $\square$ are supp.
9. $m\angle X + m\angle XWY = 180$ $m\angle X + m\angle XZY = 180$	9. Def. Supp. $\angle$s
10. $90 + m\angle XWY = 180$ $90 + m\angle XZY = 180$	10. Substitution Prop. (=)
11. $m\angle XWY = 90$ $m\angle XZY = 90$	11. Subtraction Prop. (=)
12. $\angle Y$, $\angle XWY$, and $\angle XZY$ are rt. $\angle$s.	12. Def. rt. $\angle$
13. $WXZY$ is a rect.	13. Def. rect.

10. Given: $\square KLMN$
Prove: $PQRS$ is a rectangle.

Proof:
The diagram indicates that $\angle KNS \cong \angle SNM \cong \angle MLQ \cong \angle QLK$ and $\angle NKS \cong \angle SKL \cong \angle LMQ \cong \angle QMN$ in $\square KLMN$. Since $\triangle KLR$, $\triangle KNS$, $\triangle MLQ$, and $\triangle MNP$ all have two angles congruent, the third angles are congruent by the third angle theorem. So $\angle QRS \cong \angle KSN \cong \angle MQL \cong \angle SPQ$. Since they are vertical angles, $\angle KSN \cong \angle PSR$ and $\angle MQL \cong \angle PQR$. Therefore, $\angle QRS \cong \angle PSR \cong \angle PQR \cong \angle SPQ$. $PQRS$ is a parallelogram since if both pairs of opposite angles are congruent, the quadrilateral is a parallelogram. Since all of the angles are congruent, and the consecutive angles are supplementary, the angles are all right. So $PQRS$ is a rectangle.

6-4 Squares and Rhombi

Pages 316–317 Check for Understanding

1. In a rhombus: the sides are all congruent, the diagonals are perpendicular, the opposite angles are congruent, the diagonals bisect a pair of opposite angles, the diagonals bisect each other, and consecutive angles are supplementary. In a square: the sides are all congruent, the diagonals are perpendicular, the opposite angles are congruent, the diagonals bisect a pair of opposite angles, the diagonals bisect each other, consecutive angles are supplementary, the diagonals are congruent, and all four angles are right. A square has all of the characteristics of a rhombus because a square is a rhombus.

2. Both definitions are correct. A square has all four sides congruent and all four angles right. A rhombus has all four sides congruent, so if it is also equiangular, its angles will be all right and it is a square. A rectangle has all four right angles. If its sides are all congruent, then it will be a square.

3. Sample answer, not drawn to scale:

```
        6 cm
      ╱‾‾‾‾‾╱
6 cm ╱     ╱ 6 cm
    ╱_____╱
      6 cm
```

4.

Property	Parallelogram	Rectangle	Rhombus	Square
The diagonals bisect each other.	yes	yes	yes	yes
The diagonals are congruent.	no	yes	no	yes
Each diagonal bisects a pair of opposite angles.	no	no	yes	yes
The diagonals are perpendicular.	no	no	yes	yes

5. See students' work.

6. Isosceles; all four sides of *PLAN* are congruent, so $\overline{PL} \cong \overline{LA}$.

7. Right; the diagonals of a rhombus are perpendicular, so $\angle PEN$ is right.

8. Yes; the diagonals of a parallelogram bisect each other, so $\overline{PE} \cong \overline{EA}$ and $\overline{EN} \cong \overline{EL}$, and $\angle PEN \cong \angle AEL$ since they are vertical angles. Thus, $\triangle PEN \cong \triangle AEL$ by SAS.

9. No; the diagonals of a rhombus are not congruent unless the rhombus is a square.

10. $m\angle RSW = \frac{1}{2}(m\angle RST)$
    $= \frac{1}{2}(67)$ or 33.5

11. $m\angle STV + m\angle TSV + m\angle TVS = 180$
    $135 + 2(m\angle SVT) = 180$
    $m\angle SVT = 22.5$

12. $m\angle SWT = 90$
    $2x + 8 = 90$
    $2x = 82$
    $x = 41$

13. $m\angle WRV = m\angle WRS$
    $5x + 5 = 7x - 19$
    $24 = 2x$
    $12 = x$

14. $PA = \sqrt{(-1-1)^2 + [0-(-1)]^2} = \sqrt{5}$
    $AR = \sqrt{(1-2)^2 + (-1-1)^2} = \sqrt{5}$
    $RK = \sqrt{(2-0)^2 + (1-2)^2} = \sqrt{5}$
    $PK = \sqrt{(-1-0)^2 + (0-2)^2} = \sqrt{5}$
    slope $\overline{PA} = \frac{-1-0}{1-(-1)} = -\frac{1}{2}$
    slope $\overline{AR} = \frac{1-(-1)}{2-1} = \frac{2}{1}$
    Since $\overline{PA} \cong \overline{AR} \cong \overline{RK} \cong \overline{PK}$ and $\overline{PA} \perp \overline{AR}$, *PARK* is a parallelogram, a rectangle, a rhombus, and a square.

15. $PA = \sqrt{[-1-(-1)]^2 + (4-10)^2} = \sqrt{36}$ or 6
    $AR = \sqrt{(-1-14)^2 + (10-10)^2} = \sqrt{225}$ or 15
    $RK = \sqrt{(14-14)^2 + (10-4)^2} = \sqrt{36}$ or 6
    $PK = \sqrt{(-1-14)^2 + (4-4)^2} = \sqrt{225}$ or 15
    $\overline{PA}$ is a vertical segment and $\overline{AR}$ is a horizontal segment, so $\overline{PA} \perp \overline{AR}$. Since $\overline{PA} \cong \overline{RK}$, $\overline{AR} \cong \overline{PK}$, and $\overline{PA} \perp \overline{AR}$, *PARK* is a parallelogram and a rectangle.

16. $PA = \sqrt{[2-(-3)]^2 + (11-1)^2} = \sqrt{125}$ or $5\sqrt{5}$
    $AR = \sqrt{(-3-8)^2 + (1-3)^2} = \sqrt{125}$ or $5\sqrt{5}$
    $RK = \sqrt{(8-13)^2 + (3-3)^2} = \sqrt{25}$ or 5
    $PK = \sqrt{(2-13)^2 + (11-3)^2} = \sqrt{185}$
    none

17. rectangle, square

18. rhombus, square

19. Given: *ABCD* is a rhombus.
    Prove: $\overline{AC} \perp \overline{BD}$

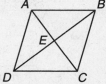

    Proof:
    The definition of a rhombus states that the four sides of the quadrilateral are congruent. Therefore, $\overline{AB} \cong \overline{BC} \cong \overline{CD} \cong \overline{AD}$. A rhombus is a parallelogram and the diagonals of a parallelogram bisect each other, so $\overline{BD}$ bisects $\overline{AC}$ at *E*. $\overline{AE} \cong \overline{CE}$ by the definition of a bisector. $\overline{BE} \cong \overline{BE}$ because congruence of segments is reflexive. Thus, $\triangle ABE \cong \triangle CBE$ by SSS. $\angle BEA \cong \angle BEC$ by CPCTC. $\angle BEA$ and $\angle BEC$ form a linear pair and if two angles form a linear pair they are supplementary. Thus, $\angle BEA$ and $\angle BEC$ are supplementary. By the definition of supplementary angles, $m\angle BEA + m\angle BEC = 180$. Also, $m\angle BEA = m\angle BEC$ by the definition of congruent angles. So by substitution, $2m\angle BEA = 180$. Then $m\angle BEA = 90$ by the Division Property of Equality. $\angle BEA$ is right by the definition of a right angle. Therefore, $\overline{AC} \perp \overline{BD}$ by the definition of perpendicular lines.

20. See students' work.

Pages 317–319 Exercises

21. Scalene; the consecutive sides of *MNOP* are not congruent.

22. Right; the diagonals are perpendicular.

23. Yes; the sides of *MNOP* are congruent and the diagonals are perpendicular, so the triangles are congruent by SAS.

24. Yes; the diagonals of a parallelogram bisect each other.

25. No; all squares are rhombi, but not all rhombi are squares.

26. Yes; if the diagonals of a parallelogram are perpendicular, then the parallelogram is a rhombus.

27. No; $MNOP$ could be a rhombus if $\overline{PO} \cong \overline{ON}$, but the conditions are not sufficient for it to be a square.

28. $m\angle ACD = m\angle BAF = 28$

29. $m\angle AFB = 90$
$16x + 6 = 90$
$16x = 84$
$x = 5.25$

30. $m\angle BCD = 2(m\angle ACD) = 2(34) = 68$
$m\angle ABC = 180 - m\angle BCD$
$\quad\quad\quad = 180 - 68$ or 112

31. $m\angle BFC = 90$
$120 - 4x = 90$
$-4x = -30$
$x = 7.5$

32. $m\angle BAC = m\angle ACD$
$4x + 6 = 12x - 18$
$-8x = -24$
$x = 3$

33. $\quad m\angle DCB = 2(m\angle DAC)$
$x^2 - 6 = 2(5x + 9)$
$x^2 - 6 = 10x + 18$
$x^2 - 10x - 24 = 0$
$(x - 12)(x + 2) = 0$
$\quad\quad x = 12 \text{ or } x = -2$

Reject $x = -2$ because $5x + 9 < 0$ and angle measures are positive.

34. $WX = \sqrt{(5-7)^2 + (6-5)^2} = \sqrt{5}$
$XY = \sqrt{(7-9)^2 + (5-9)^2} = \sqrt{20}$ or $2\sqrt{5}$
$YZ = \sqrt{(9-7)^2 + (9-10)^2} = \sqrt{5}$
$WZ = \sqrt{(5-7)^2 + (6-10)^2} = \sqrt{20}$ or $2\sqrt{5}$
slope of $\overline{WX} = \frac{5-6}{7-5} = \frac{-1}{2}$
slope of $\overline{XY} = \frac{9-5}{9-7} = \frac{4}{2}$ or $\frac{2}{1}$
Since $\overline{WX} \cong \overline{YZ}$, $\overline{WY} \cong \overline{WZ}$, and $\overline{WX} \cong \overline{XY}$, $WXYZ$ is a parallelogram and a rectangle.

35. $WX = \sqrt{(-3-1)^2 + [-3-(-6)]^2} = \sqrt{25}$ or 5
$XY = \sqrt{(1-5)^2 + [-6-(-3)]^2} = \sqrt{25}$ or 5
$YZ = \sqrt{(5-1)^2 + (-3-0)^2} = \sqrt{25}$ or 5
$WZ = \sqrt{(-3-1)^2 + (-3-0)^2} = \sqrt{25}$ or 5
slope of $\overline{WX} = \frac{-6-(-3)}{1-(-3)} = \frac{-3}{4}$
slope of $\overline{XY} = \frac{-3-(-6)}{5-4} = \frac{3}{1}$
Since $\overline{WX} \cong \overline{XY} \cong \overline{YZ} \cong \overline{WZ}$, $WXYZ$ is a parallelogram and a rhombus.

36. $WX = \sqrt{[-6-(-11)]^2 + [11-(-7)]^2} = \sqrt{349}$
$XY = \sqrt{[-11-(-7)]^2 + [-7-(-2)]^2} = \sqrt{41}$
$YZ = \sqrt{[-7-(-2)]^2 + [-2-(-6)]^2} = \sqrt{41}$
$WZ = \sqrt{[-6-(-2)]^2 + [11-(-6)]^2} = \sqrt{305}$
none

37. $WX = \sqrt{(10-6)^2 + (6-10)^2} = \sqrt{32}$ or $4\sqrt{2}$
$XY = \sqrt{(6-10)^2 + (10-14)^2} = \sqrt{32}$ or $4\sqrt{2}$
$YZ = \sqrt{(10-14)^2 + (14-10)^2} = \sqrt{32}$ or $4\sqrt{2}$
$WZ = \sqrt{(10-14)^2 + (6-10)^2} = \sqrt{32}$ or $4\sqrt{2}$
slope of $\overline{WX} = \frac{10-6}{6-10} = \frac{4}{-4}$ or -1
slope of $\overline{XY} = \frac{14-10}{10-6} = \frac{4}{4}$ or 1
Since $\overline{WX} \cong \overline{XY} \cong \overline{YZ} \cong \overline{WZ}$ and $\overline{WX} \perp \overline{XY}$, $WXYZ$ is a parallelogram, a rectangle, a rhombus, and a square.

38. rectangle, square

39. parallelogram, rectangle, rhombus, square

40. square　　　　　　**41.** rhombus, square

42. True; the set of squares is a subset of the set of rhombi.

43. False; some rhombi are not squares.

44. False; some rectangles are not squares.

45. True; the set of squares is a subset of the set of rectangles.

46. True; the set of rhombi is a subset of the set of parallelograms.

47. False; some parallelograms are not rectangles.

48. Sample answer, not drawn to scale:

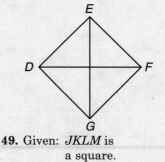

49. Given: $JKLM$ is a square.
Prove: $\overline{JL} \cong \overline{KM}$
Proof:

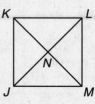

Statements	Reasons
1. $JKLM$ is a square.	**1.** Given
2. $JKLM$ is a rectangle.	**2.** Def. square
3. $\overline{JL} \cong \overline{KM}$	**3.** If a $\square$ is a rect., then its diagonals are $\cong$.

50. Given: Rhombus *MTRN*

Prove: ∠1 and ∠2 are complementary.

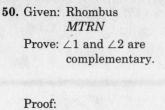

Proof:

Statements	Reasons
1. Rhombus *MTRN*	1. Given
2. $\overline{MR} \perp \overline{TN}$	2. The diagonals of a rhom. are ⊥.
3. ∠*MST* is a right angle.	3. Def. ⊥
4. $m\angle MST = 90$	4. Def. rt. ∠
5. $m\angle MST + m\angle 1 + m\angle 2 = 180$	5. Angle Sum Th.
6. $90 + m\angle 1 + m\angle 2 = 180$	6. Substitution Prop. (=)
7. $m\angle 1 + m\angle 2 = 90$	7. Subtraction Prop. (=)
8. ∠1 and ∠2 are complementary.	8. Def. comp. ∠s

51. Given: *ABCD* is a parallelogram. $AC \perp BD$

Prove: *ABCD* is a rhombus.

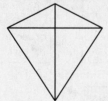

Proof:

We are given that *ABCD* is a parallelogram. The diagonals of a parallelogram bisect each other, so $\overline{AE} \cong \overline{EC}$. $\overline{BE} \cong \overline{BE}$ because congruence of segments is reflexive. We are also given that $\overline{AC} \perp \overline{BD}$. Thus, ∠*AEB* and ∠*BEC* are right angles by the definition of perpendicular lines. Then ∠*AEB* ≅ ∠*BEC* because all right angles are congruent. Therefore, △*AEB* ≅ △*BEC* by SAS. $\overline{AB} \cong \overline{BC}$ by CPCTC. Opposite sides of parallelograms are congruent, so $\overline{AB} \cong \overline{CD}$ and $\overline{BC} \cong \overline{AD}$. Then since congruence of segments is transitive, $\overline{AB} \cong \overline{CD} \cong \overline{BC} \cong \overline{AD}$. All four sides of *ABCD* are congruent, so *ABCD* is a rhombus by definition.

52. Sample answer:

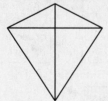

53. The flag of Denmark contains two red squares and two rectangles. The flag of St. Vincent and The Grenadines contains a blue rectangle, a green rectangle, a yellow rectangle, a blue and yellow rectangle, a yellow and green rectangle, and three green rhombi. The flag of Trinidad and Tobago contains two white parallelograms, and one black parallelogram.

54a. Each door is a rectangle made up of two congruent squares and one of their diagonals.

54b. Sample answer: Triangles are rigid and strong for construction, so using a square and a diagonal will make a sturdy door.

55. The quadrilateral formed by the back wall, the two side walls, and the short line is a square because all the sides are congruent and the angles are right. The quadrilateral formed by the front wall, the two side walls, and the short line is a square because all the sides are congruent and the angles are right. The back wall, the two side walls and the service line form a rectangle because the angles are all right, but the sides are not all congruent. The front wall, the two side walls and the service line form a rectangle because the angles are all right, but the sides are not all congruent. The two side walls, the short line, and the service line form a rectangle because the angles are all right, but the sides are not all congruent.

56. Given: ▱*WXYZ*

∠1 and ∠2 are complementary.

Prove: *WXYZ* is a rectangle.

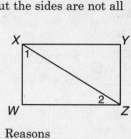

Proof:

Statements	Reasons
1. ▱*WXYZ* ∠1 and ∠2 are complementary.	1. Given
2. $m\angle 1 + m\angle 2 = 90$	2. Def. comp. ∠s
3. $m\angle 1 + m\angle 2 + m\angle W = 180$	3. Angle Sum Theorem
4. $90 + m\angle W = 180$	4. Substitution Prop. (=)
5. $m\angle W = 90$	5. Subtraction Prop. (=)
6. ∠*W* ≅ ∠*Y*	6. Opp. ∠s of a ▱ are ≅.
7. $m\angle W = m\angle Y$	7. Def. ≅ ∠s
8. $m\angle Y = 90$	8. Substitution Prop. (=)
9. ∠*W* and ∠*WXY* are supplementary. ∠*W* and ∠*YZW* are supplementary.	9. Consec. ∠s of a ▱ are supp.
10. $m\angle W + m\angle WXY = 180$ $m\angle W + m\angle YZW = 180$	10. Def. supp ∠s
11. $90 + m\angle WXY = 180$ $90 + m\angle YZW = 180$	11. Substitution Prop. (=)
12. $m\angle WXY = 90$ $m\angle YZW = 90$	12. Subtraction Prop. (=)
13. ∠*W*, ∠*Y*, ∠*WXY*, and ∠*YZW* are right angles.	13. Def. rt. ∠
14. *WXYZ* is a rect.	14. Def. rect.

57. The legs are made so that they will bisect each other, so the quadrilateral formed by the ends of the legs is always a parallelogram. Therefore, the tabletop is parallel to the floor.

58. true   **59.** Yes; if *V* is (12, 3), *TU* = *UV*.

60. $\overline{OM}$ **61.** true

62. No; slope of $\overline{AB} = \dfrac{-6-3}{-4-(-1)} = \dfrac{-9}{-3}$ or 3 and slope of $\overline{CD} = \dfrac{9-0}{1-(-2)} = \dfrac{9}{3}$ or 3, but $\overline{AB}$ and $\overline{CD}$ are the same line since A, B, C, and D are collinear.

63. False; they may be skew.

64. hypothesis: a U.S. citizen is over 18 years old
conclusion: he or she may vote

65.
$$AB + BC = AC \qquad\qquad BC = 4x - 7$$
$$9 + (4x - 7) = 18 \qquad\qquad = 4(4) - 7$$
$$4x + 2 = 18 \qquad\qquad\qquad = 16 - 7$$
$$4x = 16 \qquad\qquad\qquad\quad = 9$$
$$x = 4$$

66. domain: $\{-9, 5, 7, 8\}$; range: $\{-2, -1, 6\}$

67. $\dfrac{165 - 52}{52} = 2.17 \approx 217\%$

6-4B Modeling Mathematics: Kites

Page 320

1. See students' work.

2. $\angle ABC \cong \angle ADC$

3. See students' work.

4. See students' work.

5. Sample answer: For kite $ABCD$, $\angle B \cong \angle D$; $\overline{AC} \perp \overline{BD}$; $\overline{AC}$ bisects $\overline{BD}$; $\overline{AB} \cong \overline{AD}$; $\overline{BC} \cong \overline{CD}$; $\triangle ABC \cong \triangle ADC$. See students' justifications.

6-5 Trapezoids

Pages 324–325 Check for Understanding

1.

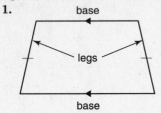

2. midpoint of $\overline{RA} = \left(\dfrac{-5 + (-4)}{2}, \dfrac{-3 + (-10)}{2}\right)$ or $M\left(-4\tfrac{1}{2}, -6\tfrac{1}{2}\right)$; midpoint of $\overline{PT} = \left(\dfrac{6 + (-1)}{2}, \dfrac{0 + 1}{2}\right)$ or $N\left(2\tfrac{1}{2}, \tfrac{1}{2}\right)$; slope of $\overline{MN} = \dfrac{-6\tfrac{1}{2} - \tfrac{1}{2}}{-4\tfrac{1}{2} - 2\tfrac{1}{2}}$ or 1;

slope of $\overline{TR} = \dfrac{1 - (-3)}{-1 - (-5)}$ or 1; slope of $\overline{AP} = \dfrac{-10 - 0}{-4 - 6}$ or 1; Since the slopes are all the same, $\overline{MN} \parallel \overline{TR} \parallel \overline{AP}$.

3a. False; a trapezoid has exactly one pair of parallel sides, a parallelogram has two pairs of parallel sides.

3b. True; this is a statement of Theorem 6-16.

3c. True; this is true by definition.

3d. False; the legs of a trapezoid are congruent only if the trapezoid is an isosceles trapezoid.

4a. Base angles are congruent.

4b. The diagonals are congruent.

4c. an isosceles trapezoid

5. True; the diagonals of an isosceles trapezoid are congruent.

6. True; the legs of an isosceles trapezoid are congruent.

7. False; if the diagonals bisected each other, $ABCD$ would be a parallelogram not a trapezoid.

8. $x^2 = 16$ **9.** $AF = QE = 17$
$x = \pm\, 4$
$x = 4 \text{ or } -4$

10. $m\angle ADQ = 180 - m\angle QUA$
$= 180 - 62 \text{ or } 118$

11. $R\left(\dfrac{3 + 7}{2}, \dfrac{2 + 4}{2}\right)$ or $(5, 3)$
$S\left(\dfrac{0 + 5}{2}, \dfrac{7 + 9}{2}\right)$ or $\left(\tfrac{5}{2}, 8\right)$

12. $RS = \sqrt{\left(5 - \tfrac{5}{2}\right)^2 + (3 - 8)^2}$
$= \sqrt{6.25 + 25} = \sqrt{31.25} \approx 5.59$

13. $NP = \sqrt{(3 - 7)^2 + (2 - 4)^2} = \sqrt{16 + 4} = \sqrt{20}$
≈ 4.47
$MQ = \sqrt{(0 - 5)^2 + (7 - 9)^2} = \sqrt{25 + 4} = \sqrt{29}$
≈ 5.39
$RS \neq \tfrac{1}{2}(NP + MQ)$ because $MNPQ$ is not a trapezoid.

14. Given: $KLMN$ is an isosceles trapezoid with bases $\overline{KL}$ and $\overline{MN}$.
Prove: $\angle 1 \cong \angle 2$
Proof:

$\boxed{\begin{array}{c}\textbf{\textit{KLMN}} \text{ is an isos. trapezoid} \\ \textbf{with bases } \overline{\textbf{\textit{KL}}} \textbf{ and } \overline{\textbf{\textit{MN}}}. \\ \text{Given}\end{array}}$

$\boxed{\begin{array}{c}\overline{KN} \cong \overline{LM} \\ \text{Def. isos.} \\ \text{trap.}\end{array}}$ $\boxed{\begin{array}{c}\overline{KM} \cong \overline{LN} \\ \text{Diagonals of} \\ \text{isos. trap. are } \cong.\end{array}}$ $\boxed{\begin{array}{c}\overline{NM} \cong \overline{NM} \\ \text{Congruence} \\ \text{of seg. is} \\ \text{reflexive.}\end{array}}$

$\boxed{\begin{array}{c}\triangle KNM \cong \triangle LMN \\ \text{SSS}\end{array}}$

$\boxed{\begin{array}{c}\angle 1 \cong \angle 2 \\ \text{CPCTC}\end{array}}$

15. Sides are trapezoids; front, back, and tops are rectangles.

Pages 325–328 Exercises

16. False; the diagonals of a rhombus are perpendicular, but the diagonals of a trapezoid are not.

17. True; $\overline{TV} \cong \overline{TV}$ because congruence of segments is reflexive, $\angle TVR \cong \angle VTS$ because base angles of an isosceles trapezoid are congruent, and $\overline{TR} \cong \overline{VS}$ because diagonals of an isosceles trapezoid are congruent; thus $\triangle TRV \cong \triangle VST$ by SAS and $\angle TRV \cong \angle VST$ by CPCTC.

18. True; base angles of an isosceles trapezoid are congruent.

19. True; $\overline{TV} \parallel \overline{SR}$ and consecutive interior angles are supplementary.

20. $MN = \frac{1}{2}(XY + WZ)$
$= \frac{1}{2}(11 + 3)$
$= \frac{1}{2}(14) = 7$

21. $m\angle XMN = m\angle WZN = 78$

22. $MN = \frac{1}{2}(XY + WZ)$
$10 = \frac{1}{2}(XY + 14)$
$20 = XY + 14$
$6 = XY$

23. $m\angle WZN = m\angle MWZ$
$90 - 4x = 15x - 5$
$95 = 19x$
$5 = x$

24. $MN = \frac{1}{2}(XY + WZ)$
$MN = \frac{1}{2}(21.7 + 93.6)$
$= \frac{1}{2}(115.3)$
$= 57.65$

25. $m\angle XWZ + m\angle XYZ = 180$
$(2x - 7) + 117 = 180$
$2x = 70$
$x = 35$

26. $MN = \frac{1}{2}(XY + WZ)$
$60 = \frac{1}{2}(4x - 1 + 6x + 11)$
$60 = 5x + 5$
$55 = 5x$
$11 = x$

27. $MN = \frac{1}{2}(XY + WZ)$
$10x + 3 = \frac{1}{2}(8x + 19 + 11)$
$10x + 3 = 4x + 15$
$6x = 12$
$x = 2$

28. $MN = \frac{1}{2}(XY + WZ)$
$2x + 1 = \frac{1}{2}(8 + 3x - 3)$
$4x + 2 = 3x + 5$
$x = 3$

29. slope of $\overline{RS} = \frac{2 - 2}{1 - (-1)} = 0$
slope of $\overline{VT} = \frac{-2 - (-2)}{-2 - 3} = 0$
slope of $\overline{RS}$ = slope of $\overline{VT} = 0$; $\overline{RS} \parallel \overline{TV}$

30. $RSTV$ is not an isosceles trapezoid because $RV = \sqrt{(-1 - (-2))^2 + (2 - (-2))^2}$ or 17, $ST = \sqrt{(1 - 3)^2 + (2 - (-2))^2}$ or $\sqrt{20}$, and $RV \neq ST$.

31. midpoint of $\overline{RV} = \left(\frac{-1 + (-2)}{2}, \frac{2 + (-2)}{2}\right)$ or $\left(-1\frac{1}{2}, 0\right)$; midpoint of $\overline{ST} = \left(\frac{1 + 3}{2}, \frac{2 + (-2)}{2}\right)$ or $(2, 0)$; slope of $\overline{AB} = 0$; slope of $\overline{RS} = 0$

32. $AB = \sqrt{\left(-1\frac{1}{2} - 2\right)^2 + (0 - 0)^2}$ or $3\frac{1}{2}$;
$RS = \sqrt{(-1 - 1)^2 + (2 - 2)^2}$ or 2;
$TV = \sqrt{(3 - (-2))^2 + (-2 - (-2))^2}$ or 5;
$\frac{5 + 2}{2} = 3\frac{1}{2}$

33. slope of $\overline{AB} = \frac{9 - 5}{4 - 1} = \frac{4}{3}$
slope of $\overline{BC} = \frac{5 - 1}{1 - 5} = \frac{4}{-4}$ or -1
slope of $\overline{CD} = \frac{1 - 5}{5 - 8} = \frac{-4}{-3}$ or $\frac{4}{3}$
slope of $\overline{AD} = \frac{9 - 5}{4 - 8} = \frac{4}{-4}$ or -1
Since $\overline{AB} \parallel \overline{CD}$ and $\overline{BC} \parallel \overline{AD}$, $ABCD$ is a parallelogram.

34. slope of $\overline{AB} = \frac{-1 - (-6)}{-2 - 0} = \frac{5}{-2}$
slope of $\overline{BC} = \frac{-6 - (-4)}{0 - 5} = \frac{-2}{-5}$ or $\frac{2}{5}$
slope of $\overline{CD} = \frac{-4 - 1}{5 - 3} = \frac{-5}{2}$
slope of $\overline{AD} = \frac{-1 - 1}{-2 - 3} = \frac{-2}{-5}$ or $\frac{2}{5}$
Since $\overline{AB} \parallel \overline{CD}$, $\overline{BC} \parallel \overline{AD}$, and $\overline{AB} \perp \overline{BC}$, $ABCD$ is a rectangle.

35. slope of $\overline{AB} = \frac{-2 - (-4)}{0 - 0}$ = undefined
slope of $\overline{BC} = \frac{-4 - (-2)}{0 - 6} = \frac{-2}{-6}$ or $\frac{1}{3}$
slope of $\overline{CD} = \frac{-2 - (-1)}{6 - 3} = \frac{-1}{3}$
slope of $\overline{AD} = \frac{-2 - (-1)}{0 - 3} = \frac{-1}{-3}$ or $\frac{1}{3}$
Since $\overline{BC} \parallel \overline{AD}$, $ABCD$ is a trapezoid.

36a. 3; $JKZX$, $IJXY$, $IKZY$

36b. Yes; the bases and legs must be congruent if they are isosceles.

36c. Answers may vary.

37. $m\angle W + m\angle Z = 180$
$x + m\angle Z = 180$
$m\angle Z = 180 - x$

38. Given: $ABCD$ is an isosceles trapezoid.
Prove: $\overline{AC} \cong \overline{BD}$

Proof:
Since $ABCD$ is an isosceles trapezoid, $\overline{AD} \cong \overline{BC}$. $\angle ADC \cong \angle BCD$ because the base angles of an isosceles trapezoid are congruent. $\overline{DC} \cong \overline{DC}$ because the congruence of segments is reflexive. So, $\triangle ADC \cong \triangle BCD$ by SAS. Therefore, $\overline{AC} \cong \overline{BD}$ by CPCTC.

39. Given: *DEFH* is a trapezoid with
bases $\overline{DE}$ and $\overline{FH}$.
$\overline{DE} \cong \overline{FG}$

Prove: *DEFG* is a parallelogram.

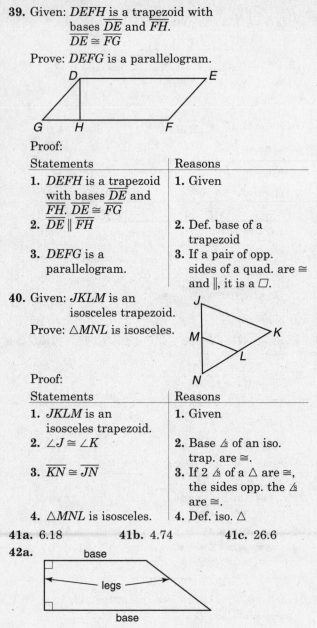

Proof:

Statements	Reasons
1. *DEFH* is a trapezoid with bases $\overline{DE}$ and $\overline{FH}$. $\overline{DE} \cong \overline{FG}$	1. Given
2. $\overline{DE} \parallel \overline{FH}$	2. Def. base of a trapezoid
3. *DEFG* is a parallelogram.	3. If a pair of opp. sides of a quad. are $\cong$ and $\parallel$, it is a $\square$.

40. Given: *JKLM* is an
isosceles trapezoid.

Prove: $\triangle MNL$ is isosceles.

Proof:

Statements	Reasons
1. *JKLM* is an isosceles trapezoid.	1. Given
2. $\angle J \cong \angle K$	2. Base $\angle$s of an iso. trap. are $\cong$.
3. $\overline{KN} \cong \overline{JN}$	3. If 2 $\angle$s of a $\triangle$ are $\cong$, the sides opp. the $\angle$s are $\cong$.
4. $\triangle MNL$ is isosceles.	4. Def. iso. $\triangle$

41a. 6.18   **41b.** 4.74   **41c.** 26.6

42a.

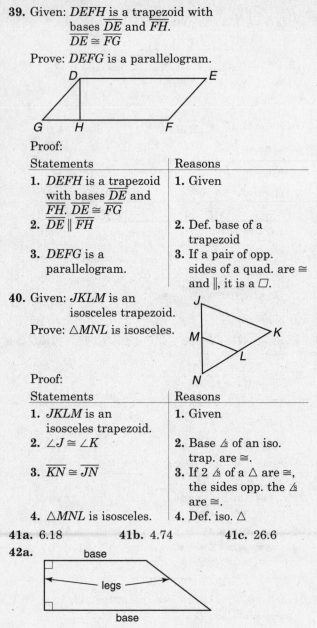

42b. It is not possible. Since pairs of base angles of an isosceles trapezoid are congruent, if two angles are right, all four angles will be right. Then the quadrilateral would be a rectangle, not a trapezoid.

43a. Sample answer: 10 and 30

43b. A measure cannot be negative and the average of the measures of the bases is 20. So the possible measures of the bases are 1 and 39, 2 and 38, $\cdots$, and 19 and 21. The measures of the bases cannot be the same or the figure would be a parallelogram. Thus, there are 19 possible combinations.

43c. There are an infinite number of combinations of possible measures if the integer restriction is removed because there is an infinite number of positive values with an average of 20.

44. Com-Pac 26: $\frac{1}{2}(12.75 + 8) = 10.375$ ft;
Pacific Seacraft 44: $\frac{1}{2}$(12 ft 4 in. + 8 ft 1 in.)
= 10 ft 2 in.;
Morris 38: $\frac{1}{2}$(11 ft 5 in. + 6 ft 8 in.)
= $\frac{1}{2}$(18 ft 1 in.) = 9 ft $\frac{1}{2}$ in.;
Precision 23: $\frac{1}{2}(9.8 + 7.4) = 8.6$ ft

45. Top is a square; sides are isosceles trapezoids.

46.

	Parallelogram	Rectangle	Square	Isosceles trapezoid
Diagonals congruent	no	yes	yes	yes
Two pairs of opposite sides congruent.	yes	yes	yes	no
One pair of opposite sides congruent	yes	yes	yes	yes
Diagonals are perpendicular.	no	no	yes	no
One pair of opposite sides parallel and congruent.	yes	yes	yes	no

47. $m\angle E + m\angle B = 180$
$m\angle E + 68 = 180$
$m\angle E = 112$

48. Since all the angles and the opposite sides are congruent, the bricks are interchangeable and can be installed in rows easily.

49. See students' work; true.

50. Two lines intersect and more than one plane contains them.

51. yes; LA or AAS

52.

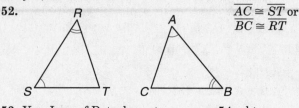

$\overline{AC} \cong \overline{ST}$ or
$\overline{BC} \cong \overline{RT}$

53. Yes; Law of Detachment   **54.** obtuse

55. 123,454,321   **56.** $\frac{12}{k} = \frac{2}{9}$
$2k = 9(12)$
$2k = 108$
$k = 54$

Chapter 6 Highlights

Page 329 Understanding and Using the Vocabulary

1. False; every parallelogram is a quadrilateral.
2. true   3. true   4. true
5. False; you can prove that a parallelogram is a rectangle by proving that the diagonals are congruent.
6. true
7. False; a square has all of the characteristics of a parallelogram, a rectangle, and a rhombus, but not the characteristics of a trapezoid.
8. true

9. False; the legs of an isosceles trapezoid are congruent.
10. true
11. False; if *QUAD* is a square, then it is also a parallelogram, a rectangle, a rhombus, and a quadrilateral. But *QUAD* is not a trapezoid.
12. False; the diagonals of an isosceles trapezoid are congruent.

Chapter 6 Study Guide and Assessment

Pages 330–332 Skills and Concepts

13. $\angle WXY$; opposite angles of a parallelogram are congruent.
14. $\overline{ZY}$; opposite sides of a parallelogram are congruent.
15. $\overline{EZ}$; diagonals of a parallelogram bisect each other.
16. $\overline{WZ}$; opposite sides of a parallelogram are congruent.
17. $\triangle ZWX$; SAS or SSS
18. $\angle 2$; Alternate Interior Angles Theorem
19. $\overline{EW}$; diagonals of a parallelogram bisect each other.
20. $\angle ZYX$ or $\angle ZWX$; Consecutive angles of a parallelogram are supplementary.

21. $6y = 30$ $(5x + 10) + 30 = 180$
    $y = 5$ $5x = 140$
                       $x = 28$

22. $x^2 - 2x = 4x + 16$ $y^2 = 25$
     $x^2 - 6x - 16 = 0$ $y = \pm 5$
     $(x - 8)(x + 2) = 0$ $y = 5$ or -5
     $x = 8$ or -2

23. Given: $\square ABCD$
           $\overline{AE} \cong \overline{CF}$

    Prove: Quadrilateral *EBFD* is a parallelogram.

Proof:

Statements	Reasons
1. $\square ABCD$ $\overline{AE} \cong \overline{CF}$	1. Given
2. $\overline{BA} \cong \overline{DC}$	2. Opp. sides of a $\square$ are $\cong$.
3. $\angle A \cong \angle C$	3. Opp. $\angle$s of a $\square$ are $\cong$.
4. $\triangle BAE \cong \triangle DCF$	4. SAS
5. $\overline{BE} \cong \overline{DF}$ $\angle BEA \cong \angle DFC$	5. CPCTC
6. $\overline{BC} \parallel \overline{AD}$	6. Def. $\square$
7. $\angle DFC \cong \angle FDE$	7. Alt. Int. $\angle$s Th.
8. $\angle BEA \cong \angle FDE$	8. Congruence of angles is transitive.
9. $\overline{BE} \parallel \overline{DF}$	9. If ⇹ and corr. $\angle$s are $\cong$, the lines are $\parallel$.
10. Quadrilateral *EBFD* is a parallelogram.	10. If a pair of opp. sides of a quad. are $\cong$ and $\parallel$, it is a $\square$.

24. $m\angle HEG + m\angle GEF = 90$
    $12x + 1 + 6x - 1 = 90$
              $18x = 90$
                $x = 5$

25. $HF = EG$
   $5x - 4 = 6x - 10$
      $-x = -6$
        $x = 6$

26. $EG = 2(JF)$
   $24x - 8 = 2(8x + 4)$
   $24x - 8 = 16x + 8$
        $8x = 16$
         $x = 2$

27. $EF = HG$
          $x^2 = 3x - 2$
    $x^2 - 3x + 2 = 0$
   $(x - 2)(x - 1) = 0$
           $x = 1$ or 2

28. $m\angle FGH = m\angle GHE$
   $10x^2 = 8x^2 + 18$
     $2x^2 = 18$
       $x^2 = 9$
        $x = \pm 3$
        $x = 3$ or -3

29. $KL = \sqrt{(4 - 0)^2 + (8 - 9)^2} = \sqrt{17}$
$LM = \sqrt{[0 - (-2)]^2 + (9 - 1)^2} = \sqrt{68}$
$MN = \sqrt{(-2 - 2)^2 + (1 - 0)^2} = \sqrt{17}$
$KN = \sqrt{(4 - 2)^2 + (8 - 0)^2} = \sqrt{68}$
slope of $\overline{KL} = \frac{9 - 8}{0 - 4} = \frac{1}{-4}$
slope of $\overline{LM} = \frac{1 - 9}{-2 - 0} = \frac{-8}{-2} = 4$
Since $\overline{KL} \cong \overline{MN}$, $\overline{LM} \cong \overline{KN}$, and $\overline{KL} \perp \overline{LM}$, *KLMN* is a parallelogram and a rectangle.

30. $KL = \sqrt{(12 - 6)^2 + [0 - (-6)^2]} = \sqrt{72}$
$LM = \sqrt{(6 - 0)^2 + (-6 - 0)^2} = \sqrt{72}$
$MN = \sqrt{(0 - 6)^2 + (0 - 6)^2} = \sqrt{72}$
$KN = \sqrt{(12 - 6)^2 + (0 - 6)^2} = \sqrt{72}$
slope of $\overline{KL} = \frac{-6 - 0}{6 - 12} = \frac{-6}{-6}$ or 1
slope of $\overline{LM} = \frac{0 - (-6)}{0 - 6} = \frac{6}{-6}$ or -1
Since $\overline{KL} \cong \overline{LM} \cong \overline{MN} \cong \overline{KN}$ and $\overline{KL} \perp \overline{LM}$, *KLMN* is a parallelogram, a rectangle, a rhombus, and a square.

31. $KL = \sqrt{(5 - 3)^2 + [4 - (-6)]^2} = \sqrt{104}$
$LM = \sqrt{(3 - 0)^2 + [-6 - (-10)^2} = \sqrt{25}$ or 5
$MN = \sqrt{(0 - 2)^2 + (-10 - 0)^2} = \sqrt{104}$
$KN = \sqrt{(5 - 2)^2 + (4 - 0)^2} = \sqrt{25}$ or 5
slope of $\overline{KL} = \frac{-6 - 4}{3 - 5} = \frac{-10}{-2} = 5$
slope of $\overline{LM} = \frac{-10 - (-6)}{0 - 3} = \frac{-4}{-3}$ or $\frac{4}{3}$
Since $\overline{KL} \parallel \overline{MN}$, and $\overline{LM} \parallel \overline{KN}$, *KLMN* is a parallelogram.

32. $KL = \sqrt{(1 - 8)^2 + (5 - 6)^2} = \sqrt{50}$
$LM = \sqrt{(8 - 15)^2 + (6 - 5)^2} = \sqrt{50}$
$MN = \sqrt{(15 - 8)^2 + (5 - 4)^2} = \sqrt{50}$
$KN = \sqrt{(1 - 8)^2 + (5 - 4)^2} = \sqrt{50}$
slope of $\overline{KL} = \frac{6 - 5}{8 - 1} = \frac{1}{7}$
slope of $\overline{LM} = \frac{5 - 6}{15 - 8} = \frac{-1}{7}$
Since $\overline{KL} \cong \overline{LM} \cong \overline{MN} \cong \overline{KN}$, *KLMN* is a parallelogram and a rhombus.

33. $PR = 2(PT) = 2(14) = 28$
34. $m\angle PQR = 2(m\angle PQT) = 2(34) = 68$

35. 90

36. $PQ = RQ$
$20 + x = 4x - 1$
$21 = 3x$
$7 = x$

37. $m\angle PQT + m\angle QPT = 90$
$m\angle PQT + 52 = 90$
$m\angle PQT = 38$

38. $PT = TR$
$4x - 8 = 16 - 2x$
$6x = 24$
$x = 4$

$QT = TS$
$6y - 9 = 3y + 9$
$3y = 18$
$y = 6$

39. $m\angle UVT = m\angle STV = 45$

40. $m\angle SUV = m\angle TSW = 35$

41. $m\angle TSU = m\angle SUV = 47$

42. length of the median $= \frac{1}{2}(ST + UV)$
$= \frac{1}{2}(23 + 19)$
$= \frac{1}{2}(42)$ or 21

43. $m\angle UWV = m\angle TWS = 127$
$m\angle UWV + m\angle WVU + m\angle WUV = 180$
$127 + m\angle WVU + 23 = 180$
$m\angle WVU = 30$

Page 332 Applications and Problem Solving

44. rhombi

45. the kite flaps and the back are all trapezoids

46.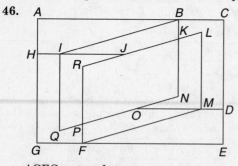

ACEG rectangle;
IBNQ, RLMF, RKNP parallelogram;
IBKJ, OPFM, ABIH, MDEF trapezoid

47. the deck top and the road surface

Page 333 Alternative Assessment: Thinking Critically

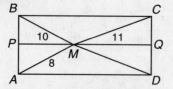

Draw a segment $\overline{PQ}$ parallel to any side and through M. In the diagram shown, $\overline{PQ}$ is parallel to $\overline{AD}$ and $\overline{BC}$. Using the Pythagorean Theorem, we can write the following equations.

$10^2 = PB^2 + PM^2$
$8^2 = PA^2 + PM^2$
$11^2 = CQ^2 + MQ^2$
$MD^2 = DQ^2 + MQ^2$

Substitute to write these equations.
$100 - PB^2 = 64 - PA^2$
$121 - CQ^2 = MD^2 - DQ^2$

Because $\overline{PQ}$ is parallel to $\overline{AD}$ and $\overline{BC}$, $PA = DQ$ and $PB = CQ$. Let $PA = DQ = x$ and $PB = CQ = y$. Then, the equations can be rewritten as follows.

$100 - y^2 = 64 - x^2$
$121 - y^2 = MD^2 - x^2$

Use elimination. Subtract the first equation from the second and then solve.

$121 - y^2 = MD^2 - x^2$
$(-)\ 100 - y^2 = \quad 64 - x^2$
$\overline{\qquad 21 = MD^2 - 64}$
$85 = MD^2$
$\sqrt{85} = MD$
$9.2 \approx MD$

College Entrance Exam Practice, Chapters 1–6

1. $a^2 + b^2 = c^2$
$1^2 + (\sqrt{2})^2 = c^2$
$1 + 2 = c^2$
$\sqrt{3} = c$

$1^2 + b^2 = (\sqrt{2})^2$
$1 + b^2 = 2$
$b^2 = 1$
$b = 1$ (D)

2. $5\%(6\%) = 0.05(0.06) = 0.003 = 0.3\%$ (B)

3. $|x - 3| < 2$
$-2 < x - 3 < 2$
$1 < x < 5$ (A)

4. $3^{-2} = \frac{1}{3^2} = \frac{1}{9}$ (C) **5.** median (C)

6. All rhombi are squares. (B)

7. $RS = \frac{6}{\sqrt{3}} = 2\sqrt{3}$
$QR = 2(RS) = 2(2\sqrt{3}) = 4\sqrt{3}$ (A)

8. $\frac{a^{-3}bc^2}{a^{-4}b^2c^{-3}} = a^{-3-(-4)}b^{1-2}c^{2-(-3)} =$
$a^1 b^{-1} c^5$ or $\frac{ac^5}{b}$ (B)

9. $4x^2y = 2^2 \cdot x^2y$
$6x^2y = 2 \cdot 3 \cdot x^2 \cdot y$
$15xy = 3 \cdot 5 \cdot x \cdot y$
LCD: $2^2 \cdot 3 \cdot 5 \cdot x^2 \cdot y = 60x^2y$

10. $P = 4x + 3y$

11. $x_1 y_1 = x_2 y_2$
$\frac{1}{2}(10) = \frac{2}{3}(y_2)$
$5 = \frac{2}{3}y_2$
$\frac{15}{2} = y_2$

12. $m\angle BAC = 60$

13. $3 - (x - 5) = 2x - 3(4 - x)$
$3 - x + 5 = 2x - 12 + 3x$
$8 - x = 5x - 12$
$20 = 6x$
$\frac{10}{3} = x$

14. $\frac{x^6 + x^6 + x^6}{x^2} = \frac{3x^6}{x^2} = 3x^4$

15. $m\angle CBE + m\angle DBE + m\angle ABD = 180$
$$m\angle CBE + 90 + x = 180$$
$$m\angle CBE = 90 - x$$

16. $x + 61 + 61 = 180$ $\qquad$ $y + 59 + 59 = 180$
$\qquad\qquad x = 58$ $\qquad\qquad\qquad\quad y = 62$ $\quad$ (B)

17. $\dfrac{1}{\frac{2}{3}} = 1 \div \dfrac{2}{3} = 1 \times \dfrac{3}{2} = \dfrac{3}{2}$

$\dfrac{2}{\frac{1}{3}} = 2 \div \dfrac{1}{3} = 2 \times 3 = 6$ $\quad$ (B)

18. The measure of an exterior angle is equal to the sum of the two remote interior angles.
$m\angle 1 > m\angle 2$ $\quad$ (A)

19. $m\angle A > m\angle B$
$m\angle A > m\angle C$
We do not know if $m\angle B$ is greater or less than the $m\angle C$. $\quad$ (D)

20. $3x - 4y = -2$ $\qquad \rightarrow \quad 3x - 4y = -2$
$(4x + 2y = 12)2$ $\quad \rightarrow \quad \underline{8x + 4y = 24}$
$\qquad\qquad\qquad\qquad\qquad\qquad 11x = 22$
$\qquad\qquad\qquad\qquad\qquad\qquad\quad x = 2$

$\qquad 4(2) + 2y = 12$
$\qquad\qquad\quad 2y = 4$
$\qquad\qquad\quad\ y = 2$
$x = y = 2$ $\quad$ (C)

Chapter 7 Connecting Proportion and Similarity

Page 341 Check for Understanding

1a. Men earn $1.31 for every dollar women earn.

1b. The proportion is $\frac{522}{399} = \frac{1.31}{1}$. It is a proportion because the ratios are equal.

2. Find the product of the means, $(30)(14)$, and of the extremes, $22x$, and set them equal. Divide each side by 22.

3. $\frac{16}{10} = \frac{8}{5}$, $\frac{16}{8} = \frac{10}{5}$, $\frac{5}{10} = \frac{8}{16}$, $\frac{5}{8} = \frac{10}{16}$

4. a, b, and d are equivalent because they have the same cross products.

5. See student's work.

6. $\frac{2}{150} = \frac{1}{75}$

7. $\frac{340}{18} = \frac{170}{9}$

8. $\frac{x}{5} = \frac{11}{35}$
$35x = 55$
$x = \frac{55}{35} = \frac{11}{7} \approx 1.57$

9. $\frac{13}{49} = \frac{26}{7x}$
$91x = 1274$
$x = 14$

10. $\frac{x-2}{x} = \frac{3}{8}$
$8(x-2) = 3x$
$8x - 16 = 3x$
$5x = 16$
$x = \frac{16}{5}$ or 3.2

11. $\frac{CD}{CE} \overset{?}{=} \frac{EF}{EG}$
$\frac{10}{20} \overset{?}{=} \frac{10}{20}$
$\frac{1}{2} = \frac{1}{2}$ ✓
yes

12. $\frac{DE}{CD} \overset{?}{=} \frac{GI}{EG}$
$\frac{10}{10} \overset{?}{=} \frac{20}{20}$
$1 = 1$ ✓
yes

13. $\frac{CE}{FG} \overset{?}{=} \frac{EH}{GH}$
$\frac{20}{10} \overset{?}{=} \frac{30}{10}$
$2 \neq 3$
no

14a. $\frac{DE}{EL} = \frac{DE}{ET + TL}$
$= \frac{DE}{DE + DE}$
$= \frac{DE}{2(DE)}$ or $\frac{1}{2}$

14b. $m\angle ADL = m\angle ALD$
$\frac{m\angle ADL}{m\angle ALD} = \frac{1}{1}$

15. $3x + 4x + 5x = 72$
$12x = 72$
$x = 6$
$3x = 3(6) = 18$ in.
$4x = 4(6) = 24$ in.
$5x = 5(6) = 30$ in.

16. $\frac{10}{8\frac{1}{3}} = \frac{50}{x}$
$10x = \frac{1250}{3}$
$x \approx 42$ in. wide

Pages 342–345 Exercises

17. $\frac{150,000}{150} = \frac{1000}{1}$

18. $\frac{2}{3}$

19. $\frac{8}{10} = \frac{4}{5}$

20. $\frac{76}{89}$

21. $\frac{a}{5.18} = \frac{1}{4}$
$4a = 5.18$
$a = 1.295$

22. $\frac{5}{n+3} = \frac{7}{4}$
$20 = 7(n+3)$
$20 = 7n + 21$
$-1 = 7n$
$n = \frac{-1}{7} \approx -0.14$

23. $\frac{7}{11} = \frac{11}{x}$
$7x = 121$
$x = \frac{121}{7} \approx 17.29$

24. $\frac{3x}{23} = \frac{48}{92}$
$276x = 1104$
$x = 4$

25. $\frac{a+1}{a-1} = \frac{5}{6}$
$6a + 6 = 5a - 5$
$a = -11$

26. $\frac{2}{3x+1} = \frac{1}{x}$
$2x = 3x + 1$
$x = -1$

27. $3x + 4x = 42$
$7x = 42$
$x = 6$
$3x = 3(6) = 18$ ft
$4x = 4(6) = 24$ ft

28. $\frac{AB}{BC} = \frac{FE}{AF}$
$\frac{4}{12} = \frac{6}{AF}$
$4AF = 72$
$AF = 18$
$AE = AF + FE = 18 + 6$ or 24
$AC = AB + BC = 4 + 12$ or 16
$\frac{AB}{BC} = \frac{CD}{DE}$
$\frac{4}{12} = \frac{CD}{9}$
$36 = 12CD$
$3 = CD$
$CE = CD + DE = 3 + 9$ or 12

29. $\frac{AB}{BC} = \frac{EF}{FG}$
$\frac{14}{2.6} = \frac{21}{FG}$
$14FG = 54.6$
$FG = 3.9$

30. $\frac{GH}{FG} = \frac{DC}{CB}$
$\frac{40}{32} = \frac{25}{CB}$
$40CB = 800$
$CB = 20$

31. $\frac{AD}{BC} = \frac{EH}{FG}$
$\frac{\frac{2}{3}}{\frac{3}{4}} = \frac{EH}{\frac{1}{2}}$
$\frac{3}{4}EH = \frac{1}{3}$
$EH = \frac{4}{9}$

32. Row 1:
$\frac{AB}{BC} = \frac{AD}{DE}$
$\frac{5}{8} = \frac{AD}{10}$
$50 = 8AD$
$6.25 = AD$

$AC = AB + BC$
$= 5 + 8$ or 13

$AE = AD + DE$
$= 6.25 + 10$ or 16.25

Row 2:
$AD = AE - DE$
$= 32 - 23.2$ or 8.8

$AC = AB + BC$
$= 5.5 + 14.5$ or 20

$\frac{AB}{BC} = \frac{AD}{DE}$
$\frac{AB}{14.5} = \frac{8.8}{23.2}$
$23.2AB = 127.6$
$AB = 5.5$

Row 3:
$DE = AE - AD = 20 - 12$ or 8
Let $x = AB$, then $BC = 16 - x$.
$$\frac{AB}{BC} = \frac{AD}{DE}$$
$$\frac{x}{16-x} = \frac{12}{8}$$
$$8x = 192 - 12x$$
$$20x = 192$$
$$x = 9.6$$
$$BC = 16 - 9.6 = 6.4$$

Row 4:
$AE = AD + DE = 17 + 17$ or 34
Let $x = AB$, then $BC = 33 - x$
$\frac{AB}{BC} = \frac{AD}{DE}, \frac{AD}{DE} = \frac{17}{17}$ or 1
$$\frac{x}{33-x} = 1$$
$$x = 33 - x$$
$$2x = 33$$
$$x = 16.5$$
$$AB = BC = 16.5$$

33. $4x + 6x + 9x = 190$
$$19x = 190$$
$$x = 10$$
$$4x = 4(10) = 40 \text{ in.}$$
$$6x = 6(10) = 60 \text{ in.}$$
$$9x = 9(10) = 90 \text{ in.}$$

34. $2x + 5x + 8x = 180$
$$15x = 180$$
$$x = 12$$
$$2x = 2(12) = 24$$
$$5x = 5(12) = 60$$
$$8x = 8(12) = 96$$

35. $\frac{32}{100} = \frac{x}{156}$
$$100x = 4992$$
$$x = 49.92$$

36. $\frac{175}{100} = \frac{x}{42}$
$$100x = 7350$$
$$x = 73.5$$

37. $\frac{x}{100} = \frac{14}{56}$
$$56x = 1400$$
$$x = 25\%$$

38. $\frac{60}{100} = \frac{32}{x}$
$$60x = 3200$$
$$x = 53\frac{1}{3}$$

39.
$$\frac{a+b}{b} = \frac{c+d}{d}$$
$$(a+b)d = (c+d)b$$
$$ad + bd = cb + db$$
$$ad + bd = cb + bd$$
$$ad + bd - bd = cb + db - bd$$
$$ad = cb$$
$$\frac{a}{b} = \frac{c}{d}$$

40.
$$\frac{a-b}{b} = \frac{c-d}{d}$$
$$(a-b)d = (c-d)b$$
$$ad - bd = cb - db$$
$$ad - bd = cb - bd$$
$$ad - bd + bd = cb - bd + bd$$
$$ad = cb$$
$$\frac{a}{b} = \frac{c}{d}$$

41. $\frac{x}{20} = \frac{6}{5}$
$$5x = 120$$
$$x = 24$$
$$\frac{6}{5} = \frac{y}{10}$$
$$60 = 5y$$
$$y = 12$$

42. $\frac{4}{3} = \frac{x+1}{x+3}$
$$4x + 12 = 3x + 3$$
$$x = -9$$
$$\frac{4}{3} = \frac{y+1}{y}$$
$$4y = 3y + 3$$
$$y = 3$$

43. This is true because one of the angles measures 90° and the other two measure 45°, the ratio of 45:90 is 1:2.

44a. $\frac{27.5}{21.3} = \frac{10}{x}$
$$x = 7.75 \text{ cm}$$
The reduced rectangle is approximately 7.75 cm by 10 cm.

44b. $\frac{27.5}{10} = 0.36$
$1 - 0.36 = 0.64$
approximately 64%

45a. stop 1: $\frac{351}{13} = 27\frac{\text{mi}}{\text{gal}}$
2: $\frac{275}{11} = 25\frac{\text{mi}}{\text{gal}}$
3: $\frac{362.5}{12.5} = 29\frac{\text{mi}}{\text{gal}}$
4: $\frac{372}{12} = 31\frac{\text{mi}}{\text{gal}}$
5: $\frac{260}{12.8} = 20.3125\frac{\text{mi}}{\text{gal}}$
6: $\frac{294.4}{10} = 29.44\frac{\text{mi}}{\text{gal}}$

45b. You cannot find the average number of miles per gallon by adding the number of miles per gallon at each stop and dividing by 6 because Keshia drove a different distance between each stop. To find the average, you must divide the total distance by the total amount of gas for all six stops. The average is about 26.86 miles per gallon.

46a. $\frac{59}{172} = 0.34$; $\frac{128}{99} = 1.29$; $\frac{168}{55} = 3.05$, $\frac{44}{200} = 0.22$;
$\frac{60}{164} = 0.37$, $\frac{109}{107} = 1.02$

46b. Sample answer: 3.05 means that there are usually 3 days with precipitation for every clear day in Buffalo.

46c. Sample answer: ranking the cities from a greatest precipitation to least precipitation: Buffalo, Boston, Montgomery, Lubbock, Albuquerque, Fresno

47a. $\frac{497,197}{45} = 11,049$; $\frac{1,629,241}{150} = 10,862$;
$\frac{538,643}{28} = 19,328$; $\frac{129,841}{10} = 12,985$;
$\frac{299,084}{22} = 13,595$

47b. You could find the ratio of people per movie screen to see which is smallest; Kansas City is the lowest at 10,862 people per screen, followed by Ann Arbor at 11,094 people per screen.

48. $\frac{1.5 \text{ cm}}{200 \text{ miles}} = \frac{2.4 \text{ cm}}{x \text{ mi}}$
$$1.5x = 480$$
$$x = 320 \text{ miles}$$

49a. $\dfrac{255{,}082{,}000 \text{ people}}{4{,}183{,}344{,}800 \text{ lbs}} = \dfrac{406{,}000 \text{ people}}{x \text{ lbs}}$

$\qquad 255{,}082{,}000x = 1.6984379888\ E\ 15$

$\qquad\qquad\qquad x = 6{,}658{,}400 \text{ lbs}$

49b. $\dfrac{6{,}658{,}400 \text{ lbs}}{406{,}000 \text{ people}} = 16.4 \text{ lbs}$ **50.** $\dfrac{262{,}017}{570{,}017} \approx 0.46$

51a.

Currency	Cost of Making (cents)	Value (cents)	Ratio (cost/value)
penny	0.8	1	$\dfrac{0.8}{1} = 0.8$
nickel	2.9	5	$\dfrac{2.9}{5} = 0.58$
dime	1.7	10	$\dfrac{1.7}{10} = 0.17$
quarter	3.7	25	$\dfrac{3.7}{25} = 0.148$
half dollar	7.8	50	$\dfrac{7.8}{50} = 0.156$
dollar bill	3	100	$\dfrac{3}{100} = 0.03$

51b. Sample answer: No, it costs the most to make a penny since the ratio is the greatest at 0.8 and it costs the least to make a dollar bill since the ratio is the smallest at 0.03.

51c. $\dfrac{500 \text{ cents}}{5 \text{ cents}} = \dfrac{x \text{ cents}}{2.9 \text{ cents}}$ $\qquad$ $\dfrac{500 \text{ cents}}{25 \text{ cents}} = \dfrac{x \text{ cents}}{3.7 \text{ cents}}$

$\qquad\quad 5x = 500(2.9)$ $\qquad\qquad 25x = 500(3.7)$

$\qquad\quad x = 290 \text{ cents}$ $\qquad\qquad\quad x = 74 \text{ cents}$

$\qquad \$2.90$ $\qquad\qquad\qquad\qquad \$0.74$

52a. An increase of almost 2 blue-collar jobs is predicted for every increase in a white-collar job in Seattle.

52b. An increase of more than 20 blue-collar jobs is predicted for a loss of every white-collar job in Pittsburgh.

52c. New York City will lose jobs. A loss of 6 blue-collar jobs is predicted for every 100 lost white-collar jobs.

53. trapazoid

54. $m\angle L = m\angle J = 72$

$\qquad m\angle J + m\angle K = 180$

$\qquad\quad 72 + m\angle K = 180$

$\qquad\qquad\qquad m\angle K = 108$

$\qquad m\angle M = m\angle K = 108$

55. $8 - 5 < x < 8 + 5$

$\qquad\quad 3 < x < 13$

It is less than 13 and greater than 3.

56. $\angle F, \angle H, \angle G$

57. $90, x + 38 = 90$

$\qquad\qquad\quad x = 52$

58. false

59. $75 \quad a + b = 180$

$\qquad\quad 75 + b = 180$

$\qquad\qquad\quad b = 105$

60. If a mineral sample is quartz, then it can scratch glass; Law of Syllogism.

61. False; A, B, and P are not necessarily collinear.

62. $2n + 6 < n - 1$

$\qquad\qquad n < -7$

$\qquad \{n \mid n < -7\}$

63. $x^2 + 6x - 16 = 0$

$\qquad (x + 8)(x - 2) = 0$

$\qquad\quad x = -8 \text{ or } x = 2$

7-2 Exploring Similar Polygons

Page 347 Modeling Mathematics

a. See students' work.

b. The measures of the corresponding sides of the original triangle and its projection are proportional.

c. You have to check that the corresponding angles are congruent.

Pages 349–350 Check for Understanding

1a. Yes; all the angles are congruent and the sides are in the ratio of 1:1.

1b. No; their corresponding sides may not be congruent.

2. They both could be right, it depends on whether you are going from a smaller polygon to a larger one or the other way around.

3. See students' work for drawings. The drawings will be similar since the measures of the corresponding sides will be proportional and the corresponding angles will be congruent.

4. The corresponding angles must be congruent: $\angle A \cong \angle M$; $\angle B \cong \angle N$; $\angle C \cong \angle O$; $\angle D \cong \angle P$.

5a. $\dfrac{8}{x} = \dfrac{2}{17}$ $\qquad\qquad$ **b.** $\dfrac{4}{30} = \dfrac{2}{15}$

$\qquad 2x = 136$

$\qquad\quad x = 68 \text{ cm}$

6. Yes; angles are congruent and sides are proportional.

$\qquad \dfrac{4.8}{6} = \dfrac{2.16}{2.7} = \dfrac{5.2}{6.5}$

7. $\dfrac{BC}{EF} = \dfrac{AB}{FG}$

$\qquad \dfrac{8}{y} = \dfrac{5}{7.5}$

$\qquad 5y = 60$

$\qquad\ y = 12; \qquad x = y = 12$

8. S; see students' drawings.

9. A; see students' drawings.

10a. $\dfrac{6}{9} = \dfrac{2}{3}$

10b. $\dfrac{2}{3} = \dfrac{14}{x}$

$\qquad 2x = 42$

$\qquad\ x = 21 \text{ in.}$

$\qquad \dfrac{2}{3} = \dfrac{12}{x}$

$\qquad 2x = 36$

$\qquad\ x = 18 \text{ in.}$

10c. $\dfrac{2}{3} = \dfrac{10}{x}$

$\qquad 2x = 30$

$\qquad\ x = 15$

$\qquad P = 9 + 15 + 18 + 21 \text{ or } 63 \text{ in.}$

11. Yes; the corresponding angles are congruent and the corresponding sides are proportional with a scale factor of $\dfrac{1}{3}$.

12a. $2.5\left(\frac{5}{4}\right)\left(\frac{5}{4}\right) = 3.9$ in. **12b.** $E = \frac{5}{4}\left(\frac{5}{4}x\right)$

$4\left(\frac{5}{4}\right)\left(\frac{5}{4}\right) = 6.3$ in. **12c.** $\frac{5}{4} \cdot \frac{5}{4} = \frac{25}{16}$

3.9 in. by 6.3 in.

Pages 351–353 Exercises

13. No; the side on the second triangle measuring 18.4 should be 21.6.

14. Yes; the corresponding angles are congruent and sides are proportional: $\frac{2.8}{8.4} = \frac{3.1}{9.3} = \frac{4}{12} = \frac{1}{3}$.

15. $\frac{ST}{RS} = \frac{WV}{WU}$ $\frac{ST}{RT} = \frac{WV}{VU}$

$\frac{49}{x} = \frac{20}{29}$ $\frac{49}{y+3} = \frac{20}{21}$

$x = 71.05$ $y = 48.45$

16. $\frac{AB}{FE} = \frac{BC}{EH}$ $\frac{DC}{GH} = \frac{BC}{EH}$

$\frac{x+2}{15} = \frac{8}{10}$ $\frac{y-3}{5} = \frac{8}{10}$

$10x + 20 = 120$ $10y - 30 = 40$

$x = 10$ $y = 7$

17. $m\angle L = m\angle G$ $m\angle J = m\angle O$

$x - 4 = 87$ $y + 30 = 60$

$x = 91$ $y = 30$

18. $m\angle S = m\angle L$

$x = 30$

$m\angle R + m\angle Q + m\angle S = 180$

$m\angle R + 80 + 30 = 180$

$m\angle R = 70$

$m\angle R = m\angle K$

$y = 70$

19–25. See students' drawings.

19. S **20.** A **21.** N **22.** S

23. S **24.** S **25.** A

26. $\frac{ST}{GF} = \frac{RT}{EF}$ **27.** $\frac{RS}{EG} = \frac{RT}{EF} = \frac{15}{11.25} = \frac{4}{3}$

$\frac{10}{GF} = \frac{15}{11.25}$

$GF = 7.5$

28. $\frac{AD}{AG} = \frac{12}{7.5} = \frac{8}{5}$ **29a.** $AG = 12 - 4.5 = 7.5$

29b. $\frac{DC}{GF} = \frac{8}{5}$ **29c.** $m\angle ADC = m\angle AGF$

$\frac{DC}{14} = \frac{8}{5}$ $m\angle ADC = 108$

$DC = 22.4$

29d. $\frac{BC}{EF} = \frac{8}{5}$

$\frac{BC}{8} = \frac{8}{5}$

$BC = 12.8$

30a. $P = AD + AB + BC + DC$

$= 12 + 26 + 12.8 + 22.4$ or 73.2

30b. $\frac{AB}{AE} = \frac{8}{5}$

$\frac{26}{AE} = \frac{8}{5}$

$AE = 16.25$

$P = AG + AE + EF + GF$

$= 7.5 + 16.25 + 8 + 14$ or 45.75

30c. $\frac{\text{perimeter of } ABCD}{\text{perimeter of } AEFG} = \frac{73.2}{45.75} = \frac{8}{5}$

31. $\triangle ABC \sim \triangle IHG \sim \triangle JKL$ and $\triangle NMO \sim \triangle RPS$

32a. Yes; the new triangle is congruent to the original, but shifted to the right two units and up two units.

32b. Yes; it is reflected over the line $y = 4$ and each side is three times larger.

33. $\frac{84 \text{ ft}}{4 \text{ ft}} = \frac{x}{\frac{1}{4} \text{ in.}}$

$4x = 21$

$x = 5\frac{1}{4}$ in.

$\frac{50 \text{ ft}}{4 \text{ ft}} = \frac{x}{\frac{1}{4} \text{ in.}}$

$4x = 12\frac{1}{2}$

$x = 3\frac{1}{8}$ in.

Students should draw a rectangle $5\frac{1}{4}$ in. by $3\frac{1}{8}$ in.

34. $\frac{91 \text{ m}}{1 \text{ m}} = \frac{x \text{ mm}}{1 \text{ mm}}$

$x = 91$ mm

$\frac{46 \text{ m}}{1 \text{ m}} = \frac{x \text{ mm}}{1 \text{ mm}}$

$x = 46$ mm

Students should draw a rectangle 91 mm by 46 mm.

35. $\frac{36 \text{ ft}}{1 \text{ ft}} = \frac{x \text{ in.}}{\frac{1}{8} \text{ in.}}$

$x = 4\frac{1}{2}$ in.

$\frac{78 \text{ ft}}{1 \text{ ft}} = \frac{x \text{ in.}}{\frac{1}{8} \text{ in.}}$

$x = 9\frac{3}{4}$ in.

Students should draw a rectangle $4\frac{1}{2}$ in. by $9\frac{3}{4}$ in.

36a. 28 square units

36b. $P = 2\ell + 2w$

$= 2(2) + 2(3)$

$= 10$ units

36c. $V = 8$ cubic units   **36d.** $112:28 = 4:1$

36e. $20:10 = 2:1$ **36f.** $64:8 = 8:1$

36g. Yes; all of the sides are changed by a scale factor of 2, so they remain in the same proportion and none of the angles are changed.

37.

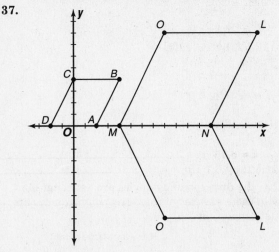

either $L(16, 8)$ and $O(8, 8)$ or $O(8, -8)$ and $L(16, -8)$

38.

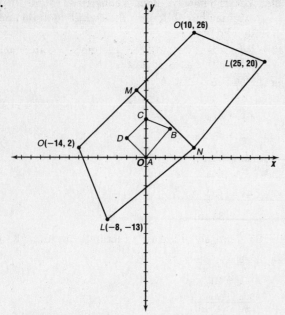

$L(25, 20)$ and $O(10, 26)$ or $L(-8, -7)$ and $O(-14, 2)$

39. In triangles ABC and DEF, $\overline{AC}$ and $\overline{DF}$ both have slope $\frac{3}{2}$, and $\overline{BC}$ and $\overline{EF}$ both have slope $\frac{-3}{2}$. Thus, $\overline{AC} \parallel \overline{DF}$ and $\overline{BC} \parallel \overline{EF}$. The horizontal axis is a transversal for both pairs of parallel lines. Thus corresponding angles A and D are $\cong$. In the same way, corresponding angles B and E are $\cong$. $\angle C \cong \angle F$ because if 2 $\angle$s in a $\triangle$ are $\cong$ to 2 $\angle$s in another $\triangle$, the third $\angle$s are also $\cong$. Using the distance formula, $\frac{AC}{DF} = \frac{AB}{DE} = \frac{BC}{EF} = \frac{3}{2}$. Corresponding sideshave the same ratio, and the angles are congruent, so the figures are similar.

40a. four times as many straws or 64 straws

40b. No; it would take 4^2 or 16 times as much paint.

40c. No; it would hold 4^3 or 64 times as much.

41a. $\frac{1 \text{ in.}}{\frac{3}{4} \text{ in.}} = \frac{18 \text{ ft}}{x \text{ ft}}$

$\qquad x = 13.5 \text{ ft}$

$\frac{1 \text{ in.}}{\frac{5}{8} \text{ in.}} = \frac{18 \text{ ft}}{x \text{ ft}}$

$\qquad x = 11.25 \text{ ft}$

13.5 ft by 11.25 ft

41b. $\frac{1 \text{ in.}}{1\frac{1}{4} \text{ in.}} = \frac{18 \text{ ft}}{x \text{ ft}}$

$\qquad x = 22.5 \text{ ft}$

$\frac{1 \text{ in.}}{\frac{3}{8} \text{ in.}} = \frac{18 \text{ ft}}{x \text{ ft}}$

$\qquad x = 6.75 \text{ ft}$

22.5 ft by 6.75 ft

42. No; the corresponding angles are not congruent and the measures of the corresponding sides are not proportional.

43. $\frac{m+3}{12} = \frac{5}{4}$ **44.** sometimes

$\quad 4m + 12 = 60$

$\qquad\quad 4m = 48$

$\qquad\quad\ m = 12$

---

45. No; one pair of sides parallel and the other pair of sides congruent is not a test for a parallelogram.

46. $\angle R, \angle Q, \angle P$

47. Let x = the number.

$400 - \left[\left(\frac{x}{2} - 17\right)3\right] = 187$

$400 - \left(\frac{3}{2}x - 51\right) = 187$

$451 - \frac{3}{2}x = 187$

$-\frac{3}{2}x = -264$

$x = 176$

48. true   **49.** 84

50. Springer spaniels are dogs.

51. $y + 6 = -\frac{5}{8}(x - 1)$

$8y + 48 = -5x + 5$

$5x + 8y = -43$

52. $f(-1) = 5(-1) + 2 = -3$

7-3   Identifying Similar Triangles

Page 354 Modeling Mathematics

a. They equal about 0.57.

b. See students' work.

c. See students' work.

d. See students' work.

Pages 357–358 Check for Understanding

1. Sample answer: Two triangles are congruent and similar by SSS Similarity and SAS Similarity. To be congruent, the parts must be congruent; to be similar, the sides must be proportional and the angles congruent. Two triangles can also be shown to be congruent by ASA Similarity and AAS Similarity. Two triangles can be shown to be similar by AA Similarity.

2. Only one; you already know the right triangles are congruent.

3. Sample answer:

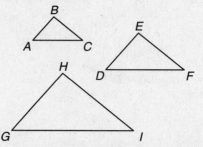

Given $\triangle ABC$, then $\triangle ABC \sim \triangle ABC$ (reflexive)

Given $\triangle ABC \sim \triangle DEF$, then $\triangle DEF \sim \triangle ABC$ (symmetric)

Given $\triangle ABC \sim \triangle DEF$ and $\triangle DEF \sim \triangle GHI$, then $\triangle ABC \sim \triangle GHI$ (transitive)

4. They both are. In both cases, the cross products will produce $rm = ks$.

5. See students' drawings. Both ratios equal $\frac{2}{3}$.

6. yes; $\triangle ABC \sim \triangle EDF$; AA Similarity

7. no; not enough information

8. true

9. $\triangle AEC \sim \triangle BDC$: parallel lines cut by a transveral yield congruent alternate interior angles, so the triangles are similar by AA.

10. If 2 ∥ lines are cut by a transversal, corres. ∠s are ≅; $\angle S \cong \angle VTU$; $\angle U \cong \angle U$, so by AA Similarity, $\triangle RSU \sim \triangle VTU$.

$$\frac{UT}{US} = \frac{UV}{UR} \qquad \frac{VT}{RS} = \frac{UV}{UR}$$
$$\frac{x}{x+12} = \frac{3}{12} \qquad \frac{y}{20} = \frac{3}{12}$$
$$12x = 3x + 36 \qquad 12y = 60$$
$$9x = 36 \qquad\qquad y = 5$$
$$x = 4$$

11. SAS Similarity
$$\frac{3}{6} = \frac{x}{9}$$
$$6x = 27$$
$$x = 4.5$$

12. $\frac{5}{6} = \frac{x}{576}$
$$6x = 2880$$
$$x = 480 \text{ ft}$$

Pages 358–361 Exercises

13. Yes; $\triangle MNO \sim \triangle PQR$; SSS Similarity

14. Yes; $\triangle STU \sim \triangle XVW$; SAS Similarity

15. No; SSA is not valid.

16. No; sides are not proportional.

17. Yes; $\triangle RST \sim \triangle JKL$; AA Similarity

18. No; sides are not proportional.

19. False; this is not true for equilateral or isosceles triangles.

20. true

21. False; the proportions are not the same.

22. $\triangle EAB \sim \triangle EFC \sim \triangle AFD$; AA Similarity

23. $\triangle QRS \sim \triangle QTR$, AA Similarity; $\triangle QRS \sim \triangle RTS$, AA Similarity; $\triangle QTR \sim \triangle RTS$, Transitive Prop of ∠s

24. $\frac{EG}{CB} = \frac{EC}{AB}$
$$\frac{3}{6} = \frac{EC}{10}$$
$$EC = 5$$

$\frac{EG}{CB} = \frac{GC}{AC}$
$$\frac{3}{6} = \frac{GC}{8}$$
$$GC = 4$$

$\frac{EF}{CB} = \frac{ED}{AB}$
$$\frac{EF}{6} = \frac{10}{10}$$
$$EF = 6$$

25. $\frac{AC}{9} = \frac{25}{AC}$
$$AC^2 = 225$$
$$AC = 15$$
$$AE + EC = AC$$
$$AE + 2AE = 15$$
$$AE = 5$$

$\frac{CB}{16} = \frac{25}{CB}$
$$CB^2 = 400$$
$$CB = 20$$
$$BF + CF = CB$$
$$BF + 2BF = 20$$
$$BF = 6\frac{2}{3}$$
$$CF = 13\frac{1}{3}$$

$\frac{CD}{9} = \frac{16}{CD}$
$$CD^2 = 144$$
$$CD = 12$$

$\frac{EF}{AB} = \frac{EC}{AC}$
$$\frac{EF}{25} = \frac{10}{15}$$
$$EF = 16\frac{2}{3}$$

26. $m\angle CFD = 50$, $m\angle GKF = 70$, $m\angle GFK = 50$, $m\angle G = 60$, $m\angle GKJ = 110$

27. $m\angle CDE = 43$, $m\angle A = 43$, $m\angle ABD = 47$, $m\angle DBE = 43$, $m\angle BDE = 47$

28.

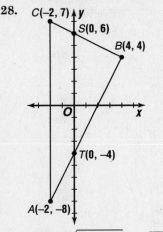

28a. $AB = \sqrt{6^2 + 12^2} = \sqrt{180}$ or $6\sqrt{5}$
$BC = \sqrt{6^2 + 3^2} = \sqrt{45}$ or $3\sqrt{5}$
$CA = |7 - (-8)| = 15$
$ST = |6 - (-4)| = 10$
$TB = \sqrt{8^2 + 4^2} = \sqrt{80}$ or $4\sqrt{5}$
$BS = \sqrt{2^2 + 4^2} = \sqrt{20}$ or $2\sqrt{5}$
$\frac{CA}{ST} = \frac{15}{10}$ or $\frac{3}{2}$, $\frac{AB}{TB} = \frac{6\sqrt{5}}{4\sqrt{5}}$ or $\frac{3}{2}$,
$\frac{BC}{BS} = \frac{3\sqrt{5}}{2\sqrt{5}}$ or $\frac{3}{2}$
Since $\frac{CA}{ST} = \frac{AB}{TB} = \frac{BC}{BS}$, $\triangle ABC \sim \triangle TBS$ by SSS Similarity.

29. Given: $\overline{LP} \parallel \overline{MN}$

Prove: $\dfrac{LJ}{JN} = \dfrac{PJ}{JM}$

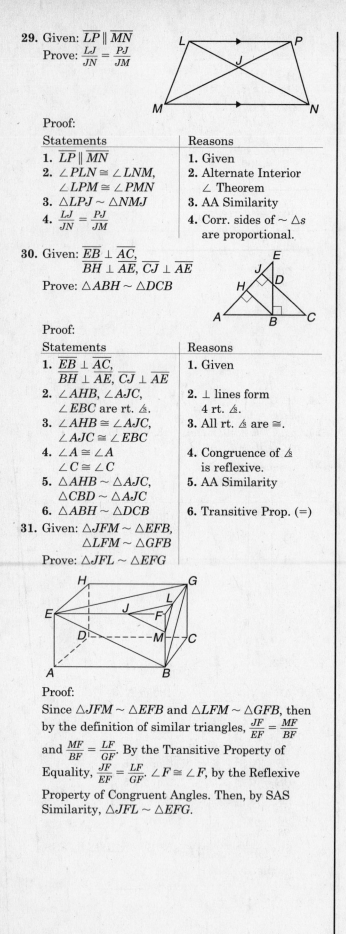

Proof:

Statements	Reasons
1. $\overline{LP} \parallel \overline{MN}$	1. Given
2. $\angle PLN \cong \angle LNM$, $\angle LPM \cong \angle PMN$	2. Alternate Interior $\angle$ Theorem
3. $\triangle LPJ \sim \triangle NMJ$	3. AA Similarity
4. $\dfrac{LJ}{JN} = \dfrac{PJ}{JM}$	4. Corr. sides of $\sim \triangle s$ are proportional.

30. Given: $\overline{EB} \perp \overline{AC}$, $\overline{BH} \perp \overline{AE}$, $\overline{CJ} \perp \overline{AE}$

Prove: $\triangle ABH \sim \triangle DCB$

Proof:

Statements	Reasons
1. $\overline{EB} \perp \overline{AC}$, $\overline{BH} \perp \overline{AE}$, $\overline{CJ} \perp \overline{AE}$	1. Given
2. $\angle AHB$, $\angle AJC$, $\angle EBC$ are rt. $\angle s$.	2. $\perp$ lines form 4 rt. $\angle s$.
3. $\angle AHB \cong \angle AJC$, $\angle AJC \cong \angle EBC$	3. All rt. $\angle s$ are $\cong$.
4. $\angle A \cong \angle A$, $\angle C \cong \angle C$	4. Congruence of $\angle s$ is reflexive.
5. $\triangle AHB \sim \triangle AJC$, $\triangle CBD \sim \triangle AJC$	5. AA Similarity
6. $\triangle ABH \sim \triangle DCB$	6. Transitive Prop. (=)

31. Given: $\triangle JFM \sim \triangle EFB$, $\triangle LFM \sim \triangle GFB$

Prove: $\triangle JFL \sim \triangle EFG$

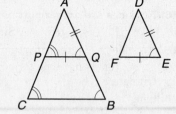

Proof:

Since $\triangle JFM \sim \triangle EFB$ and $\triangle LFM \sim \triangle GFB$, then by the definition of similar triangles, $\dfrac{JF}{EF} = \dfrac{MF}{BF}$ and $\dfrac{MF}{BF} = \dfrac{LF}{GF}$. By the Transitive Property of Equality, $\dfrac{JF}{EF} = \dfrac{LF}{GF}$. $\angle F \cong \angle F$, by the Reflexive Property of Congruent Angles. Then, by SAS Similarity, $\triangle JFL \sim \triangle EFG$.

32. Given: $\overline{JM} \parallel \overline{EB}$, $\overline{LM} \parallel \overline{GB}$

Prove: $\overline{JL} \parallel \overline{EG}$

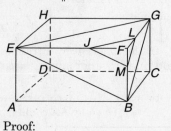

Proof:

Since $\overline{JM} \parallel \overline{EB}$ and $\overline{LM} \parallel \overline{GB}$, then $\angle MJF \cong \angle BEF$ and $\angle FML \cong \angle FBG$ because if two $\parallel$ lines are cut by a transversal, corresponding angles are $\cong$. $\angle EFB \cong \angle EFB$ and $\angle BFG \cong \angle BFG$ since congruence of angles is reflexive. Then $\triangle EFB \sim \triangle JFM$ and $\triangle FBG \sim \triangle FML$ by AA Similarity. Then $\dfrac{JF}{EF} = \dfrac{MF}{BF}, \dfrac{MF}{BF} = \dfrac{LF}{GF}$ by the definition of similar triangles. $\dfrac{JF}{EF} = \dfrac{LF}{GF}$ by the Transitive Property of Equality and $\angle EFG \cong \angle EFG$ since congruence of $\angle s$ is reflexive. Thus, $\triangle JFL \sim \triangle EFG$ by SAS Similarity and $\angle FJL \cong \angle FEG$ by the definition of similar triangles. $\overline{JL} \parallel \overline{EG}$ because if 2 lines are cut by a transversal so the corresponding angles are congruent, then the lines are parallel.

33. Given: $\angle B \cong \angle E$

$\dfrac{AB}{DE} = \dfrac{BC}{EF}$

Prove: $\triangle ABC \sim \triangle DEF$

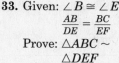

Proof:

Statements	Reasons
1. Draw $\overline{QP} \parallel \overline{BC}$ so that $\overline{QP} \cong \overline{EF}$.	1. Parallel Postulate
2. $\angle APQ \cong \angle C$	2. Corresponding $\angle s$ Postulate
3. $\angle B \cong \angle E$	3. Given
4. $\angle AQP \cong \angle E$	4. Transitive Prop. of $\cong \angle s$
5. $\triangle ABC \sim \triangle AQP$	5. AA Similarity
6. $\dfrac{AB}{AQ} = \dfrac{BC}{QP}$	6. Def. of $\sim \triangle s$
7. $\dfrac{AB}{DE} = \dfrac{BC}{EF}$	7. Given
8. $AB \cdot QP = AQ \cdot BC$, $AB \cdot EF = DE \cdot BC$	8. Equality of cross products
9. $QP = EF$	9. Def. of $\cong$ segments
10. $AB \cdot ERF = AQ \cdot BC$	10. Substitution Prop. (=)
11. $AQ \cdot BC = DE \cdot BC$	11. Substitution Prop. (=)
12. $AQ = DE$	12. Div. Prop. (=)
13. $AQ \cong DE$	13. Def. of $\cong$ segments
14. $\triangle AQP \cong \triangle DEF$	14. SAS
15. $\angle APQ \cong \angle F$	15. CPCTC
16. $\angle C \cong \angle F$	16. Transitive Prop. of $\cong \angle s$
17. $\triangle ABC \sim \triangle DEF$	17. AA Similarity

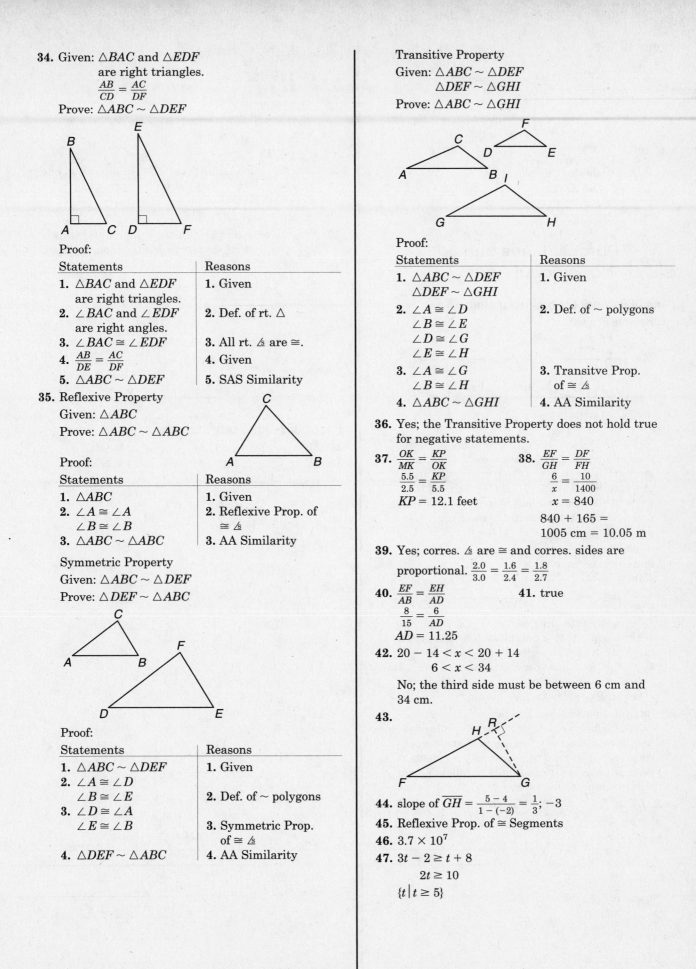

34. Given: △BAC and △EDF
are right triangles.
$\frac{AB}{CD} = \frac{AC}{DF}$
Prove: △ABC ~ △DEF

Proof:

Statements	Reasons
1. △BAC and △EDF are right triangles.	1. Given
2. ∠BAC and ∠EDF are right angles.	2. Def. of rt. △
3. ∠BAC ≅ ∠EDF	3. All rt. ∠s are ≅.
4. $\frac{AB}{DE} = \frac{AC}{DF}$	4. Given
5. △ABC ~ △DEF	5. SAS Similarity

35. Reflexive Property
Given: △ABC
Prove: △ABC ~ △ABC

Proof:

Statements	Reasons
1. △ABC	1. Given
2. ∠A ≅ ∠A ∠B ≅ ∠B	2. Reflexive Prop. of ≅ ∠s
3. △ABC ~ △ABC	3. AA Similarity

Symmetric Property
Given: △ABC ~ △DEF
Prove: △DEF ~ △ABC

Proof:

Statements	Reasons
1. △ABC ~ △DEF	1. Given
2. ∠A ≅ ∠D ∠B ≅ ∠E	2. Def. of ~ polygons
3. ∠D ≅ ∠A ∠E ≅ ∠B	3. Symmetric Prop. of ≅ ∠s
4. △DEF ~ △ABC	4. AA Similarity

Transitive Property
Given: △ABC ~ △DEF
△DEF ~ △GHI
Prove: △ABC ~ △GHI

Proof:

Statements	Reasons
1. △ABC ~ △DEF △DEF ~ △GHI	1. Given
2. ∠A ≅ ∠D ∠B ≅ ∠E ∠D ≅ ∠G ∠E ≅ ∠H	2. Def. of ~ polygons
3. ∠A ≅ ∠G ∠B ≅ ∠H	3. Transitve Prop. of ≅ ∠s
4. △ABC ~ △GHI	4. AA Similarity

36. Yes; the Transitive Property does not hold true for negative statements.

37. $\frac{OK}{MK} = \frac{KP}{OK}$
$\frac{5.5}{2.5} = \frac{KP}{5.5}$
$KP = 12.1$ feet

38. $\frac{EF}{GH} = \frac{DF}{FH}$
$\frac{6}{x} = \frac{10}{1400}$
$x = 840$
$840 + 165 = 1005$ cm $= 10.05$ m

39. Yes; corres. ∠s are ≅ and corres. sides are proportional. $\frac{2.0}{3.0} = \frac{1.6}{2.4} = \frac{1.8}{2.7}$

40. $\frac{EF}{AB} = \frac{EH}{AD}$
$\frac{8}{15} = \frac{6}{AD}$
$AD = 11.25$

41. true

42. $20 - 14 < x < 20 + 14$
$6 < x < 34$

No; the third side must be between 6 cm and 34 cm.

43.

44. slope of $\overline{GH} = \frac{5-4}{1-(-2)} = \frac{1}{3}$; -3

45. Reflexive Prop. of ≅ Segments

46. 3.7×10^7

47. $3t - 2 \geq t + 8$
$2t \geq 10$
$\{t \mid t \geq 5\}$

1. $\frac{1}{3} = \frac{t}{8-t}$
   $8 - t = 3t$
   $4t = 8$
   $t = 2$

2. No; corres. $\angle$s are not congruent.

3. $\frac{4 \text{ drinks}}{3 \text{ days}} = \frac{x \text{ drinks}}{365 \text{ days}}$
   $x \approx 487$ soft drinks

4. yes; AA Similarity

5. yes; SAS Similarity

7-4 Parallel Lines and Proportional Parts

Page 366 Check for Understanding

1. Sample answer:

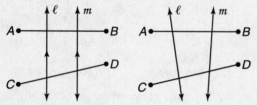

2. Sample answer: Given three or more parallel lines intersecting two transversals, Corollary 7-1 states that the parts of the transversals are proportional. Corollary 7-2 states that if the parts of one transversal are congruent, then the parts of every transversal are congruent.

3. when the segment is drawn through the midpoints of the two sides

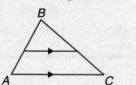

4. Draw a ray extending from one of the endpoints of the segment. Mark off an arc on the ray. Then mark off three more arcs of equal lengths. Construct four lines connecting these points. To separate a segment into five congruent parts, mark off five arcs of equal length.

5. Sample answer: alternate interior angles, corresponding angles, lines perpendicular to same line, line intersects two sides of triangle and separates sides into corresponding segments of proportional lengths then it is parallel to third side of triangle.

6a. LT 6b. RL

7a. true

7b. false
   $\frac{LR}{TR} = \frac{RW}{RS}$
   $\frac{3}{8} = \frac{6}{RS}$
   $RS = 16$

8. $AB = 2(EC)$
   $x + 12 = 2(5x - 3)$
   $x + 12 = 10x - 6$
   $18 = 9x$
   $x = 2$
   $AE = ED$
   $y + 8 = 2y - 4$
   $y = 12$

9. Yes; if 3 or more $\parallel$ lines cut off $\cong$ segments on one transversal, then they cut off $\cong$ segments on every transversal.

10. no; must have $\overline{DG} \parallel \overline{EF}$

11. Yes; if 3 or more $\parallel$ lines intersect 2 transversals, then they cut off the transversals proportionately.

12. $\frac{x}{8} = \frac{2.5}{6}$
    $x = 3\frac{1}{3}$ ft
    $\frac{y}{8} = \frac{2}{6}$
    $y = 2\frac{2}{3}$ ft
    $\frac{z}{8} = \frac{1.5}{6}$
    $z = 2$ ft

Pages 367–369 Exercises

13. DF 14. AC 15. GB

16. IE 17. true   18. true

19. false; $\frac{BD}{DC} = \frac{2}{3}$

20. $\frac{6}{x+y} = \frac{10}{35}$
    $10x + 10y = 210$
    $10\left(\frac{5}{2}y\right) + 10y = 210$
    $\frac{25}{2}y = 210$
    $y = 6$
    $\frac{x}{y} = \frac{25}{10}$
    $10x = 25y$
    $x = \frac{5}{2}y$
    $x = \frac{5}{2}(6)$ or 15

21. $3y - 9 = 2y + 6$
    $y = 15$
    $\frac{x+2}{\frac{5}{3}x} + 11 = \frac{1}{2}$
    $\frac{5}{3}x + 11 = 2x + 4$
    $\frac{1}{3}x = 7$
    $x = 21$

22. $\frac{x}{3} = \frac{x+3}{4}$
    $4x = 3x + 9$
    $x = 9$
    $\frac{y}{3} = \frac{2y-5}{4}$
    $4y = 6y - 15$
    $-2y = -15$
    $y = 7.5$

23. $\frac{ED}{DC} = \frac{AB}{BC}$
    $\frac{8}{20} = \frac{x}{25}$
    $20x = 200$
    $x = 10$

24. $\frac{BC}{AB} = \frac{DC}{ED}$
    $\frac{12}{6} = \frac{x-4}{8}$
    $96 = 6x - 24$
    $120 = 6x$
    $x = 20$

25.
$$\frac{DC}{ED} = \frac{CB}{AB}$$
$$\frac{15}{x-5} = \frac{18}{x-4}$$
$$15x - 60 = 18x - 90$$
$$3x = 30$$
$$x = 10$$

26. The slope of $\overline{SM} = \frac{14-12}{3-5} = -1 =$ slope of ,
$\overline{TW} = \frac{26-20}{11-17} = -1$. $RS = RM = 2\sqrt{13}$;
$ST = MW = 4\sqrt{13}$, so $\frac{RS}{ST} = \frac{RM}{MW} = \frac{2\sqrt{13}}{4\sqrt{13}} = \frac{1}{2}$

27. $\left(\frac{x_1+x_2}{2}, \frac{y_1+y_2}{2}\right) = (1, 1)$

$\frac{-3+x_2}{2} = 1 \qquad\qquad \frac{4+y_2}{2} = 1$
$\quad x_2 = 5 \qquad\qquad\qquad y_2 = -2$

$B(5, -2)$

$\left(\frac{x_1+x_2}{2}, \frac{y_1+y_2}{2}\right) = (4, 3)$

$\frac{-3+x_2}{2} = 4 \qquad\qquad \frac{4+y_2}{2} = 3$
$\quad x_2 = 11 \qquad\qquad\qquad y_2 = 2$

$C(11, 2)$

28. $BC = \frac{1}{2}(FD) \qquad AB = \frac{1}{2}(FE) \qquad AC = \frac{1}{2}(DE)$

$\quad 11 = \frac{1}{2}FD \qquad\quad 15 = \frac{1}{2}FE \qquad\quad 13 = \frac{1}{2}DE$

$\quad 22 = FD \qquad\qquad 30 = FE \qquad\qquad 26 = DE$

Perimeter of $\triangle DEF = 22 + 30 + 26 = 78$

29. $AB = \frac{1}{2}(EF) \qquad BC = \frac{1}{2}(DF) \qquad AC = \frac{1}{2}(DE)$

$\quad EF = 2(CF) \qquad\quad DF = 2(AD) \qquad\quad = \frac{1}{2}(18)$ or 9

$\quad AB = CF = 7 \qquad BC = AD = 10$

30.

8 cm

31.

1   4

1   4

32. Given: $\frac{DB}{AD} = \frac{EC}{AE}$
Prove: $\overline{DE} \parallel \overline{BC}$

Proof:

Statements	Reasons
1. $\frac{DB}{AD} = \frac{EC}{AE}$	**1.** Given
2. $\frac{AD+DB}{AD} = \frac{AE+EC}{AE}$	**2.** Addition Prop. (=)
3. $AB = AD + DB$ $\quad AC = AE + EC$	**3.** Segment Addition Postulate
4. $\frac{AB}{AD} = \frac{AC}{AE}$	**4.** Substitution Prop. (=)
5. $\angle A \cong \angle A$	**5.** Reflexive Prop. of $\cong$ $\angle$s
6. $\triangle ADE \sim \triangle ABC$	**6.** SAS Similarity
7. $\angle ADE \cong \angle ABC$	**7.** Def. of $\sim$ polygons
8. $\overline{DE} \parallel \overline{BC}$	**8.** If $\leftrightarrow$ and corr. $\angle$s are $\cong$, then the lines are $\parallel$.

33. Given: D is the midpoint of $\overline{AB}$. E is the midpoint of $\overline{AC}$.
Prove: $DE \parallel BC$; $DE = \frac{1}{2}BC$

Proof:

Statements	Reasons
1. D is the midpoint of $\overline{AB}$. E is the midpoint of $\overline{AC}$.	**1.** Given
2. $\overline{AD} \cong \overline{DB}$ $\quad \overline{AE} \cong \overline{EC}$	**2.** Def. of midpoint
3. $AD = DB$ $\quad AE = EC$	**3.** Def. of $\cong$ segments
4. $AB = AD + DB$ $\quad AC = AE + EC$	**4.** Segment Addition Postulate
5. $AB = AD + AD$ $\quad AC = AE + AE$	**5.** Substitution Prop. (=)
6. $AB = 2AD$ $\quad AC = 2AE$	**6.** Substitution Prop. (=)
7. $\frac{AB}{AD} = 2$ $\quad \frac{AC}{AE} = 2$	**7.** Division Prop. (=)
8. $\frac{AB}{AD} = \frac{AC}{AE}$	**8.** Transitive Prop. (=)
9. $\angle A \cong \angle A$	**9.** Reflexive Prop. of $\cong$ angles
10. $\triangle ADE \sim \triangle ABC$	**10.** SAS Similarity
11. $\angle ADE \cong \angle ABC$	**11.** Def. of $\sim$ polygons
12. $\overline{DE} \parallel \overline{BC}$	**12.** If $\leftrightarrow$ and corr. $\angle$s are $\cong$ the lines are $\parallel$.
13. $\frac{BC}{DE} = \frac{AB}{AD}$	**13.** Def of $\sim$ polygons
14. $\frac{BC}{DE} = 2$	**14.** Substitution Prop. (=)
15. $2DE = BC$	**15.** Mult. Prop. (=)
16. $DE = \frac{1}{2}BC$	**16.** Division Prop. (=)

34. $|x_2 - x_1| = 3, \frac{3}{3}$ or 1

$|y_2 - y_1| = 12; \frac{12}{3}$ or 4

$P(2 + 1, 12 - 4) = (3, 8)$ or

$P(5 - 1, 0 + 4) = (4, 4)$

35. From N to P = 3 units right, 4 units down, for a distance of 5 units. From P to L = twice the distance, so $L[11 + 2(3), 16 + 2(-4)]$ or $L(17, 8)$. From N to R = 5 units left and 12 units down. From R to M is twice the distance, so $M[(3 + 2(-5), 8 + 2(-12)]$ or $M(-7, -16)$.

36a. Rhombus; see students' work.

36b. Sample answer: no, there will be an odd number of sides so you cannot get all sets of sides to be parallel.

37. $\frac{x}{2} = \frac{7}{9}, \qquad \frac{y}{3} = \frac{7}{9}, \qquad \frac{2}{5} = \frac{7}{9}$

$9x = 14 \qquad 9y = 21 \qquad 9z = 35$

$x = \frac{14}{9}$ cm, $\quad y = \frac{7}{3}$ cm, $\quad z = \frac{35}{9}$ cm

38a. The bar connects the midpoints of each leg of the letter and is parallel to the base. Therefore, the length of the bar is one-half the length of the base because if a segment has endpoints at the midpoints of two sides of a triangle, it is parallel to the third side of the triangle and its length is one-half the length of the third side.

38b. $\frac{3}{x} = \frac{1}{\frac{1}{12}}$

$x = \frac{3}{12} = 0.25$ cm

39. $\triangle ABC \sim \triangle ADE$ by SAS Similarity, so $\frac{AD}{AB} = \frac{DE}{BC}$.

$AD = 60$ and $AB = 100$ so $\frac{60}{100} = \frac{DE}{BC}$.

$\frac{3}{5} = \frac{DE}{BC}$ and $\frac{3}{5}BC = DE$.

40. yes; SSS Similarity

41. $\frac{AC}{DF} = \frac{BC}{x} \qquad\qquad \frac{AC}{DF} = \frac{AB}{EF}$

$\frac{3}{1} = \frac{5}{x} \qquad\qquad\quad \frac{3}{1} = \frac{4}{y}$

$3x = 5 \qquad\qquad\quad 3y = 4$

$x = \frac{5}{3}$ or $1\frac{2}{3} \qquad\quad y = \frac{4}{3}$ or $1\frac{1}{3}$

42. Yes, if it is a square. **43.** true

44. $\triangle MNO \cong \triangle ABC$ **45.** $\angle RST \cong \angle ABC$

46. $\left(\frac{x_1 + x_2}{2}, \frac{y_1 + y_2}{2}\right) = (6, -1)$

$\frac{-2 + x_2}{2} = 6, \qquad\qquad \frac{3 + y_2}{2} = -1$

$-2 + x_2 = 12 \qquad\qquad 3 + y_2 = -2$

$x_2 = 14, \qquad\qquad\quad y_2 = -5$

$B(14, -5)$

47. $(k + 6)(k - 3)$

48. mean $= \frac{267}{10} = 26.7$

median $= \frac{27 + 29}{2} = 28$

bimodel: 23, 29

Page 369 Mathematics and Society

1. This approach avoids the possibility of making mathematical errors that could result from using a reduced scale. Also, pieces of stone could be measured directly against the blueprint lines as they were cut, to ensure proper size and fit.

2. You could use a smaller "reference" object whose size you know. For example, you could photograph a familiar person or object that is next to the building and use the photograph to determine the height and width of the building. Or you could measure shadows cast by the building and by a reference object.

3. The rough blocks could be floated down the river from a quarry site to the blueprint area where the measuring and cutting took place. This would have been much easier than trying to transport the stones over land. It also avoided potential problems caused by rough terrain and bad weather.

7-5 Parts of Similar Triangles

Pages 372–373 Check for Understanding

1. 3 to 1, by Proportional Perimeter Theorem

2. $\triangle EFG \sim \triangle RST$ and one of the following: $\overline{FH}$ and $\overline{SW}$ are altitudes, angle bisectors, or medians.

3. Sample answer: Two of the three sets of altitudes are also sides of the triangles.

4. No; the correct ratio is $\frac{AD}{DC} = \frac{AB}{BC}$.

5. AB; Angle Bisector Theorem

6. DF; the medians of two similar triangles are proportional to the corresponding sides.

7. $\frac{x}{20} = \frac{12}{16}$ **8.** $\frac{18}{24} = \frac{x}{9}$

$x = 15$ $\qquad\qquad\qquad x = 6.75$

9. $\frac{5}{x} = \frac{7 - x}{2}$

$7x - x^2 = 10$

$x^2 - 7x + 10 = 0$

$(x - 5)(x - 2) = 0$

$x = 5$ or $x = 2$

When solved algebraically, $x = 5$ or 2, which means $FB = 2$ or 5. Geometrically, $FB = 5$ is not possible. In $\triangle FBG$, which is a right triangle, the hypotenuse is 5 and since the hypotenuse is the longest side of the triangle, leg FB cannot also be 5 units long. Thus FB must equal 2. **Note:** If $FB = 2$, then $x = 5$. This means that the two figures would actually be congruent, but that's ok since congruent triangles are similar.

10. Given: $\overline{VR} \parallel \overline{WS}$
$\overline{WS}$ bisects $\angle RWT$.
Prove: $\frac{RW}{WT} = \frac{RS}{ST}$

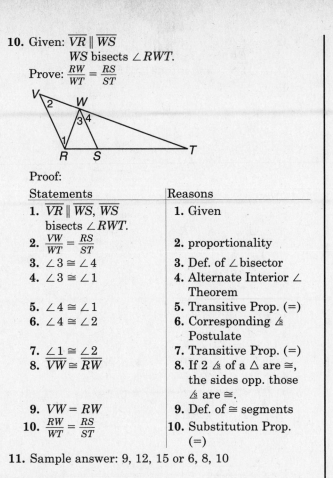

Proof:

Statements	Reasons
1. $\overline{VR} \parallel \overline{WS}$, $\overline{WS}$ bisects $\angle RWT$.	1. Given
2. $\frac{VW}{WT} = \frac{RS}{ST}$	2. proportionality
3. $\angle 3 \cong \angle 4$	3. Def. of $\angle$ bisector
4. $\angle 3 \cong \angle 1$	4. Alternate Interior $\angle$ Theorem
5. $\angle 4 \cong \angle 1$	5. Transitive Prop. (=)
6. $\angle 4 \cong \angle 2$	6. Corresponding $\angle$s Postulate
7. $\angle 1 \cong \angle 2$	7. Transitive Prop. (=)
8. $\overline{VW} \cong \overline{RW}$	8. If 2 $\angle$s of a $\triangle$ are $\cong$, the sides opp. those $\angle$s are $\cong$.
9. $VW = RW$	9. Def. of $\cong$ segments
10. $\frac{RW}{WT} = \frac{RS}{ST}$	10. Substitution Prop. (=)

11. Sample answer: 9, 12, 15 or 6, 8, 10

Pages 373–377 Exercises

12. $BD = 6$ $\qquad \frac{DC}{DF} = \frac{BC}{BF}$
$ BF = 4$ $\qquad \frac{DC}{2} = \frac{8}{4}$
$ DC = 4$

13. $\frac{FC}{GC} = \frac{1}{2}$
$\frac{4.3}{GC} = \frac{1}{2}$
$GC = 8.6$

14. $\frac{FC}{GC} = \frac{1}{2}$
$\frac{FC}{14} = \frac{1}{2}$
$FC = 7$

15. $\frac{FC}{FG} = \frac{CD}{ED}$ $\qquad CD = ED$
$\frac{FC}{18} = \frac{16}{16}$
$FC = 18$

16. CD $\qquad\qquad$ **17.** DB

18. $\frac{12}{32} = \frac{x-5}{2x-3}$
$24x - 36 = 32x - 160$
$8x = 124$
$x = 15\frac{1}{2}$ or 15.5

19. $\frac{11}{20-x} = \frac{14}{x}$
$11x = 280 - 14x$
$25x = 280$
$x = 11\frac{1}{5}$ or 11.2

20. $\frac{10}{x} = \frac{12}{18-x}$
$180 - 10x = 12x$
$180 = 22x$
$x = 8\frac{4}{22}$ or $8\frac{2}{11}$

21. $\frac{x}{26.2} = \frac{24.22}{17.3}$
$17.3x = 634.564$
$x = 36.68$

22. $\frac{6}{4} = \frac{x+3}{x}$
$6x = 4x + 12$
$x = 6$

23. $\frac{9}{x} = \frac{2x}{8}$
$2x^2 = 72$
$x^2 = 36$
$x = 6$

24. $\frac{AS}{RS} = \frac{SN}{SV}$
$\frac{7}{18} = \frac{SN}{9}$
$SN = 3.5$

25. $\frac{AB}{RT} = \frac{SN}{SV}$
$\frac{16}{36} = \frac{13}{SV}$
$SV = 29.25$

26. $\frac{AS}{RS} = \frac{AB}{RT}$
$\frac{18}{40} = \frac{22}{RT}$
$RT = 48\frac{8}{9}$

$\frac{SB}{ST} = \frac{AS}{RS}$
$\frac{24}{ST} = \frac{18}{40}$
$ST = 53\frac{3}{9}$

perimeter of $\triangle RTS = RT + ST + RS$
$= 48\frac{8}{9} + 53\frac{3}{9} + 40$
$= 142\frac{2}{9}$

27. $\frac{8}{3x-6} = \frac{3}{x+2}$
$8x + 16 = 9x - 18$
$x = 34$
$UB = x + 2 = 34 + 2$ or 36

28. $\frac{10}{8} = \frac{\text{perimeter of } \triangle RST}{\text{perimeter of } \triangle ABC}$
$\frac{10}{8} = \frac{P}{28}$
$P = 35$

perimeter of $\triangle RST = 35$
$10 + (x - 1.5) + (x - 4) = 35$
$x = 15.25$

29. $\frac{BC}{CF} = \frac{BA}{AF}$
$\frac{10}{CF} = \frac{6}{24 - CF}$
$CF = 15$

$\frac{BC}{BD} = \frac{CF}{DE}$
$\frac{10}{BD} = \frac{15}{33}$
$BD = 22$

$CD + BC = BD$
$CD + 10 = 22$
$CD = 12$

30. $AB = 6$, $AC = 8$, and by the Pythagorean Theorem, $BC = 10$. The perimeter of $\triangle ABC = 24$. Since $\overline{BC} \parallel \overline{EF}$, $\angle ABC \cong \angle DEF$. Triangle $ABD \sim \triangle DEF$, by AA Similarity.

$\frac{AB}{DE} = \frac{\text{perimeter of } \triangle ABC}{\text{perimeter of } \triangle DEF}$
$\frac{6}{9} = \frac{24}{x}$
$6x = 216$
$x = 36$

31. $\frac{24}{x} = \frac{30}{20-x}$
$30x = 480 - 24x$
$x = 8\frac{8}{9}$
$20 - x = 11\frac{1}{9}$

The measures of the segments are $8\frac{8}{9}$ and $11\frac{1}{9}$.

32. 1

33. $\frac{AB}{RS} = \frac{\text{perimeter of } \triangle ABC}{\text{perimeter of } \triangle RST}$
$\frac{10.2}{12.24} = \frac{\text{perimeter of } \triangle ABC}{32}$
perimeter of $\triangle ABC = 26\frac{2}{3}$

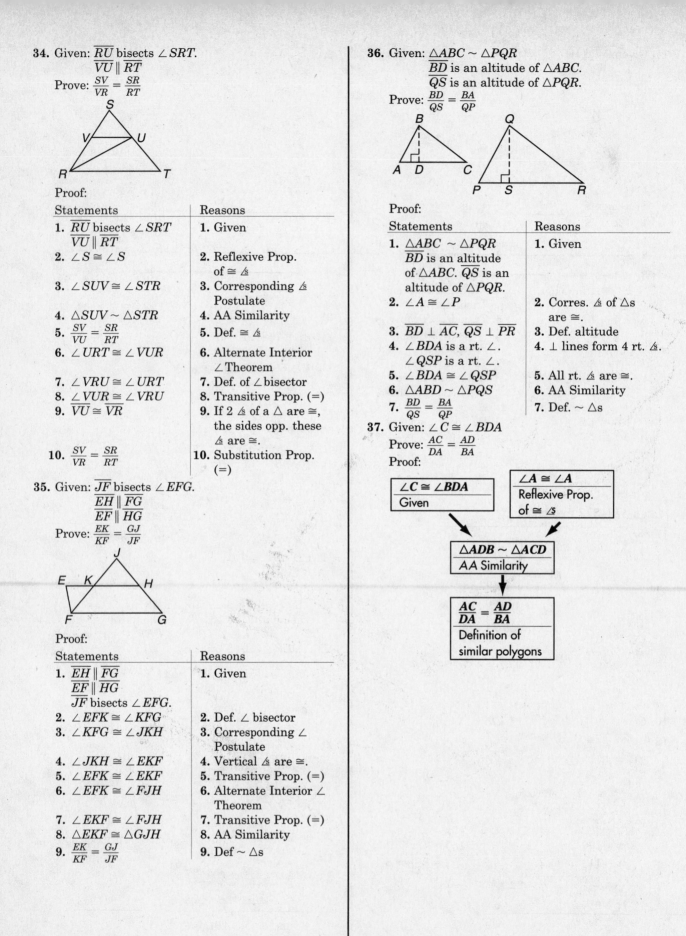

34. Given: $\overline{RU}$ bisects $\angle SRT$.
$\overline{VU} \parallel \overline{RT}$
Prove: $\dfrac{SV}{VR} = \dfrac{SR}{RT}$

Proof:

Statements	Reasons
1. $\overline{RU}$ bisects $\angle SRT$ $\overline{VU} \parallel \overline{RT}$	1. Given
2. $\angle S \cong \angle S$	2. Reflexive Prop. of $\cong \angle s$
3. $\angle SUV \cong \angle STR$	3. Corresponding $\angle s$ Postulate
4. $\triangle SUV \sim \triangle STR$	4. AA Similarity
5. $\dfrac{SV}{VU} = \dfrac{SR}{RT}$	5. Def. $\cong \angle s$
6. $\angle URT \cong \angle VUR$	6. Alternate Interior $\angle$ Theorem
7. $\angle VRU \cong \angle URT$	7. Def. of $\angle$ bisector
8. $\angle VUR \cong \angle VRU$	8. Transitive Prop. (=)
9. $\overline{VU} \cong \overline{VR}$	9. If 2 $\angle s$ of a $\triangle$ are $\cong$, the sides opp. these $\angle s$ are $\cong$.
10. $\dfrac{SV}{VR} = \dfrac{SR}{RT}$	10. Substitution Prop. (=)

35. Given: $\overline{JF}$ bisects $\angle EFG$.
$\overline{EH} \parallel \overline{FG}$
$\overline{EF} \parallel \overline{HG}$
Prove: $\dfrac{EK}{KF} = \dfrac{GJ}{JF}$

Proof:

Statements	Reasons
1. $\overline{EH} \parallel \overline{FG}$ $\overline{EF} \parallel \overline{HG}$ $\overline{JF}$ bisects $\angle EFG$.	1. Given
2. $\angle EFK \cong \angle KFG$	2. Def. $\angle$ bisector
3. $\angle KFG \cong \angle JKH$	3. Corresponding $\angle$ Postulate
4. $\angle JKH \cong \angle EKF$	4. Vertical $\angle s$ are $\cong$.
5. $\angle EFK \cong \angle EKF$	5. Transitive Prop. (=)
6. $\angle EFK \cong \angle FJH$	6. Alternate Interior $\angle$ Theorem
7. $\angle EKF \cong \angle FJH$	7. Transitive Prop. (=)
8. $\triangle EKF \cong \triangle GJH$	8. AA Similarity
9. $\dfrac{EK}{KF} = \dfrac{GJ}{JF}$	9. Def $\sim \triangle s$

36. Given: $\triangle ABC \sim \triangle PQR$
$\overline{BD}$ is an altitude of $\triangle ABC$.
$\overline{QS}$ is an altitude of $\triangle PQR$.
Prove: $\dfrac{BD}{QS} = \dfrac{BA}{QP}$

Proof:

Statements	Reasons
1. $\triangle ABC \sim \triangle PQR$ $\overline{BD}$ is an altitude of $\triangle ABC$. $\overline{QS}$ is an altitude of $\triangle PQR$.	1. Given
2. $\angle A \cong \angle P$	2. Corres. $\angle s$ of $\triangle s$ are $\cong$.
3. $\overline{BD} \perp \overline{AC}, \overline{QS} \perp \overline{PR}$	3. Def. altitude
4. $\angle BDA$ is a rt. $\angle$. $\angle QSP$ is a rt. $\angle$.	4. $\perp$ lines form 4 rt. $\angle s$.
5. $\angle BDA \cong \angle QSP$	5. All rt. $\angle s$ are $\cong$.
6. $\triangle ABD \sim \triangle PQS$	6. AA Similarity
7. $\dfrac{BD}{QS} = \dfrac{BA}{QP}$	7. Def. $\sim \triangle s$

37. Given: $\angle C \cong \angle BDA$
Prove: $\dfrac{AC}{DA} = \dfrac{AD}{BA}$
Proof:

$\angle C \cong \angle BDA$		$\angle A \cong \angle A$
Given		Reflexive Prop. of $\cong \angle s$

$\downarrow$ $\swarrow$

$\triangle ADB \sim \triangle ACD$
AA Similarity

$\downarrow$

$\dfrac{AC}{DA} = \dfrac{AD}{BA}$
Definition of similar polygons

38. Given: $\triangle RST \sim \triangle ABC$

W and D are midpoints of $\overline{TS}$ and $\overline{CB}$, respectively.

Prove: $\triangle RWS \sim \triangle ADB$

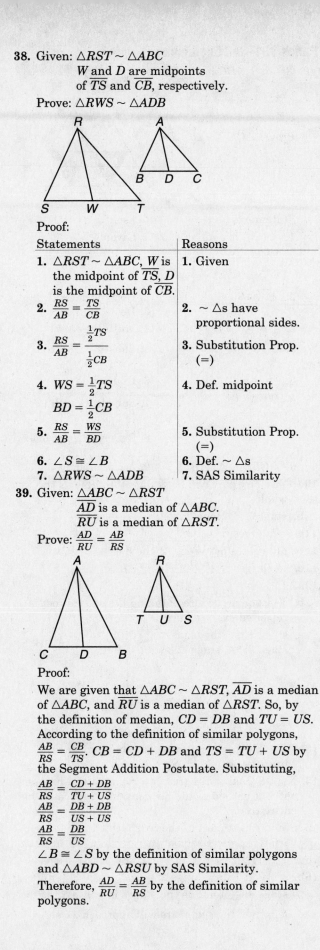

Proof:

Statements	Reasons
1. $\triangle RST \sim \triangle ABC$, W is the midpoint of $\overline{TS}$, D is the midpoint of $\overline{CB}$.	1. Given
2. $\dfrac{RS}{AB} = \dfrac{TS}{CB}$	2. $\sim \triangle$s have proportional sides.
3. $\dfrac{RS}{AB} = \dfrac{\frac{1}{2}TS}{\frac{1}{2}CB}$	3. Substitution Prop. (=)
4. $WS = \frac{1}{2}TS$ $BD = \frac{1}{2}CB$	4. Def. midpoint
5. $\dfrac{RS}{AB} = \dfrac{WS}{BD}$	5. Substitution Prop. (=)
6. $\angle S \cong \angle B$	6. Def. $\sim \triangle$s
7. $\triangle RWS \sim \triangle ADB$	7. SAS Similarity

39. Given: $\triangle ABC \sim \triangle RST$

$\overline{AD}$ is a median of $\triangle ABC$.

$\overline{RU}$ is a median of $\triangle RST$.

Prove: $\dfrac{AD}{RU} = \dfrac{AB}{RS}$

Proof:

We are given that $\triangle ABC \sim \triangle RST$, $\overline{AD}$ is a median of $\triangle ABC$, and $\overline{RU}$ is a median of $\triangle RST$. So, by the definition of median, $CD = DB$ and $TU = US$. According to the definition of similar polygons, $\dfrac{AB}{RS} = \dfrac{CB}{TS}$. $CB = CD + DB$ and $TS = TU + US$ by the Segment Addition Postulate. Substituting,

$\dfrac{AB}{RS} = \dfrac{CD + DB}{TU + US}$

$\dfrac{AB}{RS} = \dfrac{DB + DB}{US + US}$

$\dfrac{AB}{RS} = \dfrac{DB}{US}$

$\angle B \cong \angle S$ by the definition of similar polygons and $\triangle ABD \sim \triangle RSU$ by SAS Similarity. Therefore, $\dfrac{AD}{RU} = \dfrac{AB}{RS}$ by the definition of similar polygons.

40. Given: $\triangle ABC$

$\overline{DC}$ bisects $\triangle ACB$.

Prove: $\dfrac{AD}{DB} = \dfrac{AC}{BC}$

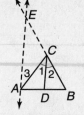

Proof:

Construct a line through point A parallel to $\overline{DC}$ meeting BC at E. Since $\overline{DC} \parallel \overline{AE}$, $\dfrac{AD}{DB} = \dfrac{EC}{BC}$. We are given that $\overline{DC}$ bisects $\angle ACB$. So, by the definition of bisector, $\angle 1 \cong \angle 2$. $\angle 1 \cong \angle 3$ because they are alternate interior angles and $\angle 2 \cong \angle E$ because they are corresponding angles. Therefore, since congruence of angles is transitive, $\angle 3 \cong \angle E$. $\overline{EC} \cong \overline{AC}$ since if two angles of a triangle are congruent, the sides opposite the angles are congruent. Therefore, $EC = AC$ and $\dfrac{AD}{DB} = \dfrac{AC}{BC}$ by substitution.

41a. 6; 24; 1:2; 1:4

41b. 35.5; 319.5; 1:3; 1:9

41c. 16.1; 578.3; 1:6; 1:36

Sample answer: If the ratio of the measures of the sides of two similar triangles is a : b, then the ratio of their areas is $a^2 : b^2$.

42a. $\dfrac{5}{a} = \dfrac{b}{b}$ and $\dfrac{b}{b} = \dfrac{w}{c}$

42b. proportional to corresponding length, width, or height relationship

42c. No; the ratio of volumes is 1 to 27.

43. Yes; the enlarged picture will take approximately 109.2 cm of piping.

$P = 2\ell + 2w$
$\quad = 2(18) + 2(24)$
$\quad = 84$

Enlarged 30% = 84(1.3) = 109.2

44. $\dfrac{10}{5} = \dfrac{x}{165}$

$x = 330$ cm

45. $\dfrac{300}{600} = \dfrac{1}{2}$; yes; proportional perimeters

46. See students' work.

47. $\dfrac{10}{7} = \dfrac{12}{x}$

$10x = 84$

$x = 8.4$

48. $\dfrac{2}{3} = \dfrac{2}{3} = \dfrac{2}{3}$

yes; SSS Similarity

49. $\dfrac{2}{3} = \dfrac{x}{21}$

$3x = 42$

$x = 14$ seniors

50. true

51. Yes; diagonals bisect each other.

52.

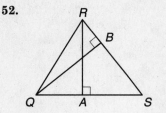

53. No; the measures of corresponding sides are not equal.

54. No; the product of the slopes is not -1.

55. If a geometry test score is 89, then it is above average.

56. $|3 - t| \leq 1$
$-1 \leq 3 - t \leq 1$
$-4 \leq \quad -t \quad \leq -2$
$4 \geq \quad t \quad \geq 2$
$\{t \mid 2 \leq t \leq 4\}$

57. $\frac{150}{25} = \frac{x}{100}$
$25x = 15{,}000$
$x = 600\%$

7-6 Fractals and Self-Similarity

Page 378 Modeling Mathematics

a. 81

b. stage 0: 48 units; stage 1: 24 units; stage 2: 12 units; stage 3: 6 units; stage 4: 3 units

c. The perimeter will approach 0.

Page 381 Check for Understanding

1. See students' work.

2. You can use the formula from the lesson: $5n = 2^{n-1}$ or you can generate the sum of the next row by multiplying the previous sum by 2.

3. Stage 1: 3, stage 2: 12, stage 3: 48, multiply the previous number by 4, so there would be 192 segments in stage 4.

4. 9 holes, 73 holes

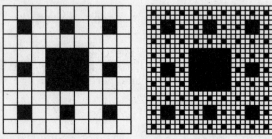

5. Yes; any part contains the same figure as the whole, 9 squares with the middle one shaded.

6. 5th = 10 + 5 or 15   6th = 15 + 6 or 21
7th = 21 + 7 or 28

7. 1, 3, 6, 10, 15, $\cdots$, each difference is 1 more than the preceding difference. The triangular numbers are the numbers in the diagonal.

8. Sample answer: broccoli, leaf veins

Pages 381–383 Exercises

9. Given: $\triangle ABC$ is equilateral.
$CD = \frac{1}{3}CB$
$CE = \frac{1}{3}CA$
Prove: $\triangle CED \sim \triangle CAB$

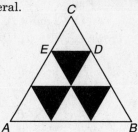

Proof:

Statements	Reasons
1. $\triangle ABC$ is equilateral. $CD = \frac{1}{3}CB$ $CE = \frac{1}{3}CA$	1. Given
2. $\overline{AC} \cong \overline{BC}$	2. Def. equilateral
3. $AC = BC$	3. Def $\cong$ segments
4. $\frac{1}{3}AC = \frac{1}{3}CB$	4. Mult. Prop. (=)
5. $CD = CE$	5. Substitution Prop. (=)
6. $\frac{CD}{CB} = \frac{CE}{CB}$	6. Division Prop. (=)
7. $\frac{CD}{CB} = \frac{CE}{CA}$	7. Substitution Prop. (=)
8. $\angle C \cong \angle C$	8. Reflexive Prop. of $\cong$ $\angle$s
9. $\triangle CED \sim \triangle CAB$	9. AA Similarity

10a. Yes; any part will be exactly the same as the whole.

10b. stage 1: 6, stage 2: 36

11a. converges to 1

11b. alternates between 0.2 and 5.0

11c. converges to 1

12a. 1

12b. Yes; the procedure of taking the square root is repeated over and over.

13a. stage 1: 2, stage 2: 6, stage 3: 14, stage 4: 30

Stage 3   Stage 4

13b. Sample answer: At stage n, the number of branches would be $S_n = 2(1 - 2^n)$.

14. No; the base of the tree or a segment of a branch without an end would not contain a replica of the entire tree.

15. Similar to stage 1 of the Sierpinski triangle variation from Exercise 10.

16a. $S_n = 4^{n-1}$; $S_8 = 4^{8-1} = 16{,}384$

16b. stage 1: 1 unit, stage 2: $\frac{1}{3}$ unit, stage 3: $\frac{1}{9}$ unit, stage 4: $\frac{1}{27}$ unit; as the stages increase, the length of the segments will approach zero.

17a. stage 1: 3 units

stage 2: $3 \cdot \frac{4}{3}$ or 4 units

stage 3: $3 \cdot \frac{4}{3} \cdot \frac{4}{3} = 3\left(\frac{4}{3}\right)^2$ or $5\frac{1}{3}$ units

stage 4: $3 \cdot \frac{4}{3} \cdot \frac{4}{3} \cdot \frac{4}{3} = 3\left(\frac{4}{3}\right)^3$ or $7\frac{1}{9}$ units

17b. $P = 3\left(\frac{4}{3}\right)^{n-1}$; as stages increase, perimeter increases and will approach infinity.

18. The original triangle and the new triangles are equilateral and thus, all of the angles are equal to 60. By AA Similarity, the triangles are similar.

19a. Trisect each of the three edges; replace the middle section on the center edge with three segments of length equal to the length removed; replace the first section on each of the outside edges with three segments of length equal to that removed. Repeat.

19b. See students' work.

20. Figure 1 is real trees, Figure 2 is a fractal mountainscape, Figure 3 is a fractal representation of Yellowstone Lake, Figure 4 is a real creek; all the images possess self-similarity.

21a. $1 + 1 + 1 + 1 + \cdots + 1 = 25$

21b. $1 + 2 + 3 + 4 + 5 + \cdots + 50 = 1275$

22. See students' work.

23. perimeter of $\triangle WVU = UV + VW + UW$
$$= 500 + 400 + 300 \text{ or } 1200$$

$\dfrac{ST}{UV} = \dfrac{\text{perimeter of } \triangle RST}{\text{perimeter of } \triangle UVW}$

$\dfrac{1000}{500} = \dfrac{\text{perimeter of } \triangle RST}{1200}$

perimeter of $\triangle RST = 2400$ units

24. $\dfrac{x}{16} = \dfrac{y}{20}$

$16y = 20x$

$y = \frac{5}{4}x$

$\dfrac{16}{x} = \dfrac{y}{45}$

$xy = 720$

$x\left(\frac{5}{4}x\right) = 720$

$\frac{5}{4}x^2 = 720$

$x^2 = 576$

$x = 24$

$y = \frac{5}{4}x = \frac{5}{4}(24)$ or 30

25. slope of $\overline{RS} = \dfrac{-4 - 3}{-1 - 1} = \dfrac{7}{2}; -\dfrac{2}{7}$

26. No; the sum of the angle measures does not equal 180.

27. no conclusion

28. 1.0×10^{-8}

29. $\{(-1, -1), (0, 2), (2, 8), (4, 14)\}$

Pages 384–385

1a. The midpoint of $\overline{PA}$ is (0.1, 0.2) in $\triangle L$; the midpoint of $\overline{PB}$ is (0.6, 0.2) in $\triangle R$; the midpoint of $\overline{PC}$ is (0.35, 0.65) in $\triangle T$.

1b. The midpoint of $\overline{PA}$ is (0.25, 0.1) in $\triangle L$; the midpoint of $\overline{PB}$ is (0.75, 0.1) in $\triangle R$; the midpoint of $\overline{PC}$ is (0.5, 0.55) in $\triangle T$.

1c. $\frac{1}{27}$　　**1d.** $\frac{1}{9}$　　**1e.** $\frac{1}{9}$

2a. The midpoint of $\overline{PA}$ is (0.15, 0.25) in $\triangle L$; the midpoint of $\overline{PB}$ is (0.65, 0.25) in $\triangle R$; the midpoint of $\overline{PC}$ is (0.4, 0.7) in $\triangle T$.

2b. The first midpoint toward A is (0.15, 0.25) in $\triangle L$, the second midpoint toward A is (0.075, 0.125) in $\triangle L$, the third midpoint toward B is (0.5375, 0.0625) in $\triangle R$.

3a. $\frac{1}{9}$　　**3b.** $\frac{1}{3}$　　**3c.** $\frac{1}{27}$

4. See students' work.

Chapter 7 Highlights

Page 387 Understanding and Using the Vocabulary

1. false; proportional
2. true
3. false; two, two
4. false; ratio
5. true
6. false; extremes
7. true
8. false; proportional
9. true
10. true
11. false; $ad = bc$
12. true

Chapter 7 Study Guide and Assessment

Pages 388–390 Skills and Concepts

13. $\dfrac{15}{30} = \dfrac{1}{2}$　　**14.** $\dfrac{15}{55} = \dfrac{3}{11}$

15. $\dfrac{x}{8} = \dfrac{6}{15}$
$15x = 48$
$x = 3.2$

16. $\dfrac{7}{x} = \dfrac{2}{3}$
$21 = 2x$
$x = 10.5$

17. $\dfrac{1}{a} = \dfrac{5}{a + 5}$
$a + 5 = 5a$
$a = 1.25$

18. $\dfrac{k + 3}{4} = \dfrac{5k - 2}{9}$
$9k + 27 = 20k - 8$
$k = \dfrac{35}{11}$

19. $\dfrac{JK}{AB} = \dfrac{JL}{AC}$
$\dfrac{7}{AB} = \dfrac{6}{8}$
$6AB = 56$
$AB = 9\frac{1}{3}$

20. $\dfrac{KL}{BC} = \dfrac{JL}{AC}$
$\dfrac{7}{BC} = \dfrac{6}{14}$
$6BC = 98$
$BC = 16\frac{1}{3}$

21. false   **22.** true

23. $\frac{5}{x} = \frac{12}{24}$

$12x = 120$

$x = 10$

24. $\frac{13}{y-2} = \frac{12}{24}$

$12y - 24 = 312$

$y = 28$

25. no; not enough information

26. yes; $\triangle HGI \sim \triangle KJL$; SAS Similarity

27. $\frac{PE}{DP} = \frac{EQ}{QF}$

$\frac{x+2}{12} = \frac{3}{8}$

$8x + 16 = 36$

$x = 2.5$

28. $\frac{TS}{SR} = \frac{TV}{VP}$

$\frac{5+x}{3} = \frac{8+x}{4}$

$20 + 4x = 24 + 3x$

$x = 4$

29. $\frac{BC}{YZ} = \frac{BM}{YN}$

$\frac{9}{12} = \frac{7}{YN}$

$9YN = 84$

$YN = 9\frac{1}{3}$

30. $\frac{PQ}{ST} = \frac{PM}{SV}$

$\frac{10}{4} = \frac{2x+9}{6x+1}$

$60x + 10 = 8x + 36$

$52x = 26$

$x = \frac{1}{2}$

perimeter of $\triangle STV = 4 + 3 + \left[6\left(\frac{1}{2}\right) + 1\right] = 11$

$\frac{10}{4} = \frac{\text{perimeter of } \triangle PQM}{\text{perimeter of } \triangle RST}$

$\frac{10}{4} = \frac{\text{perimeter of } \triangle PQM}{11}$

perimeter of $\triangle PQM = 27.5$

31.

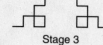

Stage 3

32. Sample answer: The smaller pieces are duplicates of the whole head.

Page 390 Applications and Problem Solving

33. $\frac{1}{6}(174) = 29$

34. $\frac{1 \text{ cm}}{15 \text{ km}} = \frac{7.9 \text{ cm}}{x \text{ km}}$

$x = 118.5 \text{ km}$

35. $\frac{36 \text{ cm}}{90 \text{ m}} = \frac{x \text{ cm}}{78 \text{ m}}$

$90x = 2808$

$x = 31.2 \text{ cm}$

36. $AT = TC = 4$ and $DT = TB = 7$

37. $2^1 = 2$

$2^2 = 4$

$2^3 = 8$

$2^4 = 16$

$2^5 = 32$

The units digit of 2^{125} is 2.

Page 391 Alternative Assessment: Thinking Critically

diameter of medium bowl $= d$

diameter of larger bowl $= 1.3d$

Volume of medium bowl $= \frac{2}{3}\pi\left(\frac{1}{2}d\right)^3 = \frac{1}{12}\pi d^3$

larger bowl $= \frac{2}{3}\pi(.65d)^3$

$\frac{2 \text{ cups}}{x \text{ cups}} = \frac{\frac{1}{12}\pi d^3}{\frac{2}{3}\pi(0.65)^3 d^3} = \frac{\text{volume of medium bowl}}{\text{volume of larger bowl}}$

$x = 4.394 \text{ cups}$

CHAPTER 8 Applying Right Triangles and Trigonometry

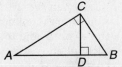

Modeling Mathematics
The Pythagorean Theorem

Page 396

1. yes

2. $a^2 + b^2 = c^2$

3. The sum of the areas of the two smaller squares is equal to the area of the larger square.

8-1 Geometric Mean and the Pythagorean Theorem

Pages 400–401 Check for Understanding

1. If x is the geometric mean, $\frac{5}{x} = \frac{x}{7}$. To find the mean, solve the equation for x.

2.

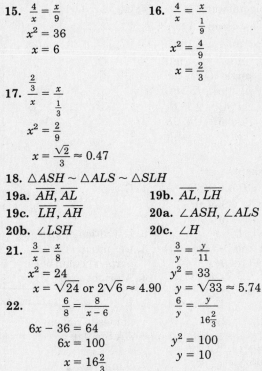

$\angle A \cong \angle A$ and $\angle CDA \cong \angle ACB$, so $\triangle ACD \sim \triangle ABC$ by AA. $\angle B \cong \angle B$ and $\angle ACB \cong \angle CDB$, so $\triangle ABC \sim \triangle CBD$ by AA. $\triangle ACD \sim \triangle ABC \sim \triangle CBD$ by the Transitive Property.

3. Since the numbers in a Pythagorean triple satisfy the equation $a^2 + b^2 = c^2$, they represent the sides of a right triangle by the converse of the Pythagorean Theorem.

4.

For leg $\overline{AC}$, $\overline{AB}$ is the hypotenuse and $\overline{AD}$ is the segment adjacent to the leg. For leg $\overline{BC}$, $\overline{AB}$ is the hypotenuse and $\overline{BD}$ is the segment adjacent to the leg.

5. Sierra; SU is the geometric mean between RS and TS only if the triangle is a right triangle and $\overline{SU}$ is the altitude from the right angle.

6a. 1 unit^2; 1 unit^2; 2 units^2

6b. The sum of the areas of the squares built on the legs equals the area of the square built on the hypotenuse.

6c. See students' work; the sum of the areas of the squares built on the legs equals the area of the square built on the hypotenuse.

7. $\frac{4}{x} = \frac{x}{25}$
$x^2 = 100$
$x = 10$

8a. $\triangle PTG \sim \triangle PGA \sim \triangle GTA$

8b. $\angle PAG, \angle TAG$

9. $\frac{5}{x} = \frac{x}{2}$
$x^2 = 10$
$x = \sqrt{10} \approx 3.16$

$\frac{2}{y} = \frac{y}{7}$
$y^2 = 14$
$y = \sqrt{14} \approx 3.74$

10. $\frac{y-4}{6} = \frac{6}{4}$
$4y - 16 = 36$
$4y = 52$
$y = 13$

$\frac{4}{x} = \frac{x}{13}$
$x^2 = 52$
$x = \sqrt{52}$
$x = 2\sqrt{13} \approx 7.21$

11. $7^2 + y^2 = 10^2$
$49 + y^2 = 100$
$y^2 = 51$
$y = \sqrt{51} \approx 7.14$

12. $4^2 + 7.5^2 \stackrel{?}{=} 8.5^2$
$16 + 56.25 \stackrel{?}{=} 72.25$
$72.25 \stackrel{?}{=} 72.25$
yes

13. Row 2: $6^2 + 8^2 = c^2$
$100 = c^2$
$10 = c$

Row 3: $9^2 + 12^2 = c^2$
$225 = c^2$
$15 = c$

Row 4: $12^2 + 16^2 = c^2$
$400 = c^2$
$20 = c$

13a. yes; 3, 4, 5

13b. Each triple is a multiple of the triple 3, 4, and 5.

13c. Sample answer: The triples are all multiples of the triple 3, 4, and 5.

13d. Yes; the measures of the sides are always multiples of 3, 4, and 5.

14. $16^2 + x^2 = 180^2$
$256 + x^2 = 32{,}400$
$x^2 = 32{,}144$
$x = \sqrt{32{,}144} \approx 179.29$ feet

Pages 401–404 Exercises

15. $\frac{4}{x} = \frac{x}{9}$
$x^2 = 36$
$x = 6$

16. $\frac{4}{x} = \frac{x}{\frac{1}{9}}$
$x^2 = \frac{4}{9}$
$x = \frac{2}{3}$

17. $\frac{\frac{2}{3}}{x} = \frac{x}{\frac{1}{3}}$
$x^2 = \frac{2}{9}$
$x = \frac{\sqrt{2}}{3} \approx 0.47$

18. $\triangle ASH \sim \triangle ALS \sim \triangle SLH$

19a. $\overline{AH}, \overline{AL}$

19b. $\overline{AL}, \overline{LH}$

19c. $\overline{LH}, \overline{AH}$

20a. $\angle ASH, \angle ALS$

20b. $\angle LSH$

20c. $\angle H$

21. $\frac{3}{x} = \frac{x}{8}$
$x^2 = 24$
$x = \sqrt{24}$ or $2\sqrt{6} \approx 4.90$

$\frac{3}{y} = \frac{y}{11}$
$y^2 = 33$
$y = \sqrt{33} \approx 5.74$

22. $\frac{6}{8} = \frac{8}{x-6}$
$6x - 36 = 64$
$6x = 100$
$x = 16\frac{2}{3}$

$\frac{6}{y} = \frac{y}{16\frac{2}{3}}$
$y^2 = 100$
$y = 10$

23.
$$\frac{y}{5} = \frac{5}{10}$$
$$10y = 25$$
$$y = 2\frac{1}{2}$$

$$x + y = 10$$
$$x + 2\frac{1}{2} = 10$$
$$x = 7\frac{1}{2}$$

24.
$$\frac{20}{24} = \frac{24}{y}$$
$$20y = 576$$
$$y = 28.8$$

$$x + 20 = y$$
$$x + 20 = 28.8$$
$$x = 8.8$$

25.
$$\frac{x}{25} = \frac{25}{5x}$$
$$5x^2 = 625$$
$$x^2 = 125$$
$$x = \sqrt{125}$$
$$= 5\sqrt{5} \approx 11.18$$

$$\frac{5\sqrt{5}}{y} = \frac{y}{30\sqrt{5}}$$
$$y^2 = 750$$
$$y = \sqrt{750}$$
$$= 5\sqrt{30} \approx 27.39$$

26.
$$\frac{x}{6} = \frac{6}{x-9}$$
$$x^2 - 9x = 36$$
$$x^2 - 9x - 36 = 0$$
$$(x-12)(x+3) = 0$$
$$x = 12 \text{ or } x = -3$$
Disregard $x = -3$

$$\frac{9}{y} = \frac{y}{3}$$
$$y^2 = 27$$
$$y = \sqrt{27} \text{ or } 3\sqrt{3} \approx 5.20$$

27.
$$2.7^2 + 3.6^2 = x^2$$
$$7.29 + 12.96 = x^2$$
$$20.25 = x^2$$
$$\sqrt{20.25} = x$$
$$4.5 = x$$

28.
$$x^2 + 25^2 = 33^2$$
$$x^2 + 625 = 1087$$
$$x^2 = 464$$
$$x = \sqrt{464} \text{ or }$$
$$4\sqrt{29} \approx 21.54$$

29.
$$x^2 + 15^2 = 25^2$$
$$x^2 + 225 = 625$$
$$x^2 = 400$$
$$x = \sqrt{400}$$
$$\text{or } 20$$

30.
$$5^2 + 12^2 \overset{?}{=} 13^2$$
$$25 + 144 \overset{?}{=} 169$$
$$169 = 169 \checkmark$$
yes

31.
$$20^2 + 21^2 \overset{?}{=} 28^2$$
$$400 + 441 \overset{?}{=} 784$$
$$841 \neq 784$$
no

32.
$$12^2 + 34^2 \overset{?}{=} 37^2$$
$$144 + 1156 \overset{?}{=} 1369$$
$$1300 \neq 1369$$
no

33. Sample answers: 16, 30, 34; 24, 45, 51

34. Sample answers: 14, 48, 50; 21, 72, 75

35. Sample answers: 18, 80, 82; 27, 120, 123

36. Given: $\angle PQR$ is a right angle. $\overline{QS}$ is an altitude of $\triangle PQR$.

Prove: $\triangle PSQ \sim \triangle PQR$
$\triangle PQR \sim \triangle QSR$
$\triangle PSQ \sim \triangle QSR$

Proof:

Statements	Reasons
1. $\angle PQR$ is a right angle. $\overline{QS}$ is an altitude of $\triangle PQR$.	1. Given
2. $\overline{QS} \perp \overline{RP}$	2. Definition of altitude
3. $\angle 1$ and $\angle 2$ are right angles.	3. Definition of perpendicular lines
4. $\angle 1 \cong \angle PQR$ $\angle 2 \cong \angle PQR$	4. All right $\angle$s are $\cong$.
5. $\angle P \cong \angle P$ $\angle R \cong \angle R$	5. Congruence of angles is reflexive.
6. $\triangle PSQ \sim \triangle PQR$ $\triangle PQR \sim \triangle QSR$	6. AA Similarity
7. $\triangle PSQ \sim \triangle QSR$	7. Similarity of triangles is transitive.

37. Given: $\angle ADC$ is a right angle. $\overline{DB}$ is an altitude of $\triangle ADC$.

Prove: $\frac{AB}{DB} = \frac{DB}{CB}$

Proof:

It is given that $\triangle ADC$ is a right triangle and $\overline{DB}$ is an altitude of $\triangle ADC$. $\triangle ADC$ is a right triangle by the definition of a right triangle. Therefore, $\triangle ADB \sim \triangle DCB$, because if the altitude is drawn from the vertex of the right angle to the hypotenuse of a right triangle, then the two triangles formed are similar to the given triangle and to each other. So $\frac{AB}{DB} = \frac{DB}{CB}$ by definition of similar polygons.

38. Given: $\angle ADC$ is a right angle. $\overline{DB}$ is an altitude of $\triangle ADC$.

Prove: $\frac{AB}{AD} = \frac{AD}{AC}$
$\frac{BC}{DC} = \frac{DC}{AC}$

Proof:

Statements	Reasons
1. $\angle ADC$ is a right angle. $\overline{DB}$ is an altitude of $\triangle ADC$	1. Given
2. $\triangle ADC$ is a right triangle.	2. Definition of right triangle
3. $\triangle ABD \sim \triangle ADC$ $\triangle DBC \sim \triangle ADC$	3. If the altitude is drawn from the vertex of the rt. $\angle$ to the hypotenuse of a rt. $\triangle$, then the 2 $\triangle$s formed are similar to the given $\triangle$ and to each other.
4. $\frac{AB}{AD} = \frac{AD}{AC}$ $\frac{BC}{DC} = \frac{DC}{AC}$	4. Definition of similar polygons

39. Given: $\triangle ABC$ with sides of measures a, b, and c, where $c^2 = a^2 + b^2$

Prove: $\triangle ABC$ is a right triangle.

Proof:

Draw $\overline{DE}$ on line ℓ with measure equal to a. At D, draw line $m \perp \overline{DE}$. Locate point F on m so that $DF = b$. Draw $\overline{FE}$ and call its measure x. Because $\triangle FED$ is a right triangle, $a^2 + b^2 = x^2$. But $a^2 + b^2 = c^2$, so $x^2 = c^2$ or $x = c$. Thus, $\triangle ABC \cong \triangle FED$ by SSS. This means $\angle C \cong \angle D$. Therefore, $\angle C$ must be a right angle, making $\triangle ABC$ a right triangle.

40. $(CB)^2 + (AC)^2 = (AB)^2$ by the Pythagorean Theorem
$|x_2 - x_1|^2 + |y_2 - y_1|^2 = d^2$ because $CB = x_2 - x_1$, $AC = y_2 - y_1$, and $AB = d$
$(x_2 - x_1)^2 + (y_2 - y_1)^2 = d^2$ because $|x_2 - x_1|^2 = (x_2 - x_1)^2$, $|y_2 - y_1|^2 = (y_2 - y_1)^2$
Take the square root of each side to get $(x_2 - x_1)^2 + (y_2 - y_1)^2 = d$.

41a. 3, 4, 5; 6, 8, 10; 12, 16, 20; 24, 32, 40; 27, 36, 45

41b. yes

42.

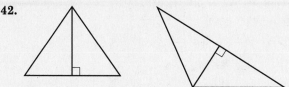

No; the smaller triangles formed when the altitudes are drawn are right triangles but the original triangles are not. Therefore, they cannot be similar.

43. $\frac{x}{3} = \frac{3}{5}$ $\quad$ $5 - \frac{9}{5} = \frac{16}{5}$ $\quad$ $\frac{\frac{9}{5}}{y} = \frac{y}{\frac{16}{5}}$
$5x = 9$ $\qquad\qquad\qquad\qquad$ $y^2 = \frac{144}{25}$
$x = \frac{9}{5}$ $\qquad\qquad\qquad\qquad$ $y = \frac{12}{5} = 2.4$ yd

44. top: $\qquad\qquad$ bottom:
$3^2 + 12^2 = x^2$ $\qquad$ $24^2 + 1.5^2 = x^2$
$9 + 144 = x^2$ $\qquad$ $576 + 2.25 = x^2$
$153 = x^2$ $\qquad\quad$ $578.25 = x^2$
$\sqrt{153} = x$ $\qquad\quad$ $\sqrt{578.25} = x$
$\quad x \approx 12.369$ $\qquad\qquad x \approx 24.047$
$2(12.369 + 24.047) = 2(36.416)$
$\qquad\qquad\qquad\quad \approx 72.83$ ft

45. no; Sample counterexample: isosceles triangle with sides measuring 4, 4, and 7
$\sqrt{4} + \sqrt{4} \overset{?}{=} \sqrt{7}$
$2 + 2 \overset{?}{=} 2.65$
$4 \neq 2.65$

46. $197 - 71 + 1 = 127$ pages

47. $\frac{1 \text{ cm}}{20 \text{ miles}} = \frac{12.7 \text{ cm}}{x \text{ miles}}$
$\qquad x = 20(12.7)$ or 254 miles

48. $M = \frac{1}{2}(10 + 22) = \frac{1}{2}(32)$ or 16 in.

49. $\quad LN = MP$
$3x - 2 = 2x + 3$
$\qquad x = 5$
$LN = 3x - 2 = 3(5) - 2$ or 13

50. False; the diagonals of a rhombus bisect opposite angles.

51. Given: $\overline{GH} \cong \overline{HJ}$
$\qquad\quad GL < JL$
Prove: $m\angle 1 < m\angle 2$

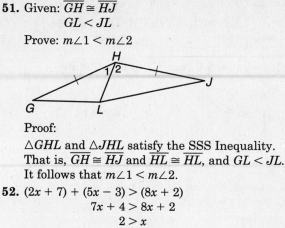

Proof:
$\triangle GHL$ and $\triangle JHL$ satisfy the SSS Inequality. That is, $\overline{GH} \cong \overline{HJ}$ and $\overline{HL} \cong \overline{HL}$, and $GL < JL$. It follows that $m\angle 1 < m\angle 2$.

52. $(2x + 7) + (5x - 3) > (8x + 2)$
$\qquad\quad 7x + 4 > 8x + 2$
$\qquad\qquad\quad 2 > x$
$(2x + 7) + (8x + 2) > (5x - 3)$
$\qquad\quad 10x + 9 > 5x - 3$
$\qquad\qquad 5x > -12$
$\qquad\qquad\quad x > \frac{-12}{5}$
$(5x - 3) + (8x + 2) > (2x + 7)$
$\qquad\quad 13x - 1 > 2x + 7$
$\qquad\qquad 11x > 8$
$\qquad\qquad\quad x > \frac{8}{11}$
$\left\{ x \mid \frac{8}{11} < x < 2 \right\}$

53. $4x + 8x + 12x = 180$
$\qquad\qquad 24x = 180$
$\qquad\qquad\quad x = 7.5$
$4x = 4(7.5) = 30$
$8x = 8(7.5) = 60$
$12x = 12(7.5) = 90$

54. $7x + 12 = 4x + 42$
$\qquad\quad 3x = 30$
$\qquad\qquad x = 10$

55.

x	y
0	1
1	4
-1	-2

$y = 3x + 1$

56. $(6t + 7a) - (3t + 12a) = 6t + 7a - 3t - 12a$
$\qquad\qquad\qquad\qquad\qquad\;\; = 3t - 5a$

Page 404 Mathematics and Society

1. 3

2. The viewer can see a more close-up image; the viewer can constantly be changing her or his position to get the best view or the view of most interest.

3. See students' work. Responses could include many types of teaching/training environments—architecture, engineering, and airline flight training.

Pages 408–409 Check for Understanding

1.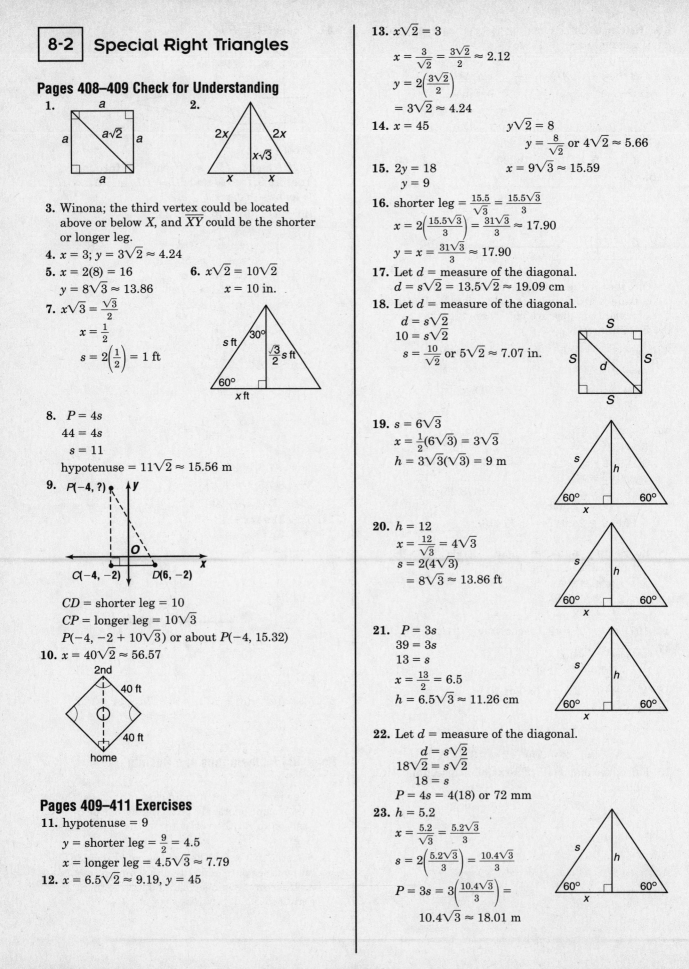

2.

3. Winona; the third vertex could be located above or below X, and $\overline{XY}$ could be the shorter or longer leg.

4. $x = 3$; $y = 3\sqrt{2} \approx 4.24$

5. $x = 2(8) = 16$
   $y = 8\sqrt{3} \approx 13.86$

6. $x\sqrt{2} = 10\sqrt{2}$
   $x = 10$ in.

7. $x\sqrt{3} = \frac{\sqrt{3}}{2}$
   $x = \frac{1}{2}$
   $s = 2\left(\frac{1}{2}\right) = 1$ ft

8. $P = 4s$
   $44 = 4s$
   $s = 11$
   hypotenuse $= 11\sqrt{2} \approx 15.56$ m

9. $P(-4, ?)$

   $CD =$ shorter leg $= 10$
   $CP =$ longer leg $= 10\sqrt{3}$
   $P(-4, -2 + 10\sqrt{3})$ or about $P(-4, 15.32)$

10. $x = 40\sqrt{2} \approx 56.57$

Pages 409–411 Exercises

11. hypotenuse $= 9$
    $y =$ shorter leg $= \frac{9}{2} = 4.5$
    $x =$ longer leg $= 4.5\sqrt{3} \approx 7.79$

12. $x = 6.5\sqrt{2} \approx 9.19$, $y = 45$

13. $x\sqrt{2} = 3$
    $x = \frac{3}{\sqrt{2}} = \frac{3\sqrt{2}}{2} \approx 2.12$
    $y = 2\left(\frac{3\sqrt{2}}{2}\right)$
    $ = 3\sqrt{2} \approx 4.24$

14. $x = 45$ $\qquad y\sqrt{2} = 8$
    $\qquad\qquad\quad y = \frac{8}{\sqrt{2}}$ or $4\sqrt{2} \approx 5.66$

15. $2y = 18 \qquad x = 9\sqrt{3} \approx 15.59$
    $y = 9$

16. shorter leg $= \frac{15.5}{\sqrt{3}} = \frac{15.5\sqrt{3}}{3}$
    $x = 2\left(\frac{15.5\sqrt{3}}{3}\right) = \frac{31\sqrt{3}}{3} \approx 17.90$
    $y = x = \frac{31\sqrt{3}}{3} \approx 17.90$

17. Let $d =$ measure of the diagonal.
    $d = s\sqrt{2} = 13.5\sqrt{2} \approx 19.09$ cm

18. Let $d =$ measure of the diagonal.
    $d = s\sqrt{2}$
    $10 = s\sqrt{2}$
    $s = \frac{10}{\sqrt{2}}$ or $5\sqrt{2} \approx 7.07$ in.

19. $s = 6\sqrt{3}$
    $x = \frac{1}{2}(6\sqrt{3}) = 3\sqrt{3}$
    $h = 3\sqrt{3}(\sqrt{3}) = 9$ m

20. $h = 12$
    $x = \frac{12}{\sqrt{3}} = 4\sqrt{3}$
    $s = 2(4\sqrt{3})$
    $ = 8\sqrt{3} \approx 13.86$ ft

21. $P = 3s$
    $39 = 3s$
    $13 = s$
    $x = \frac{13}{2} = 6.5$
    $h = 6.5\sqrt{3} \approx 11.26$ cm

22. Let $d =$ measure of the diagonal.
    $d = s\sqrt{2}$
    $18\sqrt{2} = s\sqrt{2}$
    $18 = s$
    $P = 4s = 4(18)$ or 72 mm

23. $h = 5.2$
    $x = \frac{5.2}{\sqrt{3}} = \frac{5.2\sqrt{3}}{3}$
    $s = 2\left(\frac{5.2\sqrt{3}}{3}\right) = \frac{10.4\sqrt{3}}{3}$
    $P = 3s = 3\left(\frac{10.4\sqrt{3}}{3}\right) =$
    $10.4\sqrt{3} \approx 18.01$ m

24. The diagonals of a rectangle are congruent and bisect each other.

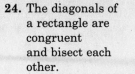

$AC = 12$

$AD = \frac{1}{2}(AC) = \frac{1}{2}(12)$ or 6

$DC = AD(\sqrt{3}) = 6\sqrt{3}$

$P = 2\ell + 2w$
$= 2(6\sqrt{3}) + 2(6)$
$= 12\sqrt{3} + 12$
≈ 32.78 in.

25. Let s = side of the square.

$s^2 + s^2 + s^2 + s^2 = 196$
$4s^2 = 196$
$s^2 = 49$
$s = 7$
$d = s\sqrt{2} = 7\sqrt{2} \approx 9.90$

26.

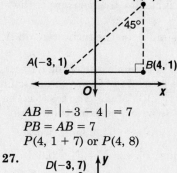

$AB = |-3 - 4| = 7$
$PB = AB = 7$
$P(4, 1 + 7)$ or $P(4, 8)$

27.

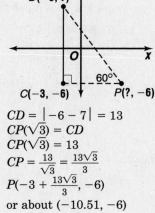

$CD = |-6 - 7| = 13$
$CP(\sqrt{3}) = CD$
$CP(\sqrt{3}) = 13$
$CP = \frac{13}{\sqrt{3}} = \frac{13\sqrt{3}}{3}$
$P(-3 + \frac{13\sqrt{3}}{3}, -6)$
or about $(-10.51, -6)$

28.

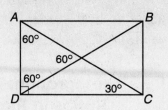

$CD = |2 - 10| = 8$
$PD = \frac{1}{2}(CD) = \frac{1}{2}(8)$ or 4

$PC = \sqrt{3}(PD) = 4\sqrt{3}$
$PC = \sqrt{(x - 2)^2 + [y - (-5)]^2}$
$4\sqrt{3} = \sqrt{(x - 2)^2 + (y + 5)^2}$
$48 = (x - 2)^2 + (y + 5)^2$
$48 = (x - 2)^2 = (y + 5)^2$

$PD = \sqrt{(x - 10)^2 + [y - (-5)]^2}$
$4 = \sqrt{(x - 10)^2 + (y + 5)^2}$
$16 = (x - 10)^2 + (y + 5)^2$
$16 - (x - 10)^2 = (y + 5)^2$
$16 - (x - 10)^2 = 48 - (x - 2)^2$
$16 - (x^2 - 20x + 100) = 48 - (x^2 - 4x + 4)$
$-x^2 + 20x - 84 = -x^2 + 4x + 44$
$16x = 128$
$x = 8$

$16 = (x - 10)^2 + (y + 5)^2$
$16 = (8 - 10)^2 + (y + 5)^2$
$12 = (y + 5)^2$
$\pm\sqrt{12} = y + 5$
$y = -5 \pm 2\sqrt{3}$

Disregard $y = -5 - 2\sqrt{3}$ which would be a coordinate below $\overline{CD}$.

$P(8, -5 + 2\sqrt{3})$ or about $(8, -1.54)$

29.

$a = \frac{1}{2}(4)\sqrt{3} = 2\sqrt{3}$
$b = \frac{1}{2}(2\sqrt{3})\sqrt{3} = 3$
$c = \frac{1}{2}(3)\sqrt{3} = \frac{3}{2}\sqrt{3}$
$x = \frac{1}{2}\left(\frac{3}{2}\sqrt{3}\right)\sqrt{3} = \frac{9}{4}$ or 2.25

30a. $BC = CF = s$
$BF = s\sqrt{2}$
$(BA)^2 + (BF)^2 = (AF)^2$
$s^2 + (s\sqrt{2})^2 = (AF)^2$
$s^2 + 2s^2 = (AF)^2$
$3s^2 = (AF)^2$
$s\sqrt{3} = AF$

30b. If $\overline{BD}$ is drawn, $BF = FD = BD$. So $\triangle BFD$ is equilateral and $m\angle BFD = 60°$.

31a.

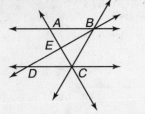

31b. $m\angle BCD = 120$, $m\angle BCE = 60$, $m\angle ABC = 180 -$ 120 or 60, $m\angle EBC = 30$, $m\angle BEC = 180 - 60 -$ 30 or 90; $\triangle BEC$ is a $30° - 60° - 90°$ triangle.

31c. $\frac{22\sqrt{3}}{3} \approx 12.70$; $\frac{44\sqrt{3}}{3} \approx 25.40$

32.

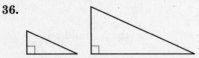

$a = 0.5 = \frac{1}{2}$

$x\sqrt{3} = \frac{1}{2}$

$x = \frac{1}{2\sqrt{3}}$ or $\frac{\sqrt{3}}{6}$

$s = 2\left(\frac{\sqrt{3}}{6}\right)$ or $\frac{\sqrt{3}}{3}$

$P = 6\left(\frac{\sqrt{3}}{3}\right)$ or $2\sqrt{3} \approx 3.46$ mi

33. 6 yd = 18 ft

$h = 18 + 5$ or 23 ft

34. $5^2 + 12^2 = c^2$

$25 + 144 = c^2$

$169 = c^2$

$13 = c$

The plywood needs to be 13 ft long.

35. AA Similarity, SSS Similarity, SAS Similarity

36.

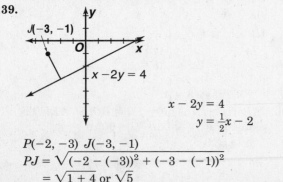

37. $\overline{QS}$ and $\overline{RT}$ are diagonals.

$QS = \sqrt{[1 - (-1)]^2 + [4 - (-6)]^2} = \sqrt{2^2 + 10^2} =$ $\sqrt{104}$ or $2\sqrt{26}$

$RT = \sqrt{[5 - (-5)]^2 + [0 - (-2)]^2} = \sqrt{10^2 + 2^2} =$ $\sqrt{104}$ or $2\sqrt{26}$

Since $\overline{QS} \cong \overline{RT}$, $QRST$ is a rectangle.

38. $KL = \sqrt{(5 - 0)^2 + (8 - (-4))^2} = 13$

$LM = \sqrt{(0 - (-1))^2 + (-4 - 1)^2} = \sqrt{26} \approx 5.1$

$KM = \sqrt{(5 - (-1))^2 + (8 - 1)^2} = \sqrt{85} \approx 9.2$

$13 + 5.1 > 9.2$

$13 + 9.2 > 5.1$

$5.1 + 9.2 > 13$

Yes; the lengths of the segments satisfy the Triangle Inequality Theorem.

39.

$x - 2y = 4$

$y = \frac{1}{2}x - 2$

$P(-2, -3)$ $J(-3, -1)$

$PJ = \sqrt{(-2 - (-3))^2 + (-3 - (-1))^2}$

$= \sqrt{1 + 4}$ or $\sqrt{5}$

40. $\frac{8k^4}{2k} = \frac{2k(4k^3)}{2k} = 4k^3$

41. $8g(g + 4)$

8-3 | **Integration: Trigonometry Ratios in Right Triangles**

Page 413 Modeling Mathematics

a. See students' work. The fractions are equivalent.

b. See students' work. The fractions are equivalent.

c. See students' work. The fractions are equivalent.

Pages 415–416 Check for Understanding

1. triangle measurement

2. All three ratios involve two sides of a right triangle. The sine ratio is the measure of the opposite side divided by the measure of the hypotenuse. The cosine ratio is the measure of the adjacent side divided by the measure of the hypotenuse. The tangent ratio is the measure of the opposite side divided by the measure of the adjacent side.

3. The triangles are similar, so the ratios remain the same.

4. The cos is the ratio of the measure of the adjacent side divided by the measure of the hypotenuse for a given angle in a right triangle. The $\cos^{-1}$ is the measure of the angle with a certain cosine ratio.

5a. $\frac{AE}{ED}$, $\frac{AG}{GF}$, $\frac{AB}{BC}$ **5b.** See students' work.

5c. The ratios are equal.   **6.** $\cos M = \frac{20}{29} \approx 0.6897$

7. $\tan E = \frac{20}{21} \approx 0.9524$ **8.** $\sin E = \frac{20}{29} \approx 0.6897$

9. 0.2419   **10.** 0.6293   **11.** 63.5   **12.** 37.1

13. $\tan x° = \frac{16}{10}$ **14.** $\cos 17° = \frac{x}{9.7}$

$\qquad x = 58.0°$ $\qquad\qquad\qquad x = 9.7 \cos 17°$

$\qquad\qquad\qquad\qquad\qquad\qquad x = 9.3$

15. $BC = 3$, $AC = 8$

$\tan A = \frac{3}{8}$

$A \approx 20.6$

16. Let x = maximum height.

$\sin 75° = \frac{x}{10}$

$x = 10 \sin 75°$

$x \approx 9.66$ ft

Pages 416–419 Exercises

17. $\sin A = \frac{5}{5\sqrt{26}} = \frac{\sqrt{26}}{26} \approx 0.1961$

18. $\cos x° = \frac{5}{5\sqrt{26}} = \frac{\sqrt{26}}{26} \approx 0.1961$

19. $\cos A = \frac{25}{5\sqrt{26}} = \frac{5\sqrt{26}}{26} \approx 0.9806$

20. $\sin x° = \frac{25}{5\sqrt{26}} = \frac{5\sqrt{26}}{26} \approx 0.9806$

21. $\tan x° = \frac{25}{5} = 5 = 5.0000$

22. $\tan A = \frac{5}{25} = \frac{1}{5} = 0.2000$

23. $\cos B = \frac{1}{\sqrt{26}} = \frac{\sqrt{26}}{26} \approx 0.1961$

24. $\sin y° = \frac{1}{\sqrt{26}} = \frac{\sqrt{26}}{26} \approx 0.1961$

25. $\tan B = \frac{5}{1} = 5 = 5.000$

26. 0.1219   **27.** 0.9135   **28.** 1.3764   **29.** 0.9511

30. 0.7431   **31.** 0.3640   **32.** 46.4   **33.** 75.6

34. 84.0   **35.** 27.2   **36.** 83.0   **37.** 23.2

38. $\sin 63° = \frac{x}{50}$ **39.** $\sin x° = \frac{7}{13}$
      $x = 50 \sin 63°$ $x = 32.6°$
      $x = 44.6$

40. $\tan 25° = \frac{x}{15}$ **41.** $\cos 32° = \frac{x}{24}$
      $x = 15 \tan 25°$ $x = 24 \cos 32°$
      $x = 7.0$ $x = 20.4$

42. $\tan x° = \frac{12}{15}$ **43.** $\cos 18° = \frac{5.8}{x}$
      $x = 38.7°$ $x = \frac{5.8}{\cos 18°}$
                        $x = 6.1$

44. $CL = \sqrt{(2-7)^2 + (-2-(-2))^2} = 5$
     $JC = \sqrt{(2-2)^2 + (2-(-2))^2} = 4$
     $\tan J = \frac{5}{4}$
     $m\angle J \approx 51.3$

45. $BC = \sqrt{(-1-(-6))^2 + (-5-(-5))^2} = 5$
     $BD = \sqrt{(-1-(-1))^2 + (-5-2)^2} = 7$
     $\tan C = \frac{7}{5}$
     $m\angle C \approx 54.5$

46. $XZ = \sqrt{(-5-0)^2 + (0-\sqrt{35})^2} = \sqrt{60} \approx 7.746$
     $XY = \sqrt{(-5-7)^2 + (0-0)^2} = 12$
     $\cos X = \frac{7.746}{12}$
     $m\angle X \approx 49.8$

47. $\tan 32° = \frac{24}{x}$
         $x = \frac{24}{\tan 32°}$
         $x \approx 38.4$

         $\cos 32° = \frac{y}{x}$
         $\cos 32° = \frac{y}{38.4}$
            $y = 38.4 \cos 32°$
            $y \approx 32.6$

48. $\tan 55° = \frac{x}{9}$
       $x = 9 \tan 55°$
       $x \approx 12.9$

       $\sin 47° = \frac{x}{y}$
       $\sin 47° = \frac{12.9}{y}$
         $y = \frac{12.9}{\sin 47°}$
         $y \approx 17.6$

49. $\sin x° = \frac{18}{27}$
       $x = 41.8°$
     $18^2 + b^2 = 27^2$
         $b^2 = 405$
           $b = \sqrt{405} \approx 20.12$
     $\tan y° = \frac{10.06}{18}$
         $y = 29.2°$

50a. Let h = measure of *the hypotenuse, so*
     $x^2 + y^2 = h^2$.
       For $x = 0.2$
   $0.2^2 + y^2 = 1^2$
         $y^2 = 0.96$
         $y = 0.96$
         $y = \sqrt{0.96} \approx 0.98$
  $\sin O = \frac{y}{h} = \frac{0.98}{1}$ or 0.98
  $\cos O = \frac{x}{h} = \frac{0.2}{1}$ or 0.2
       For $x = 0.4$
   $0.4^2 + y^2 = 1^2$
         $y^2 = 0.84$
         $y = \sqrt{0.84} \approx 0.92$
  $\sin O = \frac{y}{h} = \frac{0.92}{1}$ or 0.92
  $\cos O = \frac{x}{h} = \frac{0.4}{1}$ or 0.4
       For $x = 0.6$
   $0.6^2 + y^2 = 1^2$
         $y^2 = 0.64$
         $y = \sqrt{0.64} = 0.8$
  $\sin O = \frac{y}{h} = \frac{0.8}{1}$ or 0.8
  $\cos O = \frac{x}{h} = \frac{0.6}{1}$ or 0.6
       For $x = 0.8$
   $0.8^2 + y^2 = 1$
         $y^2 = 0.36$
         $y = \sqrt{0.36} = 0.6$
  $\sin O = \frac{y}{h} = \frac{0.6}{1}$ or 0.6
  $\cos O = \frac{x}{h} = \frac{0.8}{1}$ or 0.8

50b. $x = \cos O$
     $y = \sin O$

51. $\tan T = \frac{10}{14}$ **52.** $\tan A = \frac{6.3}{9.8}$
     $m\angle T \approx 35.5$ $A \approx 32.7°$

53a. $\tan 0.00021° = \frac{1}{x}$
      $x = \frac{1}{\tan 0.00021°}$
      $x \approx 272.837$ astronomical units

53b. The stellar parallax would be too small.

54. shorter leg $= \frac{14}{\sqrt{3}} = \frac{14\sqrt{3}}{3}$
     hypotenuse $= 2\left(\frac{14\sqrt{3}}{3}\right) = \frac{28\sqrt{3}}{3}$

55. $\frac{8}{x} = \frac{x}{9}$
     $x^2 = 72$
      $x = \sqrt{72} = 6\sqrt{2} \approx 8.49$

56. $\frac{\text{perimeter of } \triangle XYZ}{\text{perimeter of } \triangle XWV} = \frac{YZ}{WV}$
           $\frac{34}{14} = \frac{YZ}{4}$
        $14YZ = 136$
          $YZ \approx 9.7$

57. $\frac{6}{10} = 9j$
     $6j = 90$
     $j = 15$

58. $AC = 2(AR)$
$6g + 2 = 2(4g - 2)$
$6g + 2 = 8g - 4$
$6 = 2g$
$3 = g$
$RC = AR$
$RC = 4g - 2 = 4(3) - 2$ or 10

59. $17° < 22°$ therefore Oak St. is shorter than Maple St. Isabel should take Walnut St. to Oak St.

60. Show that he wasn't at the movies.

61. $7r + 12 = 9r - 3$ $25 + 7 = 35 - 5$
$2r = 15$ $s = 12$
$r = 7.5$

62. Given: $\overline{AB} \perp \overline{BD}$
$\overline{DE} \perp \overline{DB}$
$\overline{DB}$ bisects $\overline{AE}$.

Prove: $\angle A \cong \angle E$

Proof:

Statements	Reasons
1. $\overline{AB} \perp \overline{BD}$ $\overline{DE} \perp \overline{DB}$ $\overline{DB}$ bisects $\overline{AE}$.	1. Given
2. $\angle B$ is a right angle. $\angle D$ is a right angle.	2. Def. $\perp$ lines
3. $\angle B \cong \angle D$	3. All right $\angle$ are $\cong$.
4. $\overline{AC} \cong \overline{EC}$	4. Definition segment bisector
5. $\angle 1 \cong \angle 2$	5. Vertical $\angle$ are $\cong$.
6. $\triangle ABC \cong \triangle EDC$	6. AAS
7. $\angle A \cong \angle E$	7. CPCTC

63. $\angle HGI$

64. Let $x =$ the number;
$x + 11 \geq 25$
$x \geq 14$
$\{x \mid x \geq 14\}$

65. $y = 2x$ $3x + (2x) = 10$ $y = 2(2)$
$3x + y = 10$ $5x = 10$ $y = 4$
$x = 2$

$(2, 4)$

Page 419 Self Test

1. $\frac{15}{x} = \frac{x}{9}$
$x^2 = 135$
$x = \sqrt{135} = 3\sqrt{15} \approx 11.62$

2. $\frac{7}{x} = \frac{x}{4}$ **3.** $\frac{x}{6} = \frac{6}{9}$
$x^2 = 28$ $9x = 36$
$x = 2\sqrt{7} \approx 5.29$ $x = 4$

4. $x^2 + (\sqrt{12})^2 = (\sqrt{13})^2$
$x^2 + 12 = 13$
$x^2 = 1$
$x = 1$

5. $d = s\sqrt{2} = 7.5\sqrt{2} \approx 10.61$

6. shorter leg $= \frac{1}{2}(6) = 3$
altitude = longer leg $= 3\sqrt{3} \approx 5.20$

7. $\sin D = \frac{3}{\sqrt{13}} = \frac{3\sqrt{13}}{13} \approx 0.8321$

8. $\cos D = \frac{2}{\sqrt{13}} = \frac{2\sqrt{13}}{13} \approx 0.5547$

9. $\tan E = \frac{2}{3} \approx 0.6667$

10. $\tan A = \frac{10}{66}$
$A \approx 8.6°$

8-4 **Angles of Elevation and Depression**

Page 422 Check for Understanding

1. Sample answer: the angle formed by the horizontal and the line of sight looking at something below

2. Sample answer:

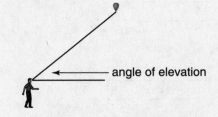

angle of elevation

3. Use sin if the measures of the side opposite the angle and the hypotenuse are known. Use cos if the measures of the side adjacent to the angle and the hypotenuse are known. Use tan if the measures of the 2 legs are known.

4. $\sin = \frac{\text{opposite}}{\text{hypotenuse}}$
$\cos = \frac{\text{adjacent}}{\text{hypotenuse}}$
$\tan = \frac{\text{opposite}}{\text{adjacent}}$
See students' work.

5. $\angle OCP$; $\angle DPC$

6. $\sin 15° = \frac{QR}{37}$ **7.** $\cos P = \frac{2.3}{5.5}$
$QR = 37 \sin 15°$ $m\angle P \approx 65.3$
$QR \approx 9.6$

8. $\tan A = \frac{173 - 5}{50}$ **9.** $\tan 75° = \frac{570 - 6}{x}$
$A \approx 73.4°$ $x = \frac{564}{\tan 75°}$
$x \approx 151.1$ ft

10a. $\tan 35° = \frac{x}{200}$
$x = 200 \tan 35°$
$x \approx 140.0$ m

10b. Yes; 140 m is higher than 61 m.

Pages 423–425 Exercises

11. $\angle GEF$; $\angle HFE$ **12.** $\angle BFT$; $\angle ATF$

13. $\angle KHJ$; $\angle IJH$ **14.** $\angle RUS$; $\angle TSU$

15. $\tan Y = \frac{54}{28}$ **16.** $\sin 28° = \frac{YZ}{15}$
$Y \approx 62.6°$ $YZ = 15 \sin 28°$
$YZ \approx 7.0$

17. $\cos 66° = \frac{7}{xy}$

$xy = \frac{7}{\cos 66°}$

$xy \approx 17.2$

18. $\cos Y = \frac{4}{15}$

$m\angle Y \approx 74.5$

19. $\cos X = \frac{4.5}{6.6}$

$m\angle X \approx 47.0$

20. $\sin 65.5° = \frac{xz}{22.4}$

$xz = 22.4 \sin 65.5°$

$xz \approx 20.4$

21a. $\tan A = \frac{625 - 5}{40}$

$m\angle A \approx 86.3$

21b. $\tan 75° = \frac{625 - 5}{x}$

$x = \frac{620}{\tan 75°}$

$x \approx 166.1$ ft

22. $\tan A = \frac{9}{175}$

$m\angle A \approx 2.9$

23. $\sin 14° = \frac{43}{x}$

$x = \frac{43}{\sin 14°}$

$x \approx 177.7$ yd

24. $\sin 35° = \frac{x}{55}$

$x = 55 \sin 35°$

$x \approx 31.5$ ft

25. $\tan A = \frac{40}{630}$

$m\angle A \approx 3.6$

26.

Let $x°$ = angle of depression.

$\cos y° = \frac{130}{550}$

$y \approx 76.3°$

$x + y = 90$

$x + 76.3° \approx 90°$

$x \approx 13.7$

27a. $\sin 70° = \frac{x}{210}$

$x = 210 \sin 70°$

$x = 197.3$

$13 + 197.3 \approx 210.3$ ft

27b. $\sin 20° = \frac{x}{210}$

$x = 210 \sin 20°$

$x \approx 71.82$

$420 - 2(71.82) \approx 276.4$ ft

28.

$\tan 29° = \frac{1335}{x}$

$x \approx 2408.4$

$\tan 42° = \frac{1335}{y}$

$y \approx 1482.7$

$x - y \approx 2408.4 - 1482.7 \approx 925.7$ ft

29.

$\tan 23.9° = \frac{h}{x}$

$h \approx x \tan 23.9°$

$\tan 11.5° = \frac{h}{0.5 + x}$

$h \approx (0.5 + x) \tan 11.5°$

$x \tan 23.9° = (5280 + x) \tan 11.5°$

$x = \frac{5280 \tan 11.5°}{\tan 239 - \tan 11.5} \approx 2240.9$

$h = (2240.9) \tan 23.9°$

≈ 993.0 ft

30a. $\sin 21.8° = \frac{6}{x}$

$x = \frac{6}{\sin 21.8°}$

$x = 16.16$ in.

diagonal of base

$(16.16)^2 + (4)^2 = y^2$

$277.03 = y^2$

$y \approx 16.64$ in.

diagonal of box

30b. $16.16 + 4 = 20.16$ in.

31. $\frac{\sin M}{\sin G}$

32. $\tan 33.7° = \frac{64}{x}$

$x = \frac{64}{\tan 33.7°}$

$x \approx 95.96$ ft

33a. $\tan 66° = \frac{6 + 1}{x}$

$x = \frac{7}{\tan 66°}$

$x \approx 3.12$ ft

33b. $\tan 19° = \frac{1 + x}{3.12}$

$x + 1 = 3.12 \tan 19°$

$x = .07$

$6 - .07 = 5.93$

the bottom 5.93 ft of the window

33c. See students' work.

34.

$\tan 35° = \frac{h}{x}$

$h = x \tan 35°$

$\tan 54° = \frac{h}{7 - x}$

$h = (7 - x) \tan 54°$

$x \tan 35° = (7 - x) \tan 54°$

$x = \frac{7 \tan 54°}{\tan 35° + \tan 54°}$

$x \approx 4.64$

$h = (4.64) \tan 35° \approx 3.25$ mi

35a. $\sin A = \frac{16}{20} = \frac{4}{5} = 0.8000$

35b. $\cos B = \frac{16}{20} = \frac{4}{5} = 0.8000$

35c. $\tan A = \frac{16}{12} = \frac{4}{3} \approx 1.3333$

36. $P = 3s$
$42 = 3s$
$s = 14$
$x = \frac{1}{2}s = \frac{1}{2}(14)$ or 7
altitude $= h = 7\sqrt{3} \approx 12.12$

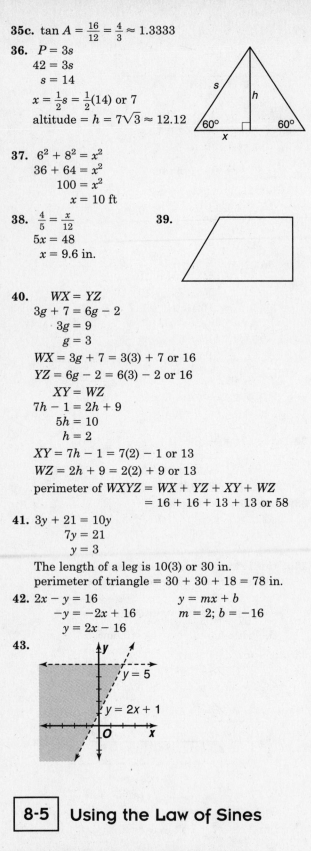

37. $6^2 + 8^2 = x^2$
$36 + 64 = x^2$
$100 = x^2$
$x = 10$ ft

38. $\frac{4}{5} = \frac{x}{12}$
$5x = 48$
$x = 9.6$ in.

39.

40. $WX = YZ$
$3g + 7 = 6g - 2$
$3g = 9$
$g = 3$
$WX = 3g + 7 = 3(3) + 7$ or 16
$YZ = 6g - 2 = 6(3) - 2$ or 16
$XY = WZ$
$7h - 1 = 2h + 9$
$5h = 10$
$h = 2$
$XY = 7h - 1 = 7(2) - 1$ or 13
$WZ = 2h + 9 = 2(2) + 9$ or 13
perimeter of $WXYZ = WX + YZ + XY + WZ$
$= 16 + 16 + 13 + 13$ or 58

41. $3y + 21 = 10y$
$7y = 21$
$y = 3$
The length of a leg is 10(3) or 30 in.
perimeter of triangle $= 30 + 30 + 18 = 78$ in.

42. $2x - y = 16$ $\qquad y = mx + b$
$-y = -2x + 16$ $\qquad m = 2; b = -16$
$y = 2x - 16$

43.

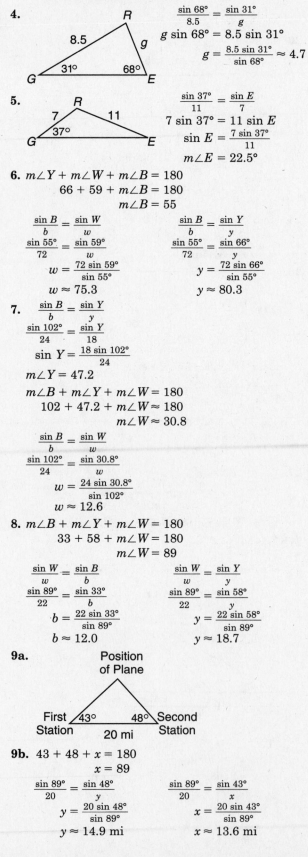

8-5	Using the Law of Sines

Pages 428–429 Check for Understanding

1. Law of Sines can be used with any triangle. However, $\sin = \frac{\text{opposite}}{\text{hypotenuse}}$ can only be used for right triangles.

2. Sample answer: Solving a triangle means finding all the missing measures.

3. The Law of Sines can be used if:
- the measures of 2 angles and a side are known or
- the measures of 2 sides and an angle opposite one of the sides are known.

4.
$\frac{\sin 68°}{8.5} = \frac{\sin 31°}{g}$
$g \sin 68° = 8.5 \sin 31°$
$g = \frac{8.5 \sin 31°}{\sin 68°} \approx 4.7$

5.
$\frac{\sin 37°}{11} = \frac{\sin E}{7}$
$7 \sin 37° = 11 \sin E$
$\sin E = \frac{7 \sin 37°}{11}$
$m\angle E = 22.5°$

6. $m\angle Y + m\angle W + m\angle B = 180$
$66 + 59 + m\angle B = 180$
$m\angle B = 55$

$\frac{\sin B}{b} = \frac{\sin W}{w}$ $\qquad$ $\frac{\sin B}{b} = \frac{\sin Y}{y}$
$\frac{\sin 55°}{72} = \frac{\sin 59°}{w}$ $\qquad$ $\frac{\sin 55°}{72} = \frac{\sin 66°}{y}$
$w = \frac{72 \sin 59°}{\sin 55°}$ $\qquad$ $y = \frac{72 \sin 66°}{\sin 55°}$
$w \approx 75.3$ $\qquad$ $y \approx 80.3$

7. $\frac{\sin B}{b} = \frac{\sin Y}{y}$
$\frac{\sin 102°}{24} = \frac{\sin Y}{18}$
$\sin Y = \frac{18 \sin 102°}{24}$
$m\angle Y = 47.2$
$m\angle B + m\angle Y + m\angle W = 180$
$102 + 47.2 + m\angle W \approx 180$
$m\angle W \approx 30.8$

$\frac{\sin B}{b} = \frac{\sin W}{w}$
$\frac{\sin 102°}{24} = \frac{\sin 30.8°}{w}$
$w = \frac{24 \sin 30.8°}{\sin 102°}$
$w \approx 12.6$

8. $m\angle B + m\angle Y + m\angle W = 180$
$33 + 58 + m\angle W = 180$
$m\angle W = 89$

$\frac{\sin W}{w} = \frac{\sin B}{b}$ $\qquad$ $\frac{\sin W}{w} = \frac{\sin Y}{y}$
$\frac{\sin 89°}{22} = \frac{\sin 33°}{b}$ $\qquad$ $\frac{\sin 89°}{22} = \frac{\sin 58°}{y}$
$b = \frac{22 \sin 33°}{\sin 89°}$ $\qquad$ $y = \frac{22 \sin 58°}{\sin 89°}$
$b \approx 12.0$ $\qquad$ $y \approx 18.7$

9a.

Position of Plane

First Station $43°$ $\qquad$ $48°$ Second Station
20 mi

9b. $43 + 48 + x = 180$
$x = 89$

$\frac{\sin 89°}{20} = \frac{\sin 48°}{y}$ $\qquad$ $\frac{\sin 89°}{20} = \frac{\sin 43°}{x}$
$y = \frac{20 \sin 48°}{\sin 89°}$ $\qquad$ $x = \frac{20 \sin 43°}{\sin 89°}$
$y \approx 14.9$ mi $\qquad$ $x \approx 13.6$ mi

10.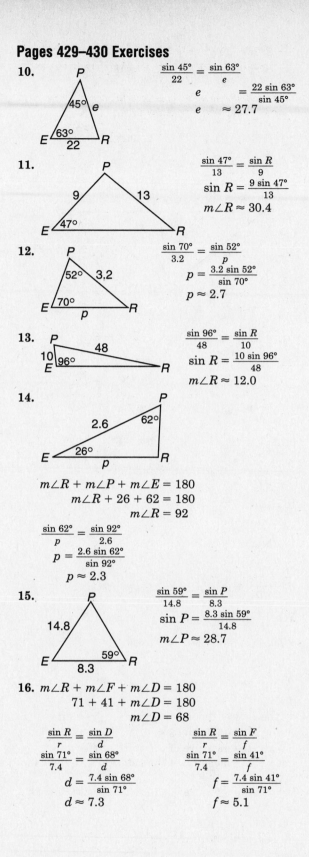

$$\frac{\sin 45°}{22} = \frac{\sin 63°}{e}$$
$$e = \frac{22 \sin 63°}{\sin 45°}$$
$$e \approx 27.7$$

11.

$$\frac{\sin 47°}{13} = \frac{\sin R}{9}$$
$$\sin R = \frac{9 \sin 47°}{13}$$
$$m\angle R \approx 30.4$$

12.

$$\frac{\sin 70°}{3.2} = \frac{\sin 52°}{p}$$
$$p = \frac{3.2 \sin 52°}{\sin 70°}$$
$$p \approx 2.7$$

13.

$$\frac{\sin 96°}{48} = \frac{\sin R}{10}$$
$$\sin R = \frac{10 \sin 96°}{48}$$
$$m\angle R \approx 12.0$$

14.

$$m\angle R + m\angle P + m\angle E = 180$$
$$m\angle R + 26 + 62 = 180$$
$$m\angle R = 92$$

$$\frac{\sin 62°}{p} = \frac{\sin 92°}{2.6}$$
$$p = \frac{2.6 \sin 62°}{\sin 92°}$$
$$p \approx 2.3$$

15.

$$\frac{\sin 59°}{14.8} = \frac{\sin P}{8.3}$$
$$\sin P = \frac{8.3 \sin 59°}{14.8}$$
$$m\angle P \approx 28.7$$

16. $m\angle R + m\angle F + m\angle D = 180$
$$71 + 41 + m\angle D = 180$$
$$m\angle D = 68$$

$$\frac{\sin R}{r} = \frac{\sin D}{d}$$
$$\frac{\sin 71°}{7.4} = \frac{\sin 68°}{d}$$
$$d = \frac{7.4 \sin 68°}{\sin 71°}$$
$$d \approx 7.3$$

$$\frac{\sin R}{r} = \frac{\sin F}{f}$$
$$\frac{\sin 71°}{7.4} = \frac{\sin 41°}{f}$$
$$f = \frac{7.4 \sin 41°}{\sin 71°}$$
$$f \approx 5.1$$

17.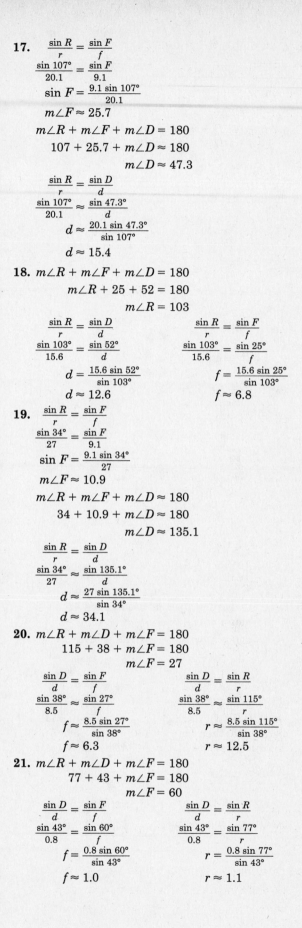

$$\frac{\sin R}{r} = \frac{\sin F}{f}$$
$$\frac{\sin 107°}{20.1} = \frac{\sin F}{9.1}$$
$$\sin F = \frac{9.1 \sin 107°}{20.1}$$
$$m\angle F \approx 25.7$$
$$m\angle R + m\angle F + m\angle D = 180$$
$$107 + 25.7 + m\angle D \approx 180$$
$$m\angle D \approx 47.3$$

$$\frac{\sin R}{r} = \frac{\sin D}{d}$$
$$\frac{\sin 107°}{20.1} \approx \frac{\sin 47.3°}{d}$$
$$d \approx \frac{20.1 \sin 47.3°}{\sin 107°}$$
$$d \approx 15.4$$

18. $m\angle R + m\angle F + m\angle D = 180$
$$m\angle R + 25 + 52 = 180$$
$$m\angle R = 103$$

$$\frac{\sin R}{r} = \frac{\sin D}{d}$$
$$\frac{\sin 103°}{15.6} = \frac{\sin 52°}{d}$$
$$d = \frac{15.6 \sin 52°}{\sin 103°}$$
$$d \approx 12.6$$

$$\frac{\sin R}{r} = \frac{\sin F}{f}$$
$$\frac{\sin 103°}{15.6} = \frac{\sin 25°}{f}$$
$$f = \frac{15.6 \sin 25°}{\sin 103°}$$
$$f \approx 6.8$$

19.

$$\frac{\sin R}{r} = \frac{\sin F}{f}$$
$$\frac{\sin 34°}{27} = \frac{\sin F}{9.1}$$
$$\sin F = \frac{9.1 \sin 34°}{27}$$
$$m\angle F \approx 10.9$$
$$m\angle R + m\angle F + m\angle D \approx 180$$
$$34 + 10.9 + m\angle D \approx 180$$
$$m\angle D \approx 135.1$$

$$\frac{\sin R}{r} = \frac{\sin D}{d}$$
$$\frac{\sin 34°}{27} \approx \frac{\sin 135.1°}{d}$$
$$d \approx \frac{27 \sin 135.1°}{\sin 34°}$$
$$d \approx 34.1$$

20. $m\angle R + m\angle D + m\angle F = 180$
$$115 + 38 + m\angle F = 180$$
$$m\angle F = 27$$

$$\frac{\sin D}{d} = \frac{\sin F}{f}$$
$$\frac{\sin 38°}{8.5} \approx \frac{\sin 27°}{f}$$
$$f \approx \frac{8.5 \sin 27°}{\sin 38°}$$
$$f \approx 6.3$$

$$\frac{\sin D}{d} = \frac{\sin R}{r}$$
$$\frac{\sin 38°}{8.5} \approx \frac{\sin 115°}{r}$$
$$r \approx \frac{8.5 \sin 115°}{\sin 38°}$$
$$r \approx 12.5$$

21. $m\angle R + m\angle D + m\angle F = 180$
$$77 + 43 + m\angle F = 180$$
$$m\angle F = 60$$

$$\frac{\sin D}{d} = \frac{\sin F}{f}$$
$$\frac{\sin 43°}{0.8} = \frac{\sin 60°}{f}$$
$$f = \frac{0.8 \sin 60°}{\sin 43°}$$
$$f \approx 1.0$$

$$\frac{\sin D}{d} = \frac{\sin R}{r}$$
$$\frac{\sin 43°}{0.8} = \frac{\sin 77°}{r}$$
$$r = \frac{0.8 \sin 77°}{\sin 43°}$$
$$r \approx 1.1$$

22. $\dfrac{\sin D}{d} = \dfrac{\sin R}{r}$

$\dfrac{\sin 107°}{30} = \dfrac{\sin R}{9.5}$

$\sin R = \dfrac{9.5 \sin 107°}{30}$

$m\angle R \approx 17.6$

$m\angle R + m\angle D + m\angle F = 180$

$17.6 + 107 + m\angle F \approx 180$

$m\angle F \approx 55.4$

$\dfrac{\sin D}{d} = \dfrac{\sin F}{f}$

$\dfrac{\sin 107°}{30} \approx \dfrac{\sin 55.4°}{f}$

$f \approx \dfrac{30 \sin 55.4°}{\sin 107°}$

$f \approx 25.8$

23. $\dfrac{\sin D}{d} = \dfrac{\sin F}{f}$

$\dfrac{\sin 88°}{21} = \dfrac{\sin F}{16}$

$\sin F = \dfrac{16 \sin 88°}{21}$

$m\angle F \approx 49.6$

$m\angle R + m\angle D + m\angle F \approx 180$

$m\angle R + 88 + 49.6 \approx 180$

$m\angle R \approx 42.4$

$\dfrac{\sin D}{d} = \dfrac{\sin R}{r}$

$\dfrac{\sin 88°}{21} = \dfrac{\sin 42.4°}{r}$

$r = \dfrac{21 \sin 42.4°}{\sin 88°}$

$r \approx 14.2$

24. $m\angle R + m\angle D + m\angle F = 180$

$m\angle R + 51 + 45 = 180$

$m\angle R = 84$

$\dfrac{\sin F}{f} = \dfrac{\sin D}{d}$ $\dfrac{\sin F}{f} = \dfrac{\sin R}{r}$

$\dfrac{\sin 45°}{23} = \dfrac{\sin 51°}{d}$ $\dfrac{\sin 45°}{23} = \dfrac{\sin 84°}{r}$

$d = \dfrac{23 \sin 51°}{\sin 45°}$ $r = \dfrac{23 \sin 84°}{\sin 45°}$

$d \approx 25.3$ $r \approx 32.3$

25. Let x = measure of each base angle. Let y = measure of leg.

$x + x + 36 = 180$ $\dfrac{\sin 72°}{y} = \dfrac{\sin 36°}{22}$

$2x = 144$

$x = 72$ $y = \dfrac{22 \sin 72°}{\sin 36°}$

$y \approx 35.6$

perimeter $= 22 + 35.6 + 35.6 \approx 93.2$ cm

26. Let ABC be the triangle. Let $m\angle A = 40$ and $m\angle B = 65$, then $m\angle C = 180 - 40 - 65$ or 75. Since $m\angle C > m\angle B > m\angle A$, $\overline{AB}$ is the longest side.

$\dfrac{\sin 75°}{34} = \dfrac{\sin 65°}{AB}$ $\dfrac{\sin 75°}{34} = \dfrac{\sin 40°}{BC}$

$AB = \dfrac{34 \sin 65°}{\sin 75°}$ $BC = \dfrac{34 \sin 40°}{\sin 75°}$

$AB \approx 31.9$ ft $BC \approx 22.6$ ft

27. $m\angle EPR = 32$

$m\angle EPR + m\angle PRE + m\angle E = 180$

$32 + 88 + m\angle E = 180$

$m\angle E = 60$

$\dfrac{\sin E}{PR} = \dfrac{\sin \angle EPR}{RE}$ $\dfrac{\sin \angle PRE}{PE} = \dfrac{\sin \angle EPR}{RE}$

$\dfrac{\sin 60°}{PR} = \dfrac{\sin 32°}{6}$ $\dfrac{\sin 88°}{PE} = \dfrac{\sin 32°}{6}$

$PR = \dfrac{6 \sin 60°}{\sin 32°}$ $PE = \dfrac{6 \sin 88°}{\sin 32°}$

$PR \approx 9.8$ $PE \approx 11.3$

28.

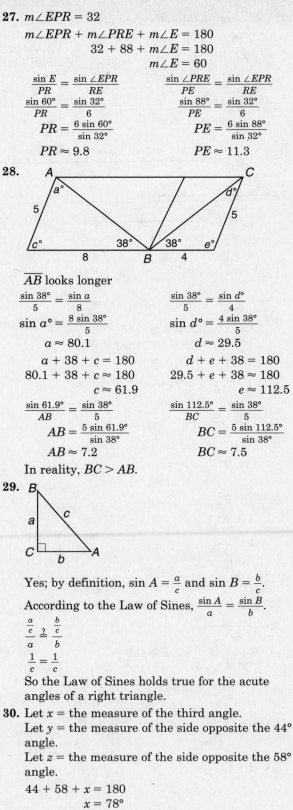

$\overline{AB}$ looks longer

$\dfrac{\sin 38°}{5} = \dfrac{\sin a}{8}$ $\dfrac{\sin 38°}{5} = \dfrac{\sin d°}{4}$

$\sin a° = \dfrac{8 \sin 38°}{5}$ $\sin d° = \dfrac{4 \sin 38°}{5}$

$a \approx 80.1$ $d \approx 29.5$

$a + 38 + c = 180$ $d + e + 38 = 180$

$80.1 + 38 + c \approx 180$ $29.5 + e + 38 \approx 180$

$c \approx 61.9$ $e \approx 112.5$

$\dfrac{\sin 61.9°}{AB} = \dfrac{\sin 38°}{5}$ $\dfrac{\sin 112.5°}{BC} = \dfrac{\sin 38°}{5}$

$AB = \dfrac{5 \sin 61.9°}{\sin 38°}$ $BC = \dfrac{5 \sin 112.5°}{\sin 38°}$

$AB \approx 7.2$ $BC \approx 7.5$

In reality, $BC > AB$.

29.

Yes; by definition, $\sin A = \dfrac{a}{c}$ and $\sin B = \dfrac{b}{c}$.

According to the Law of Sines, $\dfrac{\sin A}{a} = \dfrac{\sin B}{b}$.

$\dfrac{\frac{a}{c}}{a} \overset{?}{=} \dfrac{\frac{b}{c}}{b}$

$\dfrac{1}{c} = \dfrac{1}{c}$

So the Law of Sines holds true for the acute angles of a right triangle.

30. Let x = the measure of the third angle.
Let y = the measure of the side opposite the 44° angle.
Let z = the measure of the side opposite the 58° angle.

$44 + 58 + x = 180$

$x = 78°$

$\dfrac{\sin 78°}{30} = \dfrac{\sin 44°}{y}$ $\dfrac{\sin 78°}{30} = \dfrac{\sin 58°}{z}$

$y = \dfrac{30 \sin 44°}{\sin 78°}$ $z = \dfrac{30 \sin 58°}{\sin 78°}$

$y \approx 21.3$ ft $z \approx 26$ ft

perimeter $= 21.3 + 30 + 26 \approx 77.3$ ft

31. Let z = the measure of third angle.
Let x = the measure of the side opposite the 52° angle.
Let y = the measure of the side opposite
$z + 37 + 52 = 180$

$\frac{\sin 91°}{5} = \frac{\sin 37°}{y}$ $\frac{\sin 91°}{5} = \frac{\sin 52°}{x}$

$y = \frac{5 \sin 37°}{\sin 91°}$ $x = \frac{5 \sin 52°}{\sin 91°}$

$y \approx 3.0$ mi $x \approx 3.9$ mi

32a. $23 + 120 + x = 180$ **32b.** $120 + 23 = 143$
$x = 37$

$\frac{\sin 37°}{55} = \frac{\sin 23°}{x}$

$x = \frac{55 \sin 23°}{\sin 37°}$

$x \approx 35.7$ mi

32c. $\frac{\sin 37°}{55} = \frac{\sin 120°}{x}$

$x = \frac{55 \sin 120°}{\sin 37°} \approx 79.1$

$(55 + 35.7) - 79.1 \approx 11.6$ mi

33. $\tan 23 = \frac{x}{100}$

$x = 100 \tan 23°$

$x \approx 42.45$

height of building = $42.45 + 1.55 \approx 44.0$ ft

34. $d = s\sqrt{2}$
$7\sqrt{2} = s\sqrt{2}$
$s = 7$
$P = 4s = 4(7) = 28$ units

35. $\frac{5}{15} = \frac{9}{x}$ $\frac{5}{15} = \frac{12}{y}$
$5x = 135$ $5y = 180$
$x = 27$ $y = 36$

36. $x + 5x + 6x = 180$ **37.** See students' work.
$12x = 180$
$x = 15$
$15, 5(15) = 75, 6(15) = 90$

38. $9x + 12 = 15x$
$12 = 6x$
$x = 2$
$15x = 15(2) = 30$
$180 - 30 = 150$
$30, 150, 30, 150$

39. $9x^2 + 2xy$

40. $y(y - 12) = 0$ $y - 12 = 0$
$y = 0$ $y = 12$
$\{0, 12\}$

8-6 | Using the Law of Cosines

Pages 433–434 Check for Understanding

1. The Law of Cosines can be used if
 a. the measures of 3 sides are known or
 b. the measures of 2 sides and the included angle are known.

2. Both the Law of Sines and the Law of Cosines are used to solve triangles. The Law of Sines can be used if the measures of 2 angles and a side are known or the measures of 2 sides and an angle opposite one of the sides are known. The Law of Cosines can be used if the measures of 3 sides are known or if the measures of 2 sides and the included angle are known.

3a. With the information given, only the Law of Cosines can be used to solve for u.

3b. See students' work.

3c. See students' work.

4a.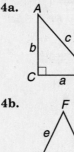

$\sin A = \frac{a}{c}$ $\sin B = \frac{b}{c}$

$\cos A = \frac{b}{c}$ $\cos B = \frac{a}{c}$

$\tan A = \frac{a}{b}$ $\tan B = \frac{b}{a}$

4b.

$\frac{\sin D}{d} = \frac{\sin E}{e} = \frac{\sin F}{f}$

The Law of Sines can be used if the 2 angles and a side are known or the measures of 2 sides and an angle opposite one of the sides are known.

4c.

$g^2 = h^2 + i^2 - 2hi \cos G$

$h^2 = g^2 + i^2 - 2gi \cos H$

$i^2 = g^2 + h^2 - 2gh \cos I$

The Law of Cosines can be used if the measures of the 3 sides are known or the measures of 2 sides and the included angle are known.

5a. Law of Sines

5b. $\frac{\sin E}{4.1} = \frac{\sin 72°}{4.5}$

$\sin E = \frac{4.1 \sin 72°}{4.5}$

$m\angle E \approx 60.1$

$m\angle E + m\angle D + m\angle F = 180$

$60.1 + 72 + m\angle F \approx 180$

$m\angle F \approx 47.9$

$\frac{\sin 47.9°}{f} = \frac{\sin 72°}{4.5}$

$f \approx \frac{4.5 \sin 47.9°}{\sin 72°}$

$f \approx 3.5$

6a.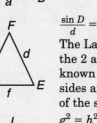

6b. Law of Cosines; two sides and the included angle require the Law of Cosines.

6c. $g^2 = n^2 + w^2 - 2nw \cos G$

$g^2 = 25^2 + 19^2 - 2(25)(19) \cos 58°$

$g = \sqrt{25^2 + 19^2 - 2(25)(19) \cos 58°}$

$g \approx 22.0$

6c. $\dfrac{\sin N}{n} = \dfrac{\sin G}{g}$

$\dfrac{\sin N}{25} = \dfrac{\sin 58°}{22}$

$\sin N = \dfrac{25 \sin 58°}{22}$

$m\angle N \approx 74.5$

$m\angle N + m\angle W + m\angle G = 180$

$74.5° + m\angle W + 58° \approx 180$

$m\angle W \approx 47.5°$

7. $m\angle A + m\angle B + m\angle C = 180$

$40 + 59 + m\angle C = 180$

$m\angle C = 81$

$\dfrac{\sin A}{a} = \dfrac{\sin C}{c}$ $\dfrac{\sin C}{c} = \dfrac{\sin B}{b}$

$\dfrac{\sin 40°}{a} = \dfrac{\sin 81°}{14}$ $\dfrac{\sin 81°}{14} = \dfrac{\sin 59°}{b}$

$a = \dfrac{14 \sin 40°}{\sin 81°}$ $b = \dfrac{14 \sin 59°}{\sin 81°}$

$a \approx 9.1$ $b \approx 12.1$

8. $a^2 = b^2 + c^2 - 2bc \cos A$

$5^2 = 10^2 + 13^2 - 2(10)(13) \cos A$

$\cos A = \dfrac{10^2 + 13^2 - 5^2}{2(10)(13)}$

$m\angle A \approx 20.2$

$\dfrac{\sin B}{b} = \dfrac{\sin A}{a}$

$\dfrac{\sin B}{10} = \dfrac{\sin 20.2°}{5}$

$\sin B = \dfrac{10 \sin 20.2°}{5}$

$m\angle B \approx 43.7$

$m\angle A + m\angle B + m\angle C = 180$

$20.2 + 43.7 + m\angle C = 180$

$m\angle C \approx 116.1$

9. $\dfrac{\sin B}{b} = \dfrac{\sin A}{a}$

$\dfrac{\sin 19°}{61} = \dfrac{\sin A}{51}$

$\sin A = \dfrac{51 \sin 19°}{61}$

$A \approx 15.8$

$m\angle A + m\angle B + m\angle C = 180$

$15.8 + 61 + m\angle C \approx 180$

$m\angle C \approx 145.2$

$\dfrac{\sin C}{c} = \dfrac{\sin B}{b}$

$\dfrac{\sin 145.2}{c} \approx \dfrac{\sin 19}{61}$

$c \approx \dfrac{61 \sin 145.2}{\sin 19}$

$c \approx 106.9$

10. $b^2 = a^2 + c^2 - 2ac \cos B$

$b^2 = 20^2 + 24^2 - 2(20)(24) \cos 47°$

$b = \sqrt{20^2 + 24^2 - 2(20)(24) \cos 47°}$

$b \approx 17.9$

$\dfrac{\sin B}{b} = \dfrac{\sin A}{a}$

$\dfrac{\sin 47°}{17.9} = \dfrac{\sin A}{20}$

$\sin A = \dfrac{20 \sin 47°}{17.9}$

$m\angle A \approx 54.8$

$m\angle B + m\angle A + m\angle C = 180$

$47 + 54.8 + m\angle C \approx 180$

$m\angle C \approx 78.2$

11. $4.9^2 = 6.8^2 + 8.4^2 - 2(6.8)(8.4) \cos A$

$\cos A = \dfrac{6.8^2 + 8.4^2 - 4.9^2}{2(6.8)(8.4)}$

$m\angle A \approx 35.7$

12. $a^2 = 180^2 + 240^2 - 2(180)(240) \cos 25°$

$a = \sqrt{180^2 + 240^2 - 2(180)(240) \cos 25°}$

$a \approx 108.1$ yd

Pages 434–436 Exercises

13. Law of Cosines;

$t^2 = s^2 + r^2 - 2rs \cos T$

$t^2 = 10^2 + 11^2 - 2(10)(11) \cos 38°$

$t = \sqrt{10^2 + 11^2 - 2(10)(11) \cos 38°}$

$t \approx 6.9$

$\dfrac{\sin R}{r} = \dfrac{\sin T}{t}$

$\dfrac{\sin R}{11} \approx \dfrac{\sin 38}{6.9}$

$\sin R \approx \dfrac{11 \sin 38}{6.9}$

$m\angle R \approx 79.0$

$m\angle R + m\angle S + m\angle T = 180$

$79 + m\angle S + 38 \approx 180$

$m\angle S \approx 63.0$

14. Law of Sines;

$\dfrac{\sin C}{c} = \dfrac{\sin A}{a}$

$\dfrac{\sin C}{8} = \dfrac{\sin 40°}{10}$

$\sin C = \dfrac{8 \sin 40°}{10}$

$m\angle C \approx 30.9$

$m\angle A + m\angle B + m\angle C = 180$

$40 + m\angle B + 30.9 \approx 180$

$m\angle B \approx 109.1$

$\dfrac{\sin B}{b} = \dfrac{\sin A}{a}$

$\dfrac{\sin 109.1°}{b} \approx \dfrac{\sin 40°}{10}$

$b \approx \dfrac{10 \sin 109.1°}{\sin 40°}$

$b \approx 14.7$

15. Law of Cosines;

$x^2 = y^2 + z^2 - 2yz \cos X$

$7^2 = 5^2 + 6^2 - 2(5)(6) \cos X$

$\cos X = \dfrac{5^2 + 6^2 - 7^2}{2(5)(6)}$

$m\angle X \approx 78.5$

$\dfrac{\sin X}{x} = \dfrac{\sin Y}{y}$

$\dfrac{\sin 78.5°}{7} \approx \dfrac{\sin Y}{5}$

$\sin Y \approx \dfrac{5 \sin 78.5°}{7}$

$m\angle Y \approx 44.4$

$m\angle X + m\angle Y + m\angle Z = 180$

$78.5 + 44.4\ m\angle Z = 180$

$m\angle Z \approx 57.1$

16.

Law of Sines;

$$\frac{\sin R}{r} = \frac{\sin D}{d}$$

$$\frac{\sin 42°}{r} = \frac{\sin 77°}{6}$$

$$r = \frac{6 \sin 42°}{\sin 77°}$$

$$r \approx 4.1$$

$$m\angle G + m\angle R + m\angle D = 180$$
$$m\angle G + 42 + 77 = 180$$
$$m\angle G = 61$$

$$\frac{\sin G}{g} = \frac{\sin D}{d}$$

$$\frac{\sin 61°}{g} = \frac{\sin 77°}{6}$$

$$g = \frac{6 \sin 61°}{\sin 77°}$$

$$g \approx 5.4$$

17.

Law of Cosines;

$$d^2 = r^2 + g^2 - 2rg \cos D$$
$$d^2 = 9.1^2 + 8.3^2 - 2(9.1)(8.3) \cos 32°$$
$$d = \sqrt{9.1^2 + 8.3^2 - 2(9.1)(8.3) \cos 32°}$$
$$d \approx 4.9$$

$$\frac{\sin G}{g} = \frac{\sin D}{d}$$

$$\frac{\sin G}{8.3} = \frac{\sin 32°}{4.9}$$

$$\sin G = \frac{8.3 \sin 32°}{4.9}$$

$$m\angle G \approx 63.8$$

$$m\angle G + m\angle D + m\angle R = 180$$
$$63.8 + 32 + m\angle R \approx 180$$
$$m\angle R \approx 84.2$$

18.

Law of Cosines;

$$d^2 = g^2 + r^2 - 2rg \cos D$$
$$22^2 = 16^2 + 13^2 - 2(16)(13) \cos D$$
$$\cos D = \frac{16^2 + 13^2 - 22^2}{2(16)(13)}$$
$$m\angle D \approx 98.2$$

$$\frac{\sin G}{g} = \frac{\sin D}{d}$$

$$\frac{\sin G}{16} = \frac{\sin 98.2°}{22}$$

$$\sin G = \frac{16 \sin 98.2°}{22}$$

$$m\angle G \approx 46.0$$

$$m\angle D + m\angle G + m\angle R \approx 180$$
$$98.2 + 46.0 + m\angle R \approx 180$$
$$m\angle R \approx 35.8$$

19.

Law of Sines;

$$\frac{\sin D}{d} = \frac{\sin G}{g}$$

$$\frac{\sin 28°}{14.9} = \frac{\sin 99°}{g}$$

$$g = \frac{14.9 \sin 99°}{\sin 28°}$$

$$g \approx 31.3$$

$$m\angle R + m\angle D + m\angle G = 180$$
$$53 + 28 + m\angle G = 180$$
$$m\angle G = 99$$

$$\frac{\sin D}{d} = \frac{\sin R}{r}$$

$$\frac{\sin 28°}{14.9} = \frac{\sin 53°}{r}$$

$$r = \frac{14.9 \sin 53°}{\sin 28°}$$

$$r \approx 25.3$$

20.
$$\frac{\sin J}{j} = \frac{\sin H}{h}$$

$$\frac{\sin J}{44} = \frac{\sin 23°}{54}$$

$$\sin J = \frac{44 \sin 23°}{54}$$

$$m\angle J \approx 18.6$$

$$m\angle H + m\angle J + m\angle K = 180$$
$$23 + 18.6 + m\angle K \approx 180$$
$$m\angle K \approx 138.4$$

$$\frac{\sin K}{k} = \frac{\sin H}{h}$$

$$\frac{\sin 138.4°}{k} = \frac{\sin 23°}{54}$$

$$k = \frac{54 \sin 138.4°}{\sin 23°}$$

$$k \approx 91.8$$

21.
$$k^2 = j^2 + h^2 - jh \cos K$$
$$65^2 = 33^2 + 56^2 - 2(33)(56) \cos K$$
$$\cos K = \frac{33^2 + 56^2 - 65^2}{2(33)(56)}$$
$$m\angle K = 90.0$$

$$\frac{\sin K}{k} = \frac{\sin H}{h}$$

$$\frac{\sin 90°}{65} = \frac{\sin H}{56}$$

$$\sin H = \frac{56 \sin 90°}{65}$$

$$m\angle H \approx 59.5$$

$$m\angle J + m\angle H + m\angle K = 180$$
$$m\angle J + 59.5 + 90 \approx 180$$
$$m\angle J \approx 30.5$$

22. $h^2 = j^2 + k^2 - 2jk \cos H$
$$h^2 = 19^2 + 28^2 - 2(19)(28) \cos 49°$$
$$h = \sqrt{19^2 + 28^2 - 2(19)(28) \cos 49°}$$
$$h \approx 21.1$$

$$\frac{\sin J}{j} = \frac{\sin H}{h}$$

$$\frac{\sin J}{19} = \frac{\sin 49°}{21.1}$$

$$\sin J = \frac{19 \sin 49°}{21.1}$$

$$m\angle J \approx 42.8$$

$$m\angle J + m\angle H + m\angle K = 180$$
$$42.8 + 49 + m\angle K = 180$$
$$m\angle K \approx 88.2$$

23. $m\angle J + m\angle H + m\angle K = 180$

$46 + 55 + m\angle K = 180$

$m\angle K = 79$

$\dfrac{\sin H}{h} = \dfrac{\sin K}{k}$ $\dfrac{\sin K}{k} = \dfrac{\sin J}{j}$

$\dfrac{\sin 55°}{h} = \dfrac{\sin 79°}{15}$ $\dfrac{\sin 79°}{16} = \dfrac{\sin 46°}{j}$

$h = \dfrac{15 \sin 55°}{\sin 79°}$ $j = \dfrac{16 \sin 46°}{\sin 79°}$

$h \approx 13.4$ $j \approx 11.7$

24. $h^2 = j^2 + k^2 - 2jk \cos H$

$669^2 = 364^2 + 436^2 - 2(364)(436) \cos H$

$\cos H = \dfrac{364^2 + 436^2 - 669^2}{2(364)(436)}$

$m\angle H \approx 113.2$

$\dfrac{\sin J}{j} = \dfrac{\sin H}{h}$

$\dfrac{\sin J}{364} \approx \dfrac{\sin 113.2°}{669}$

$\sin J \approx \dfrac{364 \sin 113.2°}{669}$

$m\angle J \approx 30.0$

$m\angle H + m\angle J + m\angle K = 180$

$113.2 + 30 + m\angle K \approx 180$

$m\angle K \approx 36.8$

25. $j^2 = k^2 + h^2 - 2hk \cos J$

$j^2 = 6.7^2 + 6.3^2 - 2(6.7)(6.3) \cos 55°$

$j = \sqrt{6.7^2 + 6.3^2 - 2(6.7)(6.3) \cos 55°}$

$j \approx 6.0$

$\dfrac{\sin J}{j} = \dfrac{\sin H}{h}$

$\dfrac{\sin 55°}{6} = \dfrac{\sin H}{6.3}$

$\sin H = \dfrac{6.3 \sin 55°}{6}$

$m\angle H \approx 59.3$

$m\angle J + m\angle H + m\angle K = 180$

$55 + 59.3 + m\angle K \approx 180$

$m\angle K \approx 65.7$

26. $j^2 = k^2 + h^2 - 2hk \cos J$

$j^2 = 10^2 + 5^2 - 2(10)(5) \cos 27°$

$j = \sqrt{10^2 + 5^2 - 2(10)(5) \cos 27°}$

$j \approx 6.0$

$\dfrac{\sin J}{j} = \dfrac{\sin H}{h}$

$\dfrac{\sin 27}{6} \approx \dfrac{\sin H}{5}$

$\sin H \approx \dfrac{5 \sin 27°}{6}$

$m\angle H \approx 22.2$

$m\angle J + m\angle H + m\angle K = 180$

$27 + 22.2 + m\angle K \approx 180$

$m\angle K \approx 130.8$

27. $h^2 = j^2 + k^2 - 2jk \cos H$

$22^2 = 27^2 + 7^2 - 2(27)(7) \cos H$

$\cos H = \dfrac{27^2 + 7^2 - 22^2}{2(27)(7)}$

$m\angle H \approx 49.9$

$\dfrac{\sin J}{j} = \dfrac{\sin H}{h}$

$\dfrac{\sin J}{27} = \dfrac{\sin 49.9°}{22}$

$\sin J = \dfrac{27 \sin 49.9°}{22}$

$m\angle J \approx 69.8$

$m\angle J + m\angle H + m\angle K = 180$

$69.8 + 49.9 + m\angle K \approx 180$

$m\angle K \approx 60.3$

28. $j^2 = h^2 + k^2 - 2hk \cos J$

$j^2 = 14^2 + 21^2 - 2(14)(21) \cos 60°$

$j = \sqrt{14^2 + 21^2 - 2(14)(21) \cos 60°}$

$j \approx 18.5$

$\dfrac{\sin J}{j} = \dfrac{\sin H}{h}$

$\dfrac{\sin 60°}{18.5} = \dfrac{\sin H}{14}$

$\sin H = \dfrac{14 \sin 60°}{18.5}$

$m\angle H \approx 40.9$

$m\angle J + m\angle H + m\angle K = 180$

$60 + 40.9 + m\angle K \approx 180$

$m\angle K \approx 79.1$

29. $h^2 = j^2 + k^2 - 2jk \cos H$

$14^2 = 15^2 + 16^2 - 2(15)(16) \cos H$

$\cos H = \dfrac{15^2 + 16^2 - 14^2}{2(15)(16)}$

$m\angle H \approx 53.6$

$\dfrac{\sin H}{h} = \dfrac{\sin J}{j}$

$\dfrac{\sin 53.6°}{14} = \dfrac{\sin J}{15}$

$\sin J = \dfrac{15 \sin 53.6°}{14}$

$m\angle J \approx 59.6$

$m\angle H + m\angle J + m\angle K = 180$

$53.6 + 59.6 + m\angle K \approx 180$

$m\angle K \approx 66.8$

30. $\dfrac{\sin H}{h} = \dfrac{\sin K}{k}$

$\dfrac{\sin 51°}{40} = \dfrac{\sin K}{35}$

$\sin K = \dfrac{35 \sin 51°}{40}$

$m\angle K \approx 42.8°$

$m\angle J + m\angle K + m\angle H = 180$

$m\angle J + 42.8 + 51 \approx 180$

$m\angle J \approx 86.2$

$\dfrac{\sin J}{j} = \dfrac{\sin H}{h}$

$\dfrac{\sin 86.2°}{j} = \dfrac{\sin 51°}{40}$

$j = \dfrac{40 \sin 86.2°}{\sin 51°}$

$j \approx 51.4$

31. $h^2 = j^2 + k^2 - 2jk \cos H$

$5^2 = 6^2 + 7^2 - 2(6)(7) \cos H$

$\cos H = \dfrac{6^2 + 7^2 - 5^2}{2(6)(7)}$

$m\angle H \approx 44.4$

$\dfrac{\sin J}{j} = \dfrac{\sin H}{h}$

$\dfrac{\sin J}{6} = \dfrac{\sin 44.4°}{5}$

$\sin J \approx \dfrac{6 \sin 44.4°}{5}$

$m\angle K \approx 57.1°$

$m\angle J + m\angle H + m\angle K = 180$

$57.1 + 44.4 + m\angle K \approx 180$

$m\angle K \approx 78.5$

32. $BD^2 = AB^2 + AD^2 - 2(AB)(AD)\cos A$
$7^2 = 5^2 + 6^2 - 2(5)(6)\cos A$
$\cos A = \frac{5^2 + 6^2 - 7^2}{2(5)(6)}$
$m\angle A \approx 78.5°$
$m\angle A = m\angle C \approx 78.5$
$m\angle A + m\angle B = 180$
$78.5 + m\angle B \approx 180$
$m\angle B \approx 101.5$
$m\angle B = m\angle D = 101.5$

33. $FH^2 = EH^2 + EF^2 - 2(EH)(EF)\cos E$
$FH^2 = 8^2 + 11^2 - 2(8)(11)\cos 110°$
$FH = \sqrt{8^2 + 11^2 - 2(8)(11)\cos 110°}$
$FH \approx 15.7$
$EG^2 = EF^2 + FG^2 - 2(EF)(FG)\cos F$
$EG^2 = 11^2 + 8^2 - 2(8)(11)\cos 70°$
$EG^2 = \sqrt{11^2 + 8^2 - 2(8)(11)\cos 70°}$
$EG \approx 11.2$

34. $85^2 = 50^2 + 70^2 - 2(50)(70)\cos C$
$\cos C = \frac{50^2 + 70^2 - 85^2}{2(50)(70)}$
$m\angle C \approx 88.6$

35. $9^2 + 13^2 = x^2$
$81 + 169 = x^2$
$x^2 = 250$
$x \approx 15.8$
15.8, 15.8, 15.8, 15.8;
$26^2 = 15.8^2 + 15.8^2 - 2(15.8)(15.8)\cos X$
$\cos X = \frac{15.8^2 + 15.8^2 - 26^2}{2(15.8)(15.8)}$
$m\angle X \approx 110.7$
$180 - 110.7 \approx 69.3$
69.3, 110.7, 69.3, 110.7

36a. The Pythagorean Theorem states that the sum of the squares of the measures of the legs ($a - x$ and h) is equal to the square of the measure of the hypotenuse.

36b. $(a - x)^2 = a^2 - 2ax + x^2$

36c. By the Pythagorean Theorem, $x^2 + h^2 = b^2$.

36d. Since $\cos C = \frac{x}{b}$, $b\cos C = x$

36e. Commutative Property (=)

37. $x^2 = 4.3^2 + 8.8^2 - 2(4.3)(8.8)\cos 44°$
$x = \sqrt{4.3^2 + 8.8^2 - 2(4.3)(8.8)\cos 44°}$
$x \approx 6.4$ light-years

38. $x^2 = 14^2 + 14^2 - 2(14)(14)\cos 30°$
$x = \sqrt{14^2 + 14^2 - 2(14)(14)\cos 30°}$
$x \approx 7.2$ in.

39. $12^2 = 40^2 + 45^2 - 2(40)(45)\cos J$
$\cos J = \frac{40^2 + 45^2 - 12^2}{2(40)(45)}$
$m\angle J \approx 14.8$
Liz
$12^2 = 20^2 + 30^2 - 2(20)(30)\cos L$
$\cos L = \frac{20^2 + 30^2 - 12^2}{2(20)(30)}$
$m\angle L \approx 15.6$

40. 9; 1 half-dollar, 1 quarter, 2 dimes, 1 nickel, 4 pennies

41. $m\angle R + m\angle P + m\angle Q = 180$
$50 + 75 + m\angle Q = 180$
$m\angle Q = 55$

$\frac{\sin R}{r} = \frac{\sin P}{p}$ $\quad$ $\frac{\sin R}{r} = \frac{\sin Q}{q}$
$\frac{\sin 50°}{10} = \frac{\sin 75°}{p}$ $\quad$ $\frac{\sin 50°}{10} = \frac{\sin 55°}{q}$
$p = \frac{10\sin 75°}{\sin 50°}$ $\quad$ $q \approx 10.7$
$p \approx 12.6$

42. $\sin 55° = \frac{100}{x}$
$x = \frac{100}{\sin 55°}$
$x \approx 122.08$ ft

43. $\frac{8}{x} = \frac{x}{3}$ $\qquad$ $\frac{3}{y} = \frac{y}{11}$
$x^2 = 24$ $\qquad$ $y^2 = 33$
$x = \sqrt{24}$ $\qquad$ $y = \sqrt{33} \approx 5.74$
$x = 2\sqrt{6} \approx 4.90$

44. Both pairs of opposite sides are congruent. One pair of opposite sides are both parallel and congruent. The diagonals bisect each other. Both pairs of opposite angles are congruent.

45. (4, 3), (−2, 7), (−4, −5)

46. He must check that all sides are the same length.

47. True; Sample explanation: A 3−4−5 triangle is a right triangle with sides of different lengths.

48. $\frac{-2 - 0}{8 - 3} = \frac{-2}{5}$

49. $x^2 + 9x + 18$

50. $\frac{z}{z+4} \div \frac{z+9}{z+4} = \frac{z}{z+4} \cdot \frac{z+4}{z+9} = \frac{z}{z+9}$

Chapter 8 Highlights

Page 437 Understanding and Using the Vocabulary

1. sine
2. extremes
3. Law of Cosines
4. angle of depression
5. trigonometry
6. tangent
7. Pythagorean triple
8. geometric mean
9. Law of Sines
10. Pythagorean Theorem
11. trigonometric ratios
12. cosine
13. means
14. angle of elevation

Chapter 8 Study Guide and Assessment

Pages 438–440 Skills and Concepts

15. $\frac{9}{x} = \frac{x}{27}$
$x^2 = 243$
$x = \sqrt{243}$
$x = 9\sqrt{3} \approx 15.59$

16. $\frac{13}{x} = \frac{x}{39}$
$x^2 = 507$
$x = \sqrt{507}$
$x = 13\sqrt{3} \approx 22.52$

17. $\frac{6}{x} = \frac{x}{\frac{2}{3}}$
$x^2 = 4$
$x = 2$

18. $\frac{\frac{3}{4}}{x} = \frac{x}{\frac{8}{3}}$
$x^2 = 2$
$x = \sqrt{2} \cong 1.41$

19. $\frac{4}{KL} = \frac{KL}{18}$

$KL^2 = 72$

$KL = \sqrt{72}$

$KL = 6\sqrt{2} \approx 8.49$

20. $\frac{4}{LN} = \frac{LN}{6}$

$LN^2 = 24$

$LN = \sqrt{24}$

$LN = 2\sqrt{6} \approx 4.90$

21. $\frac{14}{19} = \frac{19}{KM}$

$14KM = 361$

$KM \approx 25.79$

22. $\frac{\frac{1}{3}}{LK} = \frac{LK}{\left(\frac{1}{3} + \frac{1}{4}\right)}$

$LK^2 = \frac{7}{36}$

$LK^2 = \sqrt{\frac{7}{36}}$

$LK = \frac{\sqrt{7}}{6} \approx 0.44$

23. $\frac{3}{LM} = \frac{LM}{(3 + 7)}$

$LM^2 = 30$

$LM = \sqrt{30} \approx 5.48$

24. $\frac{KN}{0.6} = \frac{0.6}{1.5}$

$1.5\,KN = 0.36$

$KN = 0.24$

25. $8^2 + 15^2 = x^2$

$64 + 225 = x^2$

$289 = x^2$

$x = 17$

26. $x^2 + 8.0^2 = 9.4^2$

$x^2 + 64 = 88.36$

$x^2 = 24.36$

$x \approx 4.94$

27. $19^2 + 24^2 \overset{?}{=} 30^2$

$361 + 576 \overset{?}{=} 900$

$937 \neq 900$

No

28. $4^2 + 7.5^2 \overset{?}{=} 8.5^2$

$16 + 56.25 \overset{?}{=} 72.25$

$72.25 = 72.25$

Yes

29. $x = 3\sqrt{2} \approx 4.24$

30. $2x = 42$

$x = 21$

31. shorter leg $= \frac{1}{2}(3.1) = 1.55$

longer leg $= x - 1.55\sqrt{3} \approx 2.68$

32. $x = \frac{14.2}{\sqrt{2}} = \frac{14.2\sqrt{2}}{2} = 7.1\sqrt{2}$

$x \approx 10.04$

33. $\sin M = \frac{15}{17} \approx 0.8824$

34. $\tan M = \frac{15}{8} \approx 1.8750$

35. $\cos K = \frac{15}{17} \approx 0.8824$

36. $\tan K = \frac{8}{15} \approx 0.5333$

37. $\tan 23° = \frac{120}{x}$

$x = \frac{120}{\tan 23°}$

$x \approx 282.7$ m

38. $\tan 44° = \frac{30}{x}$

$x = \frac{30}{\tan 44°}$

$x \approx 31.1$ m

39. $\tan X = \frac{30}{400}$

$m\angle X \approx 4.3°$

40. $\frac{\sin A}{a} = \frac{\sin B}{b}$

$\frac{\sin A}{4.2} = \frac{\sin 22°}{6.8}$

$\sin A = \frac{4.2 \sin 22°}{6.8}$

$m\angle A \approx 13.4$

$m\angle A + m\angle B + m\angle C = 180$

$13.4 + 22 + m\angle C = 180$

$m\angle C \approx 144.6$

$\frac{\sin C}{c} = \frac{\sin B}{b}$

$\frac{\sin 144.6°}{c} = \frac{\sin 22°}{6.8}$

$c = \frac{6.8 \sin 144.6°}{\sin 22°}$

$c \approx 10.5$

41. $m\angle A + m\angle B + m\angle C = 180$

$m\angle A + 46 + 83 = 180$

$m\angle A = 51$

$\frac{\sin B}{b} = \frac{\sin A}{a}$

$\frac{\sin 46°}{65} = \frac{\sin 51°}{a}$

$a = \frac{65 \sin 51°}{\sin 46°}$

$a \approx 70.2$

$\frac{\sin B}{b} = \frac{\sin C}{c}$

$\frac{\sin 46°}{65} = \frac{\sin 83°}{c}$

$c = \frac{65 \sin 83°}{\sin 46°}$

$c \approx 89.7$

42. $\frac{\sin A}{a} = \frac{\sin B}{b}$

$\frac{\sin 65°}{80} = \frac{\sin B}{10}$

$\sin B = \frac{10 \sin 65°}{80}$

$m\angle B \approx 6.5$

$m\angle A + m\angle B + m\angle C = 180$

$65 + 6.5 + m\angle C \approx 180$

$m\angle C \approx 108.5$

$\frac{\sin A}{a} = \frac{\sin C}{c}$

$\frac{\sin 65°}{80} = \frac{\sin 108.5°}{c}$

$c = \frac{80 \sin 108.5°}{\sin 65°}$

$c \approx 83.7$

43. $m\angle A + m\angle B + m\angle C = 180$

$30 + m\angle B + 70 = 180$

$m\angle B = 80$

$\frac{\sin B}{b} = \frac{\sin A}{a}$

$\frac{\sin 80°}{b} = \frac{\sin 30°}{7.5}$

$b = \frac{7.5 \sin 80°}{\sin 30°}$

$b \approx 14.8$

$\frac{\sin A}{a} = \frac{\sin C}{c}$

$\frac{\sin 30°}{7.5} = \frac{\sin 70°}{c}$

$c = \frac{7.5 \sin 70°}{\sin 30°}$

$c \approx 14.1$

44. $c^2 = a^2 + b^2 - 2ab \cos C$

$c^2 = 8^2 + 12^2 - 2(8)(12) \cos 55°$

$c = \sqrt{8^2 + 12^2 - 2(8)(12) \cos 55°}$

$c \approx 9.9$

$\frac{\sin C}{c} = \frac{\sin A}{a}$

$\frac{\sin 55°}{9.9} = \frac{\sin A}{8}$

$\sin A = \frac{8 \sin 55°}{9.9}$

$m\angle A \approx 41.4$

$m\angle A + m\angle B + m\angle C = 180$

$41.4 + 55 + m\angle C \approx 180$

$m\angle C \approx 68.6$

45. $b^2 = a^2 + c^2 - 2ac \cos B$

$b^2 = 44^2 + 32^2 - 2(44)(32) \cos 44°$

$b = \sqrt{44^2 + 32^2 - 2(44)(32) \cos 44°}$

$b \approx 30.6$

$\frac{\sin B}{b} = \frac{\sin A}{a}$

$\frac{\sin 44°}{30.6} \approx \frac{\sin A}{49}$

$\sin A \approx \frac{44 \sin 44°}{30.6}$

$m\angle A \approx 87.3$

$m\angle A + m\angle B + m\angle C = 180$

$87.3 + 44 + m\angle C \approx 180$

$m\angle C \approx 48.7$

46. $c^2 = a^2 + b^2 - 2ab \cos C$

$c^2 = 4.5^2 + 4.9^2 - 2(4.5)(4.9) \cos 78°$

$c = \sqrt{4.5^2 + 4.9^2 - 2(4.5)(4.9) \cos 78°}$

$c \approx 5.9$

$\dfrac{\sin C}{c} = \dfrac{\sin A}{a}$

$\dfrac{\sin 78°}{5.9} \approx \dfrac{\sin A}{4.5}$

$\sin A \approx \dfrac{4.5 \sin 78°}{5.9}$

$m\angle A \approx 48.2$

$m\angle A + m\angle B + m\angle C = 180$

$48.2 + m\angle B + 78 \approx 180$

$m\angle B \approx 53.8$

47. $a^2 = b^2 + c^2 - 2bc \cos A$

$6^2 = 9^2 + 8^2 - 2(9)(8) \cos A$

$\cos A = \dfrac{9^2 + 8^2 - 6^2}{2(9)(8)}$

$m\angle A \approx 40.8$

$\dfrac{\sin A}{a} = \dfrac{\sin B}{b}$

$\dfrac{\sin 40.8°}{6} = \dfrac{\sin B}{9}$

$\sin B \approx \dfrac{9 \sin 40.8°}{6}$

$m\angle B \approx 78.6$

$m\angle A + m\angle B + m\angle C = 180$

$40.8 + 78.6 + m\angle C \approx 180$

$m\angle C \approx 60.6$

Page 440 Applications and Problem Solving

48. $\sin 70° = \dfrac{x}{65}$

$x = 65 \sin 70°$

$x \approx 61.1$ m

49. $\tan 15° = \dfrac{x}{2}$

$x = 2 \tan 15°$

$x \approx 0.5$ mi

50. $\tan 22° = \dfrac{75}{x}$

$x = \dfrac{75}{\tan 22°}$

$x \approx 185.6$

51. $\sin x° = \dfrac{10}{75}$

$m\angle x \approx 7.7$

52. $c^2 = a^2 + b^2 - 2ab \cos C$

$c^2 = 1000^2 + 700^2 - 2(1000)(700) \cos 160°$

$c = \sqrt{1000^2 + 700^2 - 2(1000)(700) \cos 160°}$

$c \approx 1675.0$ km

53. Sample answer: Look for a pattern; 2.

Page 441 Alternative Assessment: Thinking Critically

Yes; If you know the angle of the Sun at any point of time a sundial is useful throughout the year.

College Entrance Exam Practice, Chapters 1–8

Pages 442–443

1. $8(2)(2)(3) = 96$ (C)

2. $A = \dfrac{1}{2}bh \qquad\qquad b = h$

$36 = \dfrac{1}{2}b^2$

$72 = b^2$

$6\sqrt{2} = b$

b = measure of a leg

measure of hypotenuse = $6\sqrt{2}(\sqrt{2})$ or 12

$P = 6\sqrt{2} + 6\sqrt{2} + 12 = (12\sqrt{2} + 12)$ units   (A)

3. $af = 6 \qquad\qquad ag = 24$

$f = \dfrac{6}{a} \qquad\qquad g = \dfrac{24}{a}$

$fg = 1 \qquad\qquad f = \dfrac{6}{12} = \dfrac{1}{2}$

$\dfrac{6}{a} \cdot \dfrac{24}{a} = 1 \qquad\quad g = \dfrac{24}{12} = 2$

$\dfrac{144}{a^2} = 1 \qquad\qquad afg = 12\left(\dfrac{1}{2}\right)(2) = 12$

$a^2 = 144 \qquad\qquad$ (C)

$a = 12$

4. $\sqrt{25 \cdot 64} = 5(8) = 40$ (D)

5. $x - \dfrac{2}{x - 3} = \dfrac{x - 1}{3 - x}$ LCD: $x - 3$

$x(x - 3) - 2 = -(x - 1)$

$x^2 - 3x - 2 = -x + 1$

$x^2 - 2x - 3 = 0$

$(x - 3)(x + 1) = 0$

$x = 3, -1$ (C)

6. Let D be the point where the segment from B meets $\overline{AC}$.

$m\angle BAD = m\angle ABD = m\angle DBC = m\angle BCD = 45$

four   (D)

7. $a + b$ (C)

8. Let y = measure of the supplement to $x°$ angle.

$y = 30 + 60$ by Exterior Angles Theorem

$x + y = 180$

$x + 90 = 180$

$x = 90$ (D)

9. $\dfrac{x}{10} = \dfrac{x + 6}{x + 3}$

$x^2 + 3x = 10x + 60$

$x^2 - 7x - 60 = 0$

$(x - 12)(x + 5) = 0$

$x = 12$ or $x = -5$

Disregard $x = -5$ (C)

10. $A = \dfrac{1}{2}bh$

$30 = \dfrac{1}{2}x(8)$

$30 = 4x$

$x = 7.5$ units

11. $\sin \theta = \dfrac{\text{opposite}}{\text{hypotenuse}} = \dfrac{3}{5}$

$\cos \theta = \dfrac{\text{adjacent}}{\text{hypotenuse}} = \dfrac{4}{5}$

$\tan \theta = \dfrac{\text{opposite}}{\text{adjacent}} = \dfrac{3}{4}$

12.

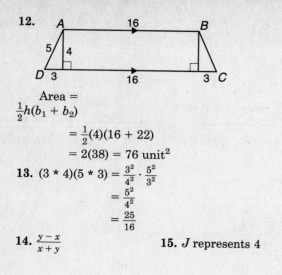

Area =
$$\frac{1}{2}h(b_1 + b_2)$$
$$= \frac{1}{2}(4)(16 + 22)$$
$$= 2(38) = 76 \text{ unit}^2$$

13. $(3 * 4)(5 * 3) = \frac{3^2}{4^2} \cdot \frac{5^2}{3^2}$
$$= \frac{5^2}{4^2}$$
$$= \frac{25}{16}$$

14. $\frac{y - x}{x + y}$

15. J represents 4

16. $A = \frac{1}{2}bh$
$$A = \frac{1}{2}(10x)(6x)$$
$$= 30x^2$$

17. $BC^2 = 2^2 + 3^2$ $\sqrt{13} + 2 + 3 > \sqrt{3} + 2 + 3$ (A)
$BC = \sqrt{13}$

18. $x + x + \frac{x}{2} = 180$ $72 > 60$ (A)
$x = 72$

19. $(3 + 5)^2 = 8^2 = 64$ $3^2 + 5^2 = 9 + 25 = 34$
$64 > 34$ (A)

20. (D)

21. a is negative $a < b$ (B)
b is zero

Geometry Chapter 8

CHAPTER 9 Analyzing Circles

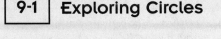
Page 447 Modeling Mathematics

a. See students' work.

b. It's about 3.14.

c. It is constant.

Page 449 Check for Understanding

1. The point stays in one place and is the center of the circle. The tip of the pencil moves around the point, always at the same distance from the point.

2. The diameter contains the center of the circle.

3. Fernando is correct since not all chords pass through the center of the circle.

4. The measure of the diameter is twice the measure of the radius, $d = 2r$.

5. Circle is derived from the Latin *circus*, which means ring.

6. $\overline{AL}$, $\overline{NO}$

7. $\frac{1}{2}(9.4) = 4.7$

8. Yes; $\overline{AL}$ is longer because it is a diameter.

9. $d = 2(7) = 14$, $C = 2\pi r = 2\pi(7) = 14\pi \approx 44.0$

10. $C = \pi d$
    $76.4 = \pi d$, $r = \frac{1}{2}d$
    $d = \frac{76.4}{\pi} \approx 24.3$ $= \frac{1}{2}(24.3) \approx 12.2$

11. $C = \pi d = 9\pi$

12a. $QR + RT = QT$
    $1 + RT = 4$
    $RT = 3$

12b. $AR = AQ + QR$
    $2(6) = AQ + 1.2$
    $AQ = 10.8$

13. $C = \pi d = 60$ $C = \pi(19.1 + 12)$
    $d = \frac{60}{\pi}$ $= 31.1\pi$
    $d \approx 19.1$ ≈ 97.7 ft

Pages 449–451 Exercises

14. M 15. $\overline{RI}$ 16. $RI = 2(5) = 10$

17. No; it is a radius.

18. Yes; they are both radii of $\odot M$.

19. $\overline{RM}$, $\overline{AM}$, $\overline{DM}$, $\overline{IM}$

20. Yes; since $\overline{RI}$ is a diameter

21. $MA = \frac{1}{2}(RI) = \frac{1}{2}(11.8) = 5.9$

22. It is isoceles, since $AM = RM$.

23. $d = 2(5) = 10$, $C = \pi d = 10\pi \approx 31.4$

24. $r = \frac{1}{2}d = \frac{1}{2}(26.8) = 13.4$, $C = \pi d = 26.8\pi \approx 84.2$

25. $C = 136.9 = \pi d$, $r = \frac{1}{2}(43.6) \approx 21.8$
    $d = \frac{136.9}{\pi} \approx 43.6$

26. $d = 2r = 2\left(\frac{x}{6}\right) = \frac{x}{3} \approx 0.3x$

    $C = 2\pi r = \frac{\pi}{3}x \approx 0.9x$ or

    $C = \pi d = 0.3\pi x \approx 1.0x$

27. $r = \frac{1}{2}d = \frac{1}{2}(2x) = x$, $C = \pi d = 2\pi x \approx 6.3x$

28. $C = 2368 = \pi d$, $r = \frac{1}{2}(753.8) \approx 376.9$
    $d = \frac{2368}{\pi} \approx 753.8$

29. $C = \pi d = 8\pi$ cm

30. $5^2 + 12^2 = d^2$ $C = \pi d = 13\pi$ cm
    $169 = d^2$
    $d = \sqrt{169}$ or 13

31. $C = \pi d = \pi(6\sqrt{2}) = 6\sqrt{2}\pi$ cm

32. $JE + EK = JK$
    $2 + EK = 7$
    $EK = 5$

33. $IJ + JE = IE$
    $IJ + 2 = 2(4)$
    $IJ = 6$

34. $IC = IE + JC - JE$
    $= 2(4) + 2(7) - 2 = 20$

35. perimeter of $\triangle ASK = AS + SK + AK$
    $= 4 + 7 + (4 + 7) - 2$
    $= 20$

36. $AS = IA$ and $KS = KC$ since all radii of a circle are congruent. Therefore, the perimeter of $\triangle ASK = IA + AK + KC$ or IC.

37. The circumference is doubled.

38. The circumference is divided by 3.

39. Given: $\odot P$ with diameter $\overline{SA}$ and chord $\overline{KR}$
    Prove: $SA > KR$

    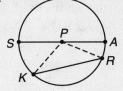

    Proof:
    By the Segment Addition Postulate, $SA = SP + PA$. Draw $\overline{PK}$ and $\overline{PR}$ since through any two points there is one line. Since all radii of a circle are congruent, $\overline{SP} \cong \overline{PK}$ and $\overline{PA} \cong \overline{PR}$. By substitution, $SA = PK + PR$. By the Triangle Inequality Theorem, $PK + PR > KR$. By substitution, $SA > KR$.

40. $P = 120 + 120 + \pi(53)$
    $P \approx 406.5$
    4 laps $\approx 4(406.5) \approx 1626.0$ yards

41. $d \approx 11.8$ cm, $C \approx \pi(11.8) \approx 37.1$ cm
    $\frac{C}{d} \approx 3.144$ or π

42. $C = \pi d = 125\pi \approx 392.7$ m

43. $C = \pi d = 10\pi \approx 31.416$
    100 revolutions $= 100(31.416) \approx 3141.6$ cm

44. $C = 2\pi r = 2\pi(33) = 66\pi$
    number of revolutions $= \frac{10(100,000)}{66\pi}$
    ≈ 4822.9 revolutions

45a. $C = \pi d = \pi(25) \approx 79$ ft

  b. $C = \pi d = \pi(42) \approx 132$ ft

46. $C = \pi(8000 + 250 + 250) = 8500\pi$
    number of orbits $= \frac{4,164,183}{8500\pi} \approx 156$ orbits

47. $x^2 = 96.4^2 + 112.7^2 - 2(96.4)(112.7)\cos 35°$
$x = \sqrt{96.4^2 + 112.7^2 - 2(96.4)(112.7)\cos 35°}$
≈ 64.8

perimeter of $\triangle GEF = 96.4 + 112.7 + 64.8 = 273.9$ cm

48. $\tan 47° = \frac{x}{6500}$
$x = 6500 \tan 47°$
$x \approx 6970$ ft

49. $s^2 = 15^2 + 8^2$
$s^2 = 225 + 64$
$s = \sqrt{289}$ or 17
$P = 4s = 4(17) = 68$ in.

50. The measures of the angles in each triangle are 90, 67, and 23. The triangles are similar by AA similarity.

51. $\frac{x}{5} = \frac{7}{2}$
$2x = 35$
$x = 17.5$

52. $M = \frac{1}{2}(b_1 + b_2)$
$18 = \frac{1}{2}(29 + b_2)$
$36 = 29 + b_2$
$b_2 = 7$ in.

53. $7 + 9 > 11$
$7 + 11 > 9$
$9 + 11 > 7$
Yes; the sum of any two sides is greater than the length of the third side.

54. slope of $\overline{WC} = \frac{-9-3}{2-0} = \frac{-12}{2} = -6$

55.
$3x - 2y = 8 \qquad\qquad 3x - 2(-4) = 8$
$\underline{-3x + 4y = -16} \qquad 3x + 8 = 8$
$\qquad -6y = 24 \qquad\qquad\qquad x = 0$
$\qquad\quad y = -4 \qquad (0, -4)$

56. $(a^3 b)(a^2 b^2) = a^{3+2} b^{1+2}$ or $a^5 b^3$

9-2 Angles and Arcs

Pages 454–455 Check for Understanding

1. to make it clear which points the arc goes through

2a. $\widehat{BNR}$ has endpoints B and R and is a minor arc; $\widehat{BRN}$ has endpoints B and N and is a major arc.

2b. Subtract $360 - 25$ to get 335.

3. A diameter divides a circle into two semicircles. Each semicircle has an arc measure of 180.

4. The word *minor* denotes something smaller, and the word *major* denotes something greater, just as a minor arc is a smaller part of a circle and a major arc is a greater part of a circle.

5a. $m\widehat{SCT} = 360 - m\widehat{ST} = 360 - 30 = 330$

5b. 150, 180; yes; arcs can be added similar to the way angles are added by the Angle Addition Postulate.

6. semicircle; 180

7. minor; $m\widehat{TR} = m\angle TSR = 42$
$m\widehat{TK} = m\widehat{RK} - m\widehat{TSR}$
$= 180 - 42$ or 138

8. major; $m\widehat{TR} = m\widehat{TSR} = 42$
$m\widehat{TRK} = m\widehat{RK} + m\widehat{TSR}$
$= 180 + 42$ or 222

9. $m\angle LJM = 180 - m\angle KJL = 180 - 140 = 40$
$\widehat{LM} = \frac{40}{360} \cdot 2\pi(18)$
$= 4\pi \approx 12.6$

10. $\widehat{KL} = \frac{140}{360} \cdot 2\pi(18) \approx 44.0$

11. $m\angle LMK = 360 - m\angle KJL$
$= 360 - 140 = 220$
$\widehat{LMK} = \frac{220}{360} \cdot 2\pi(18) \approx 69.1$

12. $m\angle ICR + m\angle RCL = 180$
$(3x + 5) + (x - 1) = 180$
$4x = 176$
$x = 44$

13. $m\angle ICR = 3(44) + 5 = 137$

14. $m\widehat{ILR} = m\widehat{IL} + m\widehat{LR}$
$= m\angle ICL + m\angle RCL$
$= 180 + (44) - 1$
$= 223$

15. true; def. of concentric circles

16. false; def. of concentric circles

17. true; concentric circles have the same center.

18a.

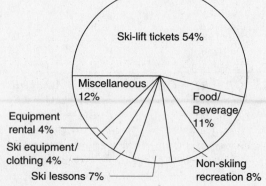

18b. The circle represents the sum of all parts of the whole.

Pages 456–458 Exercises

19. minor, $m\widehat{TG} = m\angle TEG = 21$

20. major, $m\widehat{ATR} = m\widehat{AT} + m\widehat{TGR}$
$= 90 + 180$ or 270

21. minor, $m\widehat{AR} = m\angle AER = 90$

22. semicircle, 180

23. minor, $m\widehat{ATG} = m\widehat{AT} + m\widehat{TG}$
$= 90 + 21$ or 111

24. major, $m\widehat{ARG} = m\widehat{AR} + m\widehat{RGT} - m\widehat{TG}$
$= 90 + 180 - 21$ or 249

25. major, $m\widehat{RAG} = m\widehat{RT} + m\widehat{TG}$
$= 180 + 21$ or 201

26. major, $m\widehat{TAG} = 360 - m\widehat{TG}$
$= 360 - 21$ or 339

27. minor, $m\widehat{GR} = 180 - m\widehat{GT}$
$= 180 - 21$ or 159

28. $\overarc{TG} = \frac{21}{360} \cdot \pi(12) \approx 2.2$

29. $\overarc{ATR} = \frac{270}{360} \cdot \pi(12) \approx 28.3$

30. $\overarc{AR} = \frac{90}{360} \cdot \pi(12) \approx 9.4$

31. $\overarc{TAR} = \frac{180}{360} \cdot \pi(12) = 18.8$

32. $\overarc{ATG} = \frac{111}{360} \cdot \pi(12) \approx 11.6$

33. $\overarc{ARG} = \frac{249}{360} \cdot \pi(12) \approx 26.1$

34. $\overarc{RAG} = \frac{201}{360} \cdot \pi(12) \approx 21.0$

35. $\overarc{TAG} = \frac{339}{360} \cdot \pi(12) \approx 35.5$

36. $\overarc{GR} = \frac{159}{360} \cdot \pi(12) \approx 16.7$

37. $m\angle AGJ + m\angle JGT = 180$
$4x + (2x + 24) = 180$
$6x = 156$
$x = 26$

38. $m\angle AGJ = 4(26)$ or 104

39. $m\angle JGT = 2(26) + 24$ or 76

40. $m\angle NGE + m\angle EGT = m\angle AGJ$
$m\overarc{NE} + m\overarc{NE} = 104$
$m\overarc{NE} = 52$

41. $m\overarc{NGT} = m\angle NGJ + m\angle JGT$
$= 180 + 76$ or 256

42. $m\overarc{JNE} = m\overarc{JAN} + m\overarc{NE}$
$= 180 + 52$ or 232

43. $m\overarc{DG} = m\angle DIG = 132$
$m\angle DGI = m\angle IDG$
$m\angle DGI + m\angle IDG + m\angle DIG = 180$
$2m\angle DGI + 132 = 180$
$m\angle DGI = 24$

44. Since $m\overarc{WN} = 60$, $m\angle WIN = 60$, but $\overline{WI} \cong \overline{IN}$, since they are radii, so $\angle IWN \cong \angle INW$.

45. False; arcs are not of the same circle.

46. true

47. False; arcs are not of the same circle.

48. true   **49.** true

50. $m\overarc{AR} = 2x$, $\overline{RT} \parallel \overline{AK}$ so $\angle 3 \cong \angle 1$ by Alternate Interior Angles Theorem. $m\angle 1 = m\overarc{AR}$ since $\angle 1$ is a central angle.

51. $AE = AC = 1$
$AD = \frac{1}{\sqrt{2}} = \frac{\sqrt{2}}{2}$
Each side measures $\frac{\sqrt{2}}{2}$.

52. Sample answer: $\angle CXD \cong \angle AXB$, but $\overarc{AB}$ is not congruent to $\overarc{CD}$.

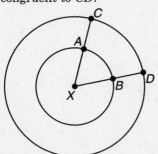

53. Sample answer:

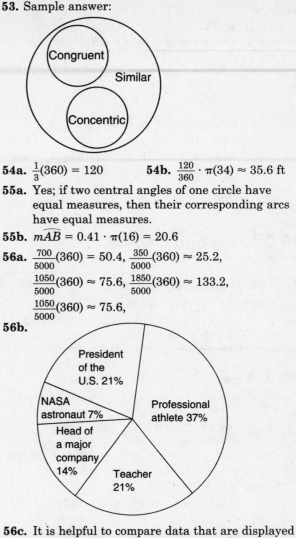

54a. $\frac{1}{3}(360) = 120$ **54b.** $\frac{120}{360} \cdot \pi(34) \approx 35.6$ ft

55a. Yes; if two central angles of one circle have equal measures, then their corresponding arcs have equal measures.

55b. $m\overarc{AB} = 0.41 \cdot \pi(16) = 20.6$

56a. $\frac{700}{5000}(360) = 50.4$, $\frac{350}{5000}(360) \approx 25.2$,
$\frac{1050}{5000}(360) \approx 75.6$, $\frac{1850}{5000}(360) \approx 133.2$,
$\frac{1050}{5000}(360) \approx 75.6$,

56b.

President of the U.S. 21%
NASA astronaut 7%
Head of a major company 14%
Professional athlete 37%
Teacher 21%

56c. It is helpful to compare data that are displayed in a graph. For example, it is easy to see that fewest students preferred trading places with an astronaut and the greatest number preferred trading places with a professional athlete.

57. $C = 2\pi r = 2\pi(22) \approx 138.2$ mm

58. $P = 4s$ $d = s\sqrt{2}$
$4s = 27$ $= 6.75\sqrt{2}$
$s = 6.75$ ≈ 9.5 cm

59. $\frac{3}{4} = \frac{x}{6}$ **60.** false
$18 = 4x$
$x = 4.5$

61. $AB = CD$
$7x - 6 = 5x + 14$
$2x = 20$
$x = 10$
$AB = 7x - 10 = 7(10) - 6 = 64$

62. If two chords are congruent, they are not equidistant from the center of the circle.

63. Let y = measure of the angle that forms a linear pair with the 115° angle. Thus, $y = 65$.
$65 + 65 + x = 180$
$x = 50$

64. Obtuse triangles have one obtuse angle and all the angles in an acute triangle are acute.

65. false

66. If a student must have a physical exam in the spring, then he or she plays a fall sport.

67. $(3x^2y^4)(5x^4y) = 3 \cdot 5x^{2\,+\,4}y^{4\,+\,1} = 15x^6y^5$

68. $\dfrac{9}{n-3} \cdot \dfrac{n^2-9}{12} = \dfrac{9(n+3)(n-3)}{12(n-3)} = \dfrac{3(n+3)}{4} = \dfrac{3n+9}{4}$

Page 458 Mathematics and Society

1. subtraction, addition

2. Sample answer: Use different colors to represent areas of greater and lesser curvature.

3. Answers will vary.

9-3 Arcs and Chords

Page 460 Modeling Mathematics

a. They are equal; they are equal.

b. If a diameter is perpendicular to a chord, then it bisects the chord and its arc.

Pages 461–462 Check for Understanding

1. $ABCD$ is a square. All arcs are congruent and all sides (chords) are congruent.

2. Square; by Theorem 9-1, since the chords are congruent, the corresponding arcs are congruent. Then use the Arc Addition Postulate to show that the sides of the quadrilateral are congruent, forming the sides of the square.

3. Tiarri is right; to bisect $\overline{PQ}$, $\overline{AB}$ must be a diameter.

4. The intersection of ℓ and m is the center of the circle because ℓ and m contain diameters.

5. In a circle, if a diameter is perpendicular to a chord, then it bisects the chord and its arc.

6. $\widehat{QM}$

7. $OR = \frac{1}{2}(RM)$ $PO^2 + OR^2 = PR^2$
$PO^2 + 12^2 = 13^2$
$PO^2 = 25$
$PO = 5$

8. $\overline{PQ}$ or $\overline{PR}$

9. $TR = ER$, $EO = \frac{1}{2}(EN)$

$RO^2 + EO^2 = ER^2$
$RO^2 + 5.4^2 = 6.4^2$
$RO^2 = 11.8$ $RO \approx 3.4$

10. $MN = \frac{1}{2}(LN)$ $MO^2 + MN^2 = ON^2$
$6^2 + 8^2 = x^2$
$100 = x^2$
$x = 10$

11a.

11b. $12^2 + 5^2 = x^2$
$169 = x^2$
$x = 13$ in.

12. $6^2 + x^2 = 27^2$
$x^2 = 693$
$x \approx 26.325$
Each support wire is about 2(26.325) or about 52.65 cm

13. In a circle or in congruent circles, two minor arcs are congruent if and only if their corresponding chords are congruent.

14. In a circle, if a diameter is perpendicular to a chord, then it bisects the chord and its arc.

15. In a circle or in congruent circles, two chords are congruent if and only if they are equidistant from the center.

16. D **17.** S

18. $VW = 2(VA) = 2(9)$ or 18

19. $\overline{PQ}$, $\overline{VU}$, and $\overline{UW}$ **20.** $\overline{DU}$, $\overline{VU}$, $\overline{DT}$, $\overline{DR}$

21. Neither, they are $\cong$.

22. $SR = \frac{1}{2}(PR)$ $DS^2 + SR^2 = DR^2$
$14^2 + 16^2 = DR^2$
$DR = \sqrt{452} \approx 21.3$

23. They are perpendicular to the same diagonal.

24. $\overline{AU}$

25. $m\angle CAM = m\angle MTN = 28$

26. $m\widehat{SE} = m\widehat{NI}$
$m\angle IMN = 180 - (40 + 40) = 100$
$m\widehat{NI} = m\angle IMN = 100$
$m\widehat{SE} = 100$

27. $CA = CT$
$CS = \frac{1}{2}CT = \frac{1}{2}(42)$ or 21

28. a. Through any 2 pts. there is 1 line.
b. Given
c. All radii of a circle are $\cong$.
d. Reflexive Prop. of $\cong$ Segments
e. $\triangle ARP \cong \triangle BRP$
f. CPCTC
g. $AK \cong BK$

29. Since all radii of a circle are congruent, $\overline{RH} \cong \overline{MR}$. Since the corresponding chords are congruent, by Theorem 9-1, $\widehat{RH} \cong \widehat{MR}$.

30. Since $RHOM$ is a rhombus, $\overline{MR} \cong \overline{RH} \cong \overline{HO} \cong \overline{OM}$. Since all radii of a circle are congruent, $\overline{OR} \cong \overline{OM}$. Therefore, $\triangle MRO$ and $\triangle RHO$ are equilateral triangles.

31. Yes; since radii are congruent, $\odot P \cong \odot Q$. Since the corresponding chords are congruent, by Theorem 9-1, $\widehat{AB} \cong \widehat{RS}$.

32. $x^2 + 5^2 = 10^2$
$x^2 + 25 = 100$
$x^2 = 75$
$x = \sqrt{75} \approx 8.7$

33. $5^2 + \left(\frac{x}{2}\right)^2 = 13^2$
$25 + \frac{x^2}{4} = 169$
$\frac{x^2}{4} = 144$
$x^2 = 576$
$x = \sqrt{576}$ or 24

34. $BJ = 5 - 2 = 3$
$BJ^2 + BC^2 = JC^2$
$3^2 + x^2 = 5^2$
$x^2 = 16$
$x = \sqrt{16} \text{ or } 4$

35.

$12^2 + 15^2 = x^2$
$369 = x$
$x = \sqrt{369} \approx 19.2 \text{ cm}$

36.

$x^2 + 15^2 = 17^2$
$x^2 = 64$
$x = \sqrt{64} \text{ or } 8 \text{ in.}$

37.

$7^2 + \left(\frac{1}{2}x\right)^2 = 25^2$
$\frac{1}{4}x^2 = 576$
$x^2 = 2304$
$x = \sqrt{2304} = 48 \text{ mm}$

38. $MA = TH$
$8x + 4 = 12$
$8x = 8$
$x = 1$
$OQ = OP = 1$
$AP = \frac{1}{2}AM = \frac{1}{2}(12) = 6$

$AP^2 + OP^2 = OA^2$
$6^2 + 1^2 = OA^2$
$37 = OA^2$
$OA = \sqrt{37} \approx 6.1$

39. $8^2 + \left(\frac{AP}{2}\right)^2 = 16^2$
$64 + \frac{AP^2}{4} = 256$
$\frac{AP^2}{4} = 192$
$AP = \sqrt{768} \approx 27.7$

40. $152 + \left(\frac{x}{2}\right)^2 = 30^2$
$\frac{x^2}{4} = 675$
$x^2 = 2700$
$x = \sqrt{2700} \approx 52.0 \text{ units}$

41. Given: $\odot O$
$\overline{AB} \cong \overline{CD}$
Prove: $\widehat{AB} \cong \widehat{CD}$

Proof:

Statements	Reasons
1. Draw radii $\overline{OA}$, $\overline{OB}$, $\overline{OC}$, and $\overline{OD}$.	1. Through any 2 pts. there is 1 line.
2. $\overline{OA} \cong \overline{OC}$ $\overline{OB} \cong \overline{OD}$	2. All radii of a $\odot$ are $\cong$.
3. $\overline{AB} \cong \overline{CD}$	3. Given
4. $\triangle ABO \cong \triangle CDO$	4. SSS
5. $\angle AOB \cong \angle COD$	5. CPCTC
6. $\widehat{AB} \cong \widehat{CD}$	6. In a $\odot$, 2 minor arcs are $\cong$ if and only if their corr. central $\angle$s are $\cong$.

42. Given: $\odot O$
$\overline{OS} \perp \overline{RT}$
$\overline{OV} \perp \overline{UW}$
$\overline{OS} \cong \overline{OV}$
Prove: $\overline{RT} \cong \overline{UW}$

Proof:

Statements	Reasons
1. Draw radii $\overline{OT}$ and $\overline{OW}$.	1. Through any 2 pts. there is 1 line.
2. $\overline{OT} \cong \overline{OW}$	2. All radii of a $\odot$ are $\cong$.
3. $\overline{OS} \cong \overline{OV}$	3. Given
4. $\triangle STO \cong \triangle VWO$	4. HL
5. $\overline{ST} \cong \overline{VW}$	5. CPCTC
6. $ST = VW$	6. Def. $\cong$ segments
7. $\overline{RS} \cong \overline{ST}$ $\overline{UV} \cong \overline{VW}$	7. A diameter $\perp$ to a chord bisects the chord.
8. $RT = 2(ST)$ $UW = 2(VW)$	8. Def. segment bisector
9. $RT = UW$	9. Substitution Prop. (=)
10. $\overline{RT} \cong \overline{UW}$	10. Def. $\cong$ segments

43. Given: $\odot O$
$\overline{MN} \cong \overline{PQ}$
Prove: $\overline{OA} \cong \overline{OB}$

Proof:

Statements	Reasons
1. Draw radii $\overline{ON}$ and $\overline{OQ}$. Draw $\overline{OA}$ so that $\overline{OA} \perp \overline{MN}$ and draw $\overline{OB}$ so that $\overline{OB} \perp \overline{PQ}$.	1. Through any 2 pts. there is 1 line.
2. $\overline{OA}$ bisects $\overline{MN}$. $\overline{OB}$ bisects $\overline{PQ}$.	2. $\overline{OA}$ and $\overline{OB}$ can be extended to form radii, and a radius $\perp$ to a chord bisects the chord.
3. $AN = \frac{1}{2}MN$ $BQ = \frac{1}{2}PQ$	3. Def. $\perp$ bisector
4. $\overline{MN} \cong \overline{PQ}$	4. Given
5. $MN = PQ$	5. Def. $\cong$ segments
6. $AN = BQ$ $\overline{ON} \cong \overline{OQ}$	6. All radii of a $\odot$ are $\cong$.
7. $\triangle AON \cong \triangle BOQ$	7. HL
8. $\overline{OA} \cong \overline{OB}$	8. CPCTC

44. As the lengths of the chords increase, their distances to the center decrease.

45a. See students' work.

45b. It is the only point equidistant from T, S, and A.

45c. Minneapolis, Minnesota

46. Construct the perpendicular bisectors of two sides of the triangle. Their intersection is the center of the circle.

47. True; all points on a circle are equidistant from the center.

48. $C = \pi d = \pi(22) = 69.1 \text{ ft}$

49. $JK = 2(6.3) = 12.6$

$LK = 6.3\sqrt{3}$

perimeter of $\triangle JKL = 6.3 + 12.6 + 6.3\sqrt{3}$
≈ 29.8

50. $\overline{RA}, \overline{OF}, \overline{AT}, \overline{FT}, \overline{RT}, \overline{OT}$

51. false

52. yes; isosceles or equilateral

53. $\angle M$

54. hypothesis: it is raining; conclusion: I will bring an umbrella.

55. $-6rs(4r^2 + 1) + 8(rs + 2r) = -24r^3s - 6rs +$
$8rs + 16r$
$= -24r^3s + 2rs + 16r$

56. $\frac{21x^3y^5z}{7xy^6z} = \frac{21}{7} \cdot x^{3-1} \cdot y^{5-6} \cdot z^{1-1} = 3x^2y^{-1}$ or $\frac{3x^2}{y}$

9-4 Inscribed Angles

Page 466 Modeling Mathematics

a. 60, 60; the measure of each minor arc equals the measure of its central angle.

b. 120, 240

c. The measure of $\angle FAB$ is one-half the measure of $\widehat{BDF}$.

Pages 469–470 Check for Understanding

1. The measure of an inscribed angle equals one-half the measure of its intercepted arc.

2. No; Q is not the center of the circle, so $\angle SQT$ is not a central angle.

3. Since the inscribed angle intercepts a semicircle, the angle is a right angle. Therefore, the triangle is a right triangle.

4. The measure of the inscribed angle equals half the measure of the central angle.

5. Sample answer: Keep tires on a wagon, drapery rods to walls, swingset, keep lug nuts on a car; used for easy alignment of tools and grip when fastening.

6. $\angle BAC$ **7.** $\widehat{BC}$

8. $m\angle BAC = \frac{1}{2}(m\angle BPC)$
$= \frac{1}{2}(42)$ or 21

9. $m\widehat{JL} = 180 - m\widehat{LK} = 180 - 100 = 80$
$m\angle JKL = \frac{1}{2}(m\widehat{JL})$
$x = \frac{1}{2}(80) = 40$

10. $m\widehat{PE} = \frac{360}{5} = 72$

11. $m\angle PTN = \frac{1}{2}(m\widehat{PEN})$
$= \frac{1}{2}(144) = 72$

12. $m\angle PEN = \frac{1}{2}(m\widehat{PTN})$
$= \frac{1}{2}(216) = 108$

13. $m\widehat{AB} = m\angle AZB = 104$

14. $m\angle BAC = \frac{1}{2}(m\widehat{BC})$
$= \frac{1}{2}(94)$ or 47

15. $m\angle ADB = \frac{1}{2}(m\widehat{AB})$
$= \frac{1}{2}(104)$ or 52

16a. Measure 120°, draw the chords, and cut.

16b. 1 in.

Pages 470–473 Exercises

17. $\widehat{HC}$

18. $m\widehat{CH} = 2(m\angle HTC) = 2(52) = 104$

19. $\widehat{TCH}$ **20.** 90   **21.** 52

22. Sample answers: $\angle HCT, \angle HEU, \angle CEH, \angle CEU,$
$\angle CTH, \angle THU$

23. There are none shown in the figure.

24. $m\widehat{CH} = 2(m\angle HTC) = 2(52) = 104$
$m\widehat{CEH} = 360 - m\widehat{CH}$
$= 360 - 104 = 256$

25. $m\angle PQR = \frac{1}{2}m\widehat{PR}$ **26.** $m\angle MHA = m\angle ATM$
$2x + 1 = \frac{1}{2}(96)$ $x = 2x - 3$
$2x = 47$ $x = 3$
$x = 23.5$

27. $m\angle K + m\angle R + m\angle P = 180$
$\left(\frac{1}{2}x\right) + \left(\frac{1}{3}x + 5\right) + 90 = 180$
$\frac{5}{6}x = 85$
$x = 102$

28. $m\angle PRS = m\angle SRT$
$-2x + 42 = 8x - 18$
$-10x = -60$
$x = 6$
$m\angle PRS = -2x + 42 = -2(6) + 42$ or 30
$m\widehat{PS} = 2m\angle PRS = 2(30)$ or 60

29. $m\widehat{ST} = m\widehat{PS}$
$m\widehat{ST} = 60$

30. $m\widehat{RT} = 180 - m\widehat{ST}$
$= 180 - 60$ or 120
$m\angle RST = \frac{1}{2}m\widehat{RT} = \frac{1}{2}(120)$ or 60

31. $m\widehat{PR} = 180 - m\widehat{PS} = 180 - 60$ or 120
$m\angle PGR = m\widehat{PR} = 120$

32. $m\widehat{PR} = 180 - m\widehat{PS} = 180 - 60$ or 120

33. $m\widehat{PSR} = 360 - m\widehat{PR}$
$= 360 - 120$ or 240

34. $m\angle PNG = 90$ because $PSTG$ is a rhombus.

35. $m\widehat{PRT} = 360 - (m\widehat{PS} + m\widehat{ST})$
$= 360 - (60 + 60)$ or 240

36. $m\angle PSR = \frac{1}{2}m\widehat{PR} = \frac{1}{2}(120)$ or 60

37. $m\widehat{GM} = m\angle GPM = 89$

38. $m\widehat{NM} = 180 - m\widehat{GM} = 180 - 89$ or 91

39. $m\widehat{GE} = 180 - m\widehat{EN} = 180 - 66$ or 114

40. $m\angle GEN = 90$

41. $m\angle EGN = \frac{1}{2}m\widehat{EN} = \frac{1}{2}(66)$ or 33

42. $m\angle EMN = \frac{1}{2}m\widehat{EN} = \frac{1}{2}(66)$ or 33

43. $m\angle GNM = \frac{1}{2}m\widehat{GM} = \frac{1}{2}(89)$ or 44.5

44. $m\angle EGN + m\angle GNE + m\angle GEN = 180$

$m\angle EGN + \frac{1}{2}(114) + \frac{1}{2}(91) = 180$

$m\angle EGN + 57 + 45.5 = 180$

$m\angle EGN = 77.5$

45. $m\angle EGM + m\angle GEM + m\angle GME = 180$

$m\angle EGM + \frac{1}{2}(89) + \frac{1}{2}(114) = 180$

$m\angle EGM + 44.5 + 57 = 180$

$m\angle EGM = 78.5$

46. $\triangle ABC$ is equilateral.

47. Given: $\overline{BR} \parallel \overline{AC}$

Prove: $\widehat{RA} \cong \widehat{BC}$

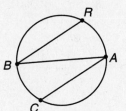

Proof:

Statements	Reasons
1. $\overline{BR} \parallel \overline{AC}$	1. Given
2. $\angle RBA \cong \angle BAC$	2. Alt. Int. $\angle$s Theorem
3. $m\angle RBA = m\angle BAC$	3. $\cong \angle$s have = measures.
4. $m\angle RBA = \frac{1}{2}m\widehat{RA}$ $m\angle BAC = \frac{1}{2}m\widehat{BC}$	4. If an $\angle$ is inscribed in a $\odot$, the measure of the $\angle = \frac{1}{2}$ the measure of its intercepted arc.
5. $\frac{1}{2}m\widehat{RA} = \frac{1}{2}m\widehat{BC}$	5. Substitution Prop. (=)
6. $m\widehat{RA} = m\widehat{BC}$	6. Mult. Prop. (=)
7. $\widehat{RA} \cong \widehat{BC}$	7. Arcs that have = measures and are in the same $\odot$ are $\cong$.

48. Given: $\widehat{MHT}$ is a semicircle.

$RH \perp TM$

Prove: $\dfrac{TR}{RH} = \dfrac{TH}{HM}$

Proof:

Statements	Reasons
1. $\widehat{MHT}$ is a semicircle. $\overline{RH} \perp \overline{TM}$	1. Given
2. $\angle THM$ is a rt. $\angle$.	2. If an inscribed $\angle$ of a $\odot$ intercepts a semicircle, then the $\angle$ is a rt. $\angle$.
3. $\angle TRH$ is a rt. $\angle$.	3. Def. $\perp$ lines
4. $\angle THM \cong \angle TRH$	4. All rt. $\angle$s are $\cong$.
5. $\angle T \cong \angle T$	5. Reflexive Prop. (=)
6. $\triangle TRH \sim \triangle THM$	6. AA Similarity
7. $\dfrac{TR}{RH} = \dfrac{TH}{HM}$	7. Def. $\sim \triangle$s

49. No; opposite angles must be congruent and supplementary. Therefore, they each must be 90°, or right angles.

50. $m\angle PRQ = m\angle PRK + m\angle KRQ$

$= \frac{1}{2}m\widehat{PK} + \frac{1}{2}m\widehat{KQ}$

$= \frac{1}{2}(m\widehat{PK} + m\widehat{KQ})$

$= \frac{1}{2}m\widehat{PQ}$

51. $m\angle PRQ = m\angle KRQ - m\angle KRP$

$= \frac{1}{2}m\widehat{KQ} - \frac{1}{2}m\widehat{KP}$

$= \frac{1}{2}(m\widehat{KQ} - m\widehat{KP})$

$= \frac{1}{2}m\widehat{PQ}$

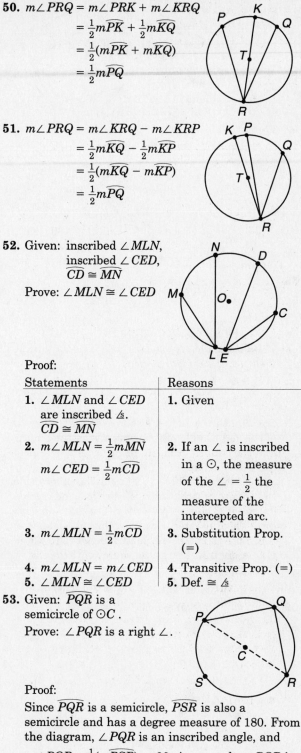

52. Given: inscribed $\angle MLN$, inscribed $\angle CED$, $\widehat{CD} \cong \widehat{MN}$

Prove: $\angle MLN \cong \angle CED$

Proof:

Statements	Reasons
1. $\angle MLN$ and $\angle CED$ are inscribed $\angle$s. $\widehat{CD} \cong \widehat{MN}$	1. Given
2. $m\angle MLN = \frac{1}{2}m\widehat{MN}$ $m\angle CED = \frac{1}{2}m\widehat{CD}$	2. If an $\angle$ is inscribed in a $\odot$, the measure of the $\angle = \frac{1}{2}$ the measure of the intercepted arc.
3. $m\angle MLN = \frac{1}{2}m\widehat{CD}$	3. Substitution Prop. (=)
4. $m\angle MLN = m\angle CED$	4. Transitive Prop. (=)
5. $\angle MLN \cong \angle CED$	5. Def. $\cong \angle$s

53. Given: $\widehat{PQR}$ is a semicircle of $\odot C$.

Prove: $\angle PQR$ is a right $\angle$.

Proof:

Since $\widehat{PQR}$ is a semicircle, $\widehat{PSR}$ is also a semicircle and has a degree measure of 180. From the diagram, $\angle PQR$ is an inscribed angle, and $m\angle PQR = \frac{1}{2}(m\widehat{PSR})$ or 90. As a result, $\angle PQR$ is a right angle.

54. Given: Quadrilateral $ABCD$ inscribed in $\odot O$

Prove: $\angle A$ and $\angle C$ are supplementary.
$\angle B$ and $\angle D$ are supplementary.

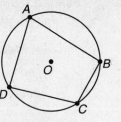

Proof:

In $\odot O$, $m\widehat{DCB} + m\widehat{DAB} = 360$.

Since $m\angle C = \frac{1}{2}m\widehat{DAB}$ and $m\angle A = \frac{1}{2}\widehat{DCB}$,

$m\angle C + m\angle A = \frac{1}{2}m\widehat{DAB} + \frac{1}{2}m\widehat{DCB}$ or

$m\angle C + m\angle A = \frac{1}{2}(m\widehat{DAB} + m\widehat{DCB}) =$

$\frac{1}{2}(360)$ or 180. Since $m\angle C + m\angle A = 180$, the angles are supplementary. A similar proof holds for angles B and D.

55. Yes; see students' work.

56. $\ell = \frac{2\pi rm}{360} = \frac{2\pi(70)(90)}{360} \approx 110 + 2(220 - 70) \approx 410$ ft

57.

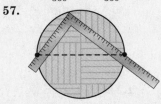

Position the carpenter's square so that the vertex of the right angle of the square is on the circle and the square forms an inscribed angle. Since the inscribed angle is a right angle, the measure of the intercepted arc is 180. So, the points where the square crosses the circle are the ends of a diameter (Theorem 9-6). Mark these points and draw the diameter. Draw another diameter using the same method. The point where the two diameters intersect is the center of the circle.

58a. 14% of 360 = .14(360) = 50.4

58b. $m\widehat{AB}$ = 53% of 360 = .53(360) = 190.8

59. $C = 2\pi r = 2\pi(8.5) \approx 53.4$ ft

60. $\frac{9}{x} = \frac{x}{21}$
$x^2 = 189$
$x = \sqrt{189} \approx 13.7$

61. See students' work.

62. $m\angle 1 + m\angle 2 = 90$
$37 + m\angle 2 = 90$
$m\angle 2 = 53$

63. Sample answer: measure the diagonals to see if they are congruent.

64. a. Given

b. Definition of bisector

c. If $\not\leftrightarrow$, alt. int. $\angle$s are $\cong$.

d. SAS

e. CPCTC

65. $m\angle 1 = m\angle 2$
$4x + 3 = 8x - 7$
$4x = 10$
$x = 2.5$

66. Sample answer: $\triangle ABC$ is a right triangle.

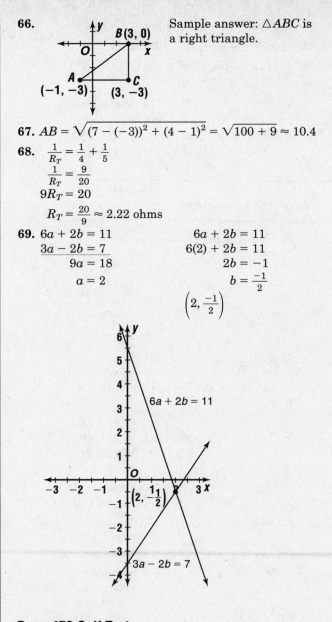

67. $AB = \sqrt{(7 - (-3))^2 + (4 - 1)^2} = \sqrt{100 + 9} \approx 10.4$

68. $\frac{1}{R_T} = \frac{1}{4} + \frac{1}{5}$
$\frac{1}{R_T} = \frac{9}{20}$
$9R_T = 20$
$R_T = \frac{20}{9} \approx 2.22$ ohms

69.
$6a + 2b = 11$
$\underline{3a - 2b = 7}$
$9a = 18$
$a = 2$

$6a + 2b = 11$
$6(2) + 2b = 11$
$2b = -1$
$b = \frac{-1}{2}$

$\left(2, \frac{-1}{2}\right)$

Page 473 Self Test

1. $\overline{PD}$, $\overline{PB}$, $\overline{PC}$

2. $C = 2\pi r = 2\pi(17) \approx 106.8$

3. $\widehat{CB} = \frac{125}{360} \cdot 2\pi(6) \approx 13.1$

4. $m\widehat{ST} = \frac{360 - 100}{4} = \frac{260}{4}$ or 65

5. $m\angle TUV = \frac{1}{2}m\widehat{TRV}$
$= \frac{1}{2}[2(65) + 100]$
$= \frac{1}{2}(230)$ or 115

9-5A Using Technology Exploring Triangles

Page 474 Exercises

1. See students' work.

2. See students' work.

3. Sample answer: the measures are equal.

4. They are right angles.

Pages 478–479 Check for Understanding

1. $\overline{AC}, \overline{BD}; \overline{AD}, \overline{BC}$

2.

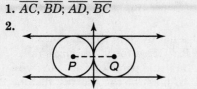

3a. 2; a tangent can be drawn to each "side" of the circle from the point outside of the circle.

3b. 0; a tangent cannot pass through a point inside the circle.

3c. 1; only one line can be drawn perpendicular to a radius of a circle at the endpoint on the circle.

4. Anjula; two lines tangent to a circle could be parallel if the points of tangency were endpoints of a diameter.

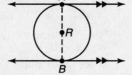

5a. $\overleftrightarrow{PQ} \perp \overleftrightarrow{RS}$

5b. They are perpendicular to each other.

6. 90

7.
$$m\angle EML + m\angle MEL + m\angle ELM = 180$$
$$66 + 90 + m\angle ELM = 180$$
$$m\angle ELM = 24$$

8. $EL = LK = 36$

9. $m\widehat{KPE} = m\angle EMK = 2(66) = 132$

10. $\triangle EML$ **11.** $\overline{KL}$

12. isosceles

13. In quadrilateral $KLEM$, $\angle K$ and $\angle E$ are right angles and the sum of their measures equals 180. Therefore, the sum of $m\angle L$ and $m\angle M$ must equal 180 and the angles must be supplementary.

14. 7

15.
$$12^2 + 16^2 = (x + 12)^2$$
$$400 = (x + 12)^2$$
$$20 = x + 12$$
$$8 = x$$

16.
$$HE^2 + HS^2 = ES^2$$
$$6400^2 + HS^2 = (6400 + 4000)^2$$
$$HS^2 = 67,200,000$$
$$HS \approx 8197.6 \text{ km}$$

Pages 479–482 Exercises

17. longer leg $= 5\sqrt{3} \approx 8.7$

18. 90

19. hypotenuse $= 2(5) = 10$

20. longer leg $= 2\sqrt{3} \approx 3.5$

21. $m\widehat{CA} = m\angle APC = 60$

22. $m\angle ADP = \frac{1}{2}\widehat{CA} = \frac{1}{2}(60) = 30$

23. 90

24. $m\angle FQD = m\angle APC = 60$
$\triangle FQD$ is a $30°-60°-90°$ $\triangle$.
$FQ = QE = 2$
$DQ = 2(FQ) = 2(2)$ or 4

25. $DJ = DF = \sqrt{3}(FQ) = 2\sqrt{3} \approx 3.5$

26. $m\widehat{FEJ} = m\angle FQE + m\angle JQE$
$= 60 + 60$ or 120

27. $m\angle QDJ = 90 - m\angle FQD = 90 - 60$ or 30

28. $AJ = AD + DJ$
$= 5\sqrt{3} + 2\sqrt{3} = 7\sqrt{3} \approx 12.1$

29. $\overline{GF}$ and $\overline{AJ}$

30. By Theorem 9-10, $\overline{GD} \cong \overline{AD}$ and $\overline{DF} \cong \overline{DJ}$. Since $GF = GD + DF$ and $AJ = AD + DJ$, then by substitution, $\overline{GF} \cong \overline{AJ}$.

31. 14   **32.** $AG = AH + HG = 4 + 6 = 10$

33.
$$AD = AB$$
$$6x + 5 = -2x + 37$$
$$8x = 32$$
$$x = 4$$

34. $12^2 + x^2 = (12 + 8)^2$ **35.** $8^2 + x^2 = 17^2$
$ x^2 = 256$ $x^2 = 225$
$ x = 16$ $x = 15$

36. $x = 2(6)$
$x = 12$

37. a. Given

b. If 2 segments from the same exterior point are tangent to a $\odot$, then they are $\cong$.

c. Radii of the same circle are $\cong$.

d. Reflexive Property (=)

e. SSS

f. CPCTC

38. $r = AB = \sqrt{(3 - 1)^2 + (2 - (-1))^2} = \sqrt{4 + 9} = \sqrt{13} \approx 3.6$

39. slope of $\overline{AB} = \frac{2 - (-1)}{3 - 1} = \frac{3}{2}$; $\ell \perp \overline{AB}$, so slope of $\ell = \frac{-2}{3}$.

40. Label points $W, X, Y,$ and Z.
If $AT = 18$ and $AX = XT$, then $AX = XT = 9$.
$TW = TX = 9$
$WG = TG - TW = 12 - 9$ or 3
$GZ = 3$
$ZN = GN - GZ = 10 - 3$ or 7
$NY = ZN = 7$
$XA = AY = 9$
$AN = XA + AY = 9 + 7$ or 16

41.

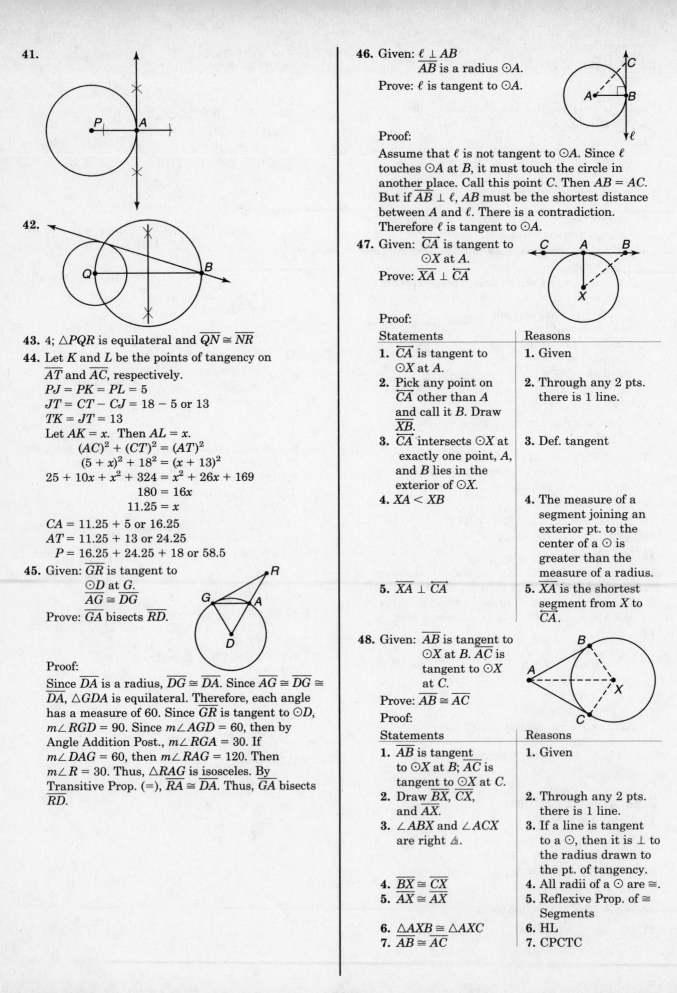

42.

43. 4; $\triangle PQR$ is equilateral and $\overline{QN} \cong \overline{NR}$

44. Let K and L be the points of tangency on $\overline{AT}$ and $\overline{AC}$, respectively.
$PJ = PK = PL = 5$
$JT = CT - CJ = 18 - 5$ or 13
$TK = JT = 13$
Let $AK = x$. Then $AL = x$.
$$(AC)^2 + (CT)^2 = (AT)^2$$
$$(5 + x)^2 + 18^2 = (x + 13)^2$$
$$25 + 10x + x^2 + 324 = x^2 + 26x + 169$$
$$180 = 16x$$
$$11.25 = x$$
$CA = 11.25 + 5$ or 16.25
$AT = 11.25 + 13$ or 24.25
$P = 16.25 + 24.25 + 18$ or 58.5

45. Given: $\overline{GR}$ is tangent to $\odot D$ at G.
$\overline{AG} \cong \overline{DG}$
Prove: $\overline{GA}$ bisects $\overline{RD}$.

Proof:
Since $\overline{DA}$ is a radius, $\overline{DG} \cong \overline{DA}$. Since $\overline{AG} \cong \overline{DG} \cong \overline{DA}$, $\triangle GDA$ is equilateral. Therefore, each angle has a measure of 60. Since $\overline{GR}$ is tangent to $\odot D$, $m\angle RGD = 90$. Since $m\angle AGD = 60$, then by Angle Addition Post., $m\angle RGA = 30$. If $m\angle DAG = 60$, then $m\angle RAG = 120$. Then $m\angle R = 30$. Thus, $\triangle RAG$ is isosceles. By Transitive Prop. (=), $\overline{RA} \cong \overline{DA}$. Thus, $\overline{GA}$ bisects $\overline{RD}$.

46. Given: $\ell \perp \overline{AB}$
$\overline{AB}$ is a radius $\odot A$.
Prove: ℓ is tangent to $\odot A$.

Proof:
Assume that ℓ is not tangent to $\odot A$. Since ℓ touches $\odot A$ at B, it must touch the circle in another place. Call this point C. Then $AB = AC$. But if $\overline{AB} \perp \ell$, AB must be the shortest distance between A and ℓ. There is a contradiction. Therefore ℓ is tangent to $\odot A$.

47. Given: $\overleftrightarrow{CA}$ is tangent to $\odot X$ at A.
Prove: $\overline{XA} \perp \overleftrightarrow{CA}$

Proof:

Statements	Reasons
1. $\overleftrightarrow{CA}$ is tangent to $\odot X$ at A.	1. Given
2. Pick any point on $\overleftrightarrow{CA}$ other than A and call it B. Draw $\overline{XB}$.	2. Through any 2 pts. there is 1 line.
3. $\overleftrightarrow{CA}$ intersects $\odot X$ at exactly one point, A, and B lies in the exterior of $\odot X$.	3. Def. tangent
4. $XA < XB$	4. The measure of a segment joining an exterior pt. to the center of a $\odot$ is greater than the measure of a radius.
5. $\overline{XA} \perp \overleftrightarrow{CA}$	5. $\overline{XA}$ is the shortest segment from X to $\overleftrightarrow{CA}$.

48. Given: $\overline{AB}$ is tangent to $\odot X$ at B. $\overline{AC}$ is tangent to $\odot X$ at C.
Prove: $\overline{AB} \cong \overline{AC}$

Proof:

Statements	Reasons
1. $\overline{AB}$ is tangent to $\odot X$ at B; $\overline{AC}$ is tangent to $\odot X$ at C.	1. Given
2. Draw $\overline{BX}$, $\overline{CX}$, and $\overline{AX}$.	2. Through any 2 pts. there is 1 line.
3. $\angle ABX$ and $\angle ACX$ are right $\angle$s.	3. If a line is tangent to a $\odot$, then it is $\perp$ to the radius drawn to the pt. of tangency.
4. $\overline{BX} \cong \overline{CX}$	4. All radii of a $\odot$ are $\cong$.
5. $\overline{AX} \cong \overline{AX}$	5. Reflexive Prop. of $\cong$ Segments
6. $\triangle AXB \cong \triangle AXC$	6. HL
7. $\overline{AB} \cong \overline{AC}$	7. CPCTC

49a. QR

49b. One definition is a ratio of the measure of the leg opposite the acute angle to the measure of the leg adjacent to the acute angle. Another definition is a line in a plane that intersects a circle in the plane in exactly one point.

50a. $RS^2 + RT^2 = ST^2$
$(432,000)^2 + RT^2 = (93,003,964)^2$
$RT = 93,002,961$ miles

50b. $\frac{NT}{MN} = \frac{RT}{RS}$
$\frac{NT}{1080} = \frac{93,002,961}{432,000}$
$NT = 232,507$ miles

50c. $NT^2 + NM^2 = MT^2$
$232,507^2 + 1080^2 = MT^2$
$MT = 232,510$ miles

50d. $OE = MT - ET - OM$
$= 232,510 - 3694 - 1080$
$= 227,466$ miles

50e. closer than 227,466 miles

51. $x^2 + 67.13^2 = (x + 65.42)^2$
$x^2 + 67.13^2 = x^2 + 130.84x + 65.42^2$
$130.84x = 226.6605$
$x = 1.73$ meters

52. $m\widehat{YZ} = 2m\angle YXZ = 2(55)$ or 110

53. $AC = 2(7)$ or 14

54. shorter leg $= \frac{6.5}{2}$
longer leg $=$ altitude $= \frac{6.5}{2}\sqrt{3} \approx 5.63$

55. $\frac{3}{5} = \frac{15}{x}$
$3x = 75$
$x = 25$ cm

56. See students' work.

57. $x - 5 > 0$
$x > 5$

58. No; the sum of measures of angles of a triangle must equal 180, and if two angles were obtuse, the sum of their measures would be greater than 180.

59. no conclusion

60. See students' work.

61. 0.02

62a. $\frac{10 - 3.5}{3.5} \approx 1.86 \approx 186\%$

62b. $\frac{36.23 - 10}{36.23} \approx 0.72 \approx 72\%$

9-6 Secants, Tangents and Angle Measures

Page 484 Modeling Mathematics

a. Exterior Angles Theorem

b. $m\angle 1 = \frac{1}{2}m\widehat{WX} + \frac{1}{2}m\widehat{ZY}$ or $\frac{1}{2}(m\widehat{WX} + m\widehat{ZY})$

c. Sample answer: The measure of an angle is half the sum of the measures of the arcs intercepted by the angle and its vertical angle.

Pages 486–487 Check for Understanding

1. Subtract the two intercepted arcs and take $\frac{1}{2}$.

2. Both are right angles since $m\widehat{JK} = m\widehat{ML}$.

3a. If $m\angle WIB = 100$, then $y = 80$.

3b. They are supplementary.

4. Since $\overline{DE}$ is tangent to $\odot P$, then $\overline{ED} \perp \overline{BD}$ so $\angle BDE$ has a measure of 90. The intercepted arc is a semicircle, so by Theorem 9-11, $m\angle BDE = \frac{1}{2}(180)$ or 90.

5. A secant "cuts" a circle into two parts or cuts away one part. A tangent only touches one point on the circle.

6. $m\angle 3 = \frac{1}{2}(128 - 84) = 22$

7. $m\widehat{AB} = 360 - 98 - 28 - 62 - 38 = 134$

8. $m\angle 1 = \frac{1}{2}m\widehat{BD} = \frac{1}{2}(134 + 38) = 86$

9. $m\angle 2 = \frac{1}{2}(m\widehat{OY} + m\widehat{AD})$
$= \frac{1}{2}(28 + 38)$ or 33

10. $m\angle 3 = \frac{1}{2}(m\widehat{AB} - m\widehat{OY})$
$= \frac{1}{2}(134 - 28)$ or 53

11. $26 = \frac{1}{2}(106 - x)$
$52 = 106 - x$
$x = 54$

12a. $(40x - 2) + (100 + 4x) + (30x + 10) +$
$(183 - 5x) = 360$
$69x + 291 = 360$
$69x = 69$
$x = 1$

12b. $m\angle AET = \frac{1}{2}(m\widehat{AT} + m\widehat{MH})$
$= \frac{1}{2}(104 + 178)$ or 141

13. $m\angle S = \frac{1}{2}(m\widehat{QUE} - m\widehat{QE})$
$11 = \frac{1}{2}[(360 - x) - x]$
$22 = 360 - 2x$
$2x = 338$
$x = 169$

Pages 487–490 Exercises

14. $m\angle 1 = \frac{1}{2}(60 - 34) = 13$

15. $m\angle 2 = \frac{1}{2}(230 + 85) = 157.5$

16. $m\angle 4 = \frac{1}{2}(360 - 102) = 129$

17. $m\angle GRE = \frac{1}{2}m\widehat{GE} = \frac{1}{2}(140) = 70$

18. $m\widehat{IR} = 360 - 140 - 80 - 130 = 10$

19. $m\angle T = \frac{1}{2}(m\widehat{GE} - m\widehat{IR})$
$= \frac{1}{2}(140 - 10)$ or 65

20. $m\angle GAE = \frac{1}{2}(m\widehat{GE} + m\widehat{IR})$
$= \frac{1}{2}(140 + 10)$ or 75

21. $m\angle IEC = \frac{1}{2}m\widehat{IC}$
$= \frac{1}{2}(10 + 130)$ or 70

22. $m\angle IED = \frac{1}{2}m\widehat{IGC}$
$= \frac{1}{2}(80 + 140)$ or 110

23. $m\angle IGA = \frac{1}{2}m\widehat{IR}$
$= \frac{1}{2}(10)$ or 5

24. $m\angle GIE = m\widehat{GI} + m\widehat{IR} + m\widehat{RE}$
$\qquad = 80 + 10 + 130$ or 220

25. $m\angle IAG = \frac{1}{2}(m\widehat{IG} + m\widehat{RE})$
$\qquad = \frac{1}{2}(80 + 130)$ or 105

26. $m\angle TIE = 180 - m\angle T - m\angle IET$
$\qquad = 180 - 5 - 65$ or 110

27. $m\angle CER = \frac{1}{2}m\widehat{ER} = \frac{1}{2}(130)$ or 65

28. $m\angle DEF = m\angle CER = 65$

29. $m\angle X = \frac{1}{2}[84 - (180 - 84 - 52)]$
$\qquad = \frac{1}{2}(40)$ or 20

30. $20 = \frac{1}{2}[(360 - 4x) - 4x]$
$\qquad 20 = 180 - 4x$
$\qquad 4x = 160$
$\qquad x = 40$

31. $m\angle X = \frac{1}{2}(28 + 24) = 26$

32. $m\angle CGD = \frac{1}{2}(116 - 38) = 39$
$\qquad 39 = \frac{1}{2}[(360 - m\widehat{AF}) - m\widehat{AF}]$
$\qquad 39 = 180 - m\widehat{AF}$
$\qquad m\widehat{AF} = 141$

33a. $m\widehat{KE} = 2m\angle KRE$
$\qquad = 2(30) = 60$
$\qquad m\angle KME = \frac{1}{2}(m\widehat{KE} + m\widehat{SR})$
$\qquad 52 = \frac{1}{2}(60 + m\widehat{SR})$
$\qquad 104 = 60 + m\widehat{SR}$
$\qquad m\widehat{SR} = 44$

33b. $m\widehat{AS} = 360 - m\widehat{AK} - m\widehat{KE} - m\widehat{ER} - m\widehat{SR}$
$\qquad = 360 - 108 - 60 - 118 - 44$
$\qquad = 30$

33c. $m\angle KPE = \frac{1}{2}(m\widehat{KE} - m\widehat{SA})$
$\qquad = \frac{1}{2}(60 - 30)$ or 15

34. $10 = \frac{1}{2}(m\widehat{EA} - m\widehat{AN})$
$\qquad 10 = \frac{1}{2}(65 - y)$
$\qquad 20 = 65 - y$
$\qquad y = 45$
$\qquad x = 360 - m\widehat{AN} - m\widehat{AE} - m\widehat{GE}$
$\qquad = 360 - 45 - 65 - 165$ or 85
$\qquad m\angle GTE = \frac{1}{2}(m\widehat{GE} - m\widehat{GN})$
$\qquad z = \frac{1}{2}(165 - 85)$ or 40

35. $m\widehat{QSD} = 360 - m\widehat{QU} - m\widehat{UD}$
$\qquad = 360 - 96 - 106$ or 158
$\qquad m\angle A = \frac{1}{2}(m\widehat{QD} - m\widehat{DU})$
$\qquad = \frac{1}{2}(158 - 106)$ or 26

36. $m\widehat{RT} = x$
$\qquad m\angle M = m\angle H$
$\qquad \frac{1}{2}[(360 - x) - x] = \frac{1}{2}x$
$\qquad 180 - x = \frac{1}{2}x$
$\qquad \frac{3}{2}x = 180$
$\qquad x = 120$

37. $m\angle E = \frac{1}{2}m\widehat{RAG}$
$\qquad 78 = \frac{1}{2}m\widehat{RAG}$
$\qquad m\widehat{RAG} = 156$
$\qquad m\widehat{REG} = 360 - 156 = 204$
$\qquad m\angle GAR = \frac{1}{2}m\widehat{REG}$
$\qquad = \frac{1}{2}(204) = 102$

38. $m\widehat{AG} = m\widehat{RAG} - m\widehat{AR}$
$\qquad = 156 - 46$ or 110

39. $m\angle TAR = \frac{1}{2}m\widehat{AR}$
$\qquad = \frac{1}{2}(46)$ or 23

40. $m\angle GAN = \frac{1}{2}m\widehat{AG}$
$\qquad = \frac{1}{2}(110)$ or 55

41. $m\angle R = \frac{1}{2}m\widehat{AGE}$
$\qquad 102 = \frac{1}{2}m\widehat{AGE}$
$\qquad m\widehat{AGE} = 204$
$\qquad m\widehat{GE} = m\widehat{AGE} - m\widehat{AG}$
$\qquad = 204 - 110$ or 94

42. $m\widehat{RE} = m\widehat{REG} - m\widehat{GE}$
$\qquad = 204 - 94$ or 110

43a. $m\angle P = \frac{1}{2}(m\widehat{RT} - m\widehat{QS})$
$\qquad 2x = \frac{1}{2}(x^2 + 4x - 63)$
$\qquad 4x = x^2 + 4x - 63$
$\qquad x^2 = 63$
$\qquad x = \sqrt{63} \approx 7.9$

43b. $m\angle P = 2(\sqrt{63}) \approx 15.9$

44a. $m\angle ACT = \frac{1}{2}(m\widehat{ABT} - m\widehat{AT})$
$\qquad 26x = \frac{1}{2}(360 - 2x^2 - 2x^2)$
$\qquad 26x = 180 - 2x^2$
$\qquad 2x^2 + 26x - 180 = 0$
$\qquad x^2 + 13x - 90 = 0$
$\qquad (x - 5)(x + 18) = 0$
$\qquad x = 5$

44b. $m\widehat{ABT} = 360 - 2x^2$
$\qquad = 360 - 2(5)^2$ or 310

45. Given: Secants $\overleftrightarrow{AC}$ and $\overleftrightarrow{BD}$ intersect at X inside $\odot P$.

Prove: $m\angle AXB = \frac{1}{2}(m\widehat{AB} + m\widehat{CD})$
Proof:

Statements	Reasons
1. Secants $\overleftrightarrow{AC}$ and $\overleftrightarrow{BD}$ intersect at X inside $\odot P$.	**1.** Given
2. Draw $\overline{BC}$.	**2.** Through any 2 pts. there is 1 line.
3. $m\angle XBC = \frac{1}{2}m\widehat{CD}$ $m\angle XCB = \frac{1}{2}m\widehat{AB}$	**3.** An $\angle$ inscribed in a $\odot$ has the measure of $\frac{1}{2}$ the measure of its intercepted arc.
4. $m\angle AXB = m\angle XCB + m\angle XBC$	**4.** Exterior Angles Theorem
5. $m\angle AXB = \frac{1}{2}m\widehat{AB} + \frac{1}{2}m\widehat{CD}$	**5.** Substitution Prop. (=)
6. $m\angle AXB = \frac{1}{2}(m\widehat{AB} + m\widehat{CD})$	**6.** Distributive Prop.

46a. Given: $\overrightarrow{AC}$ and $\overrightarrow{AT}$ are secants to the circle.

Prove: $m\angle CAT = \frac{1}{2}(m\widehat{CT} - m\widehat{BR})$

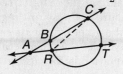

Proof:

Statements	Reasons
1. $\overrightarrow{AC}$ and $\overrightarrow{AT}$ are secants to the circle.	1. Given
2. Draw $\overline{CR}$.	2. Through any 2 pts. there is 1 line.
3. $m\angle CRT = \frac{1}{2}m\widehat{CT}$ $m\angle ACR = \frac{1}{2}m\widehat{BR}$	3. The measure of an inscribed $\angle = \frac{1}{2}$ the measure of its intercepted arc.
4. $m\angle CRT = m\angle ACR + m\angle CAT$	4. Exterior $\angle$s Theorem
5. $\frac{1}{2}m\widehat{CT} = \frac{1}{2}m\widehat{BR} + m\angle CAT$	5. Substitution Prop. (=)
6. $\frac{1}{2}m\widehat{CT} - \frac{1}{2}m\widehat{BR} = m\angle CAT$	6. Subtraction Prop. (=)
7. $\frac{1}{2}(m\widehat{CT} - m\widehat{BR}) = m\angle CAT$	7. Distributive Prop.

46b. Given: $\overrightarrow{DG}$ is a tangent to the circle. $\overrightarrow{DF}$ is a secant to the circle.

Prove: $m\angle FDG = \frac{1}{2}(m\widehat{FG} - m\widehat{GE})$

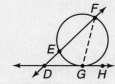

Proof:

Statements	Reasons
1. $\overrightarrow{DG}$ is a tangent to the circle. $\overrightarrow{DF}$ is a secant to the circle.	1. Given
2. Draw $\overline{FG}$.	2. Through any 2 pts. there is 1 line.
3. $m\angle DFG = \frac{1}{2}m\widehat{GE}$ $m\angle FGH = \frac{1}{2}m\widehat{FG}$	3. The measure of an inscribed $\angle = \frac{1}{2}$ the measure of its intercepted arc.
4. $m\angle FGH = m\angle DFG + m\angle FDG$	4. Exterior $\angle$s Theorem
5. $\frac{1}{2}m\widehat{FG} = \frac{1}{2}m\widehat{GE} + m\angle FDG$	5. Substitution Prop. (=)
6. $\frac{1}{2}m\widehat{FG} - \frac{1}{2}m\widehat{GE} = m\angle FDG$	6. Subtraction Prop. (=)
7. $\frac{1}{2}(m\widehat{FG} - m\widehat{GE}) = m\angle FDG$	7. Distributive Prop.

46c. Given: $\overleftrightarrow{HI}$ and $\overleftrightarrow{HJ}$ are tangents to the circle.

Prove: $m\angle IHJ = \frac{1}{2}(m\widehat{IXJ} - m\widehat{IJ})$

Proof:

Statements	Reasons
1. $\overleftrightarrow{HI}$ and $\overleftrightarrow{HJ}$ are tangents to the circle.	1. Given
2. Draw $\overline{IJ}$.	2. Through any 2 pts. there is 1 line.
3. $m\angle IJK = \frac{1}{2}m\widehat{IXJ}$ $m\widehat{HIJ} = \frac{1}{2}m\widehat{IJ}$	3. The measure of an inscribed $\angle = \frac{1}{2}$ the measure of its intercepted arc.
4. $m\angle IJK = m\angle HIJ + m\angle IHJ$	4. Exterior Angles Theorem
5. $\frac{1}{2}m\widehat{IXJ} = \frac{1}{2}m\widehat{IJ} + m\angle IHJ$	5. Substitution Prop. (=)
6. $\frac{1}{2}m\widehat{IXJ} - \frac{1}{2}m\widehat{IJ} = m\angle IHJ$	6. Subtraction Prop. (=)
7. $\frac{1}{2}(m\widehat{IXJ} - m\widehat{IJ}) = m\angle IHJ$	7. Distributive Prop.

47a. Given: $\overrightarrow{AB}$ is a tangent to $\odot O$. $\overrightarrow{AC}$ is a secant to $\odot O$. $\angle CAB$ is acute.

Prove: $m\angle CAB = \frac{1}{2}m\widehat{CA}$

Proof:

Construct diameter $\overline{AD}$. $\angle DAB$ is a right $\angle$ with measure 90, and $\widehat{DCA}$ is a semicircle with measure 180, since if a line is tangent to a $\odot$, it is $\perp$ to the radius at the point of tangency. Since $\angle CAB$ is acute, C is in the interior of $\angle DAB$, so by the Angle and Arc Addition Postulates, $m\angle DAB = m\angle DAC + m\angle CAB$ and $m\widehat{DCA} = m\widehat{DC} + m\widehat{CA}$. By substitution, $90 = m\angle DAC + m\angle CAB$ and $180 = m\widehat{DC} + m\widehat{CA}$. So, $90 = \frac{1}{2}m\widehat{DC} + \frac{1}{2}m\widehat{CA}$ by Division Prop. (=), and $m\angle DAC + m\angle CAB = \frac{1}{2}m\widehat{DC} + \frac{1}{2}m\widehat{CA}$ by substitution. $m\angle DAC = \frac{1}{2}m\widehat{DC}$ since $\angle DAC$ is inscribed, so substitution yields $\frac{1}{2}m\widehat{DC} + m\angle CAB = \frac{1}{2}m\widehat{DC} + \frac{1}{2}m\widehat{CA}$. By Subtraction Prop. (=), $m\angle CAB = \frac{1}{2}m\widehat{CA}$.

47b. Given: $\overleftrightarrow{AB}$ is a tangent to $\odot O$.
$\overrightarrow{AC}$ is a secant to $\odot O$.

Prove: $m\angle CAB = \frac{1}{2}m\widehat{CDA}$

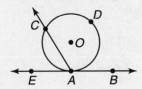

Proof:

$\angle CAB$ and $\angle CAE$ form a linear pair, so $m\angle CAB + m\angle CAE = 180$. Since $\angle CAB$ is obtuse, $\angle CAE$ is acute and Case 1 applies, so $m\angle CAE = \frac{1}{2}m\widehat{CA}$. $m\widehat{CA} + m\widehat{CDA} = 360$, so $\frac{1}{2}m\widehat{CA} + \frac{1}{2}m\widehat{CDA} = 180$ by Division Prop. (=), and $m\widehat{CAE} + \frac{1}{2}m\widehat{CDA} = 180$ by substitution.

By the Transitive Prop. (=), $m\angle CAB + m\angle CAE = m\angle CAE + \frac{1}{2}m\widehat{CDA}$, so by Subtraction Prop. (=), $m\angle CAB = \frac{1}{2}m\widehat{CDA}$.

48. The diagonals of a rectangle are $\cong$ and bisect each other, thus creating the center of the circle that circumscribes the rectangle.

49. $m\widehat{AC} = 160 - 2\,(42)$ or 76

50. $m\angle AMB = \frac{1}{2}(m\widehat{BC} - m\widehat{AB})$
$= \frac{1}{2}(118 - 71)$ or 23.5

51. 12   **52.** No, one side is not a chord.

53. $KO^2 + KL^2 = OL^2$ **54.** tangent,
$3^2 + KL^2 = 5^2$ $\tan Q = \frac{5}{4}$
$KL^2 = 16$ $m\angle Q \approx 51$
$KL = 4$
$JL = 2(KL) = 8$

55. $\frac{25.74}{1} = \frac{450}{x}$ **56.** $m\angle P + m\angle Q = 180$
$25.74x = 450$ $110 + m\angle Q = 180$
$x = \$17.48$ $m\angle Q = 70$

57. $17 + 10 \not> 29$ no
$17 + 29 > 10$ yes
$10 + 29 > 17$ yes
No; the measures do not satisfy the Triangle Inequality Theorem.

58. false   **59.** Division Prop. (=) or Mult. Prop. (=)

60. $2w$ **61.** $x^2 + 2x - 3 = 0$
$(x + 3)(x - 1) = 0$
$x = -3$ or $x = 1$

9-7 | Special Segments in a Circle

Pages 494–495 Check for Understanding

1. $\overline{SC}$ or $\overline{ST}$

2. Chords CG and EM intersect in the circle at O, so the products of the measures of the segments of those chords are equal.

3. A tangent segment is a segment from an exterior point to the point of tangency; $SN \cdot ST = (SE)^2$.

4. She is wrong. The measure of the exterior secant segment times the measure of the secant segment equals the measure of the other exterior secant segment times the measure of the other secant segment. The correct equation is $KA \cdot KN = KL \cdot KO$.

5. The distance from the center would have been 0, since a semicircle contains the diameter.

6. $3(x + 3) = 4(4 + 7)$ **7.** $x \cdot 9 = 3 \cdot 6$
$3x + 9 = 44$ $9x = 18$
$3x = 35$ $x = 2$
$x \approx 11.7$

8. $9(4 + 9) = x^2$
$x^2 = 117$
$x \approx 10.8$

9. $TE = ES = \frac{1}{2}(TS) = \frac{1}{2}(10) = 5$

10. $RE \cdot PE = TE \cdot ES$
$3 \cdot PE = 5 \cdot 5$
$3PE = 25$
$PE = 8\frac{1}{3}$

11. $PR = PE + ER$ **12.** $AP = \frac{1}{2}(PR)$
$= 8\frac{1}{3} + 3$ $= \frac{1}{2}\left(11\frac{1}{3}\right)$
$= 11\frac{1}{3}$ $= 5\frac{2}{3}$

13. $60x = 100 \cdot 100$
$60x = 10,000$
$x = 166\frac{2}{3}$
radius $= \frac{1}{2}\left(60 + 166\frac{2}{3}\right) = 113\frac{1}{3}$ cm

Pages 495–497 Exercises

14. $2x = 5 \cdot 5$ **15.** $20(20 + x) = 31^2$
$2x = 25$ $400 + 20x = 961$
$x = 12.5$ $x \approx 28.1$

16. $x(x + 10) = 8(16)$
$x^2 + 10x = 128$
$x^2 + 10x - 128 = 0$
$x = \frac{-10 \pm \sqrt{100 - 4\,(-128)}}{2} \approx 7.4$

17. $18 \cdot 3 = 2x \cdot 3x$ **18.** $10(10 + 3x) = 8(8 + 22)$
$6x^2 = 54$ $100 + 30x = 240$
$x^2 = 9$ $30x = 140$
$x = 3$ $x = 4.7$

19. $7.1(x + 7.1) = 9.8^2$
$7.1x + 50.41 = 96.04$
$7.1x = 45.63$
$x = 6.4$

20. $x(x + 3x) = 8((x + 2) + 8)$
$4x^2 = 8x + 80$
$4x^2 - 8x - 80 = 0$
$x^2 - 2x - 20 = 0$
$x = \frac{2 \pm \sqrt{4 - 4(-20)}}{2}$
$x \approx 5.6$

21. $x(x + x) = 8^2$
$2x^2 = 64$
$x^2 = 32$
$x \approx 5.7$

22. $x^2 = 20 - x$
$x^2 + x - 20 = 0$
$(x + 5)(x - 4) = 0$
$x = -5$ or $x = 4$

23. $AX = EX = 24$

24. $AD = DE = 7$
$AD^2 + AX^2 = DX^2$
$7^2 + 24^2 = DX^2$
$DX = 25$

25. $DX = DQ + QX$
$25 = 7 + QX$
$QX = 18$

26. $TX = TQ + QX$
$= 2(7) + 18$
$= 32$

27. $DQ + QX = DX$ *Segment Add. Post.*
$QX = DX - DQ$
$= 25 - 7$ $DQ = DE = 7$
$= 18$
$(EX)^2 = QX \cdot TX$ *Theorem 9-16*
$24^2 = x(x + 14)$
$0 = x^2 + 14x - 576$
$x = 18$ *quadratic formula*

28. a. Through any 2 pts. there is 1 line.
    b. If 2 inscribed ∡ of a ⊙ intercept the same arc, then the ∡ are ≅.
    c. AA Similarity
    d. Definition of similar polygons
    e. Cross products

29. $KT = MK = 8$
$TR = x, KR = 8 - x$
$x(16 - x) = 4(9)$
$16x - x^2 = 36$
$x^2 - 16x + 36 = 0$
$x = \dfrac{16 \pm \sqrt{(-16)^2 - 4(1)(36)}}{2} = 2.7$
$KR = 8 - 2.7 = 5.3$

30. $BC \cdot AC = CD \cdot CE$
$10(8 + 10) = 9(9 + DE)$
$180 = 81 + 9DE$
$99 = 9DE$
$DE = 11$

31. $12^2 = 6(x + 9)$ $3(15) = 2y$
$144 = 6x + 54$ $45 = 2y$
$6x = 90$ $y = 22.5$
$x = 15$

32. $9^2 = x(x + 17.3)$
$81 = x^2 + 17.3x$
$x^2 + 17.3x - 81 = 0$
$x = \dfrac{-17.3 \pm \sqrt{(17.3)^2 - 4(-81)}}{2} = 3.8$
$y(y + 15) = 3.8(21.1)$
$y^2 + 15y - 80.18 = 0$
$y = \dfrac{-15 \pm \sqrt{15^2 - 4(-80.18)}}{2} = 4.2$

33. Given: $\overline{EC}$ and $\overline{EB}$ are secant segments.
Prove: $EA \cdot EC = ED \cdot EB$

Proof:

Statements	Reasons
1. $\overline{EC}$ and $\overline{EB}$ are secant segments.	1. Given
2. Draw $\overline{AB}$ and $\overline{CD}$.	2. Through any 2 pts. there is 1 line.
3. $\angle DEC \cong \angle AEB$	3. Reflexive Prop. of ≅ ∡
4. $\angle ECD \cong \angle EBA$	4. If 2 inscribed ∡ of a ⊙ or ≅ ⊙s intercept ≅ arcs or the same arc, then the ∡ are ≅.
5. $\triangle ABE \sim \triangle DCE$	5. AA Similarity
6. $\dfrac{EA}{ED} = \dfrac{EB}{EC}$	6. Def. ~ polygons
7. $EA \cdot EC = ED \cdot EB$	7. Cross products

34. Given: $\odot H, \overline{AO} \perp \overline{DM}$
Prove: $OT \cdot TA = (TM)^2$

Proof:

Statements	Reasons
1. Draw $\overline{DA}$ and $\overline{OM}$ forming $\triangle ADT$ and $\triangle MOT$.	1. Through any 2 pts. there is 1 line.
2. $\odot H, \overline{AO} \perp \overline{DM}$	2. Given
3. $\overline{DT} \cong \overline{TM}$	3. In a ⊙, if a diameter is ⊥ to a chord, then it bisects the chord and its arc.
4. $\angle D \cong \angle O$ $\angle A \cong \angle M$	4. If 2 inscribed ∡ of a ⊙ intercept the same arc, then the ∡ are ≅.
5. $\triangle ADT \sim \triangle MOT$	5. AA Similarity
6. $\dfrac{DT}{OT} = \dfrac{TA}{TM}$	6. Def. ~ polygons
7. $DT \cdot TM = OT \cdot TA$	7. Cross products
8. $TM \cdot TM = OT \cdot TA$	8. Substitution Prop. (=)
9. $OT \cdot TA = TM \cdot TM$	9. Symmetric Prop. (=)
10. $OT \cdot TA = (TM)^2$	10. Def. exponents

35. Given: $\overline{XY}$ is tangent to $\odot A$.

$\overline{WY}$ is a secant segment to $\odot A$.

Prove: $(XY)^2 = WY \cdot ZY$

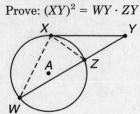

Proof:

Statements	Reasons
1. $\overline{XY}$ is tangent to $\odot A$. $\overline{WY}$ is a secant segment to $\odot A$.	1. Given
2. Draw $\overline{XZ}$ and $\overline{XW}$	2. Through any 2 pts. there is 1 line.
3. $m\angle XWZ = \frac{1}{2}m\widehat{XZ}$	3. If an $\angle$ is inscribed in a $\odot$, the measure of the $\angle = \frac{1}{2}$ the measure of its intercepted arc.
4. $m\angle YXZ = \frac{1}{2}m\widehat{XZ}$	4. If a secant and a tangent intersect at the pt. of tangency, then the measure of the $\angle$ formed $= \frac{1}{2}$ the measure of its intercepted arc.
5. $m\angle YXZ = m\angle XWZ$	5. Substitution Prop. (=)
6. $\angle YXZ \cong \angle XWZ$	6. Def. of $\cong$ $\angle s$
7. $\angle Y \cong \angle Y$	7. Reflexive Prop. of $\cong$ $\angle s$
8. $\triangle YXZ \sim \triangle YWX$	8. AA Similarity
9. $\frac{XY}{WY} = \frac{ZY}{XY}$	9. Def. $\sim$ polygons
10. $(XY)^2 = WY \cdot ZY$	10. Cross products

36a. 16 **36b.** about 2.6 **36c.** about 16.7

37. $(AB)^2 = BC(BD)$ — Th. 9-16
$= BC(BC + CD)$ — Seg. Add. Post.
$= BC(BC + BC)$ — $BC = CD$
$= BC(2BC)$
$= 2(BC)^2$
$AB = \sqrt{2}BC$

38. $113x = 340 \cdot 340$

$x = 1023$

radius $= \frac{(1023 + 113)}{2}$

$= 568$ ft

39. $3x = 3.5^2$

$x = \frac{49}{12}$

$r = \frac{1}{2}\left(\frac{49}{12} + 3\right)$

$r \approx 3.5$

ratios: 7: 3.5

40. $m\angle 1 = \frac{1}{2}(126) = 63$

41. $8^2 + 15^2 = x^2$

$289 = x^2$

$x = 17$

42. $d = 5\sqrt{2} = 30.4\sqrt{2} \approx 43.0$ yd

43. $\frac{t}{18} = \frac{5}{6}$

$6t = 90$

$t = 15$

44. $m\angle Q + m\angle R = 180$

$76 + 3x + 2x = 180$

$5x = 104$

$x = 20.8$

$m\angle TRS = 2(20.8) = 41.6$

45. Subtraction Prop. of Inequality

46. sometimes

47. $(2c - 1)(c + 7) = 2c^2 + 14c - c - 7$ or $2c^2 + 13c - 7$

48. $(5a - 2)(5a + 2)$

9-8 Integration: Algebra Equations of Circles

Pages 500–501 Check for Understanding

1. The equation of a circle is derived using the distance formula.

2. Solve the system of equations for the two lines. The solution is the point of intersection, which is the center.

3a. Mach number is the ratio of the speed of an object to the speed of sound. Mach 1 is equal to the speed of sound, about 760 mph, Mach 2 is twice the speed of sound, or about 1520 mph.

3b. Austrian physicist and philospher Ernst Mach developed the concept.

4. $(x + 2)^2 + (y + 7)^2 = 81$
$[x - (-2)]^2 + [y - (-7)]^2 = 9^2$
$(h, k) = (-2, -7); r = 9$

5. **6.**

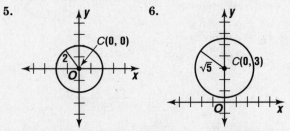

7. $(x + 2)^2 + (y - 3)^2 = 11$

8. $r = PQ = \sqrt{(2 - 0)^2 + (2 - 0)^2} = \sqrt{4 + 4} = \sqrt{8}$
$(x - 0)^2 + (y - 0)^2 = (\sqrt{8})^2$
$x^2 + y^2 = 8$

9. Center: $(0, 0)$ $r = \sqrt{(0 - 0)^2 + (4 - 0)^2} = \sqrt{16} = 4$
$(x - 0)^2 + (y - 0)^2 = 4^2$
$x^2 + y^2 = 16$

10. For any sample circle, the distance from the center of the circle to N will be 5 times the speed of sound.

Pages 501–503 Exercises

11. $\left(x - \frac{3}{4}\right)^2 + (y + 3)^2 = \frac{81}{4}$
$\left(x - \frac{3}{4}\right)^2 + [y - (-3)]^2 = \left(\frac{9}{2}\right)^2$
$(h, k) = \left(\frac{3}{4}, -3\right), r = \frac{9}{2}$

12. $(x + 4)^2 + y^2 - 121 = 0$
$[x - (-4)]^2 + (y - 0)^2 = 11^2$
$(h, k) = (-4, 0), r = 11$

13. $(x - 0.5)^2 + (y + 3.1)^2 = 17.64$
$(x - 0.5)^2 + [y - (-3.1)]^2 = 4.2^2$
$(h, k) = (0.5, -3.1), r = 4.2$

14.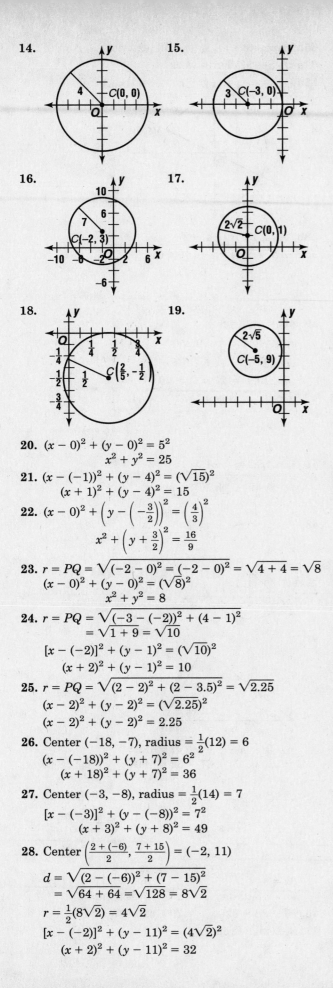

4 $C(0, 0)$

15.

3 $C(-3, 0)$

16.

10
6
7
$C(-2, 3)$
-10 -6 -2 2 6
-6

17.

$2\sqrt{2}$ $C(0, 1)$

18.

$\frac{1}{4}$ $\frac{1}{2}$ $\frac{3}{4}$
$-\frac{1}{4}$
$-\frac{1}{2}$ $\frac{1}{2}$ $C\left(\frac{2}{5}, -\frac{1}{2}\right)$
$-\frac{3}{4}$

19.

$2\sqrt{5}$
$C(-5, 9)$

20. $(x - 0)^2 + (y - 0)^2 = 5^2$
$x^2 + y^2 = 25$

21. $(x - (-1))^2 + (y - 4)^2 = (\sqrt{15})^2$
$(x + 1)^2 + (y - 4)^2 = 15$

22. $(x - 0)^2 + \left(y - \left(-\frac{3}{2}\right)\right)^2 = \left(\frac{4}{3}\right)^2$

$x^2 + \left(y + \frac{3}{2}\right)^2 = \frac{16}{9}$

23. $r = PQ = \sqrt{(-2 - 0)^2 = (-2 - 0)^2} = \sqrt{4 + 4} = \sqrt{8}$
$(x - 0)^2 + (y - 0)^2 = (\sqrt{8})^2$
$x^2 + y^2 = 8$

24. $r = PQ = \sqrt{(-3 - (-2))^2 + (4 - 1)^2}$
$= \sqrt{1 + 9} = \sqrt{10}$
$[x - (-2)]^2 + (y - 1)^2 = (\sqrt{10})^2$
$(x + 2)^2 + (y - 1)^2 = 10$

25. $r = PQ = \sqrt{(2 - 2)^2 + (2 - 3.5)^2} = \sqrt{2.25}$
$(x - 2)^2 + (y - 2)^2 = (\sqrt{2.25})^2$
$(x - 2)^2 + (y - 2)^2 = 2.25$

26. Center $(-18, -7)$, radius $= \frac{1}{2}(12) = 6$
$(x - (-18))^2 + (y + 7)^2 = 6^2$
$(x + 18)^2 + (y + 7)^2 = 36$

27. Center $(-3, -8)$, radius $= \frac{1}{2}(14) = 7$
$[x - (-3)]^2 + (y - (-8))^2 = 7^2$
$(x + 3)^2 + (y + 8)^2 = 49$

28. Center $\left(\frac{2 + (-6)}{2}, \frac{7 + 15}{2}\right) = (-2, 11)$

$d = \sqrt{(2 - (-6))^2 + (7 - 15)^2}$
$= \sqrt{64 + 64} = \sqrt{128} = 8\sqrt{2}$
$r = \frac{1}{2}(8\sqrt{2}) = 4\sqrt{2}$
$[x - (-2)]^2 + (y - 11)^2 = (4\sqrt{2})^2$
$(x + 2)^2 + (y - 11)^2 = 32$

Figure for 29–32.

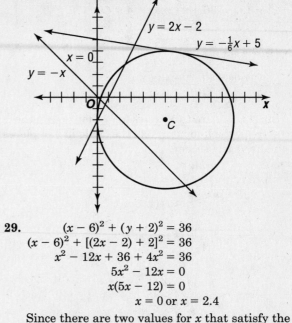

$y = 2x - 2$
$y = -\frac{1}{6}x + 5$
$x = 0$
$y = -x$
C

29. $(x - 6)^2 + (y + 2)^2 = 36$
$(x - 6)^2 + [(2x - 2) + 2]^2 = 36$
$x^2 - 12x + 36 + 4x^2 = 36$
$5x^2 - 12x = 0$
$x(5x - 12) = 0$
$x = 0$ or $x = 2.4$

Since there are two values for x that satisfy the system, the line intersects the circle in two places. Thus, it is a secant.

30. $(x - 6)^2 + (y + 2)^2 = 36$
$(0 - 6)^2 + (y + 2)^2 = 36$
$36 + y^2 + 4y + 4 = 36$
$y^2 + 4y + 4 = 0$
$(y + 2)^2 = 0$
$y = -2$

Since there is only one value for y that satisfies the system, the line intersects the circle in one point. Thus, it is a tangent.

31. $(x - 6)^2 + (y + 2)^2 = 36$
$(x - 6)^2 + \left[\left(-\frac{1}{6}x + 5\right) + 2\right]^2 = 36$
$(x - 6)^2 + \left(-\frac{1}{6}x + 7\right)^2 = 36$
$x^2 - 12x + 36 + \frac{1}{36}x^2 - \frac{7}{3}x + 49 = 36$
$36x^2 - 432x + 1296 + x^2 - 84x + 1764 = 1296$
$37x^2 - 516x + 1764 = 0$
$x = \frac{-b \pm \sqrt{b^2 - 4ac}}{2a}$
$x = \frac{-(-516) \pm \sqrt{(-516)^2 - 4(37)(1764)}}{2(37)}$
$x = \frac{516 \pm 72}{74}$
$x = 7\frac{35}{37}$ or $x = 6$

Since there are two values for x that satisfy the system, the line intersects the circle in two places. Thus, it is a secant.

32.
$$(x-6)^2 + (y+2)^2 = 36$$
$$(x-6)^2 + (-x+2)^2 = 36$$
$$x^2 - 12x + 36 + x^2 - 4x + 4 = 36$$
$$2x^2 - 16x + 4 = 36$$
$$x^2 - 8x + 2 = 0$$
$$x = \frac{-b \pm \sqrt{b^2 - 4ac}}{2a}$$
$$x = \frac{-(-8) \pm \sqrt{(-8)^2 - 4(1)(2)}}{2(1)}$$
$$x = 4 \pm \sqrt{14}$$

Since there are two values for x that satisfy the system, the line intersects the circle in two places. Thus, it is a secant.

33a.

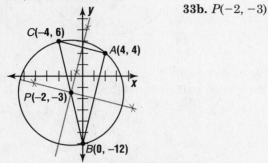

33b. $P(-2, -3)$

33c. $PA = \sqrt{(-2-4)^2 + (-3-4)^2}$
$$= \sqrt{36 + 49} = \sqrt{85} \approx 9.2$$

33d. $[x - (-2)]^2 + [y - (-3)]^2 = (\sqrt{85})^2$
$$(x+2)^2 + (y+3)^2 = 85$$

34.

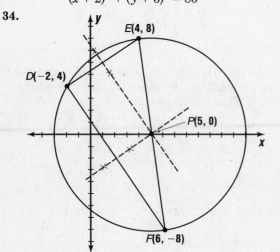

Center $(5, 0)$
radius $= \sqrt{(5-(-2))^2 + (0-4)^2}$
$$= \sqrt{49 + 16} = \sqrt{65}$$
$$(x-5)^2 + (y-0)^2 = (\sqrt{65})^2$$
$$(x-5)^2 + y^2 = 65$$

35a. Center $(3, 3)$
radius $= \sqrt{(0-3)^2 + (6-3)^2} = \sqrt{9+9} = \sqrt{18}$
$$(x-3)^2 + (y-3)^2 = (\sqrt{18})^2$$
$$(x-3)^2 + (y-3)^2 = 18$$

35b. $AB = \sqrt{(0-6)^2 + (6-0)^2} = \sqrt{72} = 6\sqrt{2}$
$BC = \sqrt{(6-6)^2 + (6-0)^2} = 6$
$AC = \sqrt{(0-6)^2 + (6-6)^2} = 6$
$AC^2 + BC^2 \overset{?}{=} AB^2$
$6^2 + 6^2 \overset{?}{=} (6\sqrt{2})^2$
$72 = 72$

right triangle

35c. diameter   **36.** exterior
37a-d. See students' work.
38a.

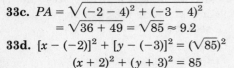

38b. $A\ (4, 2)$, $B\ (-4, -2)$

38c. $AB = \sqrt{(4-(-4))^2 + (2-(-2))^2}$
$$= \sqrt{64 + 16} = \sqrt{80}$$
$$= 4\sqrt{5} \approx 8.9$$

38d. $\overline{AB}$ is a diameter of the circle.

39. $AC = 4(2) = 8$
$$\sin \angle BCA = \frac{2}{8} = 0.2500$$
$$m\angle BCA = 14.5$$
$$m\angle BCD = 2(14.5) = 29$$

40. $(x-0)^2 + (y-0)^2 = 3^2$
$$x^2 + y^2 = 9$$

41. $10^2 = 5(5 + 3x)$
$$100 = 25 + 15x$$
$$75 = 15x$$
$$x = 5$$

42. $m\angle ABC = \frac{1}{2}m\widehat{AC}$
$$42 = \frac{1}{2}m\widehat{AC}$$
$$m\widehat{AC} = 84$$

43.

$$x^2 + 5^2 = 7^2$$
$$x^2 = 24$$
$$x = \sqrt{24}$$
$$2x = 2\sqrt{24} \approx 9.8 \text{ in.}$$

44.

$m\angle D + m\angle K + m\angle H = 180$
$m\angle D + 37 + 62 = 180$
$m\angle D = 81$

$\dfrac{\sin 81°}{d} = \dfrac{\sin 37°}{8.1}$ $\dfrac{\sin 62°}{h} = \dfrac{\sin 37°}{8.1}$

$d = \dfrac{8.1 \sin 81°}{\sin 37°}$ $h = \dfrac{8.1 \sin 62°}{\sin 37°}$

$d \approx 13.3$ $h \approx 11.9$

45. $\dfrac{6}{12} = \dfrac{9}{x}$ $\dfrac{6}{12} = \dfrac{11}{y}$

$6x = 108$ $6y = 132$

$x = 18$ units $y = 22$ units

46. $90 - 28 = 62$ $(90, 62)$
47. Reflexive Prop. (=)

48. $y = x - 3$ $y = 0 - 3$
$\qquad 2x + y = -3$ $y = -3$
$\qquad 2x + (x - 3) = -3$ $(0, -3)$
$\qquad\qquad 3x = 0$
$\qquad\qquad x = 0$

49. $y = 8000 (1 + 0.0175)^{3(5)}$
$\qquad = \$10,377.82$

Chapter 9 Highlights

Page 505 Understanding and Using the Vocabulary

1. (i) central angle   **2.** (j) concentric circles
3. (h) secant   **4.** (a) chord
5. (c) inscribed angle   **6.** (b) congruent circles
7. (f) tangent   **8.** (g) circumfrence
9. (e) adjacent arcs   **10.** (d) congruent arcs

Chapter 9 Study Guide and Assessment

Pages 506–508 Skills and Concepts

11. $\overline{AB}$

12. $AB = 2(TC) = 2(6) = 12$

13. $C = 2\pi r$
$\qquad = 2\pi(14)$
$\qquad = 28\pi \approx 88.0$

14. $(3x) + (3x - 3) + (2x + 15) = 180$
$\qquad\qquad\qquad\qquad\qquad 8x = 168$
$\qquad\qquad\qquad\qquad\qquad x = 21$
$\qquad m\widehat{YC} = m\angle YPC = 3x - 3 = 3(21) - 3$ or 60

15. $m\widehat{BC} = m\angle BPC$
$\qquad = 3(21) + (3(21) - 3)$ or 123

16. $m\widehat{AX} = m\widehat{BY}$
$\qquad m\widehat{BX} = 180 - m\widehat{AX}$
$\qquad\qquad = 180 - 3(21)$ or 117

17. $m\widehat{CA} = \frac{(2(21) + 15)}{360} \cdot \pi(9)$
$\qquad\qquad \approx 4.5$

18. $m\widehat{YAX} = \frac{180}{360} \cdot \pi(9)$
$\qquad\qquad \approx 14.1$

19. $m\widehat{ABY} = \frac{(180 + 63)}{360} \cdot \pi(9)$ **20.** $5^2 + x^2 = 13^2$
$\qquad\qquad \approx 19.$
$\qquad\qquad\qquad\qquad\qquad\qquad\qquad x^2 = 144$
$\qquad\qquad\qquad\qquad\qquad\qquad\qquad x = 12$
$\qquad\qquad\qquad\qquad\qquad\qquad 2(12) = 24$ cm

21. $12^2 + 32^2 = x^2$
$\qquad 1168 = x^2$
$\qquad x \approx 34.2$ cm

22. $x^2 + 8^2 = 10^2$
$\qquad x^2 = 36$
$\qquad x = 6$ cm

23. $3^2 + x^2 = 5^2$
$\qquad x^2 = 16$
$\qquad x = 4$ in.

24. $m\angle DAB = \frac{1}{2}m\widehat{BD} = \frac{1}{2}(72)$ or 36

25. $m\widehat{CD} = m\angle CPD = 144$

26. $m\widehat{CA} = m\widehat{BD} = 72$

27. $m\angle CDA = \frac{1}{2}m\widehat{CA} = \frac{1}{2}(72)$ or 36

28. $m\widehat{AB} = 360 - m\widehat{BD} - m\widehat{CD} - m\widehat{CA}$
$\qquad = 360 - 72 - 144 - 72$
$\qquad = 72$

29. $x^2 + 9^2 = (6 + 9)^2$ **30.** $x + 2 = 8$
$\qquad x^2 + 81 = 225$ $x = 6$
$\qquad x^2 = 144$
$\qquad x = 12$

31. $m\angle DEC = m\angle AEB = 42$

32. $m\angle AEB = \frac{1}{2}(m\widehat{AB} + m\widehat{CD})$
$\qquad 42 = \frac{1}{2}(29 + m\widehat{CD})$
$\qquad 84 = 29 + m\widehat{CD}$
$\qquad m\widehat{CD} = 55$

33. $m\angle GFD = \frac{1}{2}(m\widehat{DC} - m\widehat{BC})$
$\qquad = \frac{1}{2}(55 - 18)$ or 18.5

34. $m\widehat{AD} = 180 - m\widehat{DC}$
$\qquad = 180 - 55$ or 125

35. $m\angle AED = 180 - m\angle DEC$
$\qquad = 180 - 42$ or 138

36. $m\angle AED = \frac{1}{2}(m\widehat{AD} + m\widehat{BC})$
$\qquad 138 = \frac{1}{2}(125 + m\widehat{BC})$
$\qquad 276 = 125 + m\widehat{BC}$
$\qquad m\widehat{BC} = 151$
$\qquad m\widehat{GC} = m\widehat{BC} - m\widehat{BG}$
$\qquad = 151 - 18$ or 133

37. $4x = 3(8)$ **38.** $x^2 = 0.5(0.5 + 0.8)$
$\qquad 4x = 24$ $x^2 = 0.65$
$\qquad x = 6.0$ cm $x \approx 0.8$ ft

39. $3(x + 3) = 5(5 + 6)$ **40.** $7^2 = 5(5 + x)$
$\qquad 3x + 9 = 55$ $49 = 25 + 5x$
$\qquad 3x = 46$ $24 = 5x$
$\qquad x = 15.3$ cm $x = 4.8$ in.

41. $[x - (-4)]^2 + (y - 3)^2 = 6^2$
$\qquad (x + 4)^2 + (y - 3)^2 = 36$

42. $r = WQ = \sqrt{(0 - 0)^2 + (2 - (-2))^2} = \sqrt{16} = 4$
$\qquad$ center $(0, -2)$
$\qquad (x - 0)^2 + (y - (-2))^2 = 4^2$
$\qquad\qquad x^2 + (y + 2)^2 = 16$

43. Portion of Sales per Recording Type

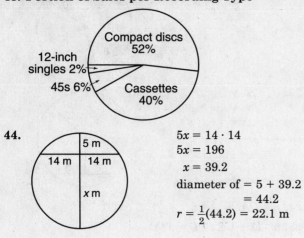

12-inch singles 2%
45s 6%
Compact discs 52%
Cassettes 40%

44.

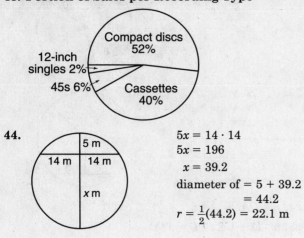

$5x = 14 \cdot 14$
$5x = 196$
$x = 39.2$
diameter of $= 5 + 39.2$
$= 44.2$
$r = \frac{1}{2}(44.2) = 22.1$ m

45. original diameter = 8 cm

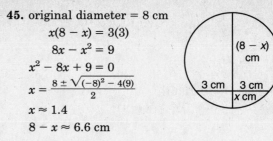

$x(8 - x) = 3(3)$
$8x - x^2 = 9$
$x^2 - 8x + 9 = 0$
$x = \dfrac{8 \pm \sqrt{(-8)^2 - 4(9)}}{2}$
$x \approx 1.4$
$8 - x \approx 6.6$ cm

Page 509 Alternative Assessment: Thinking Critically

- Rectangles are used in bar graphs. Geometric models are useful since we have formulas to compute perimeter and area. Geometric models can be misleading if they are not drawn to scale.

CHAPTER 10 Exploring Polygons and Area

Page 517 Modeling Mathematics
a. See students' work.
b. The sum of the measures of the exterior angles of any convex polygon is 360.

Pages 518–519 Check for Understanding
1a. yes **1b.** No; sides overlap.
1c. no; curved side **1d.** yes
2. Juanita is correct because $\frac{360}{15} = 24$, which is the exterior angle measure.
3. Sample answer:

The pentagon is concave because when a line segment is extended, it contains a point in the interior of the pentagon.
4. The Interior Angle Sum Theorem is for a convex polygon, and it is only dependent on the number of sides the polygon has. Therefore, the size of the polygon makes no difference, and similar polygons all have the same interior angle sum. Furthermore, the pentagons are regular, and therefore each interior angle is congruent.
5. Subtract the measure of the known interior angle from 180. Divide 360 by that result. This answer is the number of sides in the polygon.
6a. See students' work.
6b. The angles should form a circle or equal 360.
6c. yes
7. $\overline{AB}, \overline{BC}, \overline{DC}, \overline{DE}, \overline{EF}, \overline{FA}$
8. Convex; lines containing each side intersect only at the endpoints.
9. $s = 180(10 - 2) = 180(8) = 1440$
10. $s = 180(21 - 2) = 180(19) = 3420$
11. $\frac{360}{30} = 12$ sides   **12.** $\frac{360}{8} = 45$ sides
13. the measure of an interior angle = $\frac{180(8 - 2)}{8} = \frac{180(6)}{8} = 135$
14. the measure of an interior angle = $\frac{180(a - 2)}{a}$
$$180 - \frac{180(a - 2)}{a} = 180 - \frac{180a - 360}{a}$$
$$= 180 - 180 + \frac{360}{a}$$
$$= \frac{360}{a}$$
15. $180 - 120 = 60$ **16.** $180 - 150 = 30$
   $\frac{360}{60} = 6$ sides $\frac{360}{30} = 12$ sides

17. $180(5 - 2) = 180(3) = 540$
$x + 3x + 2x - 1 + 6x - 5 + 4x + 2 = 540$
$$16x = 544$$
$$x = 34$$
$3x = 102$
$2x - 1 = 67$
$6x - 5 = 199$
$4x + 2 = 138$
18. $S = 180(n - 2) = 180(3)$ or 540
each angle $= \frac{540}{5} = 108$
angle between beds $= 360 - 108 - 90 - 90 = 72$

Pages 519–521 Exercises
19. A, B, C, D, E, F **20.** no
21. Sample answers: $BCDEFA$ and $FABCDE$
22. $S = 180(11 - 2) = 180(9) = 1620$
23. $S = 180(26 - 2) = 180(24) = 4320$
24. $S = 180(90 - 2) = 180(88) = 15,840$
25. $S = 180(46 - 2) = 180(44) = 7920$
26. $S = 180(x - 2)$ **27.** $S = 180(3m - 2)$
28. $\frac{360}{72} = 5$ **29.** $\frac{360}{45} = 8$
30. $\frac{360}{18} = 20$ **31.** $\frac{360}{14.4} = 25$
32. $\frac{360}{20} = 18$ **33.** $\frac{360}{x}$
34. int. $\angle$: $\frac{180(30 - 2)}{30} = \frac{180(28)}{30} = 168$
ext. $\angle$: $180 - 168 = 12$
35. int. $\angle$: $\frac{180(16 - 2)}{16} = \frac{180(14)}{16} = 157.5$
ext. $\angle$: $180 - 157.5 = 22.5$
36. int $\angle$: $\frac{180(22 - 2)}{22} = \frac{180(20)}{22} = 163.64$
ext. $\angle$: $180 - 163.64 = 16.36$
37. int $\angle$: $\frac{180(14 - 2)}{14} = \frac{180(12)}{14} = 154.29$
ext. $\angle$: $180 - 154.29 = 25.71$
38. int. $\angle$: $\frac{180(3m - 2)}{3m} = \frac{60(3m - 2)}{m}$
ext. $\angle$: $180 - \frac{60(3m - 2)}{m} = 180 - 180 + \frac{120}{m}$
$$= \frac{120}{m}$$
39. int. $\angle$: $\frac{180(x + 2y - 2)}{x + 2y}$
ext. $\angle$:
$180 - \frac{180(x + 2y - 2)}{x + 2y} = 180 - \frac{180x - 360y - 360}{x + 2y}$
$$= \frac{180x + 360y - 180x - 360y + 360}{x + 2y}$$
$$= \frac{360}{x + 2y}$$
40. $180 - 135 = 45$ **41.** $180 - 144 = 36$
   $\frac{360}{45} = 8$ sides $\frac{360}{36} = 10$ sides
42. $180 - 157.5 = 22.5$ **43.** $180 - 176.4 = 3.6$
   $\frac{360}{22.5} = 16$ sides $\frac{360}{3.6} = 100$ sides
44. $180 - 165.6 = 14.4$ **45.** $180 - \frac{180(s - 2)}{s} = \frac{360}{s}$
   $\frac{360}{14.4} = 25$ sides $\frac{360}{s} = s$ sides
$$\frac{360}{\frac{360}{s}}$$

46. $180(4 - 2) = x + 2x + x + 2x$
$360 = 6x$
$x = 60$
$m\angle A = 60, m\angle B = 120, m\angle C = 120, m\angle D = 60$

47. $180(5 - 2) = 120 + (2y - 5) + 2y + 2y + (3y - 25)$
$540 = 90 + 9y$
$450 = 9y$
$y = 50$
$m\angle R = 3(150) - 25 = 125, m\angle S = 2(50) = 100,$
$m\angle T = 2(50) = 100, m\angle U = 2(50) - 5 = 95,$
$m\angle V = 120$

48. $\frac{360}{36} = 10$
$S = 180(10 - 2) = 1440$

49. $\frac{360}{60} = 6$
$S = 180(6 - 2) = 720$

50a. Each numbered angle is a vertical angle to an interior angle of the pentagon. The sum of the measures of the numbered angles equals the sum of the measures of the interior angles of a pentagon $S = 180(5 - 2) = 540$

50b. Each triangle contains two exterior angles of a pentagon. The sum of the angles at the points equals the sum of the measures of 5 triangles minus 2 sets of exterior angles.
$5(180) - 2(360) = 180$

51. $x + (100 + x) = 180$ $\frac{360}{40} = 9$ sides, which
$x = 40$ is a nonagon

52. $5x + x = 180$
$6x = 180$
$x = 30$
int. $\angle$: 150; ext. $\angle$: 30 $\frac{360}{30} = 12$ sides; 12-gon
or dodecagon

53. Consider the sum of the measures of the exterior angles for an n-gon. sum of measures of exterior angles
N = sum of measures of linear pairs − sum of measures of interior angles
$= n \cdot 180 - 180(n - 2)$
$= 180n - 180n + 360$
$= 360$

So, the sum of the exterior angle measures is 360 for *any* convex polygon.

54. x, z, y; the sum of the exterior angles is 360, therefore, the larger the number of sides of a polygon, the smaller each exterior angle measure will be because there will be more angles to share the 360 degrees.

55. No; the sum of the measures of the angles of any vertex is less than 360, so the polygons interlock in a plane.

56a. hexagon

56b. $\frac{180(6 - 2)}{6} = \frac{180(4)}{6}$ or 120

56c.

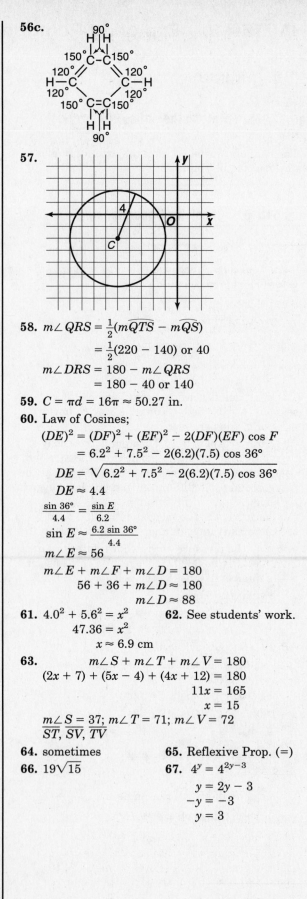

58. $m\angle QRS = \frac{1}{2}(m\widehat{QTS} - m\widehat{QS})$
$= \frac{1}{2}(220 - 140)$ or 40
$m\angle DRS = 180 - m\angle QRS$
$= 180 - 40$ or 140

59. $C = \pi d = 16\pi \approx 50.27$ in.

60. Law of Cosines;
$(DE)^2 = (DF)^2 + (EF)^2 - 2(DF)(EF) \cos F$
$= 6.2^2 + 7.5^2 - 2(6.2)(7.5) \cos 36°$
$DE = \sqrt{6.2^2 + 7.5^2 - 2(6.2)(7.5) \cos 36°}$
$DE \approx 4.4$
$\frac{\sin 36°}{4.4} = \frac{\sin E}{6.2}$
$\sin E \approx \frac{6.2 \sin 36°}{4.4}$
$m\angle E \approx 56$
$m\angle E + m\angle F + m\angle D = 180$
$56 + 36 + m\angle D \approx 180$
$m\angle D \approx 88$

61. $4.0^2 + 5.6^2 = x^2$ **62.** See students' work.
$47.36 = x^2$
$x \approx 6.9$ cm

63. $m\angle S + m\angle T + m\angle V = 180$
$(2x + 7) + (5x - 4) + (4x + 12) = 180$
$11x = 165$
$x = 15$
$m\angle S = 37; m\angle T = 71; m\angle V = 72$
$\overline{ST}, \overline{SV}, \overline{TV}$

64. sometimes   **65.** Reflexive Prop. (=)

66. $19\sqrt{15}$ **67.** $4^y = 4^{2y-3}$
$y = 2y - 3$
$-y = -3$
$y = 3$

Modeling Mathematics: Tessellations and Transformatrons

10-2A

Page 522

1. Yes; whatever space is taken out of the square is then added onto the outside of the square. The area does not change, only the shape changes.

2. Modify the bottom of the triangle to be like the right side of the triangle. Erase the bottom and right original sides of the triangle.

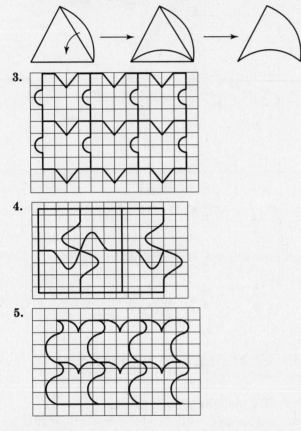

3.

4.

5.

10-2 | Tessellations

Page 523 Modeling Mathematics

a. See students' work.

b. triangle, square, hexagon

c. If a regular polygon has an interior angle with a measure that is a factor of 360, then the polygon will tessellate the plane.

Page 525 Check for Understanding

1. Each angle is a factor of 360.

2. A regular tessellation uses one type of polygon and a semi-regular tessellation uses more than one type.

3. Equilateral triangles, squares, and regular hexagons; these are the only regular polygons that have an interior angle measure that is a factor of 360.

4. Sample answer:

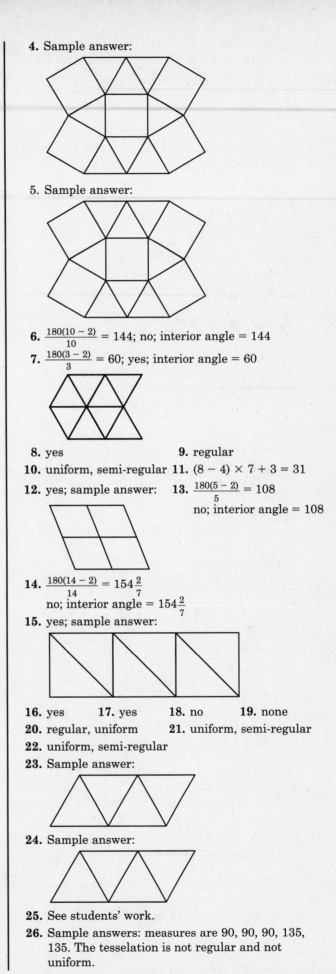

5. Sample answer:

6. $\frac{180(10-2)}{10} = 144$; no; interior angle = 144

7. $\frac{180(3-2)}{3} = 60$; yes; interior angle = 60

8. yes   9. regular

10. uniform, semi-regular 11. $(8-4) \times 7 + 3 = 31$

12. yes; sample answer: 13. $\frac{180(5-2)}{5} = 108$
                              no; interior angle = 108

14. $\frac{180(14-2)}{14} = 154\frac{2}{7}$
    no; interior angle = $154\frac{2}{7}$

15. yes; sample answer:

16. yes   17. yes   18. no   19. none

20. regular, uniform   21. uniform, semi-regular

22. uniform, semi-regular

23. Sample answer:

24. Sample answer:

25. See students' work.

26. Sample answers: measures are 90, 90, 90, 135, 135. The tesselation is not regular and not uniform.

27. Yes; a tessellation can be uniform with only one regular polygon. Therefore, it would not be semi-regular.

28. No; by definition a semi-regular tessellation must be uniform.

29.

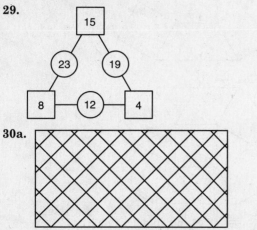

30a.

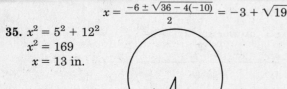

30b. triangle with two sides equal to the side of the square and one side equal to the length of the diagonal

31a. D = 5, Y = 2, N = 6, E = 9, A = 4, L = 8, S = 1, R = 7, C = 3, and T = 0

31b. More answers will result; sample answer: 561,535 + 207,535 = 769,070.

32. not regular, uniform, not semi-regular

33. $180 - 160 = 20$
$$\frac{360}{20} = 18 \text{ sides}$$

34. $(2x + 4)(x + 4) = 6^2$
$2x^2 + 12x + 16 = 36$
$2x^2 + 12x - 20 = 0$
$x^2 + 6x - 10 = 0$
$x = \frac{-6 \pm \sqrt{36 - 4(-10)}}{2} = -3 + \sqrt{19}$

35. $x^2 = 5^2 + 12^2$
$x^2 = 169$
$x = 13$ in.

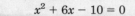

36.

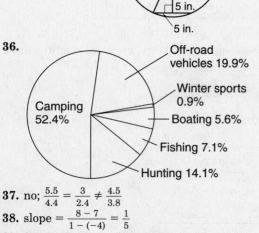

Off-road vehicles 19.9%

Winter sports 0.9%

Boating 5.6%

Fishing 7.1%

Hunting 14.1%

Camping 52.4%

37. no; $\frac{5.5}{4.4} = \frac{3}{2.4} \neq \frac{4.5}{3.8}$

38. slope $= \frac{8 - 7}{1 - (-4)} = \frac{1}{5}$

39. {(6, 6), (0, 1), (−5, 6), (9, 2)};
D = {6, 0, −5, 9};
R = {2, 1, 6};
Inverse = {(6, 6), (1, 0), (6, −5), (2, 9)}

10-3A Using Technology
Area of Parallelograms

Page 528 Exercises

1. See students' work.   **2.** See students' work.

3. See students' work.   **4.** See students' work.

5. See students' work.   **6.** The areas are the same.

7. $A = bh$

8.

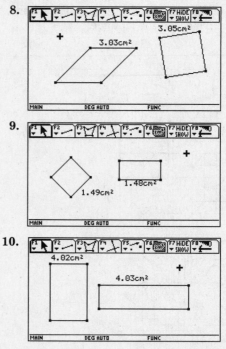

9.

10.

10-3 ## Area of Parallelograms

Page 529 Modeling Mathematics

a. See students' work.   **b.** See students' work.

c. $A = bh$

Page 532 Check for Understanding

1. Four meters is a linear measurement, while four square meters is an area measurement.

2. area of $CDEF = \frac{1}{2}$(area of $ABCD$)

3.

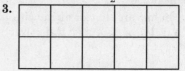

4. The two cuts are parallel to each other and at an angle less than 90 with the base. The two congruent shapes can be either right triangles or right trapezoids depending on how far in from the sides the cuts are made.

5. (3.1 cm)(6.2 cm) = 19.22 cm²

6. (13)(9) − (4)(4) − (4)(3) = 89 mm²

7. $(5.5)(6) - (1)(3) - (0.5)(3) = 28.5$ cm^2

8. $m = \frac{2 - (-1)}{1 - (-1)} = \frac{3}{2}$

$m = \frac{2 - (-1)}{6 - 4} = \frac{3}{2}$

$m = \frac{2 - 2}{6 - 1} = 0$

$m = \frac{-1 - (-1)}{4 - (-1)} = 0$

Opp. sides are parallel. → parallelgram

length of base $= \sqrt{(-1 - 4)^2 + [-1 - (-1)]^2}$
$= \sqrt{25}$ or 5

length of height $= \sqrt{(1 - 1)^2 + [2 - (-1)]^2}$
$= \sqrt{9}$ or 3

$A = 3 \cdot 5$ or 15 units^2

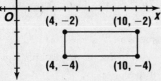

9. Divide the figure into rectangles. The two triangles form a rectangle 75 by 10.

$30(250) + 30(100) + 10(30) + 7.5(10) = 10,875$ ft^2

$\frac{10,875}{9} = 1208\frac{1}{3}$ yd^2

$\left(1208\frac{1}{3}\right)(0.52) = \$628.34$

Pages 532–534 Exercises

10. $(7 \text{ m})(7 \text{ m}) = 49$ m^2

11. $(14 \text{ m})(27.8 \text{ m}) = 389.2$ m^2

12. $\left(4\frac{1}{2} \text{ yd}\right)\left(12\frac{1}{3} \text{ yd}\right) = 55\frac{1}{2}$ yd^2

13. $(36 \text{ ft})(60 \text{ ft}) = 2160$ ft^2

14. $7(10) - 5(2) = 60$ in^2

15. $5(11) - 4(4) - 4(4) = 23$ m^2

16. $10(5\sqrt{2}) - 5(5) = 50\sqrt{2} - 25 \cong 45.71$ mm^2

17. $(18)(15) - 4(8) - 3(12) = 202$ cm^2

18. $(9.2)(9.2) + (10.8)(3.1) - (3.1)(3.1) = 108.51$ m^2

19.

19a. $m = \frac{-2 - (-4)}{4 - 4} =$ undefined

$m = \frac{-2 - (-4)}{10 - 10} =$ undefined

$m = \frac{-2 - (-2)}{4 - 10} = 0$

$m = \frac{-4 - (-4)}{4 - 10} = 0$

The opposite sides are parallel and since vertical lines are perpendicular to horizontal lines, it is a rectangle.

19b. $b = \sqrt{(4 - 10)^2 + [-4 - (-4)]^2} = \sqrt{36}$ or 6

$h = \sqrt{(4 - 4)^2 + [-2 - (-4)]^2} = \sqrt{4}$ or 2

$A = 6 \cdot 2 = 12$ units^2

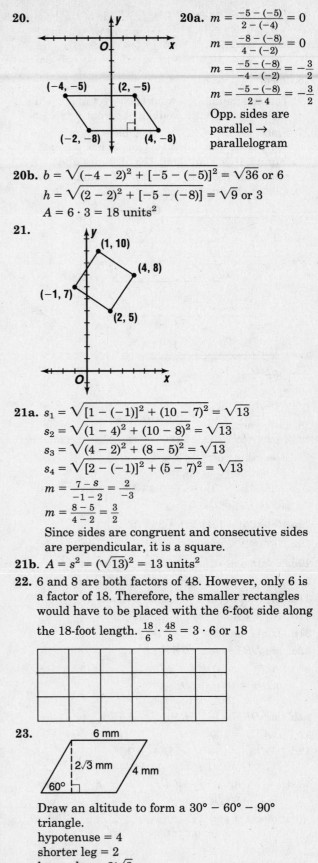

20.

20a. $m = \frac{-5 - (-5)}{2 - (-4)} = 0$

$m = \frac{-8 - (-8)}{4 - (-2)} = 0$

$m = \frac{-5 - (-8)}{-4 - (-2)} = -\frac{3}{2}$

$m = \frac{-5 - (-8)}{2 - 4} = -\frac{3}{2}$

Opp. sides are parallel → parallelogram

20b. $b = \sqrt{(-4 - 2)^2 + [-5 - (-5)]^2} = \sqrt{36}$ or 6

$h = \sqrt{(2 - 2)^2 + [-5 - (-8)]} = \sqrt{9}$ or 3

$A = 6 \cdot 3 = 18$ units^2

21.

21a. $s_1 = \sqrt{[1 - (-1)]^2 + (10 - 7)^2} = \sqrt{13}$

$s_2 = \sqrt{(1 - 4)^2 + (10 - 8)^2} = \sqrt{13}$

$s_3 = \sqrt{(4 - 2)^2 + (8 - 5)^2} = \sqrt{13}$

$s_4 = \sqrt{[2 - (-1)]^2 + (5 - 7)^2} = \sqrt{13}$

$m = \frac{7 - s}{-1 - 2} = \frac{2}{-3}$

$m = \frac{8 - 5}{4 - 2} = \frac{3}{2}$

Since sides are congruent and consecutive sides are perpendicular, it is a square.

21b. $A = s^2 = (\sqrt{13})^2 = 13$ units^2

22. 6 and 8 are both factors of 48. However, only 6 is a factor of 18. Therefore, the smaller rectangles would have to be placed with the 6-foot side along the 18-foot length. $\frac{18}{6} \cdot \frac{48}{8} = 3 \cdot 6$ or 18

23.

Draw an altitude to form a $30° - 60° - 90°$ triangle.
hypotenuse $= 4$
shorter leg $= 2$
longer leg $= 2\sqrt{3}$
$A = (6 \text{ mm})(2\sqrt{3} \text{ mm}) = 12\sqrt{3}$ mm^2

24. $(x + 5)^2 = 2.25x^2$
$x + 5 = 1.5x$
$5 = .5x$
$x = 10$

The side of the original square was 10 in.
$A = (10)^2 = 100$ in.^{2}

25. 25cm^2; $\frac{1}{4}$ area of square

26. The maximum area would be a rectangle, while the minimum area would be approaching a line.

27. Since $\triangle PNM \cong \triangle NOP$, they have the same altitudes. So the altitude from O has a length of 3 units. If you cut along the altitudes and rearrange the parts, a rectangle with base $\overline{NP}$ and height 3 is formed.

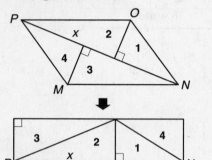

$3NP = A$
$3NP = 48$
$NP = 16$ units

28. Going across,
1 length 4 yd by 12 ft
1 length 4 yd by 14 ft
1 length 4 yd by 34 ft
    4 yd by 60 ft = 4 yd by 20 yd = 80 yd^2
see students' drawings

29a. $(30)(36) - (21)(12) = 828$ ft^2

29b. $\frac{828}{4} = 207$ ft^2

29c. Sample answer: 12 ft by 17.25 ft

29d. See students' work. **30.** 21,978 and 87,912

31a. M, N, O, P, Q **31b.** convex

31c. No; its sides are not all congruent.

31d. pentagon

32a. $m\angle DRE = m\angle ARB = 24$
$m\widehat{DE} = m\angle DRE = 24$
$m\widehat{DB} = 180 - m\widehat{DE}$
        $= 180 - 24$ or 156

32b. $m\angle DRF = m\angle DRE + m\angle FRE = 24 + 44$ or 68

32c. $m\widehat{AFD} = 180$

32d. $m\widehat{BEC} = 180 + m\widehat{ED} + m\widehat{DC}$
        $= 180 + 24 + 44$ or 248

33. Given: trapezoid $ABCD$,
        $\overline{AB} \parallel \overline{DC}$
Prove: $\angle A$ and $\angle D$
        are supplementary.
Proof:

Statements	Reasons
1. trapezoid $ABCD$, $\overline{AB} \parallel \overline{DC}$	1. Given
2. $\angle A$ and $\angle D$ are supplementary.	2. Consecutive Interior Angles Theorem

34a. $\overline{GJ}$ **34b.** $\overline{EH}$ **34c.** $\overline{FE}$

35.

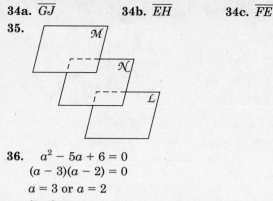

36. $a^2 - 5a + 6 = 0$
$(a - 3)(a - 2) = 0$
$a = 3$ or $a = 2$
$\{2, 3\}$

37 a. (0, 2)
$2 \stackrel{?}{>} 4(0) - 3$
$2 > -3$ ✓

b. (3, 0)
$0 \stackrel{?}{>} 4(3) - 3$
$0 \not> 9$

c. (1, −1)
$-1 > 4(1) - 3$
$-1 \not> 1$

d. (−4, 2)
$2 \stackrel{?}{>} 4(-4) - 3$
$2 > -19$ ✓

a, d

10-4 Area of Triangles, Rhombi, and Trapezoids

Page 535 Modeling Mathematics

a. areas of $\triangle BEA + \triangle DBC = \triangle ABC$

b. half

c. $A = \frac{1}{2}bh$

Pages 538–539 Check for Understanding

1. Yes; $\frac{1}{2}(3)(7) = \frac{1}{2}(7)(3)$ by the Commutative Property (=).

2a. trapezoid and square

2b. triangle   **2c.** triangle and square

2d. triangle and square

3. A rhombus is made up of two congruent triangles and using d_1 and d_2 instead of b and h, its area in reference to $A = \frac{1}{2}bh$ is $2\left[\frac{1}{2}(d_1)\left(\frac{1}{2}d_2\right)\right]$ or $\frac{1}{2}d_1d_2$.

4. See students' work. Sample answer: use trapezoid formula, use median of trapezoid, and split trapezoid up into shape of other figures and then add areas together.

5a. See students' work.
    Sample answer:

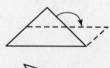

5b. Each new figure has the same area as its original triangle.

6. $\frac{1}{2}(7.3)(3.4) = (7.3)(1.7) = 12.41$ in^2

7. $\frac{1}{2}(6)(8 + 12) = \frac{1}{2}(6)(20) = 60$ cm^2

8. $A = \frac{1}{2}bh$

$24 = \frac{1}{2}(8)h$

$24 = 4h$

$h = 6$ units

9.

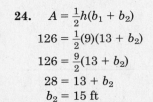

The diagonals form four congruent $30° - 60° - 90°$ triangles with the hypotenuse 12 inches long, the short leg 6 inches long and the longer leg $6\sqrt{3}$ inches long.

$A = 4\left[\frac{1}{2}(6)(6\sqrt{3})\right] = 72\sqrt{3} \approx 124.7$ in^2

10. $8(13) + 8(10) + 12(12) = 328$ ft^2

Yes; the total area is 328 ft^2.

Pages 539–541 Exercises

11. $\frac{1}{2}(7)(10.2) = (7)(5.1) = 35.7$ in^2

12. $2(2) + \frac{1}{2}(2)(\sqrt{3}) = (4 + \sqrt{3}) \approx 5.7$ ft^2

13. $3\left(\frac{1}{2}(6)(3\sqrt{3})\right) = 3(9\sqrt{3}) = 27\sqrt{3} \approx 46.8$ m^2

14. $y(y) + \frac{1}{2}y(y + y) = y^2 + \frac{1}{2}y(2y) = y^2 + y^2 = 2y^2$ mm^2

15. $\frac{1}{2}(4)(20) + \frac{1}{2}(3)(12 + 20) = 2(20) + \frac{1}{2}(3)(32)$

$= 40 + 48$

$= 88$ m^2

16. $2\left[\frac{1}{2}(12)(6\sqrt{3})\right] + 12^2 = 12(6\sqrt{3}) + 144$

$= 72\sqrt{3} + 144$

≈ 268.7 yd^2

17. $A = \frac{1}{2}bh$

$12 = \frac{1}{2}(x)(6)$

$12 = 3x$

$x = 4$

18. $A = \frac{1}{2}d_1 d_2$

$56 = \frac{1}{2}(16)(x)$

$56 = 8x$

$x = 7$

19. $A = \frac{1}{2}h(b_1 + b_2)$

$95 = \frac{1}{2}x(8 + 11)$

$95 = \frac{1}{2}x(19)$

$95 = \frac{19}{2}x$

$x = 10$

20. $A = \frac{1}{2}h(b_1 + b_2)$

$75 = \frac{1}{2}h(8 + 17)$

$75 = \frac{1}{2}h(25)$

$75 = \frac{25}{2}h$

$h = 6$ in.

21.

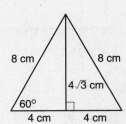

The diagonals form $30° - 60° - 90°$ triangles with the long legs are 5 inches long. The short legs are $\frac{5}{\sqrt{3}}$ inches long.

$A = \frac{1}{2}(10)\left(2\left(\frac{5}{\sqrt{3}}\right)\right)$

$= 10\left(\frac{5}{\sqrt{3}}\right)$

≈ 28.9 in^2

22. The diagonals form four congruent $30° - 60° - 90°$ triangles with the short legs 5 inches long. The long legs are $5\sqrt{3}$ inches long.

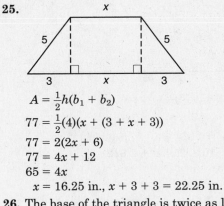

$A = 4\left[\frac{1}{2}(5)(5\sqrt{3})\right] = 50\sqrt{3} \approx 80.6$ in^2

23. $A = \frac{1}{2}(8)(4\sqrt{3})$

$= 16\sqrt{3}$

≈ 27.7 cm^2

24. $A = \frac{1}{2}h(b_1 + b_2)$

$126 = \frac{1}{2}(9)(13 + b_2)$

$126 = \frac{9}{2}(13 + b_2)$

$28 = 13 + b_2$

$b_2 = 15$ ft

25.

$A = \frac{1}{2}h(b_1 + b_2)$

$77 = \frac{1}{2}(4)(x + (3 + x + 3))$

$77 = 2(2x + 6)$

$77 = 4x + 12$

$65 = 4x$

$x = 16.25$ in., $x + 3 + 3 = 22.25$ in.

26. The base of the triangle is twice as long as the base of the parallelogram.

27. total area = area of parallelogram + area of triangle

$$= bh + \frac{1}{2}bh$$
$$= ah + \frac{1}{2}(b - a)h$$
$$= ah + \left(\frac{1}{2}b - \frac{1}{2}a\right)h$$
$$= ah + \frac{1}{2}bh - \frac{1}{2}ah$$
$$= \frac{1}{2}ah + \frac{1}{2}bh$$
$$= \frac{1}{2}h(a + b)$$

28a. $\frac{BC}{AB} = \frac{1}{2} = \frac{x}{9 - x}$ **28b.** square
$$2x = 9 - x$$
$$x = 3$$
$$BC = 3, AB = 6$$
$$AH = BC$$
$$AH^2 + AB^2 = BH^2$$
$$3^2 + 6^2 = BH^2$$
$$BH^2 = 45 \text{ m}^2$$

28c. It will always have a ratio of 5:9.

29a. 35 units^2 **29b.** 27.125 units^2

30a. $A = \frac{1}{2}(50.74)(147.08 + 57.62)$
$$= 25.37(204.7)$$
$$= 5193.239 \text{ ft}^2$$

30b. $\frac{5193.239}{43,560} \approx 0.119 = 11.9\%$

31. small trapezoid:
$$12^2 + h^2 = 20^2$$
$$h^2 = 256$$
$$h = 16$$
$$A = \frac{1}{2}(10 + 34)(16) = 352$$

Large trapezoid:

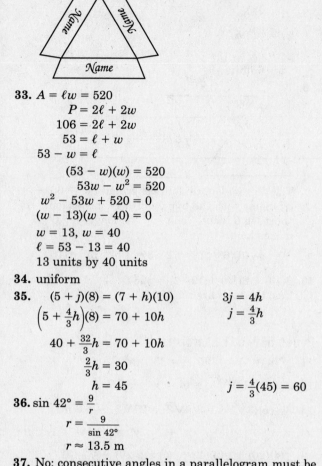

$$A = \frac{1}{2}(45 + 69)(16)$$
$$A = 912$$
$$A_{\text{roof}} = A_{\text{top}} + 2(A_{\text{trap-sm}}) + 2(A_{\text{trap-lg}})$$
$$= 45 \cdot 10 + 2(352) + 2(912)$$
$$A = 2978 \text{ ft}^2$$
$$\frac{2978}{100} = 29.78$$

Since you can't buy parts of packages, Rosa should buy 30 packages of shingles

32. Sample answer:

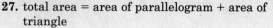

33. $A = \ell w = 520$
$$P = 2\ell + 2w$$
$$106 = 2\ell + 2w$$
$$53 = \ell + w$$
$$53 - w = \ell$$
$$(53 - w)(w) = 520$$
$$53w - w^2 = 520$$
$$w^2 - 53w + 520 = 0$$
$$(w - 13)(w - 40) = 0$$
$$w = 13, w = 40$$
$$\ell = 53 - 13 = 40$$
13 units by 40 units

34. uniform

35. $(5 + j)(8) = (7 + h)(10)$ $3j = 4h$
$$\left(5 + \frac{4}{3}h\right)(8) = 70 + 10h \qquad j = \frac{4}{3}h$$
$$40 + \frac{32}{3}h = 70 + 10h$$
$$\frac{2}{3}h = 30$$
$$h = 45 \qquad\qquad j = \frac{4}{3}(45) = 60$$

36. $\sin 42° = \frac{9}{r}$
$$r = \frac{9}{\sin 42°}$$
$$r \approx 13.5 \text{ m}$$

37. No; consecutive angles in a parallelogram must be supplementary.

38. $9g + 15 = 90$
$$9g = 75$$
$$g = \frac{75}{9} = \frac{25}{3}$$

39. $\frac{k^3\ell m^2}{x^2 y^2} \div \frac{k^3 m}{x^3 y^2} = \frac{k^3\ell m^2}{x^2 y^2} \cdot \frac{x^3 y^2}{k^3 m} = \ell m x$

40. $180 - 64 = 116$

Page 541 Self Test

1a. heptagon   **1b.** no   **1c.** convex

2. $\frac{180(20 - 2)}{20} = \frac{180(18)}{20} = 162$

3. $\frac{180(12 - 2)}{12} = \frac{180(10)}{12} = 150$

4. $180 - 160 = 20$ **5.** $180 - 168\frac{3}{4} = 11\frac{1}{4}$
$$\frac{360}{20} = 18 \qquad\qquad \frac{360}{11\frac{1}{4}} = 32$$

6. not regular, uniform, not semi-regular

7.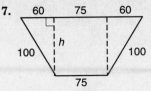

Use Pythagorean Theorem to find height.
$$h^2 + 60^2 = 100^2$$
$$h^2 = 6400$$
$$h = 80$$

$A_{\text{region}} = A_{\text{trapezoid}} - A_{\text{rectangles}}$
$A = \frac{1}{2}(80)(75 + 95) - 40(25) - 30(20) = 9200 \text{ ft}^2$

8. $1.2(2.1) + 2\left(\frac{1}{2}\right)(2.1)(0.6) = 3.78 \text{ m}^2$

9. $10^2 + \left(\frac{10}{\sqrt{2}}\right)^2 = 100 + 50 = 150 \text{ cm}^2$

10. Sample answer: $35 - 64 + 752 + 6 - 17 = 712$

10-5A Modeling Mathematics: Regular Polygons

Page 542

1. 360

2a. same number of angles as sides

2b. 60

3. They are the same.

4. 120; See students' work.   **5.** 90; See students' work.

6. 72; See students' work.   **7.** 45; See students' work.

8. 36; See students' work.   **9.** 30; See students' work.

10-5 Area of Regular Polygons and Circles

Page 547 Check for Understanding

1. The central angle of a regular hexagon is 60. Therefore, a $30° - 60° - 90°$ triangle is formed with the apothem, half of a side, and the radius. Working with the perimeter, you can find the measure of the apothem.

2. The radius is the distance from the center to a vertex, and the apothem is the distance from the center to the middle of a side. Together they form a triangle along with half of a side.

3. d represents diameter and the diameter is equal to twice the radius. Therefore, $d = 2r$ and can be substituted into the formula.

4. They will be the same when the circle is inscribed in the polygon and different when the circle is circumscribed about the polygon.

5. $OU = \sqrt{2}(a)$
$ 2 = \sqrt{2}(a)$
$\frac{2}{\sqrt{2}} = a$
$\sqrt{2} = a$
$UT = 2a = 2\sqrt{2}$
$P = 45$
$ = 4(2\sqrt{2}) = 8\sqrt{2} \approx 11.31 \text{ cm}$

6. $A = \pi r^2 = \pi(2)^2 = 4\pi \approx 12.57 \text{ cm}^2$
$C = 2\pi r = 2\pi(2) = 4\pi \approx 12.57 \text{ cm}$

7. They are close in length.

8. $a = \frac{11}{2} = 5.5 \text{ cm}$
$A = s^2 = 11^2 = 121 \text{ cm}^2$
$P = 4s = 4(11) = 44 \text{ cm}$

9. $a = \frac{4}{\sqrt{3}} = \frac{4\sqrt{3}}{3} \approx 2.3 \text{ in.}$
$A = \frac{1}{2}Pa = \frac{1}{2}(3(8))\left(\frac{4\sqrt{3}}{3}\right) = 16\sqrt{3} \approx 27.7 \text{ in}^2$
$P = 3s = 3(8) = 24 \text{ in.}$

10. $A = \pi r^2$
$10\pi = \pi r^2$
$\sqrt{10} = r$
$C = 2\pi r = 2\pi(\sqrt{10}) \approx 19.9 \text{ ft}$

11. area of the shaded region = area of square − area of equilateral triangle
The apothem radius and $\frac{1}{2}$ of a side form a $30° - 60° - 90°$ triangle.
$a = \frac{5}{\sqrt{3}} = \frac{5\sqrt{3}}{3}$

$A_{\text{region}} = A_{\text{square}} - A_{\text{triangle}}$
$\phantom{A_{\text{region}}} = 10^2 - \frac{1}{2}(3 \cdot 10)\left(\frac{5\sqrt{3}}{3}\right)$
$\phantom{A_{\text{region}}} = 100 - 25\sqrt{3}$
$\phantom{A_{\text{region}}} \approx 56.7 \text{ cm}^2$

12. area of the shaded region = area of circle − area of equilateral triangle
The apothem, radius and $\frac{1}{2}$ of a side form a $30° - 60° - 90°$ triangle. The radius is 8, so the apothem is 4 and $\frac{1}{2}$ a side is $4\sqrt{3}$.

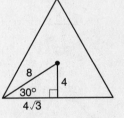

$A_{\text{region}} = A_{\text{circle}} - A_{\text{triangle}}$
$\phantom{A_{\text{region}}} = \pi(8)^2 - \frac{1}{2}(3 \cdot (2 \cdot 4\sqrt{3}))(4)$
$\phantom{A_{\text{region}}} = 64\pi - 48\sqrt{3}$
$\phantom{A_{\text{region}}} \approx 117.9 \text{ m}^2$

13. Area of the court that is painted blue $= 2(19)(12) + 2\pi(6)^2$
$ = 456 + 72\pi$
$ \approx 682.19 \text{ ft}^2$

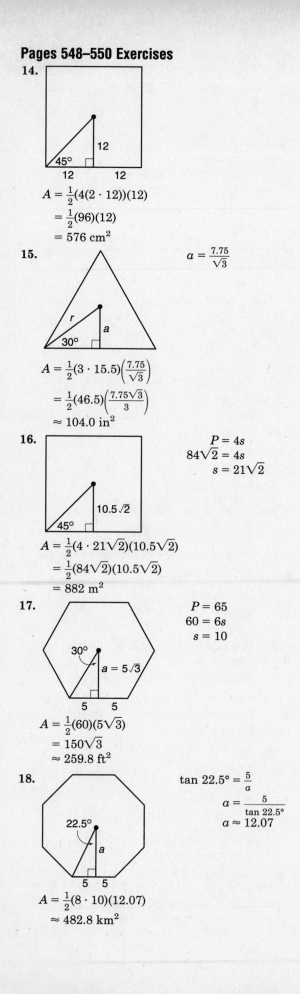

14.

$A = \frac{1}{2}(4(2 \cdot 12))(12)$

$= \frac{1}{2}(96)(12)$

$= 576 \text{ cm}^2$

15.

$a = \frac{7.75}{\sqrt{3}}$

$A = \frac{1}{2}(3 \cdot 15.5)\left(\frac{7.75}{\sqrt{3}}\right)$

$= \frac{1}{2}(46.5)\left(\frac{7.75\sqrt{3}}{3}\right)$

$\approx 104.0 \text{ in}^2$

16.

$P = 4s$

$84\sqrt{2} = 4s$

$s = 21\sqrt{2}$

$A = \frac{1}{2}(4 \cdot 21\sqrt{2})(10.5\sqrt{2})$

$= \frac{1}{2}(84\sqrt{2})(10.5\sqrt{2})$

$= 882 \text{ m}^2$

17.

$P = 65$

$60 = 6s$

$s = 10$

$A = \frac{1}{2}(60)(5\sqrt{3})$

$= 150\sqrt{3}$

$\approx 259.8 \text{ ft}^2$

18.

$\tan 22.5° = \frac{5}{a}$

$a = \frac{5}{\tan 22.5°}$

$a \approx 12.07$

$A = \frac{1}{2}(8 \cdot 10)(12.07)$

$\approx 482.8 \text{ km}^2$

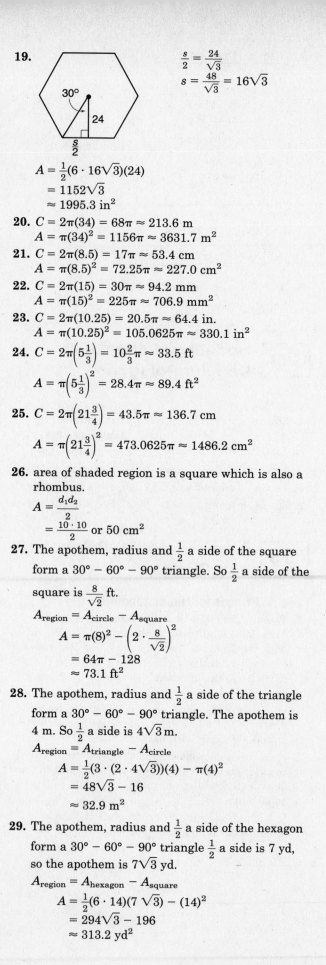

19.

$\frac{s}{2} = \frac{24}{\sqrt{3}}$

$s = \frac{48}{\sqrt{3}} = 16\sqrt{3}$

$A = \frac{1}{2}(6 \cdot 16\sqrt{3})(24)$

$= 1152\sqrt{3}$

$\approx 1995.3 \text{ in}^2$

20. $C = 2\pi(34) = 68\pi \approx 213.6 \text{ m}$
$A = \pi(34)^2 = 1156\pi \approx 3631.7 \text{ m}^2$

21. $C = 2\pi(8.5) = 17\pi \approx 53.4 \text{ cm}$
$A = \pi(8.5)^2 = 72.25\pi \approx 227.0 \text{ cm}^2$

22. $C = 2\pi(15) = 30\pi \approx 94.2 \text{ mm}$
$A = \pi(15)^2 = 225\pi \approx 706.9 \text{ mm}^2$

23. $C = 2\pi(10.25) = 20.5\pi \approx 64.4 \text{ in.}$
$A = \pi(10.25)^2 = 105.0625\pi \approx 330.1 \text{ in}^2$

24. $C = 2\pi\left(5\frac{1}{3}\right) = 10\frac{2}{3}\pi \approx 33.5 \text{ ft}$

$A = \pi\left(5\frac{1}{3}\right)^2 = 28.4\pi \approx 89.4 \text{ ft}^2$

25. $C = 2\pi\left(21\frac{3}{4}\right) = 43.5\pi \approx 136.7 \text{ cm}$

$A = \pi\left(21\frac{3}{4}\right)^2 = 473.0625\pi \approx 1486.2 \text{ cm}^2$

26. area of shaded region is a square which is also a rhombus.

$A = \frac{d_1 d_2}{2}$

$= \frac{10 \cdot 10}{2} \text{ or } 50 \text{ cm}^2$

27. The apothem, radius and $\frac{1}{2}$ a side of the square form a $30° - 60° - 90°$ triangle. So $\frac{1}{2}$ a side of the square is $\frac{8}{\sqrt{2}}$ ft.

$A_{\text{region}} = A_{\text{circle}} - A_{\text{square}}$

$A = \pi(8)^2 - \left(2 \cdot \frac{8}{\sqrt{2}}\right)^2$

$= 64\pi - 128$

$\approx 73.1 \text{ ft}^2$

28. The apothem, radius and $\frac{1}{2}$ a side of the triangle form a $30° - 60° - 90°$ triangle. The apothem is 4 m. So $\frac{1}{2}$ a side is $4\sqrt{3}$ m.

$A_{\text{region}} = A_{\text{triangle}} - A_{\text{circle}}$

$A = \frac{1}{2}(3 \cdot (2 \cdot 4\sqrt{3}))(4) - \pi(4)^2$

$= 48\sqrt{3} - 16$

$\approx 32.9 \text{ m}^2$

29. The apothem, radius and $\frac{1}{2}$ a side of the hexagon form a $30° - 60° - 90°$ triangle $\frac{1}{2}$ a side is 7 yd, so the apothem is $7\sqrt{3}$ yd.

$A_{\text{region}} = A_{\text{hexagon}} - A_{\text{square}}$

$A = \frac{1}{2}(6 \cdot 14)(7\sqrt{3}) - (14)^2$

$= 294\sqrt{3} - 196$

$\approx 313.2 \text{ yd}^2$

Geometry Chapter 10

30. The radius of each circle is 2 mm.

$A_{\text{region}} = A_{\text{rectangle}} - A_{\text{circles}}$

$\qquad = 8(4) - \pi(2)^2 - \pi(2)^2$

$\qquad = 32 - 8\pi$

$\qquad = 6.9 \text{ mm}^2$

31. The apothem of the triangle $= \dfrac{1.75}{\sqrt{3}}$ or $\dfrac{1.75\sqrt{3}}{3}$;
$P = 3 \cdot 3.5$ or 10.5 If all the radii of pentagon are drawn, the central angles are 72° angles. The apothem bisects the angle making a $36° - 54° - 90°$ triangle.

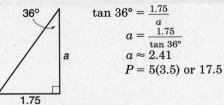

$\tan 36° = \dfrac{1.75}{a}$

$a = \dfrac{1.75}{\tan 36°}$

$a \approx 2.41$

$P = 5(3.5)$ or 17.5

$A_{\text{region}} = A_{\text{pentagon}} - A_{\text{triangle}}$

$A \approx \dfrac{1}{2}(17.5)(2.41) - \dfrac{1}{2}(10.5)\left(\dfrac{1.75\sqrt{3}}{3}\right)$

$\qquad \approx 21.0875 - 3.0625\sqrt{3}$

$\qquad \approx 15.8 \text{ in}^2$

32. The apothem, radius, and half the side of the triangle form a $30° - 60° - 90°$ triangle. The radius is 12, so half the side is $6\sqrt{3}$ and the apothem is 6. $P = 3\,[2 \cdot 6\sqrt{3}]$ or $36\sqrt{3}$. The radii and side of the hexagon form equilateral triangles with sides 12m long. The apothem of the hexagon $= \dfrac{1}{2}(12)\sqrt{3}$ or $6\sqrt{3}$. $P = 6 \cdot 12$ or 72

$A_{\text{region}} = A_{\text{hexagon}} - A_{\text{triangle}}$

$A = \dfrac{1}{2}(72)(6\sqrt{3}) - \dfrac{1}{2}(36\sqrt{3})(6)$

$\qquad = 216\sqrt{3} - 108\sqrt{3}$

$\qquad = 108\sqrt{3} \approx 187.1 \text{ m}^2$

33. The radii of the octagon form 45° central angles. The apothem bisects the angle to form a $22.5° - 67.5° - 90°$ triangle.

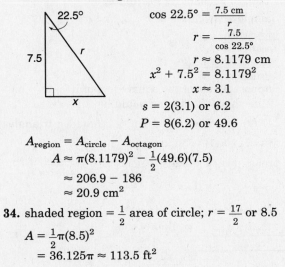

$\cos 22.5° = \dfrac{7.5 \text{ cm}}{r}$

$r = \dfrac{7.5}{\cos 22.5°}$

$r \approx 8.1179 \text{ cm}$

$x^2 + 7.5^2 = 8.1179^2$

$x \approx 3.1$

$s = 2(3.1)$ or 6.2

$P = 8(6.2)$ or 49.6

$A_{\text{region}} = A_{\text{circle}} - A_{\text{octagon}}$

$A \approx \pi(8.1179)^2 - \dfrac{1}{2}(49.6)(7.5)$

$\qquad \approx 206.9 - 186$

$\qquad \approx 20.9 \text{ cm}^2$

34. shaded region $= \dfrac{1}{2}$ area of circle; $r = \dfrac{17}{2}$ or 8.5

$A = \dfrac{1}{2}\pi(8.5)^2$

$\qquad = 36.125\pi \approx 113.5 \text{ ft}^2$

35.

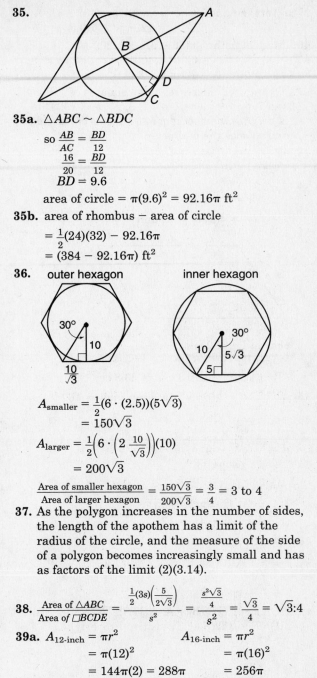

35a. $\triangle ABC \sim \triangle BDC$

so $\dfrac{AB}{AC} = \dfrac{BD}{12}$

$\dfrac{16}{20} = \dfrac{BD}{12}$

$BD = 9.6$

area of circle $= \pi(9.6)^2 = 92.16\pi \text{ ft}^2$

35b. area of rhombus − area of circle

$= \dfrac{1}{2}(24)(32) - 92.16\pi$

$= (384 - 92.16\pi) \text{ ft}^2$

36.   outer hexagon   inner hexagon

$A_{\text{smaller}} = \dfrac{1}{2}(6 \cdot (2.5))(5\sqrt{3})$

$\qquad = 150\sqrt{3}$

$A_{\text{larger}} = \dfrac{1}{2}\left(6 \cdot \left(2\,\dfrac{10}{\sqrt{3}}\right)\right)(10)$

$\qquad = 200\sqrt{3}$

$\dfrac{\text{Area of smaller hexagon}}{\text{Area of larger hexagon}} = \dfrac{150\sqrt{3}}{200\sqrt{3}} = \dfrac{3}{4} = 3 \text{ to } 4$

37. As the polygon increases in the number of sides, the length of the apothem has a limit of the radius of the circle, and the measure of the side of a polygon becomes increasingly small and has as factors of the limit $(2)(3.14)$.

38. $\dfrac{\text{Area of } \triangle ABC}{\text{Area of } \square BCDE} = \dfrac{\frac{1}{2}(3s)\left(\frac{5}{2\sqrt{3}}\right)}{s^2} = \dfrac{\frac{s^2\sqrt{3}}{4}}{s^2} = \dfrac{\sqrt{3}}{4} = \sqrt{3}{:}4$

39a. $A_{\text{12-inch}} = \pi r^2 \qquad\qquad A_{\text{16-inch}} = \pi r^2$

$\qquad = \pi(12)^2 \qquad\qquad\quad = \pi(16)^2$

$\qquad = 144\pi(2) = 288\pi \qquad = 256\pi$

two 12-inch pizzas

39b. unit cost of (2) 12-inch $= \dfrac{2(6.98)}{288\pi} \approx .015$

unit cost of 16-inch $= \dfrac{\$9.98}{256\pi} \approx .012$

No; the unit cost of two 12-inch pizzas is more expensive than the unit cost of one 16-inch pizza.

40a. area = area of square + area of circle

$= (175)^2 + \pi\left(\dfrac{175}{2}\right)^2$

$= (30{,}625 + 7656.25\pi) \approx 54{,}677.82 \text{ ft}^2$

perimeter = 2 sides + circumference of circle

$= 2(175) + 2\pi(87.5)$

$= (350 + 175\pi) \approx 899.78 \text{ ft}$

40b. Total circumference $= \pi(20) + \pi(40) + \pi(60)$
$$= 120\pi \approx 377.0 \text{ ft}$$

40c. area of path $= \pi(30 - 5)^2 - \pi(20)^2$
$$= 625\pi - 400\pi$$
$$= 225\pi \approx 706.9 \text{ ft}^2$$

41. No; they will increase by the squares of 1, 3, 5, and 7, or in other words, 1, 9, 25, and 49. This is because the apothem has a factor of the side and so does the perimeter.

42. $18 = x + x + 8$
$$x = 5$$
$$4^2 + h^2 = 5^2$$
$$h = 3$$
$$A = \frac{1}{2}bh = \frac{1}{2}(8)(3) = 12 \text{ unit}^2$$

43.

shorter leg = 2 cm
longer leg = $2\sqrt{3}$ cm
$A = 2\sqrt{3}(6) = 12\sqrt{3} \text{ cm}^2 \approx 20.8 \text{ cm}^2$

44. $\frac{180(12 - 2)}{12} = 162$; No, interior angle = 162

45. center $= \left(\frac{-1 + 5}{2}, \frac{2 + 6}{2}\right) = (2, 4)$
$$d = \sqrt{(-1 - 5)^2 + (6 - 2)^2} = \sqrt{36 + 16}$$
$$= \sqrt{52} = 2\sqrt{13}$$
$$r = \frac{1}{2}(2\sqrt{13}) = \sqrt{13}$$
$$(x - 2)^2 + (y - 4)^2 = (\sqrt{13})^2$$
$$(x - 2)^2 + (y - 4)^2 = 13$$

46. $a = \frac{1}{2}s\sqrt{3}$
$$= \frac{1}{2}\left(\frac{8}{s}\right)\sqrt{3}$$
$$= \frac{4\sqrt{3}}{s} \approx 1.4 \text{ ft}$$

47. $\triangle QRT \sim \triangle QTS$ by AA, $\triangle QTS \sim \triangle TRS$ by AA, $\triangle QRT \sim \triangle TRS$ by Transitive Property

48.

$BC = \sqrt{(5 - 3)^2 + (11 - 7)^2} = \sqrt{4 + 16} = \sqrt{20}$
$AD = \sqrt{(7 - 9)^2 + (6 - 10)^2} = \sqrt{4 + 16} = \sqrt{20}$
$CD = \sqrt{(5 - 9)^2 + (11 - 10)^2} = \sqrt{16 + 1} = \sqrt{17}$
$AB = \sqrt{(7 - 3)^2 + (6 - 7)^2} = \sqrt{16 + 1} = \sqrt{17}$
Yes; both pairs of opposite sides are congruent.

49. $(x + 16) + (8x + 7) + (11x - 3) = 180$
$$20x + 20 = 180$$
$$x = 8$$

$x + 16 = 24$
$8(8) + 7 = 71$
$11(8) - 3 = 85$
acute

50. $3y^3(7x + y^2)$ **51.** $(2a3)^2 - 2^2 \cdot (a^3)^2 = 4a^6$

10-6 Integration: Probability
Geometric Probability

Pages 554–555 Check for Understanding

1. The Length Probability Postulate is one-dimensional and the Area Probability Postulate is two-dimensional. They are similar otherwise.

2. Adina is right. Yes; you can use the probability of an event occurring to estimate the area of a region.

3a. Area Probability Postulate

3b. Length Probability Postulate

4. Sample answer: $r = 1$, $r = 5$, and $r = 7$.

5. $\frac{\text{length of } \overline{EF}}{\text{length of } \overline{DI}} = \frac{2}{9}$

6. $\frac{\text{length of } \overline{FI}}{\text{length of } \overline{DI}} = \frac{6}{9} = \frac{2}{3}$

7. Suppose a side of the square is 2 units long. One of the shaded triangles would have an area of $\frac{1}{2}(1)(2) = 1$. The total area of the shaded triangles would be $2(1) = 2 \text{ units}^2$.

probability of shaded region $= \frac{\text{area of shaded region}}{\text{total area}}$

$$= \frac{2}{2^2} = \frac{1}{2}.$$

8a. See students' work.

8b. probability $= \frac{\text{total area of cards}}{\text{area of board}}$

$$= \frac{25(2.5)(3.5)}{(6.12)(3.12)} = \frac{218.85}{2592} \approx 0.08$$

8c. No; as long as the dart is randomly thrown and the cards do not overlap, the area of the board and the cards is always the same.

9. probability $= \dfrac{\text{area of red circle}}{\text{area of target}}$

$\phantom{\text{probability }} = \dfrac{\pi(12)^2}{\pi(30)^2}$

$\phantom{\text{probability }} = \dfrac{144\pi}{900\pi}$

$\phantom{\text{probability }} = \dfrac{4}{25}$ or 0.16

Pages 555–558 Exercises

10. If a point is between 0 and 4 it is closer to point A than to point x.

probability $= \dfrac{4}{\text{length of } AB} = \dfrac{4}{12} = \dfrac{1}{3}$

11.

$\bullet$———$\bullet$——$\bullet$—$\bullet$————$\bullet$
$X \quad\; W \quad\;\; Z \; V \qquad\quad Y$

If $XY = 10$, $XZ = 5$,

$XW = WZ = 2.5$,

$WY = 7.5$, and $WV = 3.75$

probability $= \dfrac{\text{length of } XV}{\text{length of } XY}$

$\phantom{\text{probability }} = \dfrac{2.5 + 3.5}{10}$

$\phantom{\text{probability }} = \dfrac{5}{8}$ or 0.625.

12. probability $= \dfrac{\text{area of shaded region}}{\text{total area}}$

$\phantom{\text{probability }} = \dfrac{\pi r^2 - \pi\left(\dfrac{r}{2}\right)^2}{\pi r^2}$

$\phantom{\text{probability }} = \dfrac{\frac{3}{4}\pi r^2}{\pi r^2} = \dfrac{3}{4}$ or 75%

13. Suppose a side of the square is 2 units long. The area of the square is 2^2 or 4 units. The radius of the circle is 1.

probability $= \dfrac{\text{area of shaded region}}{\text{total area}}$

$\phantom{\text{probability }} = \dfrac{2^2 - \pi(1)^2}{2^2}$

$\phantom{\text{probability }} = \dfrac{4 - \pi}{4} \approx 21.5\%$

14. Suppose the diameter of the circle is 2 units long.

A side of the square would be $\dfrac{2}{\sqrt{2}}$

probability $= \dfrac{\text{area of shaded region}}{\text{total area}}$

$\phantom{\text{probability }} = \dfrac{\pi(1)^2 - \left(\dfrac{2}{\sqrt{2}}\right)^2}{\pi(1)^2}$

$\phantom{\text{probability }} = \dfrac{\pi - 2}{\pi} \approx 36.3\%$

15. $\dfrac{80°}{360°} = \dfrac{2}{9}$ **16.** $\dfrac{90°}{360°} = \dfrac{1}{4}$

17. $\dfrac{80°}{360°} = \dfrac{2}{9}$ **18.** $\dfrac{(60° + 80°)}{360°} = \dfrac{140°}{360°} = \dfrac{7}{18}$

19. probability $= \dfrac{\text{area of circle}}{\text{area of target}}$

$\phantom{\text{probability }} = \dfrac{\pi(1)^2}{\pi(4)^2}$

$\phantom{\text{probability }} = \dfrac{\pi}{16\pi} = \dfrac{1}{16}$

20. probability $= \dfrac{\text{area of 8 point region}}{\text{area of target}}$

$\phantom{\text{probability }} = \dfrac{\pi(2)^2 - \pi(1)^2}{\pi(4)^2}$

$\phantom{\text{probability }} = \dfrac{4\pi - \pi}{16\pi}$

$\phantom{\text{probability }} = \dfrac{3\pi}{16\pi}$

$\phantom{\text{probability }} = \dfrac{3}{16}$

21. probability $= \dfrac{\text{area of 6 points}}{\text{area of target}}$

$\phantom{\text{probability }} = \dfrac{\pi(3)^2 - \pi(2)^2}{\pi(4)^2}$

$\phantom{\text{probability }} = \dfrac{9\pi - 4\pi}{16\pi}$

$\phantom{\text{probability }} = \dfrac{5\pi}{16\pi}$

$\phantom{\text{probability }} = \dfrac{5}{16}$

22a. There are 15 tracks: 6 short diagonals, 3 long diagonals, and 6 sides.

probability $= \dfrac{\text{longer diagonal}}{\text{total tracks}} = \dfrac{3}{15} = \dfrac{1}{5}$

22b. probability $= \dfrac{\text{not on a side}}{\text{total tracks}} = \dfrac{15 - 6}{15}$ or $\dfrac{9}{15}$ or $\dfrac{3}{5}$

23a.

$\bullet$———$\bullet$—$\bullet$—$\bullet$—$\bullet$—$\bullet$
$A \qquad\; B \;\; C \;\; D \;\; E \;\; F$

23b. $AB = BD = DF$, $\dfrac{AB}{AF} = \dfrac{1}{3}$

23c. $BC = CD = DE = EF$, $AB = BC + CD$, $\dfrac{DE}{AF} = \dfrac{1}{6}$

23d. $\dfrac{BE}{AF} = \dfrac{3}{6} = \dfrac{1}{2}$

24. $P(\text{missed the start of the quiz}) =$

$\dfrac{\text{number of minutes late}}{\text{number of minutes of class}} = \dfrac{15 \text{ min}}{48 \text{ min}} = \dfrac{5}{16}$

25. $\dfrac{1}{3}$

26.

$A \qquad\qquad C \qquad\; D \;\; B$
12:00   12:10   12:30

If you arrive before 12:15 or after 12:25 you will miss your friend.

probability $= \dfrac{15 + 5}{30} = \dfrac{20}{30} = \dfrac{2}{3}$

27.

probability $= \dfrac{\text{area of circle}}{\text{area of square}}$

$\phantom{\text{probability }} = \dfrac{\pi(1)^2}{2^2} = \dfrac{\pi}{4} \approx 78.5\%$

28.

probability $= \dfrac{\text{area of hexagon}}{\text{area of circle}} =$

$\dfrac{\frac{1}{2}\left(6 \cdot \left(2 \cdot \frac{1}{2}\right)\right)\left(\frac{1}{2}\sqrt{3}\right)}{\pi(1)^2} = \dfrac{\frac{3\sqrt{3}}{2}}{\pi} = \dfrac{3\sqrt{3}}{2} \approx 82.7\%$

29. unshaded part = 25% of area of square

$$= \frac{1}{4}(12)(12) = 36$$

$$s^2 = 36$$

$$s = 6 \text{ cm}$$

30. probability = $\dfrac{\text{area of shaded region}}{\text{total area}}$

$$= \frac{\pi\left(\frac{7\sqrt{2}}{2}\right)^2 - (7)^2}{\pi\left(\frac{7\sqrt{2}}{2}\right)^2}$$

$$= \frac{\frac{49}{2}\pi - 49}{\frac{49}{2}\pi}$$

$$= \frac{49\pi - 98}{49\pi} = \frac{\pi - 2}{\pi} \approx 36.3\%$$

The diagonal of the square is $7\sqrt{2}$. The radius is $\frac{7\sqrt{2}}{2}$.

31a–31e. See students' work.

31f. $\frac{1}{3}$

32. Sample answer: $m\angle 1 = 90$, $m\angle 2 = 90$, $m\angle 3 = 45$, $m\angle 4 = 45$, and $m\angle 5 = 90$.

33. $\frac{130°}{360°} = \frac{13}{36} \approx 36.1\%$ **34.** $\frac{1}{3}$

35a. $A = \frac{1}{2}bh$ $35^2 + x^2 = 100^2$

$\quad\ \ = \frac{1}{2}(70)(93.67)$ $x^2 = 8775$

$\quad\ \ \approx 3279 \text{ yd}^2$ $x \approx 93.67$

35b. $A = 12(3) = 36 \text{ ft}^2$

35c. probability = $\dfrac{\text{area of rowboat}}{\text{area of triangle}}$

$$= \frac{36}{9(3279)} = \frac{36}{29,511} \approx 0.12\%$$

36. $A = \frac{1}{2}Pa$

$\quad\ \ = \frac{1}{2}(8 \cdot 6.2)(7.5)$

$\quad\ \ = 186 \text{ ft}^2$

37. $\dfrac{\text{area of new triangle}}{\text{area of old triangle}} = \dfrac{\frac{1}{2}(3b)(3h)}{\frac{1}{2}bh} = \dfrac{9bh}{bh} = \dfrac{9}{1} = 9{:}1$

38. $180 - 160 = 20$

$\frac{360}{20} = 18$ sides

39. $m\angle IJK = \frac{1}{2}m\widehat{IHK}$

$\quad 84 = \frac{1}{2}m\widehat{IHK}$

$\quad m\widehat{IHK} = 168$

$m\widehat{IJK} = 360 - m\widehat{IHK}$

$\quad\quad\quad = 360 - 168 = 192$

40.

B — 7.5 ft, 103°, A — 14 ft — C

$\dfrac{\sin 103°}{14} = \dfrac{\sin C}{7.5}$ $\dfrac{\sin 103°}{14} = \dfrac{\sin 46°}{BC}$

$\sin C = \dfrac{7.5 \sin 103°}{14}$ $BC = \dfrac{14 \sin 46°}{\sin 103°}$

$m\angle C \approx 31$ $BC \approx 10.3 \text{ ft}$

$m\angle A + m\angle B + m\angle C = 180$

$\quad m\angle A + 103 + 31 = 180$

$\quad\quad\quad\quad m\angle A = 46$

41. not enough information

42. $x = \dfrac{-(-6) \pm \sqrt{(-6)^2 - 4(2)(1)}}{2(2)}$

$\quad\ = \dfrac{6 \pm \sqrt{28}}{4}$

$\quad\ = \dfrac{6 \pm 5.29}{4}$

$\dfrac{6 + 5.29}{4} = 2.82 \qquad \dfrac{6 - 5.29}{4} = 0.18$

43. $\dfrac{18,737 - 12,809}{12,809} = 46.3\%$

$\dfrac{19,666 - 18,737}{18,737} = 5.0\%$

$\dfrac{24,398 - 19,666}{19,666} = 24.1\%$

$\dfrac{32,629 - 24,398}{24,398} = 33.7\%$

$\dfrac{40,368 - 32,629}{32,629} = 23.7\%$

$\dfrac{54,904 - 40,368}{40,368} = 36.0\%$

$\dfrac{74,560 - 54,904}{54,904} = 35.8\%$

Page 558 Mathematics and Society

1. to improve telescope operation by getting away from city lights, air pollution, and atmospheric disturbances

2. 40-meter telescope, a great improvement over a 5-meter telescope

3. no

10-7 **Integration: Graph Theory**
Polygons as Networks

Pages 561–562 Check for Understanding

1. Polygons must be closed and made of line segments that do not overlap, while networks can be open, curved, and overlap.

2. Terri was correct. Traceability has to do with degree of nodes.

3. Sample answer:

4. When a node has an odd degree, it must be a starting or finishing point because there is only one path and therefore must only exit or only enter. When a path goes through a node, it uses two edges.

5. No; it is not traceable. It has more than two nodes that have odd degrees.

6. A: degree 2, B: degree 3, C: degree 2, D: degree 2, E: degree 3, F: degree 2

7a. traceable, incomplete

7b. $\overline{AE}, \overline{ED}, \overline{DC}, \overline{CB}, \overline{BD}, \overline{DA}, \overline{AB}$

7c. $\overline{AC}, \overline{BE}, \overline{CE}$ **8a.** traceable, incomplete

8b. $\overline{AB}, \overline{BC}, \overline{CD}, \overline{DB}$ **8c.** $\overline{AC}, \overline{AD}$

9a.

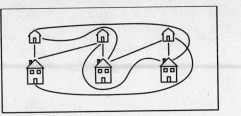

9b. yes; at least once

Pages 562–564 Exercises

10. *A*: degree 2, *B*: degree 2, *C*: degree 2, *D*: degree 2, *E*: degree 2

11. *A*: degree 4, *B*: degree 2, *C*: degree 3, *D*: degree 3, *E*: degree 2

12. *A*: degree 4, *B*: degree 4, *C*: degree 4, *D*: degree 4, *E*: degree 4

13a. traceable, complete **13b.** $\overline{AB}, \overline{BC}, \overline{CA}$

13c. none

14a. traceable, incomplete

14b. $\overline{ED}, \overline{DC}, \overline{CB}, \overline{BA}, \overline{AF}, \overline{FC}, \overline{CE}, \overline{EF}$

14c. $\overline{AC}, \overline{AD}, \overline{AE}, \overline{BD}, \overline{BE}, \overline{BF}, \overline{DF}$

15a. not traceable, incomplete

15b. none **15c.** $\overline{AC}, \overline{BD}, \overline{CE}$

16a. traceable, incomplete

16b. $\overline{CD}, \overline{DE}, \overline{EF}, \overline{FA}, \overline{AB}, \overline{BC}, \overline{CE}, \overline{EB}, \overline{BF}$

16c. $\overline{AC}, \overline{AD}, \overline{AE}, \overline{BD}, \overline{CF}, \overline{DF}$

17a. traceable, complete

17b. $\overline{AB}, \overline{BC}, \overline{CA}, \overline{AC}, \overline{CB}, \overline{BA}$

17c. none

18a. not traceable, incomplete

18b. none

18c. $\overline{AC}, \overline{AF}, \overline{AG}, \overline{AH}, \overline{BD}, \overline{BE}, \overline{BH}, \overline{BG}, \overline{CF}, \overline{CE}, \overline{CH},$
$\overline{DE}, \overline{DF}, \overline{DG}, \overline{EG}, \overline{FH}$

19. can't be traced

20. Can be traced; start at one odd vertex and finish at the other.

21. Sample answer: **22.** Sample answer:

23. Sample answer: **24a.** yes

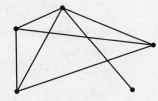

24b. sample tracing:

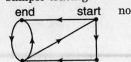

24c. No; if a network has an Euler circuit, each node has an even degree, so any path will return to its starting node.

25. When a path goes through a node, it uses two edges, so wherever you start you use one edge from that node, and the edges of every subsequent node are both used, one for entering and one for exiting. Therefore, the starting node is the only node left to go to because only one edge was used to start.

26a. *A*: degree 2, *B*: degree 3, *C*: degree 3, *D*: degree 2, *E*: degree 3, *F*: degree 3

26b. $2 + 3 + 3 + 2 + 3 + 3 = 16$

26c. The sum of the degrees of the nodes is twice the number of edges.

26d. See students' work.

27a.   **27b.** No; all four nodes have odd degree.

27c.

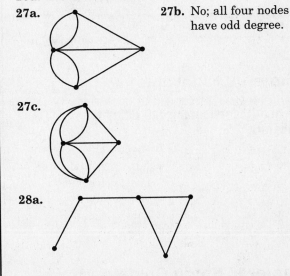

28a.

28b. Yes, exactly two nodes have odd degrees $\overline{AB}, \overline{BC}, \overline{CD}, \overline{DE}, \overline{EC}$

29. See students' work.

30. probability $= \dfrac{\text{area of triangle}}{\text{area of circle}}$

$$= \dfrac{\frac{1}{2}(5)(5)}{\pi(5)^2} = \dfrac{1}{2\pi} \approx 15.9\%$$

31. area of shaded region $=$ area of pentagon $-$ area of square

$$= \frac{1}{2}(5 \cdot 6)(4.5) - 6^2$$
$$= 67.5 - 36$$
$$= 31.5 \text{ unit}^2$$

32. $A = \frac{1}{2}d_1 d_2$
$$= \frac{1}{2}(2\sqrt{3})(1.5) = 1.5\sqrt{3} \approx 2.6 \text{ unit}^2$$

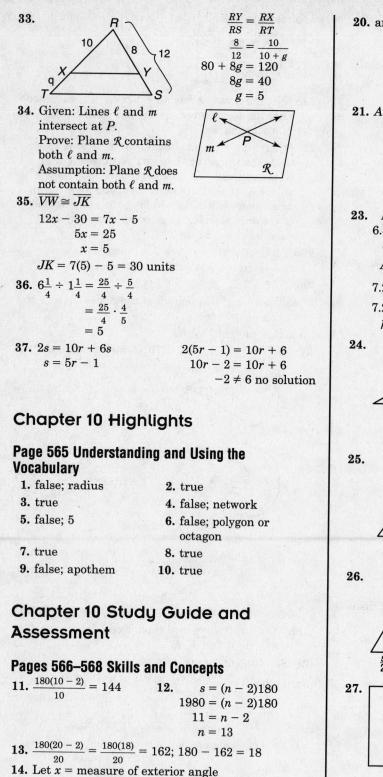

33.

$$\frac{RY}{RS} = \frac{RX}{RT}$$

$$\frac{8}{12} = \frac{10}{10 + g}$$

$$80 + 8g = 120$$

$$8g = 40$$

$$g = 5$$

34. Given: Lines ℓ and m intersect at P.
Prove: Plane $\mathcal{R}$ contains both ℓ and m.
Assumption: Plane $\mathcal{R}$ does not contain both ℓ and m.

35. $\overline{VW} \cong \overline{JK}$

$$12x - 30 = 7x - 5$$

$$5x = 25$$

$$x = 5$$

$$JK = 7(5) - 5 = 30 \text{ units}$$

36. $6\frac{1}{4} \div 1\frac{1}{4} = \frac{25}{4} \div \frac{5}{4}$

$$= \frac{25}{4} \cdot \frac{4}{5}$$

$$= 5$$

37. $2s = 10r + 6s$
$s = 5r - 1$

$$2(5r - 1) = 10r + 6$$

$$10r - 2 = 10r + 6$$

$$-2 \neq 6 \text{ no solution}$$

Chapter 10 Highlights

Page 565 Understanding and Using the Vocabulary

1. false; radius
2. true
3. true
4. false; network
5. false; 5
6. false; polygon or octagon
7. true
8. true
9. false; apothem
10. true

Chapter 10 Study Guide and Assessment

Pages 566–568 Skills and Concepts

11. $\frac{180(10 - 2)}{10} = 144$

12. $s = (n - 2)180$
$1980 = (n - 2)180$
$11 = n - 2$
$n = 13$

13. $\frac{180(20 - 2)}{20} = \frac{180(18)}{20} = 162; \; 180 - 162 = 18$

14. Let x = measure of exterior angle
$x + 11x = 180$ $\qquad \frac{360}{15} = 24$ sides
$12x = 180$
$x = 15$

15. regular, uniform   **16.** regular

17. $A = bh = 6(25) = 150 \text{ cm}^2$

18. $A = 2(4) + 2(4) + 2(5) = 26 \text{ cm}^2$

19. $18.9h = 134.19$
$h = 7.1 \text{ in.}$

20. area of figure = area of triangle + area of trapezoid

$$= \frac{1}{2}(2.4)(7.8) + \frac{1}{2}(5.8)(7.8 + 3.6)$$

$$= 9.36 + 2.9(11.4)$$

$$= 42.42 \text{ m}^2$$

21. $A = \frac{1}{2}h(b_1 + b_2)$

$$= \frac{1}{2}(10)(11 + 14)$$

$$= 5(25)$$

$$= 125 \text{ m}^2$$

22. $A = \frac{1}{2}d_1d_2$

$$54.18 = \frac{1}{2}(8.6)(d_2)$$

$$d_2 = 12.6$$

$$4.3^2 + 6.3^2 = s^2$$

$$58.18 = s^2$$

$$s \approx 7.6 \text{ cm}$$

23. $P = \text{leg} + \text{leg} + b_1 + b_2$

$$6.8 = 1.9 + 1.9 + b_1 + b_2$$

$$3 = b_1 + b_2$$

$$A = \frac{1}{2}h(b_1 + b_2)$$

$$7.2 = \frac{1}{2}h(3)$$

$$7.2 = 1.5h$$

$$h = 4.8 \text{ ft}$$

24.

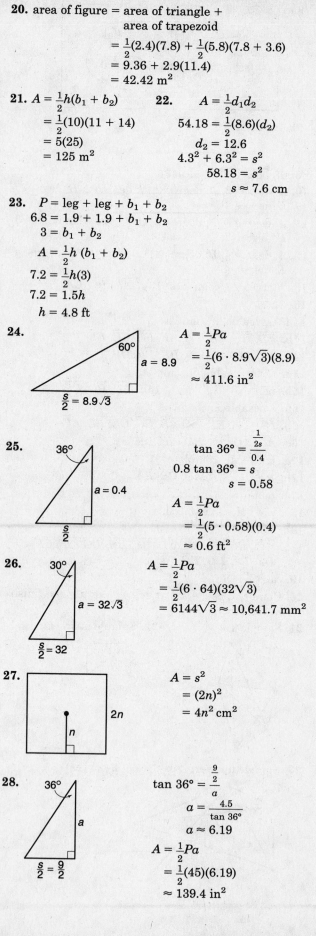

$$A = \frac{1}{2}Pa$$

$$= \frac{1}{2}(6 \cdot 8.9\sqrt{3})(8.9)$$

$$\approx 411.6 \text{ in}^2$$

25.

$$\tan 36° = \frac{\frac{1}{2}s}{0.4}$$

$$0.8 \tan 36° = s$$

$$s = 0.58$$

$$A = \frac{1}{2}Pa$$

$$= \frac{1}{2}(5 \cdot 0.58)(0.4)$$

$$\approx 0.6 \text{ ft}^2$$

26.

$$A = \frac{1}{2}Pa$$

$$= \frac{1}{2}(6 \cdot 64)(32\sqrt{3})$$

$$= 6144\sqrt{3} \approx 10,641.7 \text{ mm}^2$$

27.

$$A = s^2$$

$$= (2n)^2$$

$$= 4n^2 \text{ cm}^2$$

28.

$$\tan 36° = \frac{\frac{9}{2}}{a}$$

$$a = \frac{4.5}{\tan 36°}$$

$$a \approx 6.19$$

$$A = \frac{1}{2}Pa$$

$$= \frac{1}{2}(45)(6.19)$$

$$\approx 139.4 \text{ in}^2$$

29. $C = 2\pi r$ $A = \pi r^2$
$= 2\pi(7)$ $= \pi(7)^2$
≈ 44.0 mm ≈ 153.9 mm^2

30. $C = 2\pi r$ $A = \pi r^2$
$= 2\pi(19)$ $= \pi(19)^2$
≈ 119.4 in. ≈ 1134.1 in^2

31. $C = 2\pi r$ $A = \pi r^2$
$= 2\pi(0.9)$ $= \pi(0.9)^2$
≈ 5.7 ft ≈ 2.5 ft^2

32. $C = 2\pi r$ $A = \pi r^2$
$= 2\pi\left(3\frac{1}{3}\right)$ $= \pi\left(3\frac{1}{3}\right)^2$
≈ 20.9 cm ≈ 34.9 cm^2

33.

$r = \frac{4}{\sqrt{2}} = 2\sqrt{2}$

$C = 2\pi r$ $A = r^2$
$= 2\pi(2\sqrt{2})$ $= \pi(2\sqrt{2})^2$
$= 4\pi\sqrt{2}$ $= 8\pi$
≈ 17.8 ft ≈ 25.1 ft^2

34. $\frac{30 \text{ sec}}{7 \text{ min}} = \frac{30 \text{ sec}}{420 \text{ sec}} = \frac{1}{14}$

35. probability $= \dfrac{\text{area of shaded region}}{\text{area of circle}}$

$= \dfrac{\frac{1}{4}\pi(4.5)^2 - \frac{1}{2}(4.5)(4.5)}{\pi(4.5)^2}$

$= \dfrac{5.0625\pi - 10.125}{20.25\pi}$

$= 0.0908 = 9.08\%$

36. nodes: A, B, C, D, E; edges: $\overline{AB}, \overline{BE}, \overline{BD}, \overline{BC}, \overline{CD}$

37. yes   **38.** no; $\overline{CA}, \overline{CE}, \overline{DA}, \overline{DE}, \overline{AE}$

Page 568 Applications and Problem Solving

39. 631 and 542

40. Area $= 3(8 \cdot 8) + (10 \cdot 8)$
$= 192 + 80 = 272$ ft^2

They will need 2 gallons for 2 coats of paint.

41. Total area $=$ area of square base $+$ area of
trapezoid sides

$= 8^2 + 4\left[\frac{1}{2}(12)(8 + 10)\right]$

$= 64 + 4\,(108)$

$= 496$ in^2

Page 569 Alternative Assessment: Thinking Critically

• Subtract the areas of the regions formed by the overlapping parts.

College Entrance Exam Practice, Chapters 1–10

Pages 570–571

1. $A = \pi r^2$ Perimeter $= 12 + 12 + \frac{2\pi(12)}{6}$
$144\pi = \pi r^2$ $= 24 + 4\pi$ **(B)**
$r = 12$

2. $3x = \pm 5 - 4$
$3x = 5 - 4$ or $3x = -5 - 4$
$3x = 1$ $3x = -9$
$x = \frac{1}{3}$ $x = -3$ $\left\{\frac{1}{3}, -3\right\}$ **(A)**

3. $2x + 4 = 9$ $x - \frac{1}{2} = \frac{5}{2} - \frac{1}{2} = 2$ **(B)**
$2x = 5$
$x = \frac{5}{2}$

4. Diagonals of a square are equal. $AC = BC = r$ **(A)**

5. shaded region $= 1 - \left(\frac{1}{4} + \frac{1}{5} + \frac{1}{2}\right)$

$= 1 - \left(\frac{5 + 4 + 10}{20}\right)$

$= 1 - \frac{19}{20} = \frac{1}{20}$ **(D)**

6. $BF = \frac{EB}{\sqrt{2}} = \frac{4}{\sqrt{2}} = 2\sqrt{2}$

Area of $CDEF$ $=$ area of triangle $BEF -$
area of triangle BDC

$= \frac{1}{2}(2\sqrt{2})(2\sqrt{2}) - \frac{1}{2}(2)(2)$

$= 4 - 2 = 2$ **(A)**

7. $x - 4 = 0$ $x + 3 = 0$
$x = 4$ $x = -3$ **(A)**

8.

y-intercept: 8
slope: 4   **(C)**

$y = 4x + 8$

9. $x^2 - 11 < x^2 + 2x - 5 < x^2 + 25$
$-11 < \quad 2x - 5 \quad < 25$
$-6 < \quad\quad 2x \quad\quad < 30$
$-3 < \quad\quad x \quad\quad < 15$

10. area of figure $= \frac{1}{2}$ area of circle $+$ area of
rectangle

$= \frac{1}{2}\pi r^2 + bh$

$= \frac{1}{2}\pi\left(\frac{3x}{2}\right)^2 + 3x(x)$

$= \left(\frac{9\pi x^2}{8} + 3x^2\right)$ unit^2

11. $\frac{6(10) + 10(6)}{16} = \frac{120}{16} = 7.5$

12. length of $\overparen{PQ} = \frac{80}{360} \cdot 2\pi(8) = \frac{32\pi}{9} \approx 11.2$ units

13. $\frac{x^7}{2y^3 z}$ **14.** $6x = 3(4)$
                $x = 2$ in.

15. $s^2 = 3600$ $y^2 = 6400$
      $s = 60$ cm $y = 80$ cm
      $x = 60 + 80 = 140$ cm

16. Let s represent length of the non-base sides of the parallelogram. Since areas are equal, the height h is the same in each figure. For the parallelogram, $P = 2b + 2s$. For the rectangle, $P = 2b + 2h$. Since $s > h$, $2b + 2s > 2b + 2h$. Thus, the perimeter of R is greater than the perimeter of P.   (B)

17. not enough information   (D)

18. $858 = 2 \cdot 3 \cdot 11 \cdot 13$
      $2310 = 2 \cdot 3 \cdot 5 \cdot 7 \cdot 11$ (A)

19. perimeter of $ABCD = 2AD + 2CD$ $2AD = CD$
                              $= 3CD$
      circumference of $\odot = \pi d$
                              $= 3.14CD$ (B)

20. the altitudes are equal since the lines are parallel   (C)

CHAPTER 11 Investigating Surface Area and Volume

11-1A Modeling Mathematics: Cross Sections and Slices of Solids

Page 574

1. See students' work.
2. a triangle congruent to the bases
3. a rectangle whose length is the length of the prism

11-1 Exploring Three-Dimensional Figures

Pages 578–579 Check for Understanding

1. Yes; all of the surfaces of an obelisk are polygons.
2. A prism and a cylinder both have two parallel bases, but a cylinder's bases are circles and a prism's bases are polygons. A cone and a pyramid both have one base and a vertex, but the base of a cone is a circle and the base of a pyramid is a polygon.
3. Rachel is correct. A sphere is not a polyhedron because a polyhedron has sides that are polygons and a sphere has no flat sides.
4. Sample answers: prism: cereal box; cube: die; pyramid: Egyptian pyramids; cylinder: plumbing pipes; cone: ice cream cone; sphere: basketball
5. See students' models.   6. See students' models.

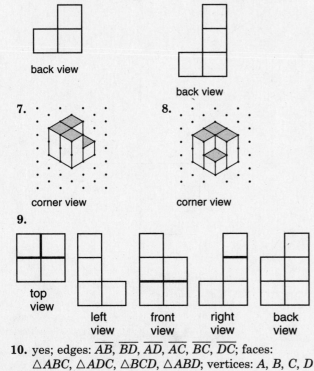

7.

corner view

8.

corner view

9.

top view   left view   front view   right view   back view

10. yes; edges: $\overline{AB}$, $\overline{BD}$, $\overline{AD}$, $\overline{AC}$, $\overline{BC}$, $\overline{DC}$; faces: $\triangle ABC$, $\triangle ADC$, $\triangle BCD$, $\triangle ABD$; vertices: A, B, C, D
11. not a polyhedron   12a. square
12b. isosceles trapezoid   12c. isosceles triangle
13. See students' work.

Pages 579–581 Exercises

14. See students' models. 15. See students' models.

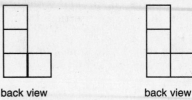

back view   back view

16. See students' models. 17. See students' models.

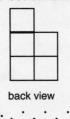

back view   back view

18.   19.

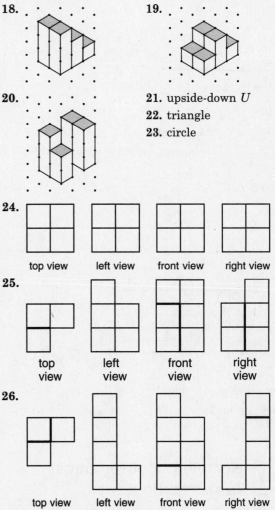

20.   21. upside-down U
22. triangle
23. circle

24.

top view   left view   front view   right view

25.

top view   left view   front view   right view

26.

top view   left view   front view   right view

27. yes; edges: $\overline{AB}$, $\overline{BC}$, $\overline{CD}$, $\overline{DE}$, $\overline{EA}$, $\overline{AF}$, $\overline{BG}$, $\overline{CH}$, $\overline{DI}$, $\overline{EJ}$, $\overline{FG}$, $\overline{GH}$, $\overline{HI}$, $\overline{IJ}$, $\overline{JF}$; faces: $ABCDE$, $ABGF$, $BCHG$, $CDIH$, $DEJI$, $EAFJ$, $FGHIJ$; vertices: A, B, C, D, E, F, G, H, I, J
28. yes; edges: $\overline{KL}$, $\overline{LM}$, $\overline{MN}$, $\overline{NK}$, $\overline{KO}$, $\overline{LP}$, $\overline{MQ}$, $\overline{NR}$, $\overline{OP}$, $\overline{PQ}$, $\overline{QR}$, $\overline{RO}$; faces: $KLMN$, $KLPO$, $LMQP$, $MNRQ$, $KNRO$, $OPQR$; vetices: K, L, M, N, O, P, Q, R

29. square   **30.** circle   **31.** triangle

32. If the plane passes through the cube so that the intersection is a quadrilateral whose vertices are two opposite vertices of the top face of the cube and two points on consecutive sides of the bottom face of the cube, then the intersection is a trapezoid.

33. The only polygon that can be formed by the intersection of a plane and a cylinder is a rectangle.

34. A cross section is the intersection of a solid with a plane parallel to the base(s). This intersection is always congruent to the base(s).

35. See students' work.

36. An MRI scan creates images of cross sections of the patient's body.

37. $A = 5$, $B = 5$, $C = 5$, $D = 5$, not traceable

38. $180(22 - 2) = 3600$ **39.** sometimes

40. $2.7^2 + 3.0^2 \overset{?}{=} 5.3^2$
    $7.29 + 9.0 \overset{?}{=} 28.09$
        $16.29 \neq 28.09$
No; the measures do not satisfy the Pythagorean Theorem.

41. slope of $\overline{AB} = \dfrac{4-3}{3-(-3)} = \dfrac{1}{6}$

    slope of $\overline{CD} = \dfrac{-1-(-2)}{1-(-4)} = \dfrac{1}{5}$

No; $\overline{AB}$ must be parallel to $\overline{CD}$ if $ABCD$ is a parallelogram.

42.

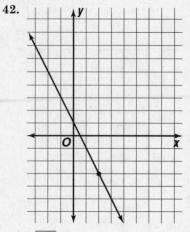

43. $\sqrt{324} = 18$

44. Yes; each element of the domain is paired with exactly one element of the range.

11-1B **Modeling Mathematics: Tetrahedron Kites**

Pages 582–583

1. equilateral   **2.** See students' work.

3. See students' work.   **4.** $\dfrac{1}{2}$

5a. See students' work.   **5b.** See students' work.

5c. See students' work.   **6.** 10; 20

11-2 **Nets and Surface Area**

Pages 586–587 Check for Understanding

1. On isometric dot paper, the dots are arranged in triangles, which aid in drawing three-dimensional objects and corner views. On rectangular dot paper, the dots are arranged in squares, which aid in drawing two-dimensional objects such as nets and right, left, top, front, and back views.

2. A net is the unfolded two-dimensional pattern of a three-dimensional object. The sum of the areas of the polygonal shapes in the net is the surface area of the polyhedron.

3. If a piece of sporting equipment has less surface area, the reduced friction allows it to travel faster.

4. No; there is no way to cover both the top and the bottom of the solid.

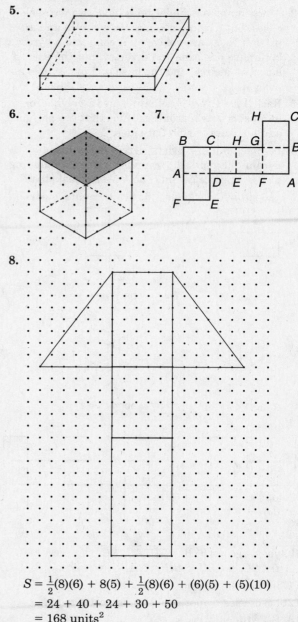

$S = \frac{1}{2}(8)(6) + 8(5) + \frac{1}{2}(8)(6) + (6)(5) + (5)(10)$
   $= 24 + 40 + 24 + 30 + 50$
   $= 168 \text{ units}^2$

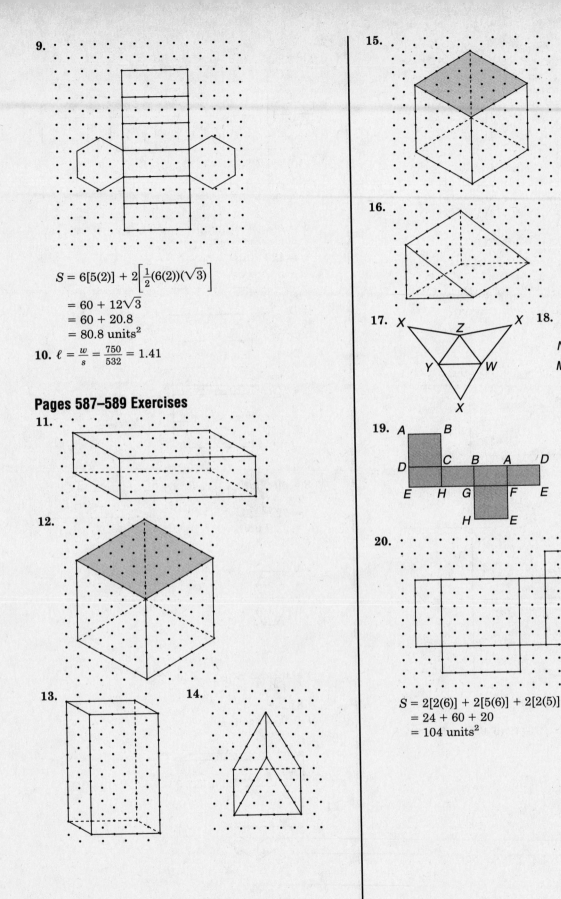

9.

$S = 6[5(2)] + 2\left[\frac{1}{2}(6(2))(\sqrt{3})\right]$

$\quad = 60 + 12\sqrt{3}$

$\quad = 60 + 20.8$

$\quad = 80.8 \text{ units}^2$

10. $\ell = \frac{w}{s} = \frac{750}{532} = 1.41$

Pages 587–589 Exercises

11.

12.

13.

14.

15.

16.

17.

18.

19.

20.

$S = 2[2(6)] + 2[5(6)] + 2[2(5)]$

$\quad = 24 + 60 + 20$

$\quad = 104 \text{ units}^2$

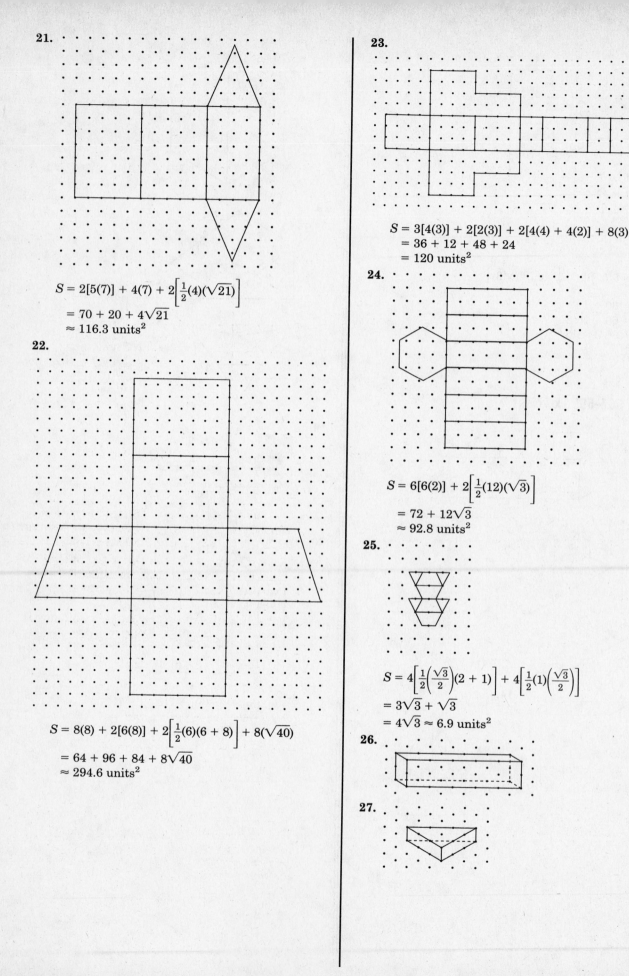

21.

$$S = 2[5(7)] + 4(7) + 2\left[\frac{1}{2}(4)(\sqrt{21})\right]$$

$$= 70 + 20 + 4\sqrt{21}$$
$$\approx 116.3 \text{ units}^2$$

22.

$$S = 8(8) + 2[6(8)] + 2\left[\frac{1}{2}(6)(6+8)\right] + 8(\sqrt{40})$$

$$= 64 + 96 + 84 + 8\sqrt{40}$$
$$\approx 294.6 \text{ units}^2$$

23.

$$S = 3[4(3)] + 2[2(3)] + 2[4(4) + 4(2)] + 8(3)$$
$$= 36 + 12 + 48 + 24$$
$$= 120 \text{ units}^2$$

24.

$$S = 6[6(2)] + 2\left[\frac{1}{2}(12)(\sqrt{3})\right]$$

$$= 72 + 12\sqrt{3}$$
$$\approx 92.8 \text{ units}^2$$

25.

$$S = 4\left[\frac{1}{2}\left(\frac{\sqrt{3}}{2}\right)(2+1)\right] + 4\left[\frac{1}{2}(1)\left(\frac{\sqrt{3}}{2}\right)\right]$$
$$= 3\sqrt{3} + \sqrt{3}$$
$$= 4\sqrt{3} \approx 6.9 \text{ units}^2$$

26.

27.

28.

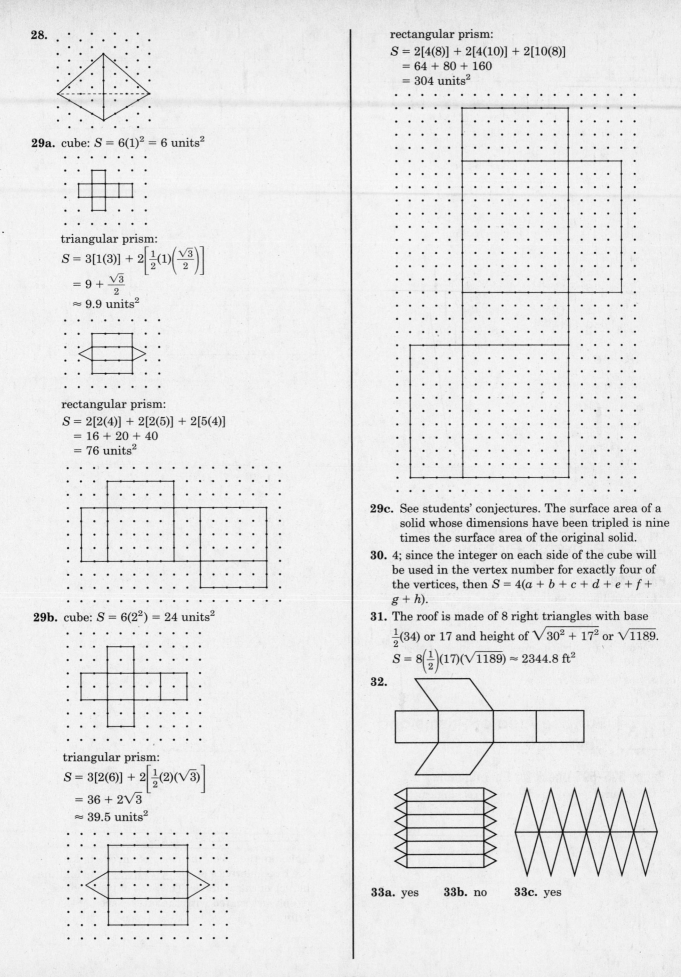

29a. cube: $S = 6(1)^2 = 6$ units^2

triangular prism:
$$S = 3[1(3)] + 2\left[\frac{1}{2}(1)\left(\frac{\sqrt{3}}{2}\right)\right]$$
$$= 9 + \frac{\sqrt{3}}{2}$$
$$\approx 9.9 \text{ units}^2$$

rectangular prism:
$$S = 2[2(4)] + 2[2(5)] + 2[5(4)]$$
$$= 16 + 20 + 40$$
$$= 76 \text{ units}^2$$

29b. cube: $S = 6(2^2) = 24$ units^2

triangular prism:
$$S = 3[2(6)] + 2\left[\frac{1}{2}(2)(\sqrt{3})\right]$$
$$= 36 + 2\sqrt{3}$$
$$\approx 39.5 \text{ units}^2$$

rectangular prism:
$$S = 2[4(8)] + 2[4(10)] + 2[10(8)]$$
$$= 64 + 80 + 160$$
$$= 304 \text{ units}^2$$

29c. See students' conjectures. The surface area of a solid whose dimensions have been tripled is nine times the surface area of the original solid.

30. 4; since the integer on each side of the cube will be used in the vertex number for exactly four of the vertices, then $S = 4(a + b + c + d + e + f + g + h)$.

31. The roof is made of 8 right triangles with base $\frac{1}{2}(34)$ or 17 and height of $\sqrt{30^2 + 17^2}$ or $\sqrt{1189}$.
$$S = 8\left(\frac{1}{2}\right)(17)(\sqrt{1189}) \approx 2344.8 \text{ ft}^2$$

32.

33a. yes   **33b.** no   **33c.** yes

34.

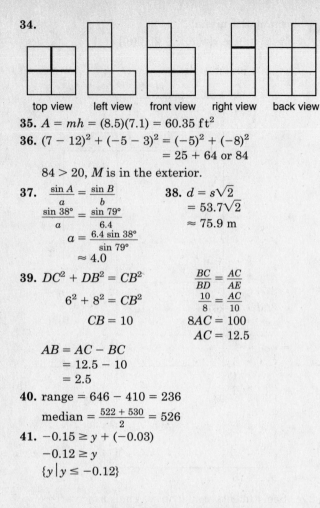

top view   left view   front view   right view   back view

35. $A = mh = (8.5)(7.1) = 60.35 \text{ ft}^2$

36. $(7 - 12)^2 + (-5 - 3)^2 = (-5)^2 + (-8)^2$
$$= 25 + 64 \text{ or } 84$$

$84 > 20$, M is in the exterior.

37. $\dfrac{\sin A}{a} = \dfrac{\sin B}{b}$

$\dfrac{\sin 38°}{a} = \dfrac{\sin 79°}{6.4}$

$a = \dfrac{6.4 \sin 38°}{\sin 79°}$

≈ 4.0

38. $d = s\sqrt{2}$
$= 53.7\sqrt{2}$
$\approx 75.9 \text{ m}$

39. $DC^2 + DB^2 = CB^2$

$6^2 + 8^2 = CB^2$

$CB = 10$

$\dfrac{BC}{BD} = \dfrac{AC}{AE}$

$\dfrac{10}{8} = \dfrac{AC}{10}$

$8AC = 100$

$AC = 12.5$

$AB = AC - BC$
$= 12.5 - 10$
$= 2.5$

40. range $= 646 - 410 = 236$

median $= \dfrac{522 + 530}{2} = 526$

41. $-0.15 \geq y + (-0.03)$
$-0.12 \geq y$
$\{y \mid y \leq -0.12\}$

11-2B **Modeling Mathematics: Plateau's Problem**

Page 590

1. See students' work.   **2.** See students' work.
3. No; it forms a shape inside of the frame.
4. Three soap surfaces meet at an angle of 120°. Four soap surfaces meet at an angle of about 110°.
5. See students' work.

11-3 **Surface Area of Prisms and Cylinders**

Pages 595–596 Check for Understanding

1a. 2 congruent triangles and 3 rectangles

1b.

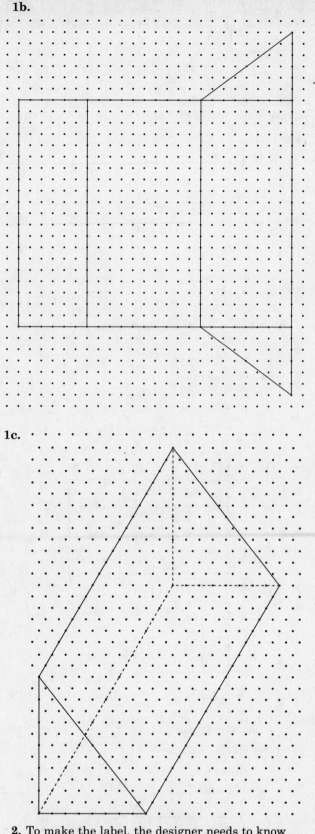

1c.

2. To make the label, the designer needs to know the circumference of the cylindrical base and the height of the cylinder. The area of the label is closely associated with the lateral area of the cylinder.

3. Lateral area is the area of all the lateral faces. Surface area is the area of the entire surface including the bases. The surface area is the sum of the areas of the bases and the lateral area.

4. In a right prism, the lateral edges of the prism are also altitudes of the prism. If this is not the case, then the prism is an oblique prism. See students' drawings.

5. Right prism; the lateral edges are perpendicular to the bases.

6. bases: pentagons; lateral faces: rectangles

7. $P = 5s = 5(6) = 30$ units

8. $L = 60(15) = 900$ units^2

9. $P = 2(8) + 2 (4)$
$P = 24$
$B = (8)(4) = 32$
$T = 24(2) + 2(32)$
$\quad = 48 + 64$
$\quad = 112$ cm^2

10. $P = 2(6.5) + 2(6.5)$
$\quad = 26$
$B = (6.5)^2 = 42.25$
$T = 26(6.5) + 2(42.25)$
$\quad = 169 + 84.5$
$\quad = 253.5$ cm^2

11. $T = 2\pi rh + 2\pi r^2$
$\quad = 2\pi(4)(6) + 2\pi(4)^2$
$\quad = 48\pi + 32\pi$
$\quad = 80\pi$
$\quad \approx 251.3$ ft^2

12. $T = 2\pi rh + 2\pi r^2$
$\quad = 2\pi(8.3)(6.6) + 2\pi(8.3)^2$
$\quad = 109.56\pi + 137.78\pi$
$\quad = 247.34\pi$
$\quad \approx 777.0$ ft^2

13. $\quad\quad T = 2\pi rh + 2\pi r^2$
$1977.7 = 2\pi r(28) + 2\pi r^2$
$\quad\quad 0 = 2\pi r^2 + 56\pi r - 1977.7$
$\quad r = \dfrac{-56\pi \pm \sqrt{(56\pi)^2 - 4(2\pi)(-1977.7)}}{4\pi}$
$\quad\quad \approx 8.6$ in.

14a. $P = 2(9) + 2(13)$
$\quad = 18 + 26 = 44$
$B = 9(13) = 117$
$T = 44(2) + 117$
$\quad = 88 + 117$
$\quad = 205$ in^2

14b. $T = 2\pi rh + \pi r^2$
$\quad = 2\pi(4.5)(2) + \pi(4.5)^2$
$\quad = 18\pi + 20.25\pi$
$\quad = 38.25\pi$
$\quad \approx 120.2$ in^2

Pages 596–598 Exercises

15. oblique prism

16. bases: rectangles; lateral faces: parallelograms

17. $P = 2(8) + 2(10) = 36$ in.

18. $L = 2(10 \cdot 6\sqrt{3}) + 2(12 \cdot 8)$
$\quad = 120\sqrt{3} + 192$
$\quad \approx 399.8$

19. $T = L + 2B$
$\quad = 399.8 + 2(8 \cdot 10)$
$\quad = 559.8$

20. $P = 8 + 8 + 14$
$\quad = 30$
$B = \frac{1}{2}(14)(\sqrt{15})$
$\quad = 7\sqrt{15}$
$T = 30(7) + 2(7\sqrt{15})$
$\quad = 210 + 14\sqrt{15}$
$\quad \approx 264.2$ in^2

21. $P = 10 + 10 + 8$
$\quad = 28$
$B = \frac{1}{2}(8)(\sqrt{84})$
$\quad = 4\sqrt{84}$
$T = 28(20.4) + 2(4\sqrt{84})$
$\quad \approx 571.2 + 73.3$
$\quad \approx 644.5$ in^2

22. $P = 14 + 14 + 18$
$\quad = 46$
$B = \frac{1}{2}(18)(\sqrt{115})$
$\quad = 9\sqrt{115}$
$T = 46(30.5) + 2(9\sqrt{115})$
$\quad = 1403 + 193$
$\quad = 1596.0$ in^2

23. $L = (12 + 9 + 8 + 7)(10)$
$\quad = 36(10)$
$\quad = 360$ cm^2
$T = 360 + 2\left[\frac{1}{2}(6)(8 + 12)\right]$
$\quad = 360 + 120$
$\quad = 480$ cm^2

24. $L = (10 + 10\sqrt{3} + 20)(10)$
$\quad = 300 + 100\sqrt{3}$
$\quad \approx 473.2$ yd^2
$T = 473.2 + 2\left[\frac{1}{2}(10)(10\sqrt{3})\right]$
$\quad = 473.2 + 100\sqrt{3}$
$\quad \approx 646.4$ yd^2

25. $L = (24 + 22 + 12 + 6 + 36 + 28)(18)$
$\quad = (128)(18)$
$\quad = 2304$ m^2
$T = 2304 + 2[(24)(28) + (12)(6)]$
$\quad = 2304 + 1488$
$\quad = 3792$ m^2

26. $T = 2\pi rh + 2\pi r^2$
$\quad = 2\pi(11)(11) + 2\pi(11)^2$
$\quad = 242\pi + 242\pi$
$\quad = 484\pi$
$\quad \approx 1520.5$ m^2

27. $T = 2\pi(13)(15.8) + 2\pi(13)^2$
$\quad = 410.8\pi + 338\pi$
$\quad = 748.8\pi$
$\quad \approx 2352.4$ m^2

28. $T = 2\pi rh + 2\pi r^2$
$\quad = 2\pi(6.8)(1.9) + 2\pi(6.8)^2$
$\quad = 25.84\pi + 92.48\pi$
$\quad = 118.32\pi$
$\quad \approx 371.7$ m^2

29. $L = 2\pi rh$
$\quad = 2\pi(7.1)(4.5)$
$\quad = 63.9\pi$
$\quad \approx 200.7$ in^2
$T = 63.9\pi + 2\pi(7.1)^2$
$\quad = 63.9\pi + 100.82\pi$
$\quad = 164.72\pi$
$\quad \approx 517.5$ in^2

30. $L = 2\pi rh$
$\quad = 2\pi(14)(14)$
$\quad = 392\pi$
$\quad \approx 1231.5 \text{ mm}^2$
$T = 392\pi + 2\pi(14)^2$
$\quad = 392\pi + 392\pi$
$\quad = 784\pi$
$\quad \approx 2463.0 \text{ mm}^2$

31. $L = 2\pi rh$
$\quad = 2\pi(0.9)(4.4)$
$\quad = 7.92\pi$
$\quad \approx 24.9 \text{ ft}^2$
$T = 7.92\pi + 2\pi(0.9)^2$
$\quad = 7.92\pi + 1.62\pi$
$\quad = 9.54\pi$
$\quad \approx 30.0 \text{ ft}^2$

32. $T = 4s^2 + 2s^2$
$\quad 864 = 6s^2$
$\quad 144 = s^2$
$\quad\quad s = 12 \text{ units}$

33. $\quad L = Ph$
$\quad 144 = (2(3w) + 2(w))(2w)$
$\quad 144 = (8w)2w$
$\quad 16w^2 = 144$
$\quad\quad w^2 = 9$
$\quad\quad w = 3$
$\quad T = 144 + 2(3 \cdot 3)(3)$
$\quad\quad = 144 + 54$
$\quad\quad = 198 \text{ cm}^2$

34. $\quad T = 2\pi rh + 2\pi r^2$
$\quad 301.6 = 2\pi r(8) + 2\pi r^2$
$\quad\quad 0 = 2\pi r^2 + 16\pi r - 301.6$
$\quad r = \dfrac{-16\pi \pm \sqrt{(16\pi)^2 - 2\,(2\pi)(-301.6)}}{4\pi}$
$\quad r = 4$
$\quad d = 2r = 2(4) = 8 \text{ m}$

35. If the height of the prism is doubled, the lateral area is doubled. The surface area is increased, but it is not doubled.

36. No; if the height of a cylinder is tripled, the lateral area is tripled. The surface area is increased, but it is not tripled.

37. $L = (10 + 7 + 10 + 7)(40)$
$\quad = 34(40)$
$\quad = 1360$
$T = 1360 + 2\left[(16)(7) + \frac{1}{2}(16)(6)\right]$
$\quad = 1360 + 320$
$\quad = 1680 \text{ ft}^2$

38. $L = 2\pi rh$
$\quad = 2\pi(2.5)(13)$
$\quad = 65\pi$
$\quad \approx 204.2 \text{ m}^2$

39. $T = \pi rh + \pi r^2$
$\quad = \pi(2.75)(18) + \pi(2.75)^2$
$\quad = 49.5\pi + 7.5625\pi$
$\quad = 57.0625\pi$
$\quad \approx 179.3 \text{ m}^2$

40.

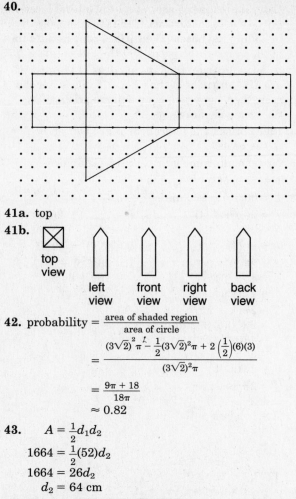

41a. top

41b.

top view

left view   front view   right view   back view

42. $\text{probability} = \dfrac{\text{area of shaded region}}{\text{area of circle}}$
$\quad = \dfrac{(3\sqrt{2})^2\pi - \frac{1}{2}(3\sqrt{2})^2\pi + 2\left(\frac{1}{2}\right)(6)(3)}{(3\sqrt{2})^2\pi}$
$\quad = \dfrac{9\pi + 18}{18\pi}$
$\quad \approx 0.82$

43. $\quad A = \frac{1}{2}d_1 d_2$
$\quad 1664 = \frac{1}{2}(52)d_2$
$\quad 1664 = 26d_2$
$\quad\quad d_2 = 64 \text{ cm}$

44. The measure of the inscribed angle is half the measure of the central angle.

45. slope of $\overline{BC} = \dfrac{2 - (-3)}{6 - 7} = -5; \dfrac{1}{5}$

46. $\quad m\angle J + m\angle K + m\angle L = 180$
$\quad (10x - 7) + 63 + (7x + 5) = 180$
$\quad\quad\quad\quad\quad 17x + 61 = 180$
$\quad\quad\quad\quad\quad\quad\quad x = 7$
$m\angle J = 10x - 7 = 10(7) - 7 \text{ or } 63$
$m\angle K = 63$
$m\angle L = 7x + 5 = 7(7) + 5 = 54$
acute; isosceles; $m\angle J = 63$, $m\angle K = 63$, and $m\angle L = 54$, thus, no angle is right or obtuse, so the triangle is acute. $m\angle J = m\angle K$ so the sides opposite these angles are congruent and $\triangle JKL$ is isosceles.

47. A triangle is equiangular if each angle measures 60°; Law of Syllogism.

48. not linear   **49.** positive

11-4 **Surface Area of Pyramids and Cones**

Page 599 Modeling Mathematics

a. triangle   **b.** Yes; see students' explanations.

c. Sample answer: They all intersect in one point.

d. The faces of the pyramid are congruent isosceles triangles that have a smaller vertex angle than those in the pyramid made from the first envelope.

Pages 603–604 Check for Understanding

1. The lateral edge of a pyramid is the side of a triangle in which one endpoint is on the base, while the other is the vertex. The lateral edge of a prism is the side of a parallelogram, and its endpoints are both on bases.

2a. As the number of sides increases, the base resembles a circle.

2b. As this takes place, the lateral faces become narrower so the lateral surface looks rounder.

3. The lateral edge is longer because it is the hypotenuse of the right triangle formed by the slant height, the lateral edge, and half of a side of the base.

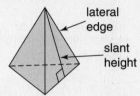

4. a cone that is oblique and not a right cone

5a. a circle with a sector missing

5b. See students' work.

5c. See students' work. The area of the surface is the same as the lateral area of the cone.

6. prism   **7.** both

8. $L = \frac{1}{2}P\ell$
$= \frac{1}{2}[4(7)](5)$
$= 70 \text{ cm}^2$
$T = 70 + 7(7)$
$= 70 + 49$
$= 119 \text{ cm}^2$

9. $L = \pi r\ell$
$= \pi(3)(5)$
$= 15\pi \approx 47.1 \text{ m}^2$
$T = 15\pi + \pi(3)^2$
$= 15\pi + 9\pi$
$= 24\pi \approx 75.4 \text{ m}^2$

10. $L = \frac{1}{2}P\ell = \frac{1}{2}[5(6)](8) = 120 \text{ ft}^2$
$A_{\text{base}} = \frac{1}{2}Pa$
$\tan 36° = \frac{3}{a}$
$a = \frac{3}{\tan 36°}$
$a \approx 4.129$
$A_{\text{base}} = \frac{1}{2}[30(4.129)] \approx 61.935 \text{ ft}^2$
$T \approx 120 + 61.9 \approx 181.9 \text{ ft}^2$

11. cone: $\ell^2 = 4^2 + 6^2$
$\ell^2 = 52$
$\ell = \sqrt{52}$
$L = 2\pi rh + \pi r\ell$
$= 2\pi(6)(6) + \pi(6)(\sqrt{52})$
$\approx 362.1 \text{ in}^2$
$T = L + B$
$\approx 362.1 + \pi(6^2)$
$\approx 475.2 \text{ in}^2$

12. slant height for 15 inch base edge:
$\ell^2 = 4^2 + \left[\frac{1}{2}(8)\right]^2$
$\ell^2 = 32$
$\ell = \sqrt{32}$
Area of $\triangle$ face: with 15-inch edge:
$A = \frac{1}{2}(15)(\sqrt{32}) = 7.5\sqrt{32}$
slant height for 8-inch base edge:
$\ell^2 = 4^2 + \left[\frac{1}{2}(15)\right]^2$
$\ell^2 = 72.25$
$\ell = 8.5$
Area of face with 8-inch edge:
$A = \frac{1}{2}(8)(8.5) = 34$
$T = 2(7.5\sqrt{32}) + 2(34) + 15(8)$
$= 15\sqrt{32} + 188$
$\approx 272.9 \text{ in}^2$

13. $\ell^2 = 481^2 + \left[\frac{1}{2}(756)\right]^2$
$\ell^2 = 374{,}245$
$\ell \approx 611.756$
$T = \frac{1}{2}P\ell$
$\approx \frac{1}{2}[4(756)](611.756)$
$\approx 924{,}974.6 \text{ ft}^2$

Pages 604–606 Exercises

14. pyramid   **15.** neither

16. prism   **17.** pyramid

18. neither   **19.** pyramid

20. pyramid

21. $\ell^2 = 8^2 + 8^2$
$\ell^2 = 128$
$\ell = 8\sqrt{2}$
$L = \pi r\ell$
$= \pi(8)(8\sqrt{2})$
$= 64\sqrt{2}\pi$
$\approx 284.3 \text{ in}^2$
$T = 64\sqrt{2}\pi + \pi r^2$
$= 64\sqrt{2}\pi + \pi(8)^2$
$= 64\sqrt{2}\pi + 64\pi \approx 485.4 \text{ in}^2$

22. $\ell^2 + 5^2 = 13^2$
$\ell^2 = 144$
$\ell = 12$
$L = \frac{1}{2}P\ell = \frac{1}{2}[4(10)](12) = 240 \text{ cm}^2$
$T = 240 + 10^2 = 340 \text{ cm}^2$

23. $L = \frac{1}{2}P\ell = \frac{1}{2}(6)(4.5)(6)$
$= 81 \text{ cm}^2$
base is hexagon
$a = \frac{1}{2}s\sqrt{3} = \frac{1}{2}(4.5)\sqrt{3} = 2.25\sqrt{3}$
$B = \frac{1}{2}Pa = \frac{1}{2}(6)(4.5)(2.25\sqrt{3}) \approx 52.6$
$T = L + B \approx 81 + 52.6 \approx 133.6 \text{ cm}^2$

24. $\ell^2 + \left[\frac{1}{2}(12)\right]^2 = 8^2$

$\ell^2 + 36 = 64$

$\ell^2 = 28$

$\ell = \sqrt{28}$ or $2\sqrt{7}$

$L = \frac{1}{2}P\ell = \frac{1}{2}[3(12)](2\sqrt{7}) = 36\sqrt{7} \approx 95.2$ cm^2

$B = \frac{1}{2}Pa = \frac{1}{2}[3(12)](2\sqrt{3}) \approx 62.4$ cm^2

$T = L + B \approx 95.2 + 62.4 \approx 157.6$ cm^2

25. $\ell^2 = 8^2 + 6^2$

$\ell^2 = 100$

$\ell = 10$

$L = \pi r\ell$

$= \pi(6)(10)$

$= 60\pi$

≈ 188.5 ft^2

$T = 60\pi + \pi r^2$

$= 60\pi + \pi(6)^2$

$= 96\pi$

≈ 301.6 ft^2

26. $L = \pi r\ell$

$= \pi(5)(13)$

$= 65\pi$

≈ 204.2 m^2

$T = 65\pi + \pi(5)^2$

$= 90\pi$

≈ 282.7 m^2

27. $T = 2\pi rh + \pi r\ell + \pi r^2$

$= 2\pi(3)(5) + \pi(3)(5) + \pi(3)^2$

$= 30\pi + 15\pi + 9\pi$

$= 54\pi$

≈ 169.6 ft^2

28. $T = 2\left(\frac{1}{2}Pl\right)$

$= \left[(6)\left(3\frac{1}{2}\right)\right]\left(5\frac{3}{8}\right)$

≈ 112.9 in^2

29. $T = \frac{1}{2}P\ell + Ph + B$

$= \frac{1}{2}[(4)(24)](17) + (4)(24)(24) + (24)^2$

$= 816 + 2304 + 576$

$= 3696$ yd^2

30. $s^2 = 100$

$s = 10$

$T = \frac{1}{2}P\ell + B$

$= \frac{1}{2}(4)(10)(13) + 100$

$= 260 + 100$

$= 360$ ft^2

31. $\triangle ABD$, $\triangle DBC$, and $\triangle ADC$ are $45° - 45° - 90°$ triangles and $h = \ell$.

$\ell^2 + (4\sqrt{2})^2 = 8^2$

$\ell^2 = 32$

$\ell = \sqrt{32}$ or $4\sqrt{2}$

$L = \frac{1}{2}P\ell$

$= \frac{1}{2}(3)(8\sqrt{2})(4\sqrt{2})$

$= 96$ units^2

$T = 96 + \frac{1}{2}((3)(8\sqrt{2}))\left(\frac{4\sqrt{2}}{\sqrt{3}}\right)$

$\approx 96 + 55.4$

≈ 151.4 units^2

32a. Since 2 is half of 4, the slant height of the whole pyramid is 2(3) or 6 yd.

$L_{\text{frustum}} = L_{\text{large pyramid}} - L_{\text{cutoff pyramid}}$

$= \frac{1}{2}(4)(4)(6) - \frac{1}{2}(4)(2)(3)$

$= 48 - 12$

$= 36$ yd^2

32b. Since the ratio of radii is $1:2$, the slant height of the large cone is 2(9) or 18 mm.

$T_{\text{frustum}} = L_{\text{entire cone}} - L_{\text{small cone}} + B_{\text{large circle}} + B_{\text{small circle}}$

$= \pi(6)(18) - \pi(3)(9) + \pi(6)^2 + \pi(3)^2$

$= 108\pi - 27\pi + 36\pi + 9\pi$

$= 126\pi$

≈ 395.8 mm^2

33. The lateral area approaches the area of the base. This can be seen by showing a series of cones cut on their slant heights and folded out into sectors. As the altitude approaches zero, the slant height approaches the radius of the base, and the sector narrows, approaching a complete circle. See students' diagrams.

34. $L = \pi r\ell = \pi(21)(47.9) = 1005.9\pi \approx 3160.1$ ft^2

35. $\ell^2 = 55^2 + \left(4\frac{1}{4}\right)^2$

$\ell^2 = 3043.0625$

$\ell \approx 55.164$

$L = \pi r\ell = \pi\left(4\frac{1}{4}\right)(55.164) = 234.4468\pi \approx 736.5$ ft^2

36. Monk's Mound is not a regular pyramid—the base is a rectangle. The lateral area is the sum of the areas of the four triangles (2 of each kind).

height of $\triangle$ with base 216.6 m:

$h^2 = (30.5)^2 + \left[\frac{1}{2}(329.4)\right]^2$

$h^2 = 28,056.34$

$h \approx 167.500$ m

height of $\triangle$ with base 329.4 m:

$h^2 = (30.5)^2 + \left[\frac{1}{2}(216.6)\right]^2$

$h^2 = 12,659.14$

$h \approx 112.513$ m

$L \approx 2\left[\frac{1}{2}(216.6)(167.500)\right] + 2\left[\frac{1}{2}(329.4)(112.513)\right]$

$\approx 36,280.5 + 37,061.8$

$\approx 73,342.3$

37. $L = Ph$

$784 = [2(3x) + 2(x)](2x)$

$784 = 16x^2$

$x^2 = 49$

$x = 7$

$T = 784 + 2(21)(7)$

$= 784 + 294$

$= 1078$ cm^2

38.

39. $A = \frac{1}{2}Pa$

$= \frac{1}{2}(9(10.4))(12.2)$

$= 570.96$ cm^2

40.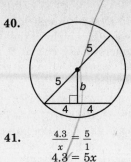

$$4^2 + b^2 = 5^2$$
$$b^2 = 9$$
$$b = 3 \text{ cm}$$

41. $\dfrac{4.3}{x} = \dfrac{5}{1}$

$4.3 = 5x$

$0.86 \text{ in.} = x$

42. The line passes through quadrants I, II, and III.

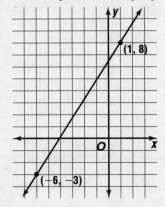

43. $x = b^2 + 18$

44. $2x + 4y = -14 \rightarrow 10x + 20y = -70$

$3x - 5y = 23 \;\; \rightarrow 12x - 20y = 92$

$\underline{22x = 22}$

$x = 1$

$2x + 4y = -14$
$2(1) + 4y = -14$
$4y = -16$
$y = -4$

$(1, -4)$

Page 606 Self Test

1.

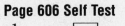

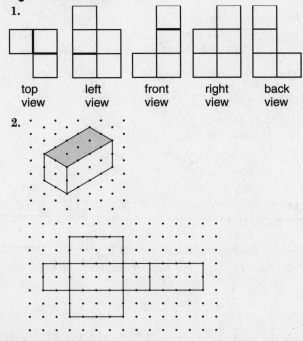

top view   left view   front view   right view   back view

2.

3. $L = Ph = [6(6)](12) = 432 \text{ in}^2$

apothem of regular hexagon:

$a = \frac{1}{2}s(\sqrt{3}) = \frac{1}{2}(6)\sqrt{3} = 3\sqrt{3}$

$B = \frac{1}{2}Pa = \frac{1}{2}(36)(3\sqrt{3}) = 54\sqrt{3}$

$T = L + 2B$
$ = 432 + 2(54\sqrt{3})$
$ = 432 + 108\sqrt{3}$
$ \approx 619.1 \text{ in}^2$

4. $L = 2\pi rh$
$ = 2\pi(4.2)(3.1)$
$ = 26.04\pi \approx 81.8 \text{ cm}^2$

$T = 26.04\pi + 2\pi(4.2)^2$
$ = 26.04\pi + 35.28\pi$
$ = 61.32\pi \approx 192.6 \text{ cm}^2$

5. $L = \frac{1}{2}P\ell$ $\ell^2 = 853^2 + 74.5^2$
$ = \frac{1}{2}[4(149)](856.247)$ $\ell^2 = 733{,}159.25$
$ \approx 255{,}161.7 \text{ ft}^2$ $\ell = 856.247$

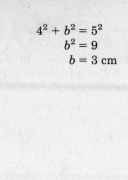

11-5   Volume of Prisms and Cylinders

Page 607 Modeling Mathematics

a. They are the same.   **b.** See students' work.

c. $V = lwh$

Pages 610–611 Check for Understanding

1. Sample answers: Soft drinks are sold by the liter, cement is sold by the cubic yard, and gasoline is sold by the gallon.

2. The volumes of two congruent geometric solids are equal.

3. You find the volume of both a prism and a cylinder by using the formula $V = Bh$. However, the base of a cylinder is always a circle, so its formula can be written as $V = \pi r^2 h$.

4. Kiki is correct. A cubic yard is 3 feet long, 3 feet wide, and 3 feet high, so the volume is $3(3(\cdot 3))$ or 27 cubic feet.

5a. 18 cubes   **5b.** $6(3)$ or 18 cubic units

5c. Yes, counting verifies the formula.

6. $V = Bh$ **7.** $V = Bh$
$ = (4 \cdot 5)(2)$ $= \pi(3)^2\left(4\frac{1}{2}\right)$
$ = 40 \text{ m}^3$ $= 40.5\pi \approx 127.2 \text{ ft}^3$

8. $b^2 = 12.5^2 - 10^2$ **9.** $V = Bh$
$b^2 = 56.25$ $= \pi(6)^2(15)$
$b = 7.5$ $= 540\pi$

$V = Bh$ $\approx 1696.5 \text{ yd}^3$
$ = \frac{1}{2}(10)(7.5)(8)$
$ = 300 \text{ in}^3$

10. $V = Bh$ **11.** $V = \frac{3}{4}Bh$
$ = \frac{1}{2}(6)(6)(3\sqrt{3})(10)$ $= \frac{3}{4}\pi(4)^2(10)$
$ = 540\sqrt{3}$ $= 120\pi \approx 377.0 \text{ ft}^3$
$ \approx 935 \text{ cm}^3$

12. $V = Bh$
$\quad = \frac{1}{2}(3)(4)(6)$
$\quad = 36 \text{ units}^3$

13. $V = Bh$
$\quad = \pi(3.5)^2(12)$
$\quad = 147\pi \approx 461.8 \text{ ft}^3$

Pages 611–613 Exercises

14. $V = Bh$
$\quad = (7.5)^2(22)$
$\quad = 1237.5\pi \approx 3887.7 \text{ ft}^3$

15. $V = Bh$
$\quad = (2.6 \cdot 4.5)(8.4)$
$\quad \approx 98.3 \text{ m}^3$

16. $V = Bh + Bh$
$\quad = (20 \cdot 8)(16) + (6 \cdot 8)(4)$
$\quad = 2560 + 192$
$\quad = 2752 \text{ cm}^3$

17. $h = 22.5^2 - 18^2$
$\quad h^2 = 182.25$
$\quad h = 13.5$
$\quad V = Bh$
$\quad = \pi(9)^2(13.5)$
$\quad = 1093.5\pi$
$\quad \approx 3435.3 \text{ mm}^3$

18. $V = Bh$
$\quad = \frac{1}{2}\left(\frac{14}{\sqrt{2}} \cdot \frac{14}{\sqrt{2}}\right)(16)$
$\quad = 784 \text{ yd}^3$

19. $V = Bh$
$\quad = \left[\frac{1}{2}(6)(12 + 8)\right](30)$
$\quad = 60(30)$
$\quad = 1800 \text{ in}^3$

20. $V = Bh$
$\quad = (6 \cdot 6)(6)$
$\quad = 216 \text{ m}^3$

21. $V = Bh$
$\quad = 25(4.2)$
$\quad = 105 \text{ m}^3$

22. $V = Bh$
$\quad = \pi(6)^2(8)$
$\quad = 288\pi \approx 904.8 \text{ cm}^3$

23. $V = Bh$
$\quad = \left[\frac{1}{2}(6 \cdot 5)(2.5\sqrt{3})\right](40)$
$\quad = 1500\sqrt{3}$
$\quad \approx 2598.1 \text{ ft}^3$

24. $\quad V = Bh$
$\quad 452.4 = \pi r^2(4)$
$\quad r^2 = 36$
$\quad r = 6$
$\quad d = 2r = 12 \text{ m}$

25. $\quad V = Bh$
$\quad 648 = 36h$
$\quad h = 18 \text{ in.}$

26. $V = Bh + Bh$
$\quad = (20 \cdot 20)(6) + (10 \cdot 10)(3)$
$\quad = 2400 + 300$
$\quad = 2700 \text{ in}^3$

27. $V = \frac{240}{360}Bh$
$\quad = \frac{2}{3}\pi(6.5)^2(18)$
$\quad = 507\pi$
$\quad \approx 1592.8 \text{ cm}^3$

28. $V = V(\text{block}) - V(\text{hole})$
$\quad = (4 \cdot 4 \cdot 4) - (\pi \cdot (1)^2 \cdot 4)$
$\quad = 64 - 4\pi$
$\quad \approx 51.4 \text{ ft}^3$

29. $V = Bh$
$\quad = \frac{1}{2}(3 \cdot 4)(6)$
$\quad = 36 \text{ units}^3$

30. $V = Bh$
$\quad = (4 \cdot 5)(2)$
$\quad = 40 \text{ m}^3$

31. $V = Bh$
$\quad = \pi(1.3)^2(4.2)$
$\quad = 7.098\pi \approx 22.3 \text{ in}^3$

32a. For cylinders A and B, and B and C: the height of the larger cylinder is twice the height of the smaller cylinder; For cylinders A and D; and D and E: the radius of the larger cylinder is twice the radius of the smaller cylinder.

32b. The lateral area of the larger cylinder is twice the lateral area of the smaller cylinder.

32c. For cylinders A and B, and B and C: The volume of the larger cylinder is twice the volume of the smaller cylinder. For cylinders A and D; and D and E: The volume of the larger cylinder is four times the volume of the smaller cylinder.

32d. If the height of a cylinder is doubled, the lateral area and volume are both doubled. If the radius of a cylinder is doubled, the lateral area is doubled and the volume is quadrupled.

33. Sample answer: True; imagine you sliced the oblique cylinder or prism parallel to its base to form a large number of pieces. Then you could slide the pieces so that they stack as a right cylinder or prism. This sliding will not affect the volume or the height. Since the volume of the right cylinder or prism is the product of the area of the base and the height, then the volume of the oblique cylinder or prism is the product of the area of the base and the height.

34a. $V = V(\text{block}) - V(\text{hole})$
$\quad = (42 \cdot 55 \cdot 80) - (\pi \cdot 18^2 \cdot 80)$
$\quad = 184{,}800 - 25{,}920\pi$
$\quad \approx 103{,}369.9 \text{ mm}^3 \text{ or } 103.4 \text{ cm}^3$

34b. $103.4 \text{ cm}^3 \cdot \frac{8.9 \text{ grams}}{\text{cm}^3} \approx 920 \text{ grams}$

35. fully expanded: $V = Bh$
$\quad = \left(\frac{1}{2} \cdot 6 \cdot 6 \cdot 3\sqrt{3}\right)(32)$
$\quad = 1728\sqrt{3} \approx 2993.0 \text{ in}^3$
fully compressed: $V = Bh$
$\quad = \left(\frac{1}{2} \cdot 6 \cdot 6 \cdot 3\sqrt{3}\right)(3)$
$\quad = 162\sqrt{3} \approx 280.6 \text{ in}^3$

36. $V = Bh$
$\quad = (78.78)(17)$
$\quad = 103{,}428 \text{ ft}^3 \times 7.5 \frac{\text{gallons}}{\text{ft}^3} = 775{,}710 \text{ gallons}$

37. $V = Bh$
$\quad = \pi(1.5)^2 18$
$\quad \approx 127.23$
$\quad 3(127.23) \approx 381.7 \text{ in}^3$

38. $r^2 = 56^2 - 32^2$
$\quad r^2 = 2112$
$\quad r \approx 46 \text{ ft}$

39. $T = Ph + 2B$
$\quad = (4 \cdot 8)(8) + 2(8)^2$
$\quad = 256 + 128$
$\quad = 384 \text{ in}^2$

40. $A = \pi r^2$
$\quad = \pi(2)^2$
$\quad = 4\pi \approx 12.6 \text{ yd}^2$

41. $S = (10 - 2)180$
$\quad = 8(180)$
$\quad = 1440$
$30, 30, 3(30) \text{ or } 90$

$x + x + 3x = 1440 - 1290$
$\quad 5x = 150$
$\quad x = 30$

42. true

43. $\overline{RS}, \overline{MN}; \overline{RT}, \overline{MO}; \overline{ST}, \overline{NO}$

44. slope of $\overline{AB} = \frac{0-4}{6-8} = \frac{-4}{-2} = 2$

slope of $\overline{CD} = \frac{-3-1}{0-2} = \frac{-4}{-2} = 2$

$\overline{AB} \parallel \overline{CD}$ since $\overline{AB}$ and $\overline{CD}$ have the same slope.

45. $2 \cdot 3 \cdot 3 \cdot 3 \cdot c \cdot c \cdot d$ **46.** 6

11-6A Modeling Mathematics: Investigating Volumes of Pyramids and Cones

Page 614

1. 3

2. The areas of the bases of the prism and the pyramid are the same.

3. The heights of the prism and the pyramid are the same.

4. $V = \frac{1}{3}Bh$

5. See students' work.   **6.** 3

7. The areas of the bases of the cone and the cylinder are the same.

8. The heights of the cone and the cylinder are the same.

9. $V = \frac{1}{3}Bh$

11-6 Volume of Pyramids and Cones

Pages 617–618 Check for Understanding

1. The volume of a cone is one-third the volume of a cylinder of the same height as the cone and with bases congruent to the base of the cone.

2. The cross sections taken at the same height in both prisms would be congruent. Each cross section is like one of the cards in the stack described in the lesson. At each level, the prisms would be the same size and shape.

3. Sample answer: Measure the radius and the height and use the formula for the volume of a cone.

4. $V = \frac{1}{3}Bh$
$= \frac{1}{3}(12 \cdot 8) \cdot 10$
$= 320 \text{ in}^3$

5. $V = \frac{1}{3}Bh$
$= \frac{1}{3}\pi(6)^2 \cdot 8$
$= 96\pi \approx 301.6 \text{ m}^3$

6. $V = \frac{1}{3}Bh$
$= \frac{1}{3}\pi(6)^2(13)$
$= 156\pi \approx 490.1 \text{ m}^3$

7. $h^2 = 15^2 - 8^2$
$h^2 = 161$
$h = \sqrt{161}$

$V = V_{\text{cube}} + V_{\text{pyramid}}$
$= Bh + \frac{1}{3}Bh$
$= (16 \cdot 16)(16) + \frac{1}{3}(16 \cdot 16)(\sqrt{161})$
$= 4096 + \frac{256}{3}\sqrt{161}$
$\approx 5178.8 \text{ mm}^3$

8. $V = \frac{1}{3}Bh$
$= \frac{1}{3}\pi(10)^2(10\sqrt{3})$
$= \frac{1000}{3}\sqrt{3}\pi$
$\approx 1813.8 \text{ ft}^3$

9. Mauna Loa: $V = \frac{1}{3}Bh$
$= \frac{1}{3}\pi(48.5)^2(9.1)$
$\approx 22{,}415.8 \text{ km}^3$

Paricutín:

$\tan 33° = \frac{410}{r}$
$r = \frac{410}{\tan 33°}$
$r \approx 631.34$

$V = \frac{1}{3}Bh$
$= \frac{1}{3}\pi(631.34)^2(410)$
$\approx 171{,}137{,}610 \text{ m}^3$

Fuji: $V = \frac{1}{3}Bh$
$= \frac{1}{3}\pi(3.776\sqrt{3})^2(3.776)$
$\approx 169.1 \text{ km}^3$

Vesuvius: $V = \frac{1}{3}Bh$
$= \frac{1}{3}\pi(60)^2(1303)$
$\approx 4{,}912{,}194 \text{ m}^3$

Pages 618-620 Exercises

10. $V = \frac{1}{3}Bh$
$= \frac{1}{3}\pi(6.5)^2(18)$
$= 253.5\pi$
$\approx 796.4 \text{ m}^3$

11. $V = \frac{1}{3}Bh$
$= \frac{1}{3}(15)(9)\left(8\frac{1}{2}\right)$
$= 382.5 \text{ in}^3$

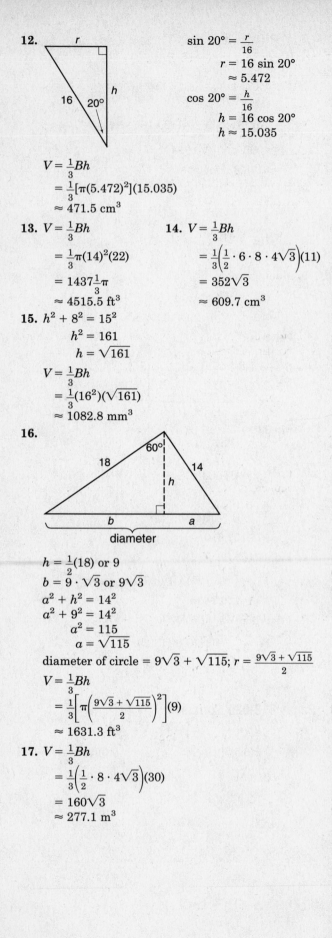

12.

$$\sin 20° = \frac{r}{16}$$
$$r = 16 \sin 20°$$
$$\approx 5.472$$
$$\cos 20° = \frac{h}{16}$$
$$h = 16 \cos 20°$$
$$h \approx 15.035$$

$$V = \frac{1}{3}Bh$$
$$= \frac{1}{3}[\pi(5.472)^2](15.035)$$
$$\approx 471.5 \text{ cm}^3$$

13. $V = \frac{1}{3}Bh$

$$= \frac{1}{3}\pi(14)^2(22)$$
$$= 1437\frac{1}{3}\pi$$
$$\approx 4515.5 \text{ ft}^3$$

14. $V = \frac{1}{3}Bh$

$$= \frac{1}{3}\left(\frac{1}{2} \cdot 6 \cdot 8 \cdot 4\sqrt{3}\right)(11)$$
$$= 352\sqrt{3}$$
$$\approx 609.7 \text{ cm}^3$$

15. $h^2 + 8^2 = 15^2$

$$h^2 = 161$$
$$h = \sqrt{161}$$

$$V = \frac{1}{3}Bh$$
$$= \frac{1}{3}(16^2)(\sqrt{161})$$
$$\approx 1082.8 \text{ mm}^3$$

16.

$$h = \frac{1}{2}(18) \text{ or } 9$$
$$b = 9 \cdot \sqrt{3} \text{ or } 9\sqrt{3}$$
$$a^2 + h^2 = 14^2$$
$$a^2 + 9^2 = 14^2$$
$$a^2 = 115$$
$$a = \sqrt{115}$$

diameter of circle $= 9\sqrt{3} + \sqrt{115}$; $r = \frac{9\sqrt{3} + \sqrt{115}}{2}$

$$V = \frac{1}{3}Bh$$
$$= \frac{1}{3}\left[\pi\left(\frac{9\sqrt{3} + \sqrt{115}}{2}\right)^2\right](9)$$
$$\approx 1631.3 \text{ ft}^3$$

17. $V = \frac{1}{3}Bh$

$$= \frac{1}{3}\left(\frac{1}{2} \cdot 8 \cdot 4\sqrt{3}\right)(30)$$
$$= 160\sqrt{3}$$
$$\approx 277.1 \text{ m}^3$$

18. $\ell^2 + \left[\frac{1}{2}(24)\right]^2 = 17^2$

$$\ell^2 = 145$$
$$\ell = \sqrt{145}$$
$$h^2 + \left[\frac{1}{2}(24)\right]^2 = \ell^2$$
$$h^2 + 144 = 145$$
$$h^2 = 1$$
$$h = 1$$

$$V = \frac{1}{3}Bh$$
$$= \frac{1}{3}(24^2)(1)$$
$$= 192 \text{ in}^3$$

19. The ratio of the radii is $\frac{12}{18}$ or $\frac{2}{3}$.

Let ℓ = slant height of large cone.
$$\frac{\ell - 10}{\ell} = \frac{2}{3}$$
$$3\ell - 30 = 2\ell$$
$$\ell = 30$$

h of large cone:
$$h^2 + 18^2 = 30^2$$
$$h^2 = 576$$
$$h = 24$$

height of frustum:
$$h^2 + (18 - 12)^2 = 10^2$$
$$h^2 = 64$$
$$h = 8$$

height of cutoff cone = $24 - 8$ or 16
$$V_{\text{frustum}} = V_{\text{large cone}} - V_{\text{cutoff cone}}$$
$$= \frac{1}{3}(\pi \cdot 18^2)(24) - \frac{1}{3}(\pi \cdot 12^2)(16)$$
$$= 2592\pi - 768\pi$$
$$= 1824\pi$$
$$\approx 5730.3 \text{ units}^3$$

20. $V = V_{\text{cylinder}} + V_{\text{cone}}$

$$= \pi(40^2)(80) + \frac{1}{3}(\pi \cdot 40^2)(40)$$
$$= \frac{448,000}{3}\pi$$
$$\approx 469,144.5 \text{ cm}^3$$

21. $\ell = 6\sqrt{3}$

$$h^2 + \left[\frac{1}{2}(12)\right]^2 = \ell^2$$
$$h^2 + 36 = 108$$
$$h^2 = 72$$
$$h = \sqrt{72} \text{ or } 6\sqrt{2}$$

$$V = 2(V_{\text{pyramid}})$$
$$= 2\left(\frac{1}{3}Bh\right)$$
$$= 2\left(\frac{1}{3}\right)(12^2)(6\sqrt{2})$$
$$= 576\sqrt{2}$$
$$\approx 814.6 \text{ yd}^3$$

22. $V = \frac{1}{3}Bh$

$$729 = \frac{1}{3}(243)h$$
$$729 = 81h$$
$$h = 9 \text{ units}$$

23. $V_{space} = V_{large\ cone} - V_{small\ cone}$
$$= \frac{1}{3}\pi(4.5)^2(5) - \frac{1}{3}\pi(3)^2(5)$$
$$= 33.75\pi - 15\pi$$
$$= 18.75\pi \approx 58.9\ in^3$$

24. $\ell = 6\sqrt{3}$
$a = 2\sqrt{3}$
$h^2 + a^2 = \ell^2$
$h^2 + 12 = 108$
$h^2 = 96$
$h = 4\sqrt{6}$
$V = \frac{1}{3}Bh$
$$= \frac{1}{3}\left[\frac{1}{2}(12)(6\sqrt{3})\right](4\sqrt{6})$$
$$= 144\sqrt{2}$$
$$\approx 203.6\ units^3$$

25a. $1493\ ft^3$ **25b.** $27,370\ in^3$ **25c.** $35\ m^3$

25d. Delete the "/3" in each of the lines that contains the volume formulas.

25e. No; the formulas are the same for a right or oblique solid.

26. $\frac{2}{3}$; the volume of each pyramid that makes up the solid on the left is $\frac{1}{3}$ of the volume of the prism, so the total volume of the solid on the left is $\frac{1}{3} + \frac{1}{3}$ or $\frac{2}{3}$ of the volume of the prism.

27. According to Cavelieri's Principle, the volume of each solid stays the same.

28.

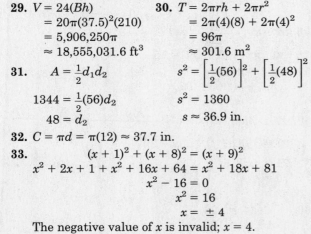

$\frac{h}{h+35} = \frac{4}{7.5}$
$7.5h = 4(h + 35)$
$3.5h = 140$
$h = 40$

$V_{frustum} = V_{large\ pyramid} - V_{small\ pyramid}$
$$= \frac{1}{3}(15 \cdot 15 \cdot 75) - \frac{1}{3}(8 \cdot 8 \cdot 40)$$
$$= 5625 - 853.3$$
$$\approx 4771.7\ ft^3$$

29. $V = 24(Bh)$
$$= 20\pi(37.5)^2(210)$$
$$= 5,906,250\pi$$
$$\approx 18,555,031.6\ ft^3$$

30. $T = 2\pi rh + 2\pi r^2$
$$= 2\pi(4)(8) + 2\pi(4)^2$$
$$= 96\pi$$
$$\approx 301.6\ m^2$$

31. $A = \frac{1}{2}d_1 d_2$

$1344 = \frac{1}{2}(56)d_2$
$48 = d_2$

$s^2 = \left[\frac{1}{2}(56)\right]^2 + \left[\frac{1}{2}(48)\right]^2$
$s^2 = 1360$
$s \approx 36.9\ in.$

32. $C = \pi d = \pi(12) \approx 37.7\ in.$

33. $(x + 1)^2 + (x + 8)^2 = (x + 9)^2$
$x^2 + 2x + 1 + x^2 + 16x + 64 = x^2 + 18x + 81$
$x^2 - 16 = 0$
$x^2 = 16$
$x = \pm 4$
The negative value of x is invalid; $x = 4$.

34. $y - y_1 = m(x - x_1)$
$y - (-3) = -1(x - 9)$
$y + 3 = -x + 9$
$x + y = 6$

35. Let x = the number
$9x \leq 108$
$x \leq 12$
$\{x \mid x \leq 12\}$

11-7 Surface Area and Volume of Spheres

Page 622 Modeling Mathematics

a. $\frac{1}{4}$ **b.** πr^2 **c.** $4\pi r^2$

Pages 625–626 Check for Understanding

1.

2. No, a polyhedron has flat faces and a sphere has no flat surfaces.

3. The volume of a sphere was generated by adding the volumes of an infinite number of small pyramids. Each pyramid has its base on the surface of the sphere and its height from the base to the center of the sphere.

4. Sample answer: Squares and circles are two-dimensional and cubes and spheres are three-dimensional. A cross section of a cube is a square, and a cross section of a sphere is a circle.

5. See students' work. **6.** sphere

7. neither **8.** false

9. true **10.** true

11. $CS^2 = CR^2 + SR^2$
$CS^2 = 4^2 + 3^2$
$CS^2 = 25$
$CS = 5$

12. $CS^2 = CR^2 + SR^2$
$13^2 = CR^2 + 12^2$
$25 = CR^2$
$5 = CR$

13. drizzle: $T < 0.005\ in^2$, $V < 0.000034\ in^3$; rain: $T > 0.005\ in^2$, $V > 0.000034\ in^3$

14. $T = 4\pi r^2 = 4\pi(12)^2 \approx 1809.6\ cm^2$
$V = \frac{4}{3}\pi r^3 = \frac{4}{3}\pi(12)^3 \approx 7238.2\ cm^3$

15. $A = \pi r^2 = 113.04$
$r^2 = 35.98$
$r = 6$
$T = 4\pi r^2 = 4\pi(6)^2 \approx 452.4\ ft^2$
$V = \frac{4}{3}\pi r^3 = \frac{4}{3}\pi(6)^3 \approx 904.8\ ft^3$

16. $V = \frac{4}{3}\pi r^3$
$\frac{32}{3} = \frac{4}{3}\pi r^3$
$8 = r^3$
$2 = r$
$T = 4\pi r^2 = 4\pi(2)^2 = 16\pi \approx 50.3\ m^2$

Pages 626–628 Exercises

17. circle **18.** sphere **19.** sphere **20.** neither

21. neither **22.** neither **23.** true **24.** false

25. true **26.** true **27.** false **28.** true

29. false   **30.** true   **31.** false

32. $OS^2 = OR^2 + SR^2$
$OS^2 = 9^2 + 12^2$
$OS^2 = 225$
$OS = 15$

33. $OS^2 = OR^2 + SR^2$ **34.** $OS^2 = OR^2 + SR^2$
    $16^2 = OR^2 + 12.8^2$ $15^2 = OR^2 + 10^2$
   $92.16 = OR^2$ $125 = OR^2$
     $9.6 = OR$ $11.2 \approx OR$

35. no   **36.** $OM = OS = 18$

37. $T = 4\pi r^2 = 4\pi(25)^2 \approx 7854.0$ in^2
   $V = \frac{4}{3}\pi r^3 = \frac{4}{3}\pi(25)^3 \approx 65{,}449.8$ in^3

38. $T = 4\pi r^2 = 4\pi(14.5)^2 \approx 2642.1$ cm^2
   $V = \frac{4}{3}\pi r^3 = \frac{4}{3}\pi(14.5)^3 \approx 12{,}770.1$ cm^3

39. $T = 4\pi r^2 = 4\pi(225)^2 \approx 636{,}172.5$ m^2
   $V = \frac{4}{3}\pi r^3 = \frac{4}{3}\pi(225)^3 \approx 47{,}712{,}938.4$ m^3

40. $T = 4\pi r^2 = 4\pi\left(6\frac{1}{2}\right)^2 \approx 530.9$ in^2
   $V = \frac{4}{3}\pi r^3 = \frac{4}{3}\pi\left(6\frac{1}{2}\right)^3 \approx 1150.3$ in^3

41. $T = 4\pi r^2 = 4\pi(1.7)^2 \approx 36.3$ m^2
   $V = \frac{4}{3}\pi r^3 = \frac{4}{3}\pi(1.7)^3 \approx 20.6$ m^3

42. $T = 4\pi r^2 = 4\pi(7)^2 \approx 615.8$ cm^2
   $V = \frac{4}{3}\pi r^3 = \frac{4}{3}\pi(7)^3 \approx 1436.8$ cm^3
      $C = 2\pi r$
   $43.96 = 2\pi r$
       $7 = r$

43. $T = 4\pi r^2$ $V = \frac{4}{3}\pi r^3$
  $16\pi = 4\pi r^2$ $= \frac{4}{3}\pi(2)^3 = \frac{32}{3}\pi$
     $4 = r^2$ ≈ 33.5 cm^3
     $r = 2$

44. $V = Bh$
  $1728 = s^3$
    $12 = s^3$

d = diagonal of cube
c = diagonal of sphere
$c = 12\sqrt{2}$
$d^2 = 12^2 + (12\sqrt{2})^2$
$d^2 = 432$
$d = 12\sqrt{3}$
$r = 6\sqrt{3}$
$V = \frac{4}{3}\pi r^3$
   $= \frac{4}{3}\pi(6\sqrt{3})^3$
   ≈ 4701 cm^3

45. surface area of smaller sphere $= 4\pi r_1{}^2$
surface area of larger sphere $= 4\pi r_2{}^2$
$4(4\pi r_1{}^2) = 4\pi r_2{}^2$
$16\pi r_1{}^2 = 4\pi r_2{}^2$
   $2r_1 = r_2$
The ratio of radii is 2:1.

46. Desta's destination is the polar opposite of the point of departure. Any city in the world would be on a great circle through these two points. So Mei's destination would be on the way.

47.

                 r = radius of slice
                 $r^2 = 13^2 - 5^2$
                 $r^2 = 144$
                 $r = 12$

   $A = \pi r^2 = \pi(12)^2 = 144\pi \approx 452.39$ cm^2

48a. yes   **48b.** no   **48c.** no

49a. $V_{\text{cone}} = \frac{1}{3}\pi r^2 h = \frac{1}{3}\pi(2)^2(10) \approx 41.89$ cm^3
   $V_{\text{ice cream}} = \frac{4}{3}\pi r^3 = \frac{4}{3}\pi(2)^3 \approx 33.51$ cm^3
   No, the ice cream will not overflow.

49b. $\frac{33.51}{41.89} \approx 80\%$

50. $T = 4\pi r^2$
  $T_{\text{hemisphere}} = \frac{1}{2}(4\pi(5)^2)$
             ≈ 157.1 ft^2
          $V = \frac{4}{3}\pi r^3$
  $V_{\text{hemisphere}} = \frac{1}{2}(\frac{4}{3}\pi(5)^3)$
            ≈ 261.8 ft^3

51. Sample answer: Buckminster Fuller designed geodesic domes. The domes are portions of spheres.

52a. $V = \frac{1}{3}Bh$
    $= \frac{1}{3}\left(\frac{1}{2}(9 \cdot 6)\right)(12)$
    $= 108$ units^2

52b. $\dfrac{\text{volume of pyramid}}{\text{volume of rectangle solid}} = \dfrac{108}{6(9)(12)}$
                     $= \dfrac{108}{648}$
                     $= \dfrac{1}{6}$
   1 to 6

53. $V_{\text{cylinder}} = \pi r^2 h$ $V_{\text{prism}} = Bh$
         $= \pi(4)^2(20)$ $= (8)(8)(18)$
         $= 320\pi \approx 1005.3$ in^3 $= 1152$ in^3
the bag shaped like a rectangular prism

54. false

55. probability $= \dfrac{\text{area of target} - \text{area of bullseye}}{\text{area of target}}$
             $= \dfrac{\pi(8)^2 - \pi(1.5)^2}{\pi(8)^2}$
             $= \dfrac{61.75}{64} \approx 0.96$

56. interior: $\dfrac{180(24 - 2)}{24} = \dfrac{3960}{24} = 165$
   exterior: $180 - 165 = 15$

57. $m\angle A + m\angle C = 180$ **58.** false
     $63 + m\angle C = 180$
         $m\angle C = 117$

59. $M = \frac{1}{2}(b_1 + b_2)$
$21 = \frac{1}{2}((3x + 4) + (5x - 2))$
$21 = 4x + 1$
$20 = 4x$
  $x = 5$

60. $32(4) = 128$
  $128 - 20 = 108$
  $108 \div 12 = 9$
    $9 + 52 = 61$ The number was 61.

61. $4n + 7 < 15$
$$4n < 8$$
$$n < 2 \quad \{n \mid n < 2\}$$

62. 614,000

Page 628 Mathematics and Society

1. Larger ball has 0.65 square inches more surface area, an increase of 7.3%.

2. Larger ball will encounter more air resistance (or drag) that will oppose its forward motion. Larger ball could have greater mass, thus not traveling as far when the same hitting force is applied.

3. See students' work. Sports or games could include football, basketball, tennis, baseball, softball, bowling, pool, billiards, and many others.

11-8 | Congruent and Similar Solids

Page 632 Check for Understanding

1. Find the ratio between each pair of corresponding linear measures. If the ratios are all the same, then the solids are similar.

2. If two solids are similar with a scale factor of a: b, then the surface areas have a ratio of a^2: b^2 and the volumes have a ratio of a^3: b^3.

3. The corresponding measures of similar solids are proportional. The corresponding measures of congruent solids are congruent. All congruent solids are also similar, but not all similar solids are congruent.

4. similar

5. $\dfrac{\text{radius of cylinder 1}}{\text{radius of cylinder 2}} = \dfrac{45}{45}$ or $\dfrac{1}{1}$

$\dfrac{\text{height of cylinder 1}}{\text{height of cylinder 2}} = \dfrac{56}{56}$ or $\dfrac{1}{1}$

The ratios are equal, so the cylinders are congruent.

6. $h^2 = 2.5^2 - 2^2$
$$h^2 = 2.25$$
$$h = 1.5$$
$\dfrac{\text{height of larger cone}}{\text{height of smaller cone}} = \dfrac{12}{1.5} = \dfrac{8}{1}$ or 8: 1

7. $\dfrac{T \text{ of larger cone}}{T \text{ of smaller cone}} = \dfrac{a^2}{b^2} = \dfrac{8^2}{1^2} = \dfrac{64}{1}$ or 64: 1

8. $\dfrac{\text{circumference of larger cone}}{\text{circumference of smaller cone}} = \dfrac{8}{1}$ or 8: 1

9. $\dfrac{\text{volume of larger cone}}{\text{volume of smaller cone}} = \dfrac{x}{(8)^3} = \dfrac{x}{512}$ m^3

10. true

11. False; if two pyramids have square bases and all the linear measurements are proportional, then they must be similar.

12. False; if the edge of one cube is twice that of another cube, then its surface area is four times that of the smaller cube.

13a. $\dfrac{\text{full-size car}}{\text{micro-car}} = \dfrac{1000}{1} = \dfrac{15}{x}$
$$1000x = 15$$
$$x = 0.015 \text{ cm or } 0.15 \text{ mm}$$

13b. $\dfrac{\text{surface area of micro-car}}{\text{surface area of full-sized}} = \dfrac{x \text{ cm}^2}{b \text{ cm}^2} = \left(\dfrac{1}{1000}\right)^2$
$$b = 1,000,000x \text{ cm}^2$$

Pages 633–635 Exercises

14. similar

15. $\dfrac{4}{14} = \dfrac{2}{7}, \dfrac{6}{16} = \dfrac{3}{8}$ neither

16. $\dfrac{10}{5} = \dfrac{2}{1}, \dfrac{6}{3} = \dfrac{2}{1}, \dfrac{16}{8} = \dfrac{2}{1}$ similar

17. $h^2 = 26^2 - 24^2$
$$h^2 = 100$$
$$h = 10$$
$\dfrac{\text{height of cylinder 1}}{\text{height of cylinder 2}} = \dfrac{10}{10} = \dfrac{1}{1}$
$\dfrac{\text{radius of cylinder 1}}{\text{radius of cylinder 2}} = \dfrac{12}{12} = \dfrac{1}{2}$
congruent

18. similar   19. neither

20. $\dfrac{\text{perimeter of rectangular prism 1}}{\text{perimeter of rectangular prism 2}} = \dfrac{2}{3}$ or 2: 3

21. $\dfrac{\text{volume of prism 1}}{\text{volume of prism 2}} = \dfrac{2^3}{3^3} = \dfrac{8}{27}$ or 8: 27

22. $\dfrac{\text{volume of prism 1}}{\text{volume of prism 2}} = \dfrac{8}{27} = \dfrac{x}{54}$
$$27x = 432$$
$$x = 16 \text{ cm}^3$$

23. $\dfrac{\text{volume of small cylinder}}{\text{volume of large cylinder}} = \left(\dfrac{4}{5}\right)^3 = \dfrac{64}{125} = \dfrac{48\pi}{x}$
$$64x = 6000\pi$$
$$x = 93.75\pi$$
$V_{\text{cylinder}} = Bh$
$$93.75\pi = \pi r^2 h$$
$$93.75\pi = \pi(5)^2 h$$
$$h = 3\tfrac{3}{4} \text{ in.}$$

24. true

25. False; if an edge length of a cube is tripled, then its volume is twenty-seven times greater.

26. true

27. False; doubling the radius of a sphere quadruples the surface area.

28. true

29a. Let x = slant height of smaller cone; then slant height of large cone = $2x$.

$\dfrac{\text{volume of frustum}}{\text{volume of original cone}} = \dfrac{(2x)^3 - (x)^3}{(2x)^3} = \dfrac{7x^3}{8x^3} = \dfrac{7}{8}$ or 7: 8

$\dfrac{\text{volume of frustum}}{\text{volume of small cone}} = \dfrac{(2x)^3 - (x)^3}{x^3} = \dfrac{7x^3}{x^3} = \dfrac{7}{1}$ or 7: 1

29b. $\dfrac{T_{\text{frustum}}}{T_{\text{original cone}}} = \dfrac{(2x) - (x)^2}{(2x)^2} = \dfrac{3x^2}{4x^2} = \dfrac{3}{4}$ or 3: 4

$\dfrac{T_{\text{frustum}}}{T_{\text{small cone}}} = \dfrac{(2x)^2 - (x)^2}{(x)^2} = \dfrac{3x^2}{x^2} = \dfrac{3}{1}$ or 3: 1

30.
$$\frac{x}{2x} = \frac{x+2}{x+3}$$
$$x(x+3) = 2x(x+2)$$
$$x^2 + 3x = 2x^2 + 4x$$
$$0 = x^2 + x$$
$$0 = x(x+1)$$
$$x = 0 \text{ or } -1$$

No; the values for which corresponding lengths would be proportional are 0 and -1. Since neither of these answers gives a length that is possible geometrically, the situation is impossible.

31. Since the only linear measure involved in a sphere is the radius, the linear measures of two spheres are always proportional.

32a. See students' work.

32b.
$$\frac{(72 \text{ in})^2}{(1 \text{ in})^2} = \frac{810 \text{ ft}^2}{x \text{ ft}^2}$$
$$\frac{5184}{1} = \frac{810}{x}$$
$$x = \frac{810}{5184} \text{ ft}^2 \text{ or } 22.5 \text{ in}^2$$

$$\frac{(72 \text{ in})^3}{(1 \text{ in})^3} = \frac{\frac{1}{2}L}{xL}$$
$$x = \frac{\frac{1}{2}}{72^3} \text{ liters or} \approx 0.0013 \text{ mL}$$

33. $\frac{1}{4} = \frac{96}{x}$ $\frac{1}{4} = \frac{75}{x}$ $\frac{1}{4} = \frac{56}{x}$
$x = 384 \text{ ft}$ $x = 300 \text{ ft}$ $x = 224 \text{ ft}$
$384 \text{ ft} \times 300 \text{ ft} \times 224 \text{ ft}$

34. $\frac{8}{20(12)} = \frac{8}{240} = \frac{1}{30}$
$$\frac{(1)^3}{(30)^3} = \frac{1}{x}$$
$$x = (30)^3 = 27{,}000 \text{ times as large}$$

35. $T = 4\pi r^2$
$$= 4\pi(6.6)^2 \approx 548.08 \text{ ft}^2$$
$V = \frac{4}{3}\pi r^3$
$$= \frac{4}{3}\pi(6.6)^3 \approx 1206.5 \text{ ft}^3$$

36. $V = Bh$
$$= (10 \cdot 12)(3)$$
$$= 360 \text{ cm}^3$$

37. $x^3 + y^3 + 2^3 = a^3$
$$3^3 + 4^3 + 5^3 = 6^3$$
$$(3 + 4 + 5)(5) = 12(5) = 60 \text{ cm}$$

38.

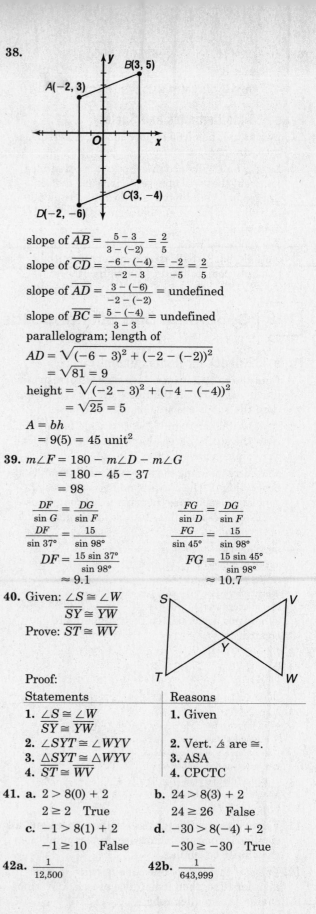

slope of $\overline{AB} = \frac{5-3}{3-(-2)} = \frac{2}{5}$

slope of $\overline{CD} = \frac{-6-(-4)}{-2-3} = \frac{-2}{-5} = \frac{2}{5}$

slope of $\overline{AD} = \frac{3-(-6)}{-2-(-2)} = \text{undefined}$

slope of $\overline{BC} = \frac{5-(-4)}{3-3} = \text{undefined}$

parallelogram; length of
$$AD = \sqrt{(-6-3)^2 + (-2-(-2))^2}$$
$$= \sqrt{81} = 9$$
$$\text{height} = \sqrt{(-2-3)^2 + (-4-(-4))^2}$$
$$= \sqrt{25} = 5$$
$$A = bh$$
$$= 9(5) = 45 \text{ unit}^2$$

39. $m\angle F = 180 - m\angle D - m\angle G$
$$= 180 - 45 - 37$$
$$= 98$$

$\frac{DF}{\sin G} = \frac{DG}{\sin F}$ $\frac{FG}{\sin D} = \frac{DG}{\sin F}$

$\frac{DF}{\sin 37°} = \frac{15}{\sin 98°}$ $\frac{FG}{\sin 45°} = \frac{15}{\sin 98°}$

$DF = \frac{15 \sin 37°}{\sin 98°}$ $FG = \frac{15 \sin 45°}{\sin 98°}$

≈ 9.1 ≈ 10.7

40. Given: $\angle S \cong \angle W$
$\overline{SY} \cong \overline{YW}$
Prove: $\overline{ST} \cong \overline{WV}$

Proof:

Statements	Reasons
1. $\angle S \cong \angle W$ $\overline{SY} \cong \overline{YW}$	1. Given
2. $\angle SYT \cong \angle WYV$	2. Vert. $\angle$s are $\cong$.
3. $\triangle SYT \cong \triangle WYV$	3. ASA
4. $\overline{ST} \cong \overline{WV}$	4. CPCTC

41. a. $2 > 8(0) + 2$ **b.** $24 > 8(3) + 2$
$2 \geq 2$ True $24 \geq 26$ False
c. $-1 > 8(1) + 2$ **d.** $-30 > 8(-4) + 2$
$-1 \geq 10$ False $-30 \geq -30$ True

42a. $\frac{1}{12{,}500}$ **42b.** $\frac{1}{643{,}999}$

Chapter 11 Highlights

Page 637 Understanding and Using the Vocabulary

1. cross section
2. prism
3. right cone
4. net
5. lateral faces
6. slant height
7. regular
8. sphere
9. similar
10. a: b

Chapter 11 Study Guide and Assessment

Pages 638–640 Skills and Concepts

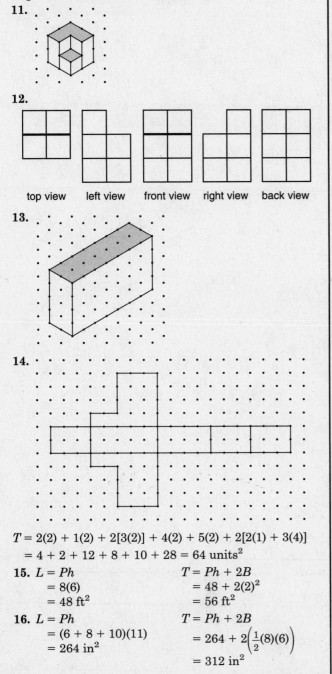

11.

12.

| top view | left view | front view | right view | back view |

13.

14.

$T = 2(2) + 1(2) + 2[3(2)] + 4(2) + 5(2) + 2[2(1) + 3(4)]$
$= 4 + 2 + 12 + 8 + 10 + 28 = 64 \text{ units}^2$

15. $L = Ph$
$\quad = 8(6)$
$\quad = 48 \text{ ft}^2$

$T = Ph + 2B$
$\quad = 48 + 2(2)^2$
$\quad = 56 \text{ ft}^2$

16. $L = Ph$
$\quad = (6 + 8 + 10)(11)$
$\quad = 264 \text{ in}^2$

$T = Ph + 2B$
$\quad = 264 + 2\left(\frac{1}{2}(8)(6)\right)$
$\quad = 312 \text{ in}^2$

17. $L = 2\pi rh$
$\quad = 2\pi(7)(10)$
$\quad \approx 439.8 \text{ cm}^2$

$T = 2\pi rh + 2\pi r^2$
$\quad = 439.8 + 2\pi(7)^2$
$\quad \approx 747.7 \text{ cm}^2$

18. $h^2 = 26^2 - 15^2$
$\quad h^2 = 451$
$\quad h \approx 21.237$
$L = 2\pi rh$
$\quad = 2\pi(7.5)(21.237)$
$\quad \approx 1000.8 \text{ m}^2$

$T = 2\pi rh + 2\pi r^2$
$\quad = 1000.8 + 2\pi(7.5)^2$
$\quad \approx 1354.2 \text{ m}^2$

19. $L = \frac{1}{2}P\ell$
$\quad = \frac{1}{2}(4 \cdot 2)(5)$
$\quad = 20 \text{ in}^2$

$T = L + B$
$\quad = 20 + (2)^2$
$\quad = 24 \text{ in}^2$

20. $L = \pi r\ell$
$\quad = \pi(3)(5)$
$\quad \approx 47.1 \text{ ft}^2$

$T = \pi r\ell + \pi r^2$
$\quad = 47.1 + \pi(3)^2$
$\quad \approx 75.4 \text{ ft}^2$

21. $\ell^2 = 5^2 - 3^2$
$\quad \ell^2 = 16$
$\quad \ell = 4$
$L = \frac{1}{2}P\ell$
$\quad = \frac{1}{2}(4 \cdot 6)(4)$
$\quad = 48 \text{ in}^2$

$T = L + B$
$\quad = 48 + (6)^2$
$\quad = 84 \text{ in}^2$

22. $L = \pi r\ell$
$\quad = \pi(3.2)(5.2)$
$\quad \approx 52.3 \text{ mm}^2$

$T = \pi r\ell + \pi r^2$
$\quad = 52.3 + \pi(3.2)^2$
$\quad \approx 84.4 \text{ mm}^2$

23. $h = \frac{1}{2}s(\sqrt{3})$
$\quad = \frac{10}{2}\sqrt{3}$
$\quad = 5\sqrt{3}$
$V = Bh$
$\quad = \frac{1}{2}(6 \cdot 10)(5\sqrt{3})(20)$
$\quad \approx 5196.2 \text{ cm}^3$

24. $V = \pi r^2 h$
$\quad = \pi(10)^2(20)$
$\quad \approx 6283.2 \text{ cm}^2$

25. $V = \pi r^2 h$
$\quad = \pi(5)^2(13)$
$\quad \approx 1021.0 \text{ ft}^2$

26. h of base $= \frac{1}{2}s\sqrt{3} = 4.5\sqrt{3}$
$V = \frac{1}{3}Bh$
$\quad = \frac{1}{3}\left(\frac{1}{2} \cdot 9 \cdot 4.5\sqrt{3}\right)(15)$
$\quad \approx 175.4 \text{ cm}^3$

27. $V = \frac{1}{3}Bh$
$\quad = \frac{1}{3}\pi(11)^2(22)$
$\quad \approx 2787.6 \text{ cm}^3$

28. $C = 2\pi r$
$\quad 62.8 = 2\pi r$
$\quad r \approx 9.9949$

$V = \frac{1}{3}Bh$
$\quad = \frac{1}{3}\pi(9.9949)^2(15)$
$\quad \approx 1569.2 \text{ mm}^3$

29. true

30. $T = 4\pi r^2$
$\quad = 4\pi(1080)^2$
$\quad \approx 14{,}657{,}415 \text{ mi}^2$

31. $A = \pi r^2$

$50.24 = \pi r^2$

$r^2 \approx 15.99188$

$r \approx 3.99898$ cm

$V = \frac{4}{3}\pi r^3$

$V = \frac{4}{3}\pi (3.99898)^3$

≈ 267.9 cm^3

32. neither   **33.** true   **34.** true

35. False; a solid is always similar to itself.

Page 640 Applications and Problem Solving

36. ceiling

37. $T = 4\pi r^2$

$= 4\pi(109)^2$

$\approx 149{,}301.0$ ft^2

$V = \frac{4}{3}\pi r^3$

$= \frac{4}{3}\pi(109)^3$

$\approx 5{,}424{,}604.8$ ft^3

38. $L = 2\pi rh$

$= 2\pi\left(\frac{1}{8}\right)(500)$

≈ 392.7 ft^2

$V = Bh$

$= \pi r^2 h$

$= \pi\left(\frac{1}{8}\right)^2(500)$

≈ 24.5 ft^3

39. $\dfrac{\text{folk guitar}}{\text{largest guitar}} = \dfrac{18}{38(18) + 2} = \dfrac{18}{458} = \dfrac{1}{25.4}$ or 1: 25.4

Page 641 Alternative Assessment: Thinking Critically

- It could mean one dimension is to two dimensions as two dimensions are to three dimensions. The analogy is valid because in each case you extend it by one dimension to get the next term. But the analogy does not work if actual values for a problem are substituted.

CHAPTER 12　Continuing Coordinate Geometry

Integration: Algebra
Graphing Linear Equations

Page 646 Modeling Mathematics
a. See students' work.　**b.** See students' work.
c. See students' work.　**d.** 160

Pages 648–649 Check for Understanding
1. Sample answer: Substitute the coordinates of the point into the equation and see if the result is a true sentence.
2. Sample answer: The x-coordinates of points on a vertical line are the same. When finding the slope, the denominator is zero and division by zero is undefined.
3. intercepts, slope-intercept; Answers may vary.
4. Yes, it can be written in the form $Ax + By = C$.
5a. See students' work.　5b. See students' work.
5c.

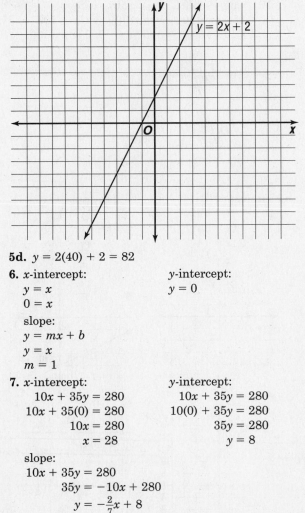

5d. $y = 2(40) + 2 = 82$
6. x-intercept:　　　y-intercept:
$y = x$　　　　　$y = 0$
$0 = x$
slope:
$y = mx + b$
$y = x$
$m = 1$
7. x-intercept:　　　　y-intercept:
$10x + 35y = 280$　　$10x + 35y = 280$
$10x + 35(0) = 280$　$10(0) + 35y = 280$
$10x = 280$　　　　$35y = 280$
$x = 28$　　　　　$y = 8$
slope:
$10x + 35y = 280$
$35y = -10x + 280$
$y = -\frac{2}{7}x + 8$
$m = -\frac{2}{7}$

8. x-intercept:
$10x - 15y = 120$
$10x - 15(0) = 120$
$10x = 120$
$x = 12$
y-intercept:
$10x - 15y = 120$
$10(0) - 15y = 120$
$-15y = 120$
$y = -8$

9. $y = -0.5x + 20$
$m = -0.5$
$b = 20$

10.

11.

12a.

12b. the acceleration, or the change in the velocity that occurs in each second that the object drops
12c. When the object is dropped, the beginning velocity is 0.

Pages 649–651 Exercises
13. x-intercept:　　y-intercept:　　slope:
$y = -x$　　　　$y = -x$　　　$y = mx + b$
$0 = -x$　　　　$y = -(0)$　　$y = -x$
$0 = x$　　　　　$y = 0$　　　$m = -1$
14. x-intercept:　　y-intercept:　　slope:
$x + 3y = 0$　　　$x + 3y = 0$　　$x + 3y = 0$
$x + 3(0) = 0$　　$0 + 3y = 0$　　$3y = -x$
$x = 0$　　　　　$y = 0$　　　$y = -\frac{1}{3}x$
　　　　　　　　　　　　　　　$m = -\frac{1}{3}$

15. *x*-intercept: *y*-intercept:
$x = 2$ none
slope:
The slope of a vertical line is undefined.

16. *x*-intercept: *y*-intercept:
none $y = 0$
slope:
The slope of a horizontal line is 0.

17. *x*-intercept: *y*-intercept:
$x = 0$ none
slope:
The slope of a vertical line is undefined.

18. *x*-intercept: *y*-intercept:

$$18x - 42y = 210 \qquad 18x - 42y = 210$$
$$18x - 42(0) = 210 \qquad 18(0) - 42y = 210$$
$$18x = 210 \qquad\qquad -42y = 210$$
$$x = 11\tfrac{2}{3} \qquad\qquad\quad y = -5$$

slope:
$$18x - 42y = 210$$
$$-42y = -18x + 210$$
$$y = \tfrac{3}{7}x - 5$$
$$m = \tfrac{3}{7}$$

19.

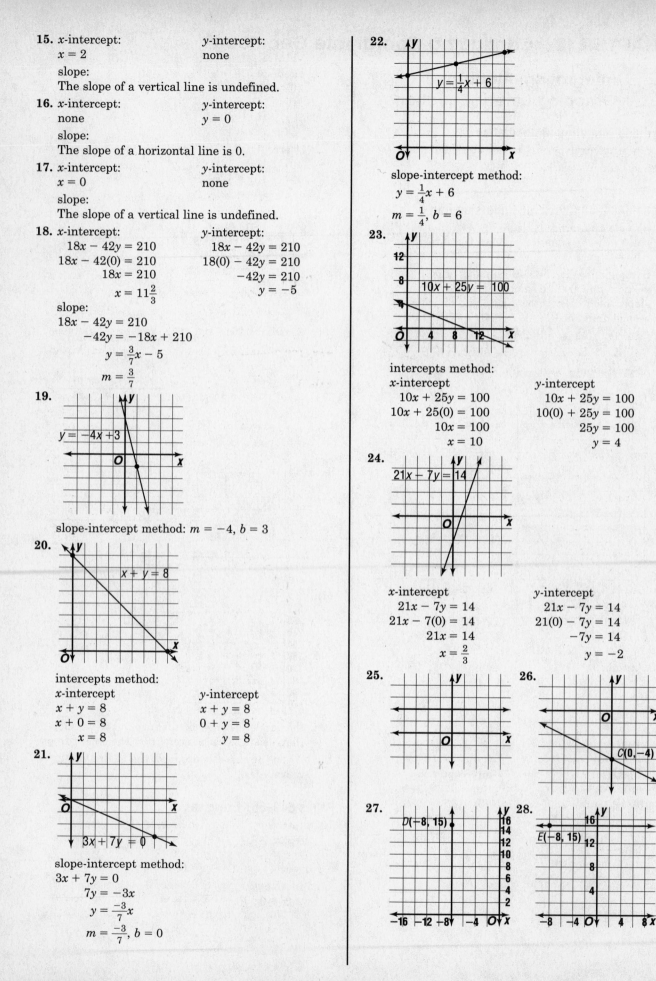

slope-intercept method: $m = -4$, $b = 3$

20.

intercepts method:

x-intercept   *y*-intercept
$x + y = 8$ $x + y = 8$
$x + 0 = 8$ $0 + y = 8$
$x = 8$ $y = 8$

21.

slope-intercept method:
$$3x + 7y = 0$$
$$7y = -3x$$
$$y = \tfrac{-3}{7}x$$
$$m = \tfrac{-3}{7}, \; b = 0$$

22.

slope-intercept method:
$$y = \tfrac{1}{4}x + 6$$
$$m = \tfrac{1}{4}, \; b = 6$$

23.

intercepts method:

x-intercept   *y*-intercept
$10x + 25y = 100$ $10x + 25y = 100$
$10x + 25(0) = 100$ $10(0) + 25y = 100$
$10x = 100$ $25y = 100$
$x = 10$ $y = 4$

24.

x-intercept   *y*-intercept
$21x - 7y = 14$ $21x - 7y = 14$
$21x - 7(0) = 14$ $21(0) - 7y = 14$
$21x = 14$ $-7y = 14$
$x = \tfrac{2}{3}$ $y = -2$

25.   **26.**

27.   **28.**

29.

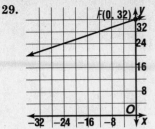

30. See students' graphs. Sample answer: All are of the form $y = -4x + b$, but all have a different value for b.

31. See students' graphs. Sample answer: All are of the form $y = mx - 1$, but all have a different value for m.

32. Sample answer: The graphs of the first and third equations are parallel and the graph of the second equation is perpendicular to the other two.

33. The slope is undefined. Sample answer: The x-coordinates of points on a vertical line are the same. When finding the slope, the denominator (the change in x) is zero and division by zero is undefined.

34a. $A = 3c$ and $B = 4c$ for any real number c, $c \neq 0$

34b. $A = 4c$ and $B = -3c$ for any real number c, $c \neq 0$

35a. The new line would be parallel to the first line with y-intercept 14.

35b. m would still be -2, b would change to 14

36. Sample answer: $y = \frac{1}{2}x + 4$

37. $y = -2.5x + 3.5$; Sample answer: The distance between two parallel lines is the length of any perpendicular segment that connects points on the two lines. The distance between the y-intercepts is 5. The y-intercept midway between the two lines is 3.5. Since the line is parallel to the other two, the slope must be the same.

38.

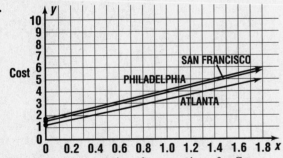

The lines representing the equations for San Francisco and Philadelphia are parallel because they have the same rate per mile, but San Francisco starts at a lower initial cost. Atlanta costs less to begin with and has a lower cost per mile so it will always be cheaper than either of the other two cities.

39a. 12; for every gram of fat in the food, there are 12 times more Calories.

39b. 180

39c.

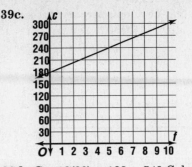

39d. $C = 12(30) + 180 = 540$ Calories

40a. $\frac{12}{100} = \frac{240}{x}$
$12x = 240(100)$
$x = 2000$ feet

40b. $\frac{2}{100} = \frac{500}{x}$ $\frac{12}{100} = \frac{500}{x}$
$2x = 500(100)$ $12x = 500(100)$
$x = 25{,}000$ feet $x = 4166\frac{2}{3}$ feet
$25{,}000 - 4166\frac{2}{3} = 20{,}833\frac{1}{3}$ feet or ≈ 3.9 miles

41a. the number of people that can be carried in x small vans

41b. x: 12; the number of small vans if all of the people were to be transported in small vans and none in the large vans; y: 8, the number of large vans if all of the people were to be transported in the large vans and none in the small vans.

41c.

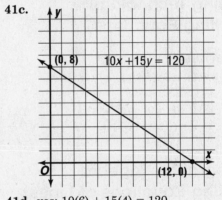

41d. yes; $10(6) + 15(4) = 120$

41e. yes; $10(3) + 15(6) = 120$

42. $\frac{1}{1000} = = \frac{\frac{5}{16}}{x}$
$x = \frac{5}{16}(1000)$
$= 312.5$ in. $= 26$ ft $\frac{1}{2}$ in.

43. $A = bh$
$108 = x(3x)$
$108 = 3x^2$
$36 = x^2$
$x = 6$
height: $3(6) = 18$ m
base: 6 m

44. $(x - h)^2 + (y - k)^2 = r^2$
$(x - 6)^2 + (y - (-5))^2 = (7\sqrt{3})^2$
$(x - 6)^2 + (y + 5)^2 = 147$

45. $\tan 22° = \frac{x}{6.9}$
$x = 6.9 \tan 22°$
≈ 2.8 miles

46. False; they can only be supplementary if it is a rectangle.

47.

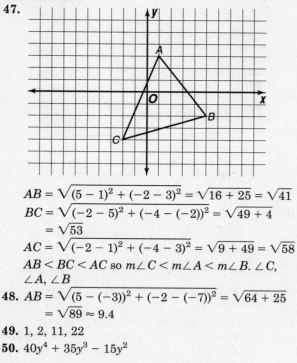

$AB = \sqrt{(5-1)^2 + (-2-3)^2} = \sqrt{16+25} = \sqrt{41}$

$BC = \sqrt{(-2-5)^2 + (-4-(-2))^2} = \sqrt{49+4}$
$= \sqrt{53}$

$AC = \sqrt{(-2-1)^2 + (-4-3)^2} = \sqrt{9+49} = \sqrt{58}$

$AB < BC < AC$ so $m\angle C < m\angle A < m\angle B. \angle C,$
$\angle A, \angle B$

48. $AB = \sqrt{(5-(-3))^2 + (-2-(-7))^2} = \sqrt{64+25}$
$= \sqrt{89} \approx 9.4$

49. 1, 2, 11, 22

50. $40y^4 + 35y^3 - 15y^2$

12-2A Using Technology Writing Equations

Page 652 Exercises

1. The slope between any two points is 0.034.

2. $b = -34$

3. $y = 0.034x - 34$; see students' work.

4. $y = 0.25x + 6$

12-2 Integration: Algebra Writing Equations of Lines

Pages 655–656 Check for Understanding

1. Sample answer: Substitute 3 for m and -10 for b into $y = mx + b$.

2. Sample answers: $y = x - 5$ and $y = 2x - 12$

3. Sample answer: You need to know what the variable represents in order to write the equation.

4. Line a goes through (0, 3) and (3, 0).

$m = \frac{3-0}{0-3} = \frac{3}{-3} = -1$
$b = 3$
$y = mx + b$
$y = -x + 3$

5. Sample answer: If the slope of line a is -1, the slope of line b must be 1 by Postulate 3–3.

6. $y - y_1 = m(x - x_1)$
$y - 5 = 4(x - 1)$
$y - 5 = 4x - 4$
$y = 4x + 1$

7. $y - y_1 = m(x - x_1)$
$y - 4 = -\frac{1}{3}(x - (-2))$
$y - 4 = -\frac{1}{3}x - \frac{2}{3}$
$y = -\frac{1}{3}x + \frac{10}{3}$

8. $y = mx + b$
$y = -3x + 5$

9. $y - y_1 = m(x - x_1)$
$y - (-1) = \frac{1}{3}(x - 6)$
$y + 1 = \frac{1}{3}x - 2$
$y = \frac{1}{3}x - 3$

10. $y - y_1 = m(x - x_1)$
$y - 0 = 5(x - (-2))$
$y = 5x + 10$

11. $m = -2 \ (4, -1)$
$y - y_1 = m(x - x_1)$
$y - (-1) = -2(x - 4)$
$y + 1 = -2x + 8$
$y = -2x + 7$

12a. $c = 29.95 + 19.95(x - 1)$; Sample answer: You must assume the fees remain constant.

12b. Sample answer: See if $89.8 = 29.95 + 19.95(3 - 1)$ is a true sentence.

Pages 656–659 Exercises

13. Line a goes through $(-6, 0)$ and $(0, 3)$.

$m = \frac{3-0}{0-(-6)} = \frac{3}{6} = \frac{1}{2}$
$b = 3$
$y = mx + b$
$y = \frac{1}{2}x + 3$

14. Line b goes through (5, 0) and (0, 5).

$m = \frac{5-0}{0-5} = \frac{5}{-5} = -1$
$b = 5$
$y = mx + b$
$y = -x + 5$

15. Line c goes through $(0, -2)$ and (3, 0).

$m = \frac{-2-0}{0-3} = \frac{-2}{-3} = \frac{2}{3}$
$b = -2$
$y = mx + b$
$y = \frac{2}{3}x - 2$

16. $y - y_1 = m(x - x_1)$
$y - (-6) = 0.3(x - 0)$
$y + 6 = 0.3x$
$y = 0.3x - 6$

17. $y - y_1 = m(x - x_1)$
$y - 19 = 0.5(x - 40)$
$y - 19 = 0.5x - 20$
$y = 0.5x - 1$

18. $y - y_1 = m(x - x_1)$
$y - (-15) = \frac{1}{3}(x - (-3))$
$y + 15 = \frac{1}{3}x + 1$
$y = \frac{1}{3}x - 14$

19. $y - y_1 = m(x - x_1)$
$y - 4 = 1(x - 2)$
$y - 4 = x - 2$
$y = x + 2$

20. $y - y_1 = m(x - x_1)$
$y - 3 = -\frac{3}{4}(x - 24)$
$y - 3 = -\frac{3}{4}x + 18$
$y = -\frac{3}{4}x + 21$

21. $y - y_1 = m(x - x_1)$
$y - 8 = 0(x - 2.5)$
$y - 8 = 0$
$y = 8$

22. $y = mx + b$
$y = 3x - 4$

23. $y = mx + b$
$y = (0)x + 6$
$y = 6$

24. $(5, 0), (0, 3)$

$m = \frac{3 - 0}{0 - 5} = -\frac{3}{5}$

$y = mx + b$

$y = -\frac{3}{5}x + 3$

25. $m = \frac{-9 - (-3)}{-1 - 2} = \frac{-6}{-3} = 2$

$y - y_1 = m(x - x_1)$

$y - (-3) = 2(x - 2)$

$y + 3 = 2x - 4$

$y = 2x - 7$

26. $m = \frac{1}{2}, (4, -1)$

$y - y_1 = m(x - x_1)$

$y - (-1) = \frac{1}{2}(x - 4)$

$y + 1 = \frac{1}{2}x - 2$

$y = \frac{1}{2}x - 3$

27. $y - y_1 = m(x - x_1)$ **28.** $y - y_1 = m(x - x_1)$

$y - 17 = -0.1(x - 20)$ $\quad y - (-7) = 5(x - (-8))$

$y - 17 = -0.1x + 2$ $\quad\quad y + 7 = 5x + 40$

$y = -0.1x + 19$ $\quad\quad\quad y = 5x + 33$

29. $m = 5, (4, 0)$ **30.** $m =$ undefined $(4, -3)$

$y - y_1 = m(x - x_1)$ $\quad\quad x = 4$

$y - 0 = 5(x - 4)$

$y = 5x - 20$

31. $m = 0, (-5, 10)$ **32.** $(5, 0), (0, -1)$

$y - y_1 = m(x - x_1)$ $\quad m = \frac{-1 - 0}{0 - 5} = \frac{1}{5}$

$y - 10 = 0(x - (-5))$ $\quad\quad y = mx + b$

$y - 10 = 0$ $\quad\quad\quad\quad y = \frac{1}{5}x - 1$

$y = 10$

33. $m = \frac{-1 - (-1)}{-2 - 4} = 0$

$y - y_1 = m(x - x_1)$

$y - (-1) = 0(x - 4)$

$y + 1 = 0$

$y = -1$

34. $m = \frac{11 - 7}{-3 - 5} = \frac{4}{-8} = -\frac{1}{2}$

$y - y_1 = m(x - x_1)$

$y - 11 = -\frac{1}{2}(x - (-3))$

$y - 11 = -\frac{1}{2}x - \frac{3}{2}$

$y = -\frac{1}{2}x + \frac{19}{2}$

35. $C = 20t + 340$ **36.** $C = 0.25$

37. line a: $y - y_1 = m(x - x_1)$

$y - 3 = -\frac{3}{5}(x - 6)$

$y - 3 = -\frac{3}{5}x + \frac{18}{5}$

$y = -\frac{3}{5}x + \frac{33}{5}$

x-intercept:

$0 = -\frac{3}{5}x + \frac{33}{5}$

$-\frac{33}{5} = -\frac{3}{5}x$

$x = 11$

line b: $m = \frac{5}{3}, (11, 0)$

$y - y_1 = m(x - x_1)$

$y - 0 = \frac{5}{3}(x - 11)$

$y = \frac{5}{3}x - \frac{55}{3}$

38. $m = \frac{7 - (-3)}{11 - 5} = \frac{10}{6} = \frac{5}{3}$

slope of perpendicular $= -\frac{3}{5}$

midpoint $= \left(\frac{5 + 11}{2}, \frac{-3 + 7}{2}\right)$ or $(8, 2)$

$y - 2 = -\frac{3}{5}(x - 8)$

$y - 2 = -\frac{3}{5}x + \frac{24}{5}$

$y = -\frac{3}{5}x + \frac{34}{5}$

39. slope of $\overline{AB} = \frac{6 - 9}{4 - 5} = \frac{-3}{-1} = 3$

slope of $\overline{BC} = -\frac{1}{3}$

$y - y_1 = m(x - x_1)$

$y - 9 = -\frac{1}{3}(x - 5)$

$y - 9 = -\frac{1}{3}x + \frac{5}{3}$

$y = -\frac{1}{3}x + \frac{32}{3}$

40. slope of $\overline{DE} = \frac{-3 - (-4)}{2 - 0} = \frac{1}{2}$

slope of $\overline{EF} = \frac{-3 - 9}{2 - (-4)} = \frac{-12}{6} = -2$

Since $\frac{1}{2} \cdot -2 = -1$, $\overline{DE} \perp \overline{EF}$ and $\triangle DEF$ is a right triangle.

41a. $y = -\frac{1}{3}x - 1$ **41b.** See students' work.

42a. $x = 0.125y + 11$ **42b.** $y = x$

$8x = y + 88$

$y = 8x - 88$

42c. Sample answer: The graph of the inverse equation is a reflection about the line $y = x$. The line $y = x$ passes through the intersection of the two inverse equations.

43a. See students' work.

43b. The y-intercepts will all change.

44. $x =$ the minutes of use during the day.

$2x + 8 =$ the minutes of use in the evening.

$0.22x + 0.10(2x + 8) = 28.52$

$0.22x + 0.20x + 0.8 = 28.52$

$0.42x = 27.72$

$x = 66$ minutes

45a. $y = \frac{192}{6}x; \quad\quad y = \frac{576}{18}x$

$y = 32x; \quad\quad y = 38x$

45b. Sample answer: Ameritech ISDN service is always cheaper for the first customer.

46. Let $t =$ number of years since 1996; $c = 82t + 1200$.

47.

$6x - 4y = 3$

$-4y = -6x + 3$

$y = \frac{3}{2}x - \frac{3}{4}$

$m = \frac{3}{2}; b = -\frac{3}{4}$

48. $V = Bh = \pi r^2 h = \pi(5)^2(2) \approx 157.1 \text{ m}^3$

49. probability $= \dfrac{\text{area of targets}}{\text{area of board}} = \dfrac{40(8)^2}{(72)(96)} =$
$= \dfrac{2560}{6912} \approx 0.37$

50. $C(2, 6)$
$r = \sqrt{(2 - 2)^2 + (6 - 1)^2} = \sqrt{25} = 5$
$(x - 2)^2 + (y - 6)^2 = 5^2$
$(x - 2)^2 + (y - 6)^2 = 25$

51. Sample answer: A circle S that has all of its points in the interior of circle R would have no common tangents with circle R.

52. $\tan X = \dfrac{7}{100}$
$m\angle X = 4$
The angle of elevation is 4°.

53. $\dfrac{EG}{JL} = \dfrac{\text{perimeter of } \triangle EFG}{\text{perimeter of } \triangle JKL}$
$\dfrac{3.6}{2.4} = \dfrac{x}{6.8}$
$2.4x = 24.48$
$x = 10.2$

54. Given: $\overline{MN} \cong \overline{QP}$
$\quad\quad\quad \overline{MQ} \cong \overline{NP}$
Prove: $\overline{MN} \parallel \overline{QP}$

Proof:

Statements	Reasons
1. $\overline{MN} \cong \overline{QP}$ $\overline{MQ} \cong \overline{NP}$	1. Given
2. $\overline{QN} \cong \overline{QN}$	2. Congruence of segments is reflexive.
3. $\triangle MNQ \cong \triangle PQN$	3. SSS
4. $\angle MNQ \cong \angle PQN$	4. CPCTC
5. $\overline{MN} \parallel \overline{QP}$	5. If ⇹ and alt. int. ∠ are $\cong$, then the lines are $\parallel$.

55. $\dfrac{2a}{7c}$; $a \neq 0$, $b \neq 0$, $c \neq 0$

56a. Yes; if each girl used only one type of cosmetic, the total of the percents would be 100%.

56b. No; a circle graph compares parts of a whole. These statistics do not represent one whole where each person is represented in just one category.

Page 659 Mathematics and Society

1. Commercial fishermen, oil companies, geologists, and the Navy itself would all have a need for accurate maps of the ocean floors.

2. North-south orbit; in this polar orbit, all of Earth's surface would eventually pass beneath the satellite's path as Earth rotates on its axis.

3. Satellites can do this job faster and cheaper than ships. It has been estimated that it would cost several billion dollars and require a hundred years for a ship to completely map Earth's oceans. By contrast, the Geosat satellite cost $80 million and did the job in 18 months.

12-3 Integration: Algebra and Statistics
Scatter Plots and Slopes

Pages 662–663 Check for Understanding

1. Sample answer: A scatter plot can be useful in analyzing relationships between data.

2. Sample answer: Use the equation of the line determined by two of the points and check to see if the third was on the line; check to see if the slope determined by the points was the same.

3. Sample answer: Neither; both procedures may have flaws and may or may not be good.

4. slope of $\overleftrightarrow{BC} = \dfrac{18 - 9}{7 - 4} = \dfrac{9}{3} = 3$
slope of $\overleftrightarrow{CD} = \dfrac{-9 - 18}{-2 - 7} = \dfrac{-27}{-9} = 3$
collinear

5. slope of $\overleftrightarrow{RS} = \dfrac{-1 - 10}{-1 - (-6)} = \dfrac{-11}{5}$
slope of $\overleftrightarrow{ST} = \dfrac{-1 - 1}{-1 - 6} = \dfrac{-2}{-7} = \dfrac{2}{7}$
not collinear

6. False; the product of the slopes is not -1.

7. false; $4 \neq -10 + 8$

8. False; T is not on the line.   **9.** true

10a.

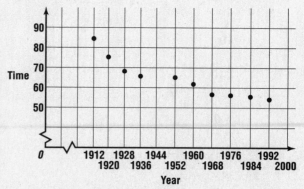

10b. Answers will vary. The points (1912, 84.6) and (1996, 54.10) produce slope of about -0.363.
$y - 84.6 = -0.363(x - 1912)$
$\quad\quad y = -0.363x + 778.656$.

10c. Using the equation $y = -0.363x + 778.656$,
$y = -0.363(2000) + 778.656 \approx 52.656$ seconds is the predicted time.

10d. Using the equation $y = -0.363x + 778.656$,
$y = -0.363(2020) + 778.656 \approx 45.369$ seconds is the predicted time . Answers will vary. Sample answer: Yes; The time would be about 9 seconds faster than the winning 1996 time. That was accomplished in the 8 years between 1912 and 1920. Sample answer: No; the times have stayed around 55 seconds for the last 20 years.

Pages 663–665 Exercises

11. slope of $\overleftrightarrow{AB} = \dfrac{4 - 0}{6 - 0} = \dfrac{4}{6} = \dfrac{2}{3}$
slope of $\overleftrightarrow{BC} = \dfrac{4 - (-2)}{6 - (-3)} = \dfrac{6}{9} = \dfrac{2}{3}$
collinear

12. slope of $\overleftrightarrow{DE} = \frac{-13 - 18}{19 - 14} = \frac{-31}{5}$

slope of $\overleftrightarrow{EF} = \frac{18 - 10}{14 - 10} = \frac{8}{4} = 2$

not collinear

13. slope of $\overleftrightarrow{MN} = \frac{10 - 10}{6 - 5} = 0$

slope of $\overleftrightarrow{NP} = \frac{-6 - 10}{5 - (-2)} = \frac{-16}{7}$

not collinear

14. slope of $\overleftrightarrow{GH} = \frac{12 - 0}{4 - 0} = \frac{12}{4} = 3$

slope of $\overleftrightarrow{HJ} = \frac{21 - 12}{7 - 4} = \frac{9}{3} = 3$

collinear

15. slope of $\overleftrightarrow{RS} = \frac{-18 - (-3)}{4 - 1} = \frac{-15}{3} = -5$

slope of $\overleftrightarrow{ST} = \frac{17 - (-18)}{-3 - 4} = \frac{35}{-7} = -5$

collinear

16. slope of $\overleftrightarrow{UV} = \frac{-9 - 3}{-2 - 4} = \frac{-12}{-6} = 2$

slope of $\overleftrightarrow{VW} = \frac{9 - (-9)}{-7 - (-2)} = \frac{18}{-5}$

not collinear

17a.

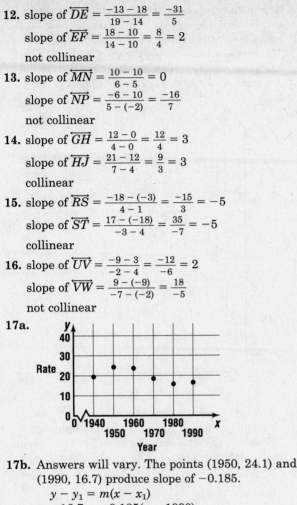

17b. Answers will vary. The points (1950, 24.1) and (1990, 16.7) produce slope of -0.185.

$y - y_1 = m(x - x_1)$

$y - 16.7 = -0.185(x - 1990)$

$y = -0.185x + 384.85$

17c. Sample answer: Each year the birth rate decreases by 0.185 so every ten years about 2 fewer children are born per 1000 people.

17d. Sample answer: $y = -0.185(2000) + 384.85 \approx 14.85$; It will be reliable only if the trend continues as it has in the past 50 years.

18. x-intercept:

$-x + 7y = 3$

$-x + 7(0) = 3$

$-x = 3$

$x = -3$

$m = \frac{8 - 0}{3 - (-3)} = \frac{8}{6} = \frac{4}{3}$

$y - y_1 = m(x - x_1)$

$y - 0 = \frac{4}{3}(x - (-3))$

$y = \frac{4}{3}x + 4$

slope of perpendicular $= \frac{-3}{4}$

$y - 8 = \frac{-3}{4}(x - 3)$

$y - 8 = \frac{-3}{4}x + \frac{9}{4}$

$y = \frac{-3}{4}x + \frac{41}{4}$

19. slope of $\overline{BC} = \frac{12 - (-4)}{6 - (-2)} = \frac{16}{8} = 2$

slope of altitude to $\overline{BC} = -\frac{1}{2}$

equation of line containing altitude to $\overline{BC}$:

$y - 18 = -\frac{1}{2}(x - 2)$

$y - 18 = -\frac{1}{2}x + 1$

$y = -\frac{1}{2}x + 19$

20. slope of $\overline{BC} = \frac{12 - (-4)}{6 - (-2)} = \frac{16}{8} = 2$

slope of perpendicular is $-\frac{1}{2}$

midpoint of $\overline{BC}$: $\left(\frac{-2 + 6}{2}, \frac{-4 + 12}{2}\right)$ or (2, 4)

equation of perpendicular bisector of $\overline{BC}$:

$y - 4 = -\frac{1}{2}(x - 2)$

$y - 4 = -\frac{1}{2}x + 1$

$y = -\frac{1}{2}x + 5$

21. midpoint of $\overline{BC}$: $\left(\frac{-2 + 6}{2}, \frac{-4 + 12}{2}\right)$ or (2, 4)

equation of median through A

slope $= \frac{4 - 18}{2 - 2} =$ undefined

$x = 2$

22. slope of $\overline{RS} = \frac{-4 - 2}{-2 - (-10)} = \frac{-6}{8} = \frac{-3}{4}$

slope of perpendicular to $\overline{RS} = \frac{4}{3}$

equation of altitude to $\overline{RS}$:

$y - 3 = \frac{4}{3}(x - (-3))$

$y - 3 = \frac{4}{3}x + 4$

$y = \frac{4}{3}x + 7$

midpoint of $\overline{RS} = \left(\frac{-10 + (-2)}{2}, \frac{2 + (-4)}{2}\right)$ or $(-6, -1)$

slope of median to $\overline{RS} = \frac{-1 - 3}{-6 - (-3)} = \frac{-4}{-3} = \frac{4}{3}$

equation of median to $\overline{RS}$:

$y - (-1) = \frac{4}{3}(x - (-6))$

$y + 1 = \frac{4}{3}x + 8$

$y = \frac{4}{3}x + 7$

$\triangle RST$ is an isosceles triangle; the equations of both lines are $y = \frac{4}{3}x + 7$; the altitude and median are the same in an isosceles triangle.

23a. midpoint of $\overline{AB} = \left(\frac{-4 + (-2)}{2}, \frac{-6 + 8}{2}\right)$ or $(-3, 1)$ D

midpoint of $\overline{AC} = \left(\frac{-4 + 6}{2}, \frac{-6 + 4}{2}\right)$ or $(1, -1)$ E

slope of $\overline{DE} = \frac{1 - (-1)}{-3 - 1} = \frac{2}{-4} = -\frac{1}{2}$

$y - (-1) = -\frac{1}{2}(x - 1)$

$y + 1 = -\frac{1}{2}x + \frac{1}{2}$

$y = -\frac{1}{2}x - \frac{1}{2}$

23b. The line through the midpoint of the two sides of a triangle is parallel to the third side and equal to half of the length of the third side. Point D will have coordinates $(-3, 1)$ and $E(1, -1)$. The slope of the line containing $\overline{BC}$ is $-\frac{1}{2}$. The slope of $\overline{DE} = -\frac{1}{2}$. The lines do not share a common point but have the same slope so they are parallel. $BC = \sqrt{(-2-6)^2 + (8-4)^2} = \sqrt{80}$ or $4\sqrt{5}$. $DE = \sqrt{(-3-1)^2 + (1-(-1))^2} = 2\sqrt{5}$. Thus, the length of the segment connecting the midpoints is one half the length of the third side.

23c. $(0,7)$ is a point on $\overline{BC}$ and on the perpendicular from $\overline{BC}$ to $D(-3, 1)$. The distance from $\overline{DE}$ to $\overline{BC}$ is $\sqrt{45} = 3\sqrt{5}$ or 6.71.

24.
$$y = 4x + 7$$
$$y = x - 2$$
$$x - 2 = 4x + 7$$
$$-3x = 9$$
$$x = -3$$

$$y = x - 2$$
$$= -3 - 2$$
$$= -5$$

$y = 4x + 7$	$y = x - 2$
$y = \frac{2}{5}x + 3\frac{2}{5}$	$y = \frac{2}{5}x + 3\frac{2}{5}$
$\frac{2}{5}x + 3\frac{2}{5} = 4x + 7$	$x - 2 = \frac{2}{5}x + 3\frac{2}{5}$
$2x + 17 = 20x + 35$	$5x - 10 = 2x + 17$
$-18x = 18$	$3x = 27$
$x = -1$	$x = 9$

$y = 4x + 7$	$y = x - 2$
$= 4(-1) + 7$	$= 9 - 2$
$= 3$	$= 7$

The coordinates of D, E, and F are $(-1, 3)$, $(9, 7)$ and $(-3, -5)$.

25. Sample answer:
$$(-3-3)^2 + (13-5)^2 = (-6)^2 + (8)^2$$
$$= 36 + 64$$
$$= 100;$$
$(9, -3)$, $(11, 11)$, $(11, -1)$ are some of the possible points.

26. Sample answer: Inside; when you substitute $(-2, 5)$ for (x, y), you get 25, which is less than 100.

27. $(3, 5)$, $(-3, 13)$
$$m = \frac{13 - 5}{-3 - 3} = \frac{8}{-6} = \frac{-4}{3}$$
slope of perpendicular $= \frac{3}{4}$
$$y - y_1 = m(x - x_1)$$
$$y - 13 = \frac{3}{4}(x - (-3))$$
$$y - 13 = \frac{3}{4}x + \frac{9}{4}$$
$$y = \frac{3}{4}x + \frac{61}{4} \text{ or } y = 0.75x + 15.25$$

28a. $D\left(\frac{4 + (-2) + 13}{3}, \frac{15 + 7 + 2}{3}\right) = D(5, 8)$

28b. slope of $\overline{AB} = \frac{15 - 7}{4 - (-2)} = \frac{8}{6} = \frac{4}{3}$
$$y - 8 = \frac{4}{3}(x - 5)$$
$$y = 8 + \frac{4}{3}(x - 5)$$

28c. Sample answer: The coordinates of D can be found by finding the average of the x-coordinates and the average of the y-coordinates.

29. Sample answer: One approach might be to use the vertical distance as a measure of error. A, B, and C are on the line $y = 2x + 10$, but D is not. The error in predicting y for $x = 6$ at point D is 14. The error in predicting using $y = 1.8x + 7.3$ for point A is 3.1, B is 2.7, C is 5.1 and D is 10.1 for a total of 21. The better line is $y = 2x + 10$.

30a.

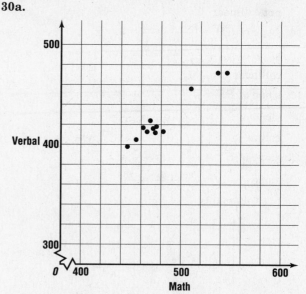

30b. Sample answer: It doesn't make any difference. It depends on which you would like to predict. However, the equation will be different depending on which you choose as the independent variable.

30c. Sample answer using $(482, 413)$ and $(469, 424)$
$$m = \frac{424 - 413}{469 - 482} = \frac{11}{-13} \approx -0.85$$
$$V - 424 = -0.85(M - 469)$$
$$V = -0.85M + 822.7$$

30d. $V = -0.85(463) + 822.7$
≈ 429

31a. See students' work.

31b. See students' work. Sample answer: $y = 0.264x + 4339.5$ where x is the original cost and y is the sum of the operating and fixed costs or the total cost of operating the car after it has been purchased.

32. false

33.

x-intercept	y-intercept
$3x - 6y = 18$	$3x - 6y = 18$
$3x - 6(0) = 18$	$3(0) - 6y = 18$
$3x = 18$	$-6y = 18$
$x = 6$	$y = -3$

slope
$$3x - 6y = 18$$
$$-6y = -3x + 18$$
$$y = \frac{1}{2}x - 3$$
$$m = \frac{1}{2}$$

34. $V = \frac{4}{3}\pi r^3$
$= \frac{4}{3}\pi(5)^3$
$\approx 523.6 \text{ in}^3$

35. False; this is only true for triangles.

36. $\frac{360}{12} = 30$ **37.** true

38. $(m + 3n)^2 = (m)^2 + 2(m)(3n) + (3n)^2$
$\qquad = m^2 + 6mn + 9n^2$

39.
$$\begin{array}{r} a + 1 - \dfrac{8}{2a+1} \\[4pt] 2a+1\overline{)2a^2 + 3a - 7} \\ \underline{2a^2 + a} \\ 2a - 7 \\ \underline{2a + 1} \\ -8 \end{array}$$

Page 665 Self Test

1. no x-intercept; y-intercept is 12; slope is 0

2. x-intercept:
$3x - 4y = 24$
$3x - 4(0) = 24$
$3x = 24$
$x = 8$

y-intercept:
$3x - 4y = 24$
$3(0) - 4y = 24$
$-4y = 24$
$y = -6$

slope
$3x - 4y = 24$
$-4y = -3x + 24$
$y = \frac{3}{4}x - 6$
$m = \frac{3}{4}$

3.

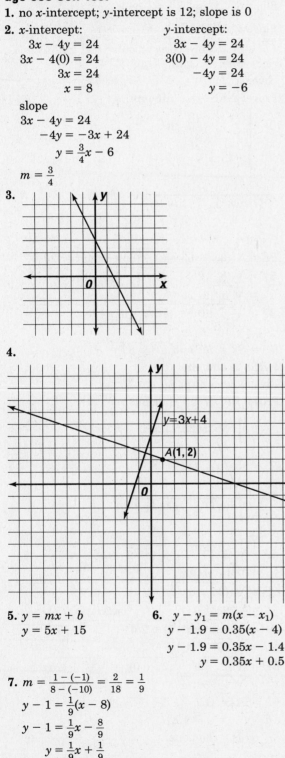

4.

5. $y = mx + b$
$y = 5x + 15$

6. $y - y_1 = m(x - x_1)$
$y - 1.9 = 0.35(x - 4)$
$y - 1.9 = 0.35x - 1.4$
$y = 0.35x + 0.5$

7. $m = \dfrac{1 - (-1)}{8 - (-10)} = \dfrac{2}{18} = \dfrac{1}{9}$
$y - 1 = \frac{1}{9}(x - 8)$
$y - 1 = \frac{1}{9}x - \frac{8}{9}$
$y = \frac{1}{9}x + \frac{1}{9}$

8. $w =$ the width
$\ell = 3w - 75$
$P = 2\ell + 2w$
$370 = 2(3w - 75) + 2w$
$520 = 8w$
$65 = w \qquad\qquad \ell = 3(65) - 75$
$w = 65$ yd $\qquad \ell = 120$ yd

9. slope of $\overleftrightarrow{AB} = \dfrac{2 - 0}{4 - 9} = \dfrac{2}{-5}$
slope of $\overleftrightarrow{BC} = \dfrac{2 - (-1)}{4 - 2} = \dfrac{3}{2}$
not collinear

10. slope of $\overleftrightarrow{LM} = \dfrac{4 - 3}{0 - 2} = \dfrac{1}{-2}$
slope of $\overleftrightarrow{MN} = \dfrac{6 - 3}{-4 - 2} = \dfrac{3}{-6} = \dfrac{-1}{2}$
collinear

12-4 Coordinate Proof

Page 666 Modeling Mathematics

a. See students' work.

b. Parallelogram; the opposite sides are congruent.

Pages 668–669 Check for Understanding

1. Sample answer: When the coordinates are 0, the computations are easier.

2. Answers will vary. Many problems that involve finding the midpoint of a segment are simpler if the sum of the coordinates has a factor of two because the result will not have any fractions.

3. Sample answer: Dashiki is correct. RJ is $a\sqrt{2}$; JK is $2a$. The sides do not have the same measures.

4. See students' work.

5. $D(0, 2c)$

6. $R(a, b)$, $S(-a, b)$

7a. Square; $AB = BC = CD = DA = a$, and $\angle DAB$ is a right angle.

7b. midpoint of $\overline{AC}$ is $\left(\dfrac{a + 0}{2}, \dfrac{a + 0}{2}\right)$ or $\left(\dfrac{a}{2}, \dfrac{a}{2}\right)$
midpoint of $\overline{DB}$ is $\left(\dfrac{0 + a}{2}, \dfrac{0 + a}{2}\right)$ or $\left(\dfrac{a}{2}, \dfrac{a}{2}\right)$
Both midpoints are $\left(\dfrac{a}{2}, \dfrac{a}{2}\right)$; $\overline{AC}$ and $\overline{BD}$ bisect each other.

7c. slope of $\overline{AC}$ is $\dfrac{a - 0}{a - 0}$ or $\dfrac{a}{a}$ or 1.

7d. slope of $\overline{DB}$ is $\dfrac{a - 0}{0 - a}$ or $\dfrac{a}{-a}$ or -1.

7e. $\overline{AC}$ and $\overline{BD}$ are perpendicular.

8. The coordinates of M, the midpoint of $\overline{BC}$, will be $\left(\dfrac{2c}{2}, \dfrac{2b}{2}\right) = (c, b)$. The distance from M to each of the vertices can be found using the distance formula.
$MB = \sqrt{(c - 0)^2 + (b - 2b)^2} = \sqrt{c^2 + b^2}$
$MC = \sqrt{(c - 2c)^2 + (b - 0)^2} = \sqrt{c^2 + b^2}$
$MA = \sqrt{(c - 0)^2 + (b - 0)^2} = \sqrt{c^2 + b^2}$
Thus, $MB = MC = MA$, and M is equidistant from the vertices.

9. Let M be the midpoint of $\overline{BC}$. The coordinates of M will be $\left(\frac{2c}{2}, \frac{2b}{2}\right) = (c, b)$.

$MA = \sqrt{(c - 0)^2 + (b - 0)^2} = \sqrt{c^2 + b^2}$
$BC = \sqrt{(2c - 0)^2 + (0 - 2b)^2} = 2\sqrt{c^2 + b^2}$
Since $2MA = BC$, $MA = \frac{1}{2}BC$.

10. Given: $\square ABCD$
Prove: $\overline{AC}$ and $\overline{DB}$ bisect each other.

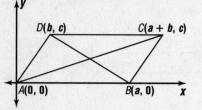

Proof:
Midpoint of $\overline{AC}$ is $\left(\frac{(a + b) + 0}{2}, \frac{c + 0}{2}\right)$ or $\left(\frac{a + b}{2}, \frac{c}{2}\right)$.

Midpoint of $\overline{BD}$ is $\left(\frac{a + b}{2}, \frac{0 + c}{2}\right)$ or $\left(\frac{a + b}{2}, \frac{c}{2}\right)$.

$\overline{AC}$ and $\overline{DB}$ bisect each other.

11. Morning Glory Pool = $(7, 32)$
Inspiration Point = $(30, 50)$
$d = \sqrt{(30 - 7)^2 + (50 - 32)^2}$
$ = \sqrt{23^2 + 18^2}$
$ = \sqrt{853}$
$ \approx 29.2$ miles

Pages 669–671 Exercises

12. $K(-b, 0)$, $N(0, c)$ 13. $D(-a, 0)$, $F(0, b)$
14. $Q(a, 0)$, $S(-b, c)$ 15. $B(a, 0)$, $D(a, d)$; $F(-b, c)$
16. Given: polygon $JFHK$
Prove: $JFHK$ is an isosceles trapezoid.

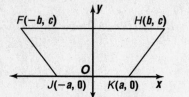

Proof:
$FJ = \sqrt{(-b - (-a))^2 + (c - 0)^2}$
$ = \sqrt{b^2 - 2ab + a^2 + c^2}$
$HK = \sqrt{(b - a)^2 + (c - 0)^2} = \sqrt{b^2 - 2ab + a^2 + c^2}$
Slope of $\overline{FH}$ is $\frac{c - c}{b - (-b)} = \frac{0}{2b}$ or 0.

Slope of $\overline{JK}$ is $\frac{0 - 0}{a - (-a)} = \frac{0}{2a}$ or 0.

$FJ = HK$ and $\overline{FH} \parallel \overline{JK}$
$FHKJ$ is an isosceles trapezoid.

17. Given: $\triangle LMN$
Prove: $\triangle LMN$ is a right triangle.

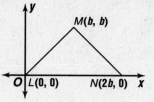

Proof:
Slope of $\overline{LM}$ is $\frac{b - 0}{b - 0} = \frac{b}{b}$ or 1.
Slope of $\overline{MN}$ is $\frac{b - 0}{b - 2b} = \frac{b}{-b}$ or -1.
$\overline{LM}$ and $\overline{MN}$ are perpendicular and $\triangle LMN$ is a right triangle.

18. Given: $\triangle RST$
Prove: $\triangle RST$ is equilateral.

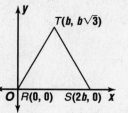

Proof:
$RS = \sqrt{(2b - 0)^2 + (0 - 0)^2} = \sqrt{4b^2}$ or $2b$
$ST = \sqrt{(b - 2b)^2 + (b\sqrt{3} - 0)^2} = \sqrt{3b^2 + b^2}$
$ = \sqrt{4b^2}$ or $2b$
$RT = \sqrt{(b - 0)^2 + (b\sqrt{3} - 0)^2} = \sqrt{3b^2 + b^2}$
$ = \sqrt{4b^2}$ or $2b$
$RS = ST = RT$ and $\overline{RS} \cong \overline{ST} \cong \overline{RT}$
$\triangle RST$ is equilateral.

19. Give: polygon $EFGH$
Prove: $EFGH$ is a rhombus.

Proof:
$EF = \sqrt{(a\sqrt{2} - 0)^2 + (a\sqrt{2} - 0)^2} = \sqrt{2a^2 + 2a^2}$
$ = \sqrt{4a^2}$ or $2a$
$FG = \sqrt{((2a + a\sqrt{2}) - a\sqrt{2})^2 + (a\sqrt{2} - a\sqrt{2})^2}$
$ = \sqrt{(2a)^2 + 0^2} = \sqrt{4a^2}$ or $2a$
$GH = \sqrt{((2a + a\sqrt{2}) - 2a)^2 + (a\sqrt{2} - 0)^2}$
$ = \sqrt{2a^2 + 2a^2} = \sqrt{4a^2}$ or $2a$
$EH = \sqrt{(0 - 0)^2 + (2a - 0)^2} = \sqrt{0^2 + (2a)^2}$
$ = \sqrt{4a^2}$ or $2a$
$EF = FG = GH = EH$
$\overline{EF} \cong \overline{FG} \cong \overline{GH} \cong \overline{EH}$
$EFGH$ is a rhombus.

20. Given: isosceles $\triangle ABC$ with $\overline{AC} \cong \overline{BC}$ and medians $\overline{AS}$ and $\overline{BR}$

Prove: $\overline{AS} \cong \overline{BR}$

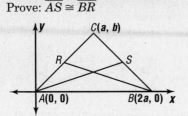

Proof:

Midpoint R of $\overline{AC}$ is $\left(\dfrac{a+0}{2}, \dfrac{b+0}{2}\right)$ or $\left(\dfrac{a}{2}, \dfrac{b}{2}\right)$.

Midpoint S of $\overline{BC}$ is $\left(\dfrac{2a+a}{2}, \dfrac{0+b}{2}\right)$ or $\left(\dfrac{3a}{2}, \dfrac{b}{2}\right)$.

$BR = \sqrt{\left(2a - \dfrac{a}{2}\right)^2 + \left(0 - \dfrac{b}{2}\right)^2} = \sqrt{\left(\dfrac{3a}{2}\right)^2 + \left(\dfrac{b}{2}\right)^2}$

$AS = \sqrt{\left(\dfrac{3a}{2} - 0\right)^2 + \left(\dfrac{b}{2} - 0\right)^2} = \sqrt{\left(\dfrac{3a}{2}\right)^2 + \left(\dfrac{b}{2}\right)^2}$

$BR = AS$ and $\overline{BR} \cong \overline{AS}$

21. Given: isosceles trapezoid $ABCD$ with $\overline{AD} \cong \overline{BC}$

Prove: $\overline{BD} \cong \overline{AC}$

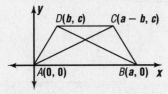

Proof:

$BD = \sqrt{(a-b)^2 + (0-c)^2} = \sqrt{(a-b)^2 + c^2}$

$AC = \sqrt{((a-b)-0)^2 + (c-0)^2} = \sqrt{(a-b)^2 + c^2}$

$BD = AC$ and $\overline{BD} \cong \overline{AC}$

22. Given: $\square ABCD$ and $\overline{AC} \cong \overline{BD}$

Prove: $\square ABCD$ is a rectangle.

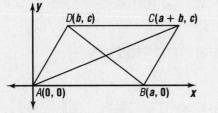

Proof:

$AC = \sqrt{(a+b-0)^2 + (c-0)^2}$

$BD = \sqrt{(b-a)^2 + (c-0)^2}$

Since $\overline{AC} \cong \overline{BD}$, $AC = BD$

$\sqrt{(a+b-0)^2 + (c-0)^2} = \sqrt{(b-a)^2 + (c-0)^2}$

$(a+b-0)^2 + (c-0)^2 = (b-a)^2 + (c-0)^2$

$(a+b)^2 + c^2 = (b-a)^2 + c^2$

$a^2 + 2ab + b^2 + c^2 = b^2 - 2ab + a^2 + c^2$

$2ab = -2ab$

$4ab = 0$

$a = 0$ or $b = 0$

Because A and B are different points, $a \neq 0$. Thus, $b = 0$. Slope of $\overline{AD}$ is undefined. Slope of $\overline{AB} = 0$. Thus, $\overline{AD} \perp \overline{AB}$. $\angle DAB$ is a right angle making $\square ABCD$ a rectangle.

23. Given: rectangle $RSTV$

Prove: $\overline{VS} \cong \overline{RT}$

Proof:

$VS = \sqrt{(0-a)^2 + (c-0)^2} = \sqrt{a^2 + c^2}$

$RT = \sqrt{(a-0)^2 + (c-0)^2} = \sqrt{a^2 + c^2}$

$VS = RT$ and $\overline{VS} \cong \overline{RT}$

24. Given: isosceles triangle ABC

$\overline{AC} \cong \overline{BC}$

R, S, and T are midpoints of their respective sides.

Prove: $\triangle RST$ is isosceles.

Proof:

Midpoint R is $\left(\dfrac{a+0}{2}, \dfrac{b+0}{2}\right)$ or $\left(\dfrac{a}{2}, \dfrac{b}{2}\right)$.

Midpoint S is $\left(\dfrac{a+2a}{2}, \dfrac{b+0}{2}\right)$ or $\left(\dfrac{3a}{2}, \dfrac{b}{2}\right)$.

Midpoint T is $\left(\dfrac{2a+0}{2}, \dfrac{0+0}{2}\right)$ or $(a, 0)$.

$RT = \sqrt{\left(\dfrac{a}{2} - a\right)^2 + \left(\dfrac{b}{2} - 0\right)^2} = \sqrt{\left(-\dfrac{a}{2}\right)^2 + \left(\dfrac{b}{2}\right)^2}$

$\quad = \sqrt{\left(\dfrac{a}{2}\right)^2 + \left(\dfrac{b}{2}\right)^2}$

$ST = \sqrt{\left(\dfrac{3a}{2} - a\right)^2 + \left(\dfrac{b}{2} - 0\right)^2} = \sqrt{\left(\dfrac{a}{2}\right)^2 + \left(\dfrac{b}{2}\right)^2}$

$RT = ST$ and $\overline{RT} \cong \overline{ST}$ and $\triangle RST$ is isosceles.

25. Given: quadrilateral *VRST*
  A, B, C, and *D* are midpoints of their respective sides.
Prove: $\overline{AC}$ and $\overline{DB}$ bisect each other.

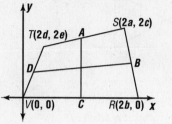

Proof:

Midpoint *A* of $\overline{TS}$ is $\left(\dfrac{2d+2a}{2}, \dfrac{2e+2c}{2}\right)$ or $(d+a, e+c)$.

Midpoint *B* of $\overline{SR}$ is $\left(\dfrac{2a+2b}{2}, \dfrac{2c+0}{2}\right)$ or $(a+b, c)$.

Midpoint *C* of $\overline{VR}$ is $\left(\dfrac{0+2b}{2}, \dfrac{0+0}{2}\right)$ or $(b, 0)$.

Midpoint *D* of $\overline{TV}$ is $\left(\dfrac{0+2d}{2}, \dfrac{0+2e}{2}\right)$ or (d, e).

Midpoint of $\overline{AC}$ is $\left(\dfrac{d+a+b}{2}, \dfrac{e+c+0}{2}\right)$ or $\left(\dfrac{a+b+d}{2}, \dfrac{c+e}{2}\right)$.

Midpoint of $\overline{DB}$ is $\left(\dfrac{d+a+b}{2}, \dfrac{e+c}{2}\right)$ or $\left(\dfrac{a+b+d}{2}, \dfrac{c+e}{2}\right)$.

$\overline{AC}$ and $\overline{DB}$ bisect each other.

26. Given: $\square ABCD$
  $\overline{BD} \perp \overline{AC}$
Prove: $\square ABCD$ is a rhombus.

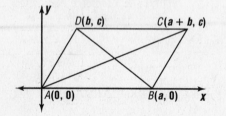

Proof:

Slope of $\overline{BD}$ is $\dfrac{c-0}{b-a}$ or $\dfrac{c}{b-a}$.

Slope of $\overline{AC}$ is $\dfrac{c-0}{a+b-0}$ or $\dfrac{c}{a+b}$.

But $\overline{BD} \perp \overline{AC}$ and $\dfrac{c}{b-a} = -\dfrac{a+b}{c}$ or $\dfrac{a+b}{-c}$.

By cross products, $-c^2 = b^2 - a^2$.

$a^2 = b^2 + c^2$ and $\sqrt{a^2} = \sqrt{b^2 + c^2}$

$AD = \sqrt{(b-0)^2 + (c-0)^2} = \sqrt{b^2 + c^2}$

$DC = \sqrt{((a+b)-b)^2 + (c-c)^2} = \sqrt{a^2}$

$BC = \sqrt{((a+b)-a)^2 + (c-0)^2} = \sqrt{b^2 + c^2}$

$AB = \sqrt{(a-0)^2 + (0-0)^2} = \sqrt{a^2}$

$AD = DC = BC = AB$

$\overline{AD} \cong \overline{DC} \cong \overline{BC} \cong \overline{AB}$

ABCD is a rhombus.

27. Given: isosceles trapezoid *ABCD*
  $\overline{AD} \cong \overline{BC}$
  Q, R, S, and *T* are midpoints of their respective sides.
Prove: *QRST* is a rhombus.

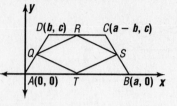

Proof:

$QR = \sqrt{\left(\dfrac{b}{2} - \dfrac{a}{2}\right)^2 + \left(\dfrac{c}{2} - c\right)^2} = \dfrac{\sqrt{b^2 - 2ab + a^2 + c^2}}{2}$

$TS = \sqrt{\left(\dfrac{2a-b}{2} - \dfrac{a}{2}\right)^2 + \left(\dfrac{c}{2} - 0\right)^2}$

$= \dfrac{\sqrt{b^2 - 2ab + a^2 + c^2}}{2}$

$QT = \sqrt{\left(\dfrac{b}{2} - \dfrac{a}{2}\right)^2 + \left(\dfrac{c}{2} - 0\right)^2}$

$= \dfrac{\sqrt{b^2 - 2ab + a^2 + c^2}}{2}$

$RS = \sqrt{\left(\dfrac{a}{2} - \dfrac{2a-b}{2}\right)^2 + \left(c - \dfrac{c}{2}\right)^2}$

$= \dfrac{\sqrt{b^2 - 2ab + a^2 + c^2}}{2}$

$QR = TS = QT = RS$, so $\overline{QR} \cong \overline{TS} \cong \overline{QT} \cong \overline{RS}$ and *QRST* is a rhombus.

28. Given: $\triangle ABC$
  S is midpoint of $\overline{AC}$.
  T is midpoint of $\overline{BC}$.
Prove: $\overline{ST} \parallel \overline{AB}$

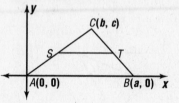

Proof:

Midpoint *S* is $\left(\dfrac{b+0}{2}, \dfrac{c+0}{2}\right)$ or $\left(\dfrac{b}{2}, \dfrac{c}{2}\right)$.

Midpoint *T* is $\left(\dfrac{a+b}{2}, \dfrac{0+c}{2}\right)$ or $\left(\dfrac{a+b}{2}, \dfrac{c}{2}\right)$.

Slope of $\overline{ST} = \dfrac{\frac{c}{2} - \frac{c}{2}}{\frac{a+b}{2} - \frac{b}{2}} = \dfrac{0}{a}$ or 0.

Slope of $\overline{AB} = \dfrac{0-0}{a-0} = \dfrac{0}{a}$ or 0. $ST \parallel AB$.

29. Given: $\triangle ABC$
  S is midpoint of $\overline{AC}$.
  T is midpoint of $\overline{BC}$.
  Prove: $ST = \frac{1}{2}AB$

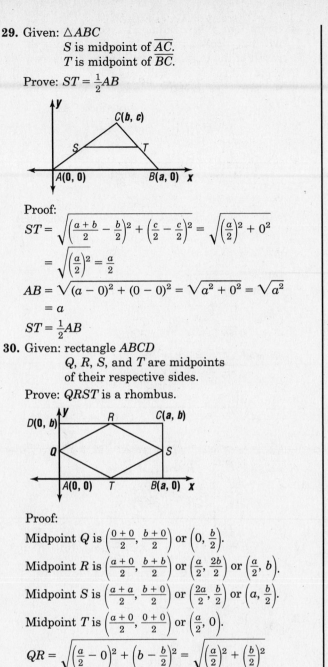

Proof:
$$ST = \sqrt{\left(\frac{a+b}{2} - \frac{b}{2}\right)^2 + \left(\frac{c}{2} - \frac{c}{2}\right)^2} = \sqrt{\left(\frac{a}{2}\right)^2 + 0^2}$$
$$= \sqrt{\left(\frac{a}{2}\right)^2} = \frac{a}{2}$$
$$AB = \sqrt{(a-0)^2 + (0-0)^2} = \sqrt{a^2 + 0^2} = \sqrt{a^2}$$
$$= a$$
$$ST = \frac{1}{2}AB$$

30. Given: rectangle $ABCD$
  Q, R, S, and T are midpoints of their respective sides.
  Prove: $QRST$ is a rhombus.

Proof:
Midpoint Q is $\left(\frac{0+0}{2}, \frac{b+0}{2}\right)$ or $\left(0, \frac{b}{2}\right)$.

Midpoint R is $\left(\frac{a+0}{2}, \frac{b+b}{2}\right)$ or $\left(\frac{a}{2}, \frac{2b}{2}\right)$ or $\left(\frac{a}{2}, b\right)$.

Midpoint S is $\left(\frac{a+a}{2}, \frac{b+0}{2}\right)$ or $\left(\frac{2a}{2}, \frac{b}{2}\right)$ or $\left(a, \frac{b}{2}\right)$.

Midpoint T is $\left(\frac{a+0}{2}, \frac{0+0}{2}\right)$ or $\left(\frac{a}{2}, 0\right)$.

$$QR = \sqrt{\left(\frac{a}{2} - 0\right)^2 + \left(b - \frac{b}{2}\right)^2} = \sqrt{\left(\frac{a}{2}\right)^2 + \left(\frac{b}{2}\right)^2}$$
$$RS = \sqrt{\left(a - \frac{a}{2}\right)^2 + \left(\frac{b}{2} - b\right)^2} = \sqrt{\left(\frac{a}{2}\right)^2 + \left(-\frac{b}{2}\right)^2}$$
$$= \sqrt{\left(\frac{a}{2}\right)^2 + \left(\frac{b}{2}\right)^2}$$
$$ST = \sqrt{\left(a - \frac{a}{2}\right)^2 + \left(\frac{b}{2} - 0\right)^2} = \sqrt{\left(\frac{a}{2}\right)^2 + \left(\frac{b}{2}\right)^2}$$
$$QT = \sqrt{\left(\frac{a}{2} - 0\right)^2 + \left(0 - \frac{b}{2}\right)^2} = \sqrt{\left(\frac{a}{2}\right)^2 + \left(-\frac{b}{2}\right)^2}$$
$$= \sqrt{\left(\frac{a}{2}\right)^2 + \left(\frac{b}{2}\right)^2}$$

$QR = RS = ST = QT$
$\overline{QR} \cong \overline{RS} \cong \overline{ST} \cong \overline{QT}$
$QRST$ is a rhombus.

31a. Answers will vary. Two possible coordinates for C are $(a, 0)$ or $(0, b)$.

31b. Answers will vary. Two possible coordinates for C are $(2a, 0)$ or $(0, 2b)$.

31c. Answers will vary. Two possible solutions are $C(a - b, a + b)$, $D(-b, a)$, and $C(a + b, b - a)$, $D(b, -a)$.

32. Sample answer: The line would be a vertical line that passes through $(22, 0)$. The equation for that line is $x = 22$.

33. The coordinates of one plane can be represented by $(4, 5)$ and the other plane by $(3, -8)$.
$$d = \sqrt{(4 - (-3))^2 + (5 - (-8))^2}$$
$$= \sqrt{7^2 + 13^2}$$
$$= \sqrt{49 + 169}$$
$$= \sqrt{218} \approx 14.8 \text{ km}$$

34a. $D\left(\frac{0+a+b}{3}, \frac{0+0+c}{3}\right) = D\left(\frac{a+b}{3}, \frac{c}{3}\right)$

34b. Label the midpoints of $\overline{AB}$, $\overline{BC}$, and $\overline{CA}$ as E, F, and G respectively. Then the coordinates of E, F, and G are $\left(\frac{a}{2}, 0\right)$, $\left(\frac{a+b}{2}, \frac{c}{2}\right)$, and $\left(\frac{b}{2}, \frac{c}{2}\right)$ respectively. slope of $\overline{AF} = \frac{c}{a+b}$ and slope of $\overline{AD} = \frac{c}{a+b}$ so D is on $\overline{AF}$; slope of $\overline{BG} = \frac{c}{b-2a}$ and slope of $\overline{BD} = \frac{c}{b-2a}$ so D is on $\overline{BG}$; slope of $\overline{CE} = \frac{2c}{2b-a}$ and slope of $\overline{CD} = \frac{2c}{2b-a}$ so D is on $\overline{AF}$. Since D is on $\overline{AF}$, $\overline{BG}$, and $\overline{CE}$, it is the intersection point of the three lines.

35a.

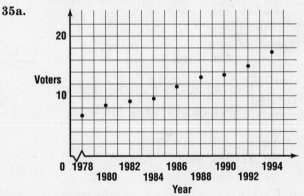

35b. Sample answer:
$$m = \frac{17.5 - 6.8}{1994 - 1978} = 0.66875$$
$$y - 17.5 = 0.66875(x - 1994)$$
$$y = 0.66875x - 1315.9875$$

35c. Sample answer:
$$y = 0.66875(2010) - 1315.9875 \approx 28.2 \text{ million}$$

36. midpoint of $\overline{TU}$ is $\left(\frac{1+7}{2}, \frac{5+1}{2}\right)$ or $(4, 3)$

slope of $\overline{VX}$ is $\frac{2-3}{-2-4}$ or $\frac{-1}{-6}$ or $\frac{1}{6}$
$$y - y_1 = m(x - x_1)$$
$$y - 3 = \frac{1}{6}(x - 4)$$
$$y - 3 = \frac{1}{6}x - \frac{2}{3}$$
$$y = \frac{1}{6}x + \frac{7}{3}$$

37. $\sin 40° = \frac{h}{12}$

$12 \sin 40° = h$

$7.713 \approx h$

Let $x = \frac{1}{2}$ length of a diagonal.

$\cos 40° = \frac{x}{12}$

$12 \cos 40° = x$

$9.193 \approx x$

length of diagonal = 2(9.193) or 18.386

$B = \frac{1}{2}d_1 d_2 \approx \frac{1}{2}(18.386)^2 \approx 169.0225$

$V = \frac{1}{3}Bh \approx \frac{1}{3}(169.0225)(7.713) \approx 435$ units^3

38. $d_1 = s\sqrt{2}$

$18.386 \approx s\sqrt{2}$

$13 \approx s$

$\ell^2 + \left[\frac{1}{2}(13)\right]^2 = 12^2$

$\ell^2 + 42.25 = 144$

$\ell^2 = 101.75$

$\ell \approx 10.087$

$L = \frac{1}{2}P\ell$

$\approx \frac{1}{2}[4(13)](10.087)$

≈ 262 units^2

$T = L + B \approx 262 + 13^2 \approx 431$ units^2

39. $C = 2\pi r - 2\pi(8) = 16\pi \approx 50.3$ inches

40. $d_1 = 2\left[\frac{1}{2}(25)\right] = 25$ units

$d_2 = 2\left[\sqrt{3}\left(\frac{1}{2}\right)(25)\right] \approx 43.3$ units

41. yes; binomial   **42.** prime

12-5A	**Modeling Mathematics**
	Representing Motion

Page 672

1. See students' work.   **2.** rectangle

3. It is a diagonal.

4. It makes the boat travel downstream as it travels across the river.

12-5	**Vectors**

Pages 676–677 Check for Understanding

1. Sample answer: Parallel vectors have the same direction but not necessarily the same magnitude. Equal vectors have both the same direction and same magnitude.

2. Sample answer: Two vectors can have the same slope and are not considered parallel when they are going in opposite directions.

3a. Sample answer: **3b.** Sample answer:

4. Sample answer: by adding the coordinates, by writing as column matrices, and by finding the result of the parallelogram created by the two vectors; Preferences will vary.

5. See students' work.

$|\overrightarrow{AB}| = \sqrt{2^2 + 11^2}$ direction of $\overrightarrow{AB}$:

$= \sqrt{125}$ $\tan X = \frac{11}{2}$

≈ 11.2 $X \approx 80°$

6. See students' work.

$|\overrightarrow{RS}| = \sqrt{(-1-4)^2 + (3-8)^2}$

$= \sqrt{50}$

≈ 7.1

direction of $\overrightarrow{RS}$

$\tan X = \frac{8-3}{4-(-1)}$

$\tan X = 1$

$X = 45°$

7. $\overrightarrow{AB} \parallel \overrightarrow{KM} \parallel \overrightarrow{TR}$

slope of $\overrightarrow{AB}$ is $\frac{2-(-2)}{1-(-1)}$ or $\frac{4}{2}$ or 2

slope of $\overrightarrow{KM}$ is $\frac{8-4}{5-3}$ or $\frac{4}{2}$ or 2

slope of $\overrightarrow{TR}$ is $\frac{8-(-4)}{-6-(-12)}$ or $\frac{12}{6}$ or 2

8. $\overrightarrow{AB} = \overrightarrow{KM}$

$\overrightarrow{AB} = \sqrt{(2-(-2))^2 + (1-(-1))^2} = \sqrt{4^2 + 2^2}$

$= \sqrt{20}$

$\overrightarrow{KM} = \sqrt{(8-4)^2 + (5-3)^2} = \sqrt{4^2 + 2^2} = \sqrt{20}$

9. $\overrightarrow{TR}$ and $\overrightarrow{AB}$ or $\overrightarrow{TR}$ and $\overrightarrow{KM}$

10. $\vec{u} + 2\vec{v} = (-4, 10) + (2 \cdot 0, 2 \cdot 5)$

$= (-4, 10) + (0, 10)$

$= (-4 + 0, 10 + 10)$

$= (-4, 20)$

11. $3\vec{w} - (\vec{u} + \vec{v}) = (3 \times 6, 3 \times 2) - ((-4, 10) + (0, 5))$

$= (18, 6) - (-4, 15)$

$= (18 - (-4), 6 - 15)$

$= (22, -9)$

12. $\begin{bmatrix} 1 \\ 3 \end{bmatrix} + \begin{bmatrix} -5 \\ 2 \end{bmatrix} = \begin{bmatrix} 1-5 \\ 3+2 \end{bmatrix}$

$= \begin{bmatrix} -4 \\ 5 \end{bmatrix}$

13. $\begin{bmatrix} 2 \\ -6 \end{bmatrix} + \begin{bmatrix} 0 \\ 3 \end{bmatrix} - \begin{bmatrix} -4 \\ -1 \end{bmatrix} = \begin{bmatrix} 2+0-(-4) \\ -6+3-(-1) \end{bmatrix}$

$= \begin{bmatrix} 6 \\ -2 \end{bmatrix}$

14.   **15.**

16a. $r \cdot t = d$

$t = \frac{d}{r} = \frac{1 \text{ km}}{4.03 \text{ km}}$ per hr = 0.25 hour or 15 minutes

16b. $\tan 29.7° = \frac{x}{1 \text{ km}}$

$x = \tan 29.7°$

≈ 0.57 km

She will land at a point 0.57 kilometer downstream from her starting point.

17. See students' work.
$$|\overrightarrow{AB}| = \sqrt{1^2 + 4^2} = \sqrt{17} \approx 4.1 \text{ units}$$
direction of $\overrightarrow{AB}$: $\tan X = \frac{4}{1}$
$$X \approx 76°$$

18. See students' work.
$$|\overrightarrow{V}| = \sqrt{(4)^2 + (-9)^2} = \sqrt{97} \approx 9.8 \text{ units}$$
direction of $\overrightarrow{V}$: $\tan X = \frac{-9}{4}$
$$X \approx -66°$$

19. See students' work.
$$|\overrightarrow{AB}| = \sqrt{(22-2)^2 + (7-4)^2}$$
$$= \sqrt{(20)^2 + (3)^2}$$
$$= \sqrt{409} \approx 20.2 \text{ units}$$
direction of $\overrightarrow{AB}$: $\tan X = \frac{22-2}{7-4}$
$$\tan X = \frac{20}{3}$$
$$X \approx 81°$$

20. See students' work.
$$|\overrightarrow{CD}| = \sqrt{(40-0)^2 + (0-(-20))^2}$$
$$= \sqrt{40^2 + 20^2}$$
$$= \sqrt{2000} \approx 44.7 \text{ units}$$
directio n of $\overrightarrow{CD} = \tan X = \frac{-20-0}{0-40}$
$$\tan X = \frac{1}{2}$$
$$X \approx 27°$$

21. See students' work.
$$|\overrightarrow{EF}| = \sqrt{(-6-0)^2 + (0-6)^2}$$
$$= \sqrt{(-6)^2 + (-6)^2} = \sqrt{72} \approx 8.5 \text{ units}$$
direction of $\overrightarrow{EF}$: $\tan X = \frac{0-6}{-6-0}$
$$\tan X = 1$$
$$X = -45°$$

22. See students' work.
$$|\overrightarrow{GH}| = \sqrt{(12-19)^2 + (-4-1)^2}$$
$$= \sqrt{(-7)^2 + (-5)^2} = \sqrt{74} \approx 8.6 \text{ units}$$
direction of $\overrightarrow{GH}$: $\tan X = \frac{-4-1}{12-19}$
$$\tan X = \frac{-5}{7}$$
$$X \approx 36°$$

23. $25 + 10 = 35$ units

24. $|\overrightarrow{AC}| = \sqrt{25^2 + 10^2} = \sqrt{725} \approx 26.9$ units

25. direction of $\overrightarrow{AC}$: $\tan X = \frac{25}{10}$
$$X \approx -68°$$

26. $\begin{bmatrix} 9 \\ 21 \end{bmatrix} + \begin{bmatrix} 8 \\ -2 \end{bmatrix} = \begin{bmatrix} 9 + 8 \\ 21 + (-2) \end{bmatrix}$
$$= \begin{bmatrix} 17 \\ 19 \end{bmatrix}$$

27. $\begin{bmatrix} 2 \\ 4 \end{bmatrix} + \begin{bmatrix} -2 \\ -3 \end{bmatrix} = \begin{bmatrix} 2 + (-2) \\ 4 + (-3) \end{bmatrix}$
$$= \begin{bmatrix} 0 \\ 1 \end{bmatrix}$$

28. $\begin{bmatrix} -5 \\ -8 \end{bmatrix} + \begin{bmatrix} 6 \\ -1 \end{bmatrix} = \begin{bmatrix} -5 + 6 \\ -8 + (-1) \end{bmatrix}$
$$= \begin{bmatrix} 1 \\ -9 \end{bmatrix}$$

29. $\begin{bmatrix} 12 \\ 4 \end{bmatrix} - \begin{bmatrix} 4 \\ -1 \end{bmatrix} = \begin{bmatrix} 12 - 4 \\ 4 - (-1) \end{bmatrix}$
$$= \begin{bmatrix} 8 \\ 5 \end{bmatrix}$$

30. $\begin{bmatrix} 5 \\ 4 \end{bmatrix} - \begin{bmatrix} 7 \\ -3 \end{bmatrix} = \begin{bmatrix} 5 - 7 \\ 4 - (-3) \end{bmatrix}$
$$= \begin{bmatrix} -2 \\ 7 \end{bmatrix}$$

31. $\begin{bmatrix} 3 \\ -3 \end{bmatrix} + \begin{bmatrix} -3 \\ 4 \end{bmatrix} - \begin{bmatrix} 2 \\ -5 \end{bmatrix} = \begin{bmatrix} 3 + (-3) - 2 \\ -3 + 4 - (-5) \end{bmatrix}$
$$= \begin{bmatrix} -2 \\ 6 \end{bmatrix}$$

32. $\overrightarrow{AB} \parallel \overrightarrow{CD} \parallel \overrightarrow{HG}$; $\overrightarrow{EF} \parallel \overrightarrow{HI}$ since they have the same direction.

33. $\overrightarrow{AB} = \overrightarrow{HG}$; $\overrightarrow{EF} = \overrightarrow{HI}$ since they have the same direction and magnitude.

34. $|\overrightarrow{AB}| = |\overrightarrow{EF}| = |\overrightarrow{HG}| = |\overrightarrow{HI}|$

35. $\overrightarrow{AD}$ **36.** $\overrightarrow{BD}$ **37.** $\overrightarrow{BE}$ **38.** $\overrightarrow{EC}$

39. $\vec{u} + 2\vec{v} = (5, 8) + (2 \cdot 3, 2 \cdot 1)$
$$= (5, 8) + (6, 2)$$
$$= (5 + 6, 8 + 2)$$
$$= (11, 10)$$

40. $\vec{u} + 2\vec{w} = \vec{v}$
$$\vec{w} = \frac{1}{2}(\vec{v} - \vec{u})$$
$$\vec{w} = \frac{1}{2}((3, 1) - (5, 8))$$
$$= \frac{1}{2}(3 - 5, 1 - 8)$$
$$= \frac{1}{2}(-2, -7)$$
$$= \left(\frac{1}{2} \cdot -2, \frac{1}{2} \cdot -7\right)$$
$$= -1, -3.5)$$

41. $\vec{w} = 4\vec{u}$
$$= (4 \cdot 5, 4 \cdot 8)$$
$$= (20, 32)$$

42. $\vec{w} = 2\vec{u} + 3\vec{u}$
$$= (2 \cdot 5, 2 \cdot 8) + (3 \cdot 5, 3 \cdot 8)$$
$$= (10, 16) + (15, 24)$$
$$= (10 + 15, 16 + 24)$$
$$= (25, 40)$$

43. $\vec{w} = \vec{v} + \vec{u}$
$$= (3, 1) + (5, 8)$$
$$= (3 + 5, 1 + 8)$$
$$= (8, 9)$$

44. $3\vec{v} - \vec{w} = \vec{u}$
$$\vec{w} = 3\vec{v} - \vec{u}$$
$$= (3 \cdot 3, 3 \cdot 1) - (5, 8)$$
$$= (9, 3) - (5, 8)$$
$$= (9 - 5, 3 - 8)$$
$$= (4, -5)$$

45. 1. Definition of vector addition
2. Definition of vector addition
3. Given
4. Substitution Property (=)
5. Distributive Property (=)
6. Substitution Property (=)
7. Multiplication Property (=)

46. Let $a = (a_1, a_2)$ and $b = (b_1, b_2)$ and $c = (c_1, c_2)$.
$(a + b) + c = [(a_1, a_2) + (b_1, b_2)] + (c_1, c_2)$
$= (a_1 + b_1, a_2 + b_2) + (c_1, c_2)$ Vector addition
$= ((a_1 + b_1) + c_1, (a_2 + b_2) + c_2)$ Vector addition
$= ((a_1 + (b_1 + c_1), a_2 + (b_2 + c_2))$ Assoc. Prop. (=)
$= (a_1 + a_2), + ((b_1 + b_2), (c_1 + c_2))$
$= a + (b + c)$

47. $\begin{bmatrix} ac \\ ab \end{bmatrix}$; the process has to model the way scalar multiplication of vectors written as ordered pairs is written.

48. slope of $\overrightarrow{RS} = \frac{12 - 2}{4 - 9} = \frac{10}{-5}$ or -2
slope of $\overrightarrow{TM} = \frac{8 - 7}{x - 2} = -2$
$\frac{1}{x - 2} = -2$
$-2(x - 2) = 1$
$-2x + 4 = 1$
$-2x = -3$
$x = 1.5$

49. A line through the origin will have equation $y = cx$ for some constant c. If (k, m) lies on the line, then $m = ck$. If (r, s) is a scalar multiple of (k, m), then $(r, s) = c(k, m) = (ck, cm)$. Substituting into $y = cx$, $cm = c(ck)$. Dividing by c, $m = ck$ which is true because (k, m) lies on the line. Therefore, (r, s) lies on the line also.

50. $\vec{a} \cdot \vec{b} = 3(-6) + (-5)(10)$
$= -18 + (-50)$
$= -68$
$\vec{a}$ and $\vec{b}$ are not perpendicular.

51. $\vec{a} \cdot \vec{b} = 3(5) + (-5)(3)$
$= 15 + (-15)$
$= 0$
$\vec{a} \perp \vec{b}$

52. $\vec{a} \cdot \vec{b} = 3(-5) + (-5)(3)$
$= -15 + (-15)$
$= -30$
$\vec{a}$ and $\vec{b}$ are not perpendicular.

53a. They have the same magnitude but opposite directions.

53b. It is a hexagon.

54. direction: $\tan X = \frac{40}{75}$
$X \approx 28°$
distance $= \sqrt{40^2 + 75^2}$
$= \sqrt{7225}$
$= 85$ miles

55. speed: $\sqrt{20^2 + 5^2} = \sqrt{425} \approx 20.62$ mph
direction: $\tan X = \frac{20}{5}$
$X \approx 76°$

56.

$m\angle DAB = 30$; $m\angle ABC = 150$
Use Law of Cosines to find AC.
$a^2 = b^2 + c^2 - 2bc \cos A$
$a^2 = 20^2 + 40^2 - 2(20)(40)\cos 150°$
$a^2 \approx 3385.64$
$a \approx 58.19$
$AC \approx 58.19$ pounds of force.
Let $x = m\angle CAB$.
$\frac{\sin A}{a} = \frac{\sin B}{b}$
$\frac{\sin 150°}{58.19} = \frac{\sin X°}{20}$
$\frac{20(\sin 150°)}{58.19} = \sin X°$
$10 \approx X$
direction of resultant $= 30° + 10°$ or $40°$

57. magnitude $= \sqrt{72^2 + 45^2}$
$= \sqrt{7209}$
≈ 84.9 newtons
direction: $\tan x = \frac{45}{72}$
$x \approx 32°$ northeast

58. Consider $\triangle ABC$ with vertices at $A(a, 0)$, $B(0, a)$, and $C\left(\frac{a}{2}, \frac{a}{2}\right)$. Midpoint M is $\left(\frac{0 + a}{2}, \frac{a + 0}{2}\right) = \left(\frac{a}{2}, \frac{a}{2}\right)$.
Slope of $\overline{AB}$ is $\frac{0 - a}{a - 0} = \frac{-a}{a} \neq -1$. or
Slope of $\overline{CM}$ is $\frac{\frac{a}{2} - 0}{\frac{a}{2} - 0} = \frac{\frac{a}{2}}{\frac{a}{2}} \neq 1$. or
Since $-1 \cdot 1 = -1$, $\overline{CM}$ is perpendicular to $\overline{AB}$.

59a. Sample answer: Using points $(1195, 229)$ and $(5821, 1134)$ the equation is $y = 0.2x - 4.8$.

59b. $y = 0.1956(2281) - 4.8$
$= 441$ thousand

60. $\ell^2 = 12^2 - 8^2$
$\ell^2 = 80$
$\ell \approx 8.944$
$h^2 = 8.944^2 - 8^2$
$h^2 = 16$
$h = 4$
$V = \frac{1}{3}Bh$
$= \frac{1}{3}(16)^2(4)$
≈ 341.3 units^3

61. $A = \frac{1}{2}bh$
$88 = \frac{1}{2}b(8)$
$88 = 4b$
$b = 22$ m

62. $\frac{180(36 - 2)}{36} = 170°$

63. $m\angle NMP = \frac{1}{2}m\widehat{NP}$
$62 = \frac{1}{2}m\widehat{NP}$
$124 = m\widehat{NP}$

64. true   **65.** $P = 35 = 72$
$s = 24$ $h = \frac{1}{2}s\sqrt{3} = 12\sqrt{3} \approx 20.8$in.

66. 16   factors: 1, 2, 4, 8, 16

67. $b_1 = \sqrt{(7-4)^2 + (3-0)^2}$
$= \sqrt{3^2 + 3^2}$
$= \sqrt{18} \text{ or } 3\sqrt{2}$
$b_2 = \sqrt{(8-2)^2 + (7-1)^2}$
$= \sqrt{6^2 + 6^2}$
$= \sqrt{72} \text{ or } 6\sqrt{2}$
median $= \frac{1}{2}(3\sqrt{2} + 6\sqrt{2})$
$= \frac{1}{2}(9\sqrt{2}) \approx 6.364$ units

68. $2m(3x - y) + 7n(3x - y) = (2m + 7n)(3x - y)$

69. $(3u^2 - 4) \div 2u = \frac{3u^2}{2u} - \frac{4}{2u}$
$= \frac{3}{2}u - \frac{2}{u}$

12-6 Coordinates in Space

Pages 683–684 Check for Understanding

1. Sample answer: First find -3 on the x-axis, 1 on the y-axis, and -2 on the z-axis. Then imagine a plane perpendicular to the x-axis at -3 and planes perpendicular to the y- and z-axes at 1 and -2. The three planes will intersect at $(-3, 1, -2)$. See students' work.

2. Sample answer: The midpoint formula in a plane is one-half the sum of the x and y values. The midpoint formula in space is one-half the sum of the x, y, and z values. The distance formula in a plane is the square root of the sum of the squares of the differences of the x and y values. The distance formula in space is the square root of the sum of the squares of the differences of the x, y, and z values.

3. The sphere has its center at $(-2, -4, 4)$ with a radius of 5.

4.

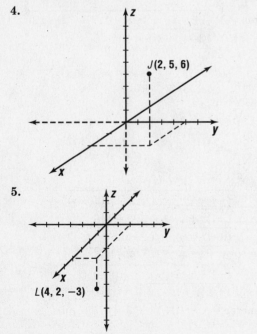

5.

6. $RS = \sqrt{(0-0)^2 + (-1-0)^2 + (6-4)^2}$
$= \sqrt{(-1)^2 + (2)^2}$
$= \sqrt{5} \approx 2.24$
midpoint $= \left(\frac{0+0}{2}, \frac{0+(-1)}{2}, \frac{4+6}{2} \right)$
$= (0, -0.5, 5)$

7. $AB = \sqrt{(19-20)^2 + (-8-(-2))^2 + (40-18)^2}$
$= \sqrt{(-1)^2 + (-6)^2 + (22)^2}$
$= \sqrt{521} \approx 22.83$
midpoint $= \left(\frac{19+20}{2}, \frac{-8+(-2)}{2}, \frac{40+18}{2} \right)$
$= (19.5, -5, 29)$

8. true   **9.** true

10. False; the point does not satisfy the equation.

11. $C = (5, -2, 0)$
radius $= \sqrt{36}$ or 6

12. $(x - (-1))^2 + (y - 2)^2 + (z - 5)^2 = 10^2$
$(x + 1)^2 + (y - 2)^2 + (z - 5)^2 = 100$

13. $C = \left(\frac{3 + (-7)}{2}, \frac{-5 + 11}{2}, \frac{18 + 32}{2} \right)$
$= (-2, 3, 25)$
radius $= \sqrt{(-2-3)^2 + (3-(-5))^2 + (25-18)^2}$
$= \sqrt{(-5)^2 + 8^2 + 7^2}$
$= \sqrt{138}$
$x - (-2))^2 + (y - 3)^2 + (z - 25)^2 = (\sqrt{138})^2$
$(x + 2)^2 + (y - 3)^2 + (z - 25)^2 = 138$

14a. $\left(3(60), 152(69), \frac{-1500}{6076.115} \right)$ or $(180, 10{,}488, -0.25)$
$\left(2(60), 154(69), \frac{-1300}{6076.115} \right)$ or $(120, 10{,}626, -0.21)$

14b. distance =
$\sqrt{(180 - 120)^2 + (10{,}488 - 10{,}626)^2 + (-0.25 - (-0.21))^2}$
$= \sqrt{22644}$
≈ 150.5

Pages 684–686 Exercises

15.

16.

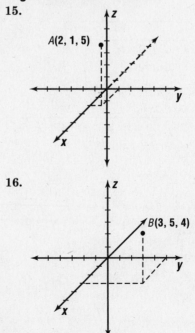

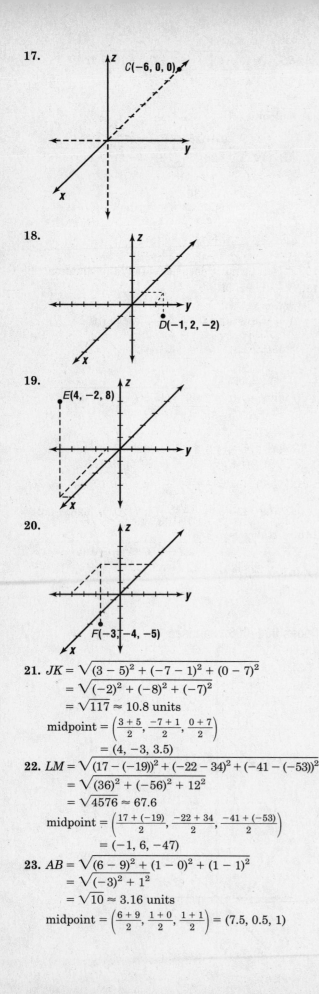

17.

18.

19.

20.

21. $JK = \sqrt{(3-5)^2 + (-7-1)^2 + (0-7)^2}$
$= \sqrt{(-2)^2 + (-8)^2 + (-7)^2}$
$= \sqrt{117} \approx 10.8$ units
midpoint $= \left(\dfrac{3+5}{2}, \dfrac{-7+1}{2}, \dfrac{0+7}{2}\right)$
$= (4, -3, 3.5)$

22. $LM = \sqrt{(17-(-19))^2 + (-22-34)^2 + (-41-(-53))^2}$
$= \sqrt{(36)^2 + (-56)^2 + 12^2}$
$= \sqrt{4576} \approx 67.6$
midpoint $= \left(\dfrac{17+(-19)}{2}, \dfrac{-22+34}{2}, \dfrac{-41+(-53)}{2}\right)$
$= (-1, 6, -47)$

23. $AB = \sqrt{(6-9)^2 + (1-0)^2 + (1-1)^2}$
$= \sqrt{(-3)^2 + 1^2}$
$= \sqrt{10} \approx 3.16$ units
midpoint $= \left(\dfrac{6+9}{2}, \dfrac{1+0}{2}, \dfrac{1+1}{2}\right) = (7.5, 0.5, 1)$

24. $CD = \sqrt{(4-7)^2 + (-8-20)^2 + (12-18)^2}$
$= \sqrt{(-3)^2 + (-28)^2 + (-6)^2}$
$= \sqrt{829} \approx 28.8$ units
midpoint $= \left(\dfrac{4+7}{2}, \dfrac{-8+20}{2}, \dfrac{12+18}{2}\right)$
$= (5.5, 6, 15)$

25. $EF = \sqrt{(3-5)^2 + (7-7)^2 + (-1-2)^2}$
$= \sqrt{(-2)^2 + (-3)^2}$
$= \sqrt{13} \approx 3.6$ units
midpoint $= \left(\dfrac{3+5}{2}, \dfrac{7+7}{2}, \dfrac{-1+2}{2}\right)$
$= (4, 7, 0.5)$

26. $GH = \sqrt{(2-(-25))^2 + (2-4)^2 + (2-18)^2}$
$= \sqrt{27^2 + (-2)^2 + (-16)^2}$
$= \sqrt{989} \approx 31.4$ units
midpoint $= \left(\dfrac{2+(-25)}{2}, \dfrac{2+4}{2}, \dfrac{2+18}{2}\right)$
$= (-11.5, 3, 10)$

27. False; $c = 0$; the points will be of the form $(0, y, z)$.

28. False, it is outside of the sphere.

29. true   **30.** true

31. False; it is a plane that contains that line.

32. $C\,(0, 3, -8)$; radius $= \sqrt{81}$ or 9

33. $C(5, -4, 10)$; radius $= \sqrt{9}$ or 3

34. $C(0, 0, 3)$; radius $= \sqrt{49}$ or 7

35. $C(-4, 2, -12)$; radius $= \sqrt{18} \approx 4.24$

36. $(x - (-5))^2 + (y - 11)^2 + (z - (-3))^2 = 4^2$
$(x + 5)^2 + (y - 11)^2 + (z + 3)^2 = 16$

37. radius $= \sqrt{(-2-5)^2 + (3-(-1))^2 + (-4-(-1))^2}$
$= \sqrt{(-7)^2 + (4)^2 + (-3)^2}$
$= \sqrt{74}$
$(x - (-2))^2 + (y - 3)^2 + (z - (-4))^2 = (\sqrt{74})^2$
$(x + 2)^2 + (y - 3)^2 + (z + 4)^2 = 74$

38. $C = \left(\dfrac{14+(-12)}{2}, \dfrac{-8+10}{2}, \dfrac{32+12}{2}\right)$
$= (1, 1, 22)$
radius $= \sqrt{(14-1)^2 + (-8-1)^2 + (32-22)^2}$
$= \sqrt{13^2 + (-9)^2 + 10^2}$
$= \sqrt{350}$
$(x - 1)^2 + (y - 1)^2 + (z - 22)^2 = \sqrt{350}^2$
$(x - 1)^2 + (y - 1)^2 + (z - 22)^2 = 350$

39. $C(-5, 4, 19)$; $r = 6$
$(x - (-5))^2 + (y - 4)^2 + (z - 19)^2 = 6^2$
$(x + 5)^2 + (y - 4)^2 + (z - 19)^2 = 36$

40. $C(2, 2, 2)$; $r = 2$
$(x - 2)^2 + (y - 2)^2 + (z - 2)^2 = 2^2$
$(x - 2)^2 + (y - 2)^2 + (z - 2)^2 = 4$

41. $AB = \sqrt{(-1-0)^2 + (3-2)^2 + (2-4)^2}$
$= \sqrt{(-1)^2 + 1^2 + (-2)^2} = \sqrt{6}$
$BC = \sqrt{(0-(-2))^2 + (2-0)^2 + (4-3)^2}$
$= \sqrt{2^2 + 2^2 + 1^2} = \sqrt{9} = 3$
$AC = \sqrt{(-1-(-2))^2 + (3-0)^2 + (2-3)^2}$
$= \sqrt{1^2 + 3^2 + (-1)^2} = \sqrt{11}$
perimeter $= \sqrt{6} + \sqrt{11} + 3 \approx 8.77$ units

42. $BA = \sqrt{(-3-2)^2 + (5-(-1))^2 + (-6-3)^2}$

$= \sqrt{(-5)^2 + 6^2 + (-9)^2}$

$= \sqrt{25 + 36 + 81}$

$= \sqrt{142}$

$AC = \sqrt{(2-7)^2 + (-1-(-7))^2 + (3-12)^2}$

$= \sqrt{(-5)^2 + 6^2 + (-9)^2}$

$= \sqrt{25 + 36 + 81}$

$= \sqrt{142}$

$BC = \sqrt{(-3-7)^2 + (5-(-7))^2 + (-6-12)^2}$

$= \sqrt{(-10)^2 + 12^2 + (-18)^2}$

$= \sqrt{100 + 144 + 324}$

$= \sqrt{568} = 2\sqrt{142}$

So $BA + AC = BC$

43. $AB = \sqrt{(3-5)^2 + (2-8)^2 + (-3-6)^2}$

$= \sqrt{(-2)^2 + (-6)^2 + (-9)^2}$

$= \sqrt{4 + 36 + 81}$

$= \sqrt{121} = 11$

$AC = \sqrt{(3-(-3))^2 + (2-(-5))^2 + (-3-3)^2}$

$= \sqrt{6^2 + 7^2 + (-6)^2}$

$= \sqrt{36 + 49 + 36}$

$= \sqrt{121} = 11$

$AB = AC = 11$ so $\triangle ABC$ is isosceles.

$BC = \sqrt{(5-(-3))^2 + (8-(-5))^2 + (6-3)^2}$

$= \sqrt{8^2 + 13^2 + 3^2}$

$= \sqrt{64 + 169 + 9}$

$= \sqrt{242}$

If $(AB)^2 + (AC)^2 = (BC)^2$; $\triangle ABC$ will be a right triangle.

$(11)^2 + (11)^2 = (\sqrt{242})^2$

$121 + 121 = 242$

$242 = 242$

$11^2 + 11^2 = 242$, so $\triangle ABC$ is a right triangle.

44a. $RS = \sqrt{(6-4)^2 + (1-5)^2 + (3-5)^2}$

$= \sqrt{4 + 16 + 4} = \sqrt{24}$

$ST = \sqrt{(4-2)^2 + (5-3)^2 + (5-1)^2}$

$= \sqrt{4 + 4 + 16} = \sqrt{24}$

$RT = \sqrt{(6-2)^2 + (1-3)^2 + (3-1)^2}$

$= \sqrt{16 + 4 + 4} = \sqrt{24}$

Each side measures $\sqrt{24}$ units.

44b. $\triangle RST$ is an equilateral triangle.

45. $T = Ph + 2B$ $V = Bh$

$= 4(5)(5) + 2(5)^2$ $= (5)^2(5)$

$= 100 + 50$ $= 125$ units^3

$= 150$ units^2

46. $RS = \sqrt{(5-3)^2 + (4-(-2))^2 + (-1-z)^2} = 7$

$2^2 + 6^2 + (-1-z)^2 = 7^2$

$40 + (-1-z)^2 = 49$

$(-1-z)^2 - 9 = 0$

$z^2 + 2z + 1 - 9 = 0$

$z^2 + 2z - 8 = 0$

$(z+4)(z-2) = 0$

$z + 4 = 0$ or $z - 2 = 0$

$z = -4$ $z = 2$

47.

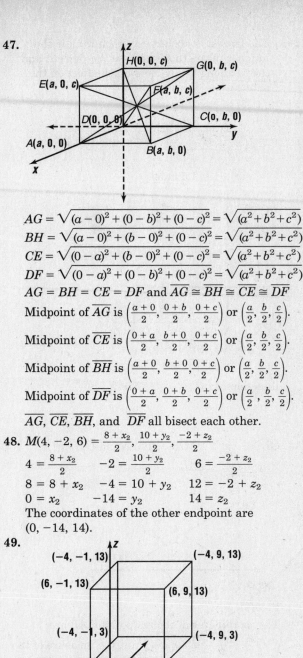

$AG = \sqrt{(a-0)^2 + (0-b)^2 + (0-c)^2} = \sqrt{a^2+b^2+c^2}$

$BH = \sqrt{(a-0)^2 + (b-0)^2 + (0-c)^2} = \sqrt{a^2+b^2+c^2}$

$CE = \sqrt{(0-a)^2 + (b-0)^2 + (0-c)^2} = \sqrt{a^2+b^2+c^2}$

$DF = \sqrt{(0-a)^2 + (0-b)^2 + (0-c)^2} = \sqrt{a^2+b^2+c^2}$

$AG = BH = CE = DF$ and $\overline{AG} \cong \overline{BH} \cong \overline{CE} \cong \overline{DF}$

Midpoint of $\overline{AG}$ is $\left(\frac{a+0}{2}, \frac{0+b}{2}, \frac{0+c}{2}\right)$ or $\left(\frac{a}{2}, \frac{b}{2}, \frac{c}{2}\right)$.

Midpoint of $\overline{CE}$ is $\left(\frac{0+a}{2}, \frac{b+0}{2}, \frac{0+c}{2}\right)$ or $\left(\frac{a}{2}, \frac{b}{2}, \frac{c}{2}\right)$.

Midpoint of $\overline{BH}$ is $\left(\frac{a+0}{2}, \frac{b+0}{2}, \frac{0+c}{2}\right)$ or $\left(\frac{a}{2}, \frac{b}{2}, \frac{c}{2}\right)$.

Midpoint of $\overline{DF}$ is $\left(\frac{0+a}{2}, \frac{0+b}{2}, \frac{0+c}{2}\right)$ or $\left(\frac{a}{2}, \frac{b}{2}, \frac{c}{2}\right)$.

$\overline{AG}$, $\overline{CE}$, $\overline{BH}$, and $\overline{DF}$ all bisect each other.

48. $M(4, -2, 6) = \frac{8+x_2}{2}, \frac{10+y_2}{2}, \frac{-2+z_2}{2}$

$4 = \frac{8+x_2}{2}$ $-2 = \frac{10+y_2}{2}$ $6 = \frac{-2+z_2}{2}$

$8 = 8 + x_2$ $-4 = 10 + y_2$ $12 = -2 + z_2$

$0 = x_2$ $-14 = y_2$ $14 = z_2$

The coordinates of the other endpoint are $(0, -14, 14)$.

49.

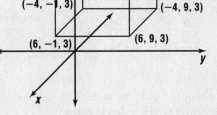

$(6, -1, 3), (6, 9, 3), (-4, 9, 3), (-4, -1, 3),$
$(6, -1, 13), (6, 9, 13), (-4, 9, 13), (-4, -1, 13)$

50a. Rochester

$= \sqrt{(0-.025)^2 + (0-1300)^2 + (0-176)^2}$

≈ 1311.9

Seattle

$= \sqrt{(0-.047)^2 + (0-2250)^2 + (0-542)^2}$

≈ 2314.4

Gainesville

$= \sqrt{(0-.038)^2 + (0-1875)^2 + (0-1377)^2}$

≈ 2326.3

Austin

$= \sqrt{(0-.035)^2 + (0-2800)^2 + (0-539)^2}$

≈ 2851.4

50b. The largest contributor to each rank is the number in the thousands, so the percent and the tax don't really have much effect on the outcomes.

51. (2, 2, 2) to block a row of Xs

52. (8, 10, 0.3) (4, 8, 0.4)

$$d = \sqrt{(8-4)^2 + (10-8)^2 + (0.3-0.4)^2}$$
$$= \sqrt{4^2 + 2^2 + (-0.1)^2}$$
$$= \sqrt{20.01} \approx 4.5 \text{ miles}$$

53.

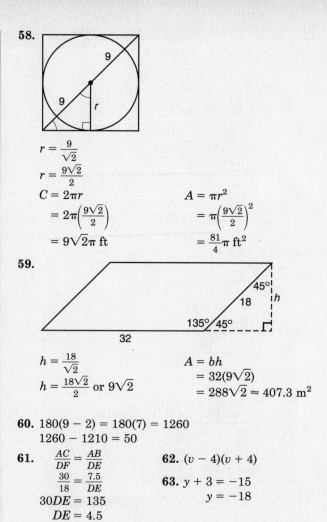

$$|\overrightarrow{LN}| = \sqrt{(-3-6)^2 + (5-7)^2}$$
$$= \sqrt{(-9)^2 + (-2)^2}$$
$$= \sqrt{81+4} = \sqrt{85} \approx 9.2$$

direction of $\overrightarrow{LN}$

$$\tan X = \frac{5-7}{-3-6}$$
$$\tan X = \frac{2}{9}$$
$$X \approx 13°$$

54. Given: right $\triangle AOB$ with median $\overline{OM}$

Prove: $OM = \frac{1}{2}AB$

Proof:
The coordinates of the midpoint of $\overline{AB}$ are $\left(\frac{0+2b}{2}, \frac{2a+0}{2}\right)$ or (b, a). Thus, the measure of the median $\overline{OM}$ is $\sqrt{(b-0)^2 + (a-0)^2}$ or $\sqrt{a^2 + b^2}$. $AB = \sqrt{(0-2b)^2 + (2a-0)^2} = \sqrt{4b^2 + 4a^2}$ or $2\sqrt{a^2 + b^2}$. $OM = \frac{1}{2}AB$. Therefore, the measure of the median to the hypotenuse is half of the measure of the hypotenuse.

55a. $y = 11x + 349$

55b. $y = 11(15) + 349 = 514$

56.
$$V = \frac{4}{3}\pi r^3$$
$$972\pi = \frac{4}{3}\pi r^3$$
$$729 = r^3$$
$$r = 9$$
$$d = 2r = 2(9) = 18 \text{ cm}$$

57.
$$L = \frac{1}{2}P\ell$$
$$= \pi r \ell$$
$$= \pi(3.2)(5.2)$$
$$\approx 52.3 \text{ mm}^2$$

58.

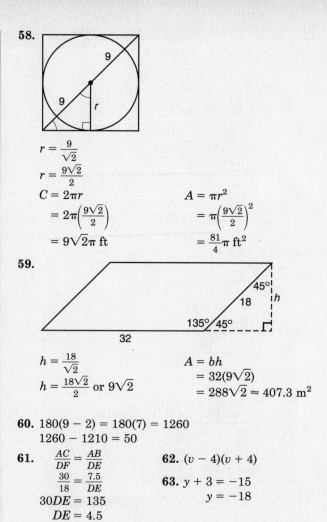

$$r = \frac{9}{\sqrt{2}}$$
$$r = \frac{9\sqrt{2}}{2}$$

$$C = 2\pi r$$
$$= 2\pi\left(\frac{9\sqrt{2}}{2}\right)$$
$$= 9\sqrt{2}\pi \text{ ft}$$

$$A = \pi r^2$$
$$= \pi\left(\frac{9\sqrt{2}}{2}\right)^2$$
$$= \frac{81}{4}\pi \text{ ft}^2$$

59.

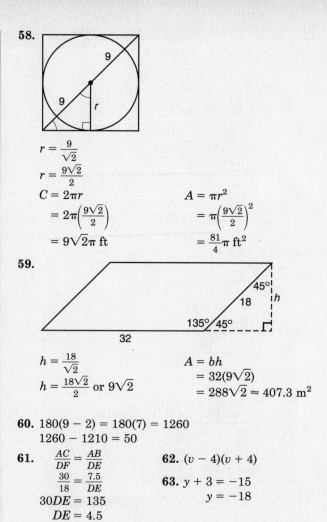

$$h = \frac{18}{\sqrt{2}}$$
$$h = \frac{18\sqrt{2}}{2} \text{ or } 9\sqrt{2}$$

$$A = bh$$
$$= 32(9\sqrt{2})$$
$$= 288\sqrt{2} \approx 407.3 \text{ m}^2$$

60. $180(9-2) = 180(7) = 1260$
$$1260 - 1210 = 50$$

61.
$$\frac{AC}{DF} = \frac{AB}{DE}$$
$$\frac{30}{18} = \frac{7.5}{DE}$$
$$30DE = 135$$
$$DE = 4.5$$

62. $(v-4)(v+4)$

63. $y + 3 = -15$
$$y = -18$$

Chapter 12 Highlights

Page 687 Understanding and Using the Vocabulary

1. coordinate proof
2. scalar multiplication
3. slope-intercept form
4. magnitude of a vector
5. standard form
6. column matrix
7. scatter plot
8. ordered triple
9. linear equation
10. point-slope form

Chapter 12 Study Guide and Assessment

Pages 688–690 Skills and Concepts

11.

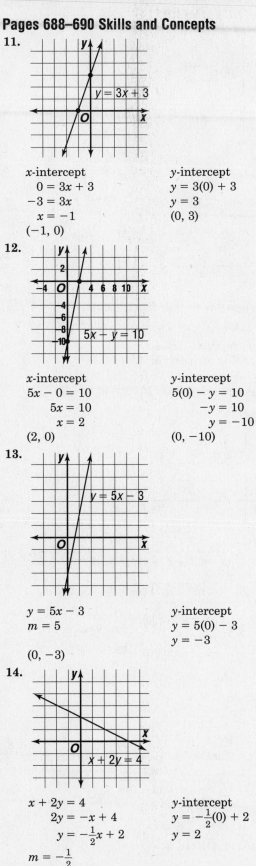

$y = 3x + 3$

x-intercept
$$0 = 3x + 3$$
$$-3 = 3x$$
$$x = -1$$
$$(-1, 0)$$

y-intercept
$$y = 3(0) + 3$$
$$y = 3$$
$$(0, 3)$$

12.

$5x - y = 10$

x-intercept
$$5x - 0 = 10$$
$$5x = 10$$
$$x = 2$$
$$(2, 0)$$

y-intercept
$$5(0) - y = 10$$
$$-y = 10$$
$$y = -10$$
$$(0, -10)$$

13.

$y = 5x - 3$

$$y = 5x - 3$$
$$m = 5$$

$$(0, -3)$$

y-intercept
$$y = 5(0) - 3$$
$$y = -3$$

14.

$x + 2y = 4$

$$x + 2y = 4$$
$$2y = -x + 4$$
$$y = -\tfrac{1}{2}x + 2$$
$$m = -\tfrac{1}{2}$$

$$(0, 2)$$

y-intercept
$$y = -\tfrac{1}{2}(0) + 2$$
$$y = 2$$

15. $y - y_1 = m(x - x_1)$ $\qquad m = 4; (0, 2)$
$$y - 2 = 4(x - 0)$$
$$y - 2 = 4x$$
$$y = 4x + 2$$

16. $y - y_1 = m(x - x_1)$
$$y - 3 = 5(x - (-1))$$
$$y - 3 = 5x + 5$$
$$y = 5x + 8$$

17. $m = \dfrac{-6 - 4}{-5 - (-7)} = \dfrac{-10}{2} = -5$
$$y - y_1 = m(x - x_1)$$
$$y - 4 = -5(x - (-7))$$
$$y - 4 = -5x - 35$$
$$y = -5x - 31$$

18. $(5, 0)(0, 3)$
$$m = \dfrac{3 - 0}{0 - 5} = -\dfrac{3}{5}$$
$$y - y_1 = m(x - x_1)$$
$$y - 0 = -\dfrac{3}{5}(x - 5)$$
$$y = -\dfrac{3}{5}x + 3$$

19. $m = 1; (0, 8)$
$$y - y_1 = m(x - x_1)$$
$$y - 8 = 1(x - 0)$$
$$y - 8 = x$$
$$y = x + 8$$

20. $m = -\dfrac{1}{3}; (6, 0)$
$$y - y_1 = m(x - x_1)$$
$$y - 0 = -\dfrac{1}{3}(x - 6)$$
$$y = -\dfrac{1}{3}x + 2$$

21. slope of $\overleftrightarrow{XY} = \dfrac{-1 - 1}{2 - 6} = \dfrac{-2}{-4} = \dfrac{1}{2}$
$$y - (-1) = \tfrac{1}{2}(x - 2)$$
$$y + 1 = \tfrac{1}{2}x - 1$$
$$y = \tfrac{1}{2}x - 2$$

slope of $\overleftrightarrow{YZ} = \dfrac{1 - (-3)}{6 - 0} = \dfrac{4}{6} = \dfrac{2}{3}$
$$y - 1 = \tfrac{2}{3}(x - 6)$$
$$y - 1 = \tfrac{2}{3}x - 4$$
$$y = \tfrac{2}{3}x - 3$$

slope of $\overleftrightarrow{XZ} = \dfrac{-1 - (-3)}{2 - 0} = \dfrac{2}{2} = 1$
$$y - (-1) = 1(x - 2)$$
$$y + 1 = x - 2$$
$$y = x - 3$$

22. midpoint of $\overline{XY} = \left(\frac{2+6}{2}, \frac{-1+1}{2}\right) = (4, 0)$

slope of median through $z = \frac{0-(-3)}{4-0} = \frac{3}{4}$

$y - 0 = \frac{3}{4}(x - 4)$

$y = \frac{3}{4}x - 3$

midpoint of $\overline{YZ} = \left(\frac{6+0}{2}, \frac{1+(-3)}{2}\right) = (3, -1)$

slope of median through $x = \frac{-1-(-1)}{3-2} = \frac{0}{1} = 0$

$y - (-1) = 0(x - 3)$

$y + 1 = 0$

$y = -1$

midpoint of $\overline{XZ} = \left(\frac{2+0}{2}, \frac{-1+(-3)}{2}\right) = (1, -2)$

slope of median through $y = \frac{-2-1}{1-6} = \frac{-3}{-5} = \frac{3}{5}$

$y - (-2) = \frac{3}{5}(x - 1)$

$y + 2 = \frac{3}{5}x - \frac{3}{5}$

$y = \frac{3}{5}x - \frac{13}{5}$

23. slope of $\overline{XY} = \frac{1}{2}$; slope of altitude to $\overline{XY} = -2$

slope of $\overline{YZ} = \frac{2}{3}$; slope of altitude to $\overline{YZ} = -\frac{3}{2}$

slope of $\overline{XZ} = 1$; slope of altitude to $\overline{XZ} = -1$

altitude to $\overline{XY}$:	altitude to $\overline{YZ}$:
$y - (-3) = -2(x - 0)$	$y - (-1) = -\frac{3}{2}(x - 2)$
$y + 3 = -2x$	
$y = -2x - 3$	$y + 1 = -\frac{3}{2}x + 3$
	$y = -\frac{3}{2}x + 2$

altitude to $\overline{XZ}$

$y - 1 = -1(x - 6)$

$y - 1 = -x + 6$

$y = -x + 7$

24. perpendicular bisector of $\overline{XY}$

slope $= -2$; midpoint $(4, 0)$

$y - 0 = -2(x - 4)$

$y = -2x + 8$

perpendicular bisector of $\overline{YZ}$

slope $= \frac{-3}{2}$; midpoint $(3, -1)$

$y - (-1) = -\frac{3}{2}(x - 3)$

$y + 1 = -\frac{3}{2}x + \frac{9}{2}$

$y = -\frac{3}{2}x + \frac{7}{2}$

perpendicular bisector of $\overline{XZ}$

slope $= -1$; midpoint $(1, -2)$

$y - (-2) = -1(x - 1)$

$y + 2 = -x + 1$

$y = -x - 1$

25. Given: trapezoid $ABCD$

M is midpoint of $\overline{AD}$.

N is midpoint of $\overline{BC}$.

Prove: $\overline{DC} \parallel \overline{MN} \parallel \overline{AB}$

Proof:

Midpoint M is $\left(\frac{b+0}{2}, \frac{c+0}{2}\right)$ or $\left(\frac{b}{2}, \frac{c}{2}\right)$.

Midpoint N is $\left(\frac{a+d}{2}, \frac{c+0}{2}\right)$ or $\left(\frac{a+d}{2}, \frac{c}{2}\right)$.

Slope of $\overline{DC}$ is $\frac{c-c}{d-b}$ or $\frac{0}{d-b}$ or 0.

Slope of $\overline{MN}$ is $\frac{\frac{c}{2}-\frac{c}{2}}{\frac{a+d}{2}-\frac{b}{2}}$ or $\frac{0}{\frac{a+d-b}{2}}$ or 0.

Slope of $\overline{AB}$ is $\frac{0-0}{a-0}$ or $\frac{0}{a}$ or 0.

$\overline{DC} \parallel \overline{MN} \parallel \overline{AB}$.

26. Given: trapezoid $ABCD$

M is midpoint of $\overline{AD}$.

N is midpoint of $\overline{BC}$.

Prove: $MN = \frac{1}{2}(DC + AB)$

Proof:

$DC = \sqrt{(d-b)^2 + (c-c)^2} = \sqrt{(d-b)^2 + 0^2}$

$\quad = d - b$

$AB = \sqrt{(a-0)^2 + (0-0)^2} = \sqrt{a^2 + 0^2} = a$

$MN = \sqrt{\left(\frac{a+d}{2} - \frac{b}{2}\right)^2 + \left(\frac{c}{2} - \frac{c}{2}\right)^2}$

$\quad = \sqrt{\left(\frac{a+d-b}{2}\right)^2 + 0} = \frac{a+d-b}{2}$

$\frac{1}{2}(DC + AB) = \frac{1}{2}((d-b) + a) = \frac{d-b-a}{2}$

or $\frac{a+d-b}{2} = MN$

27. $|\vec{V}| = \sqrt{7^2 + 1^2}$

$\quad = \sqrt{50} \approx 7.1$ units

direction of $\vec{V}$: $\tan X = \frac{1}{7}$

$\quad\quad\quad X \approx 8.1°$

28. $|\overline{AB}| = \sqrt{(7-1)^2 + (5-0)^2}$

$\quad = \sqrt{6^2 + 5^2}$

$\quad = \sqrt{61} \approx 7.8$ units

direction of $\overline{AB}$: $\tan X = \frac{5-0}{7-1}$

$\quad\quad \tan X = \frac{5}{6}$

$\quad\quad\quad X \approx 39.8°$

29. $\vec{v} + \vec{s} = (0, 8) + (4, 0)$
$= (0 + 4, 8 + 0)$
$= (4, 8)$

30. $3\vec{v} + \vec{s} = (3 \cdot 0, 3 \cdot 8) + (4, 0)$
$= (0, 24) + (4, 0)$
$= (0 + 4, 24 + 0)$
$= (4, 24)$

31. $\begin{bmatrix} 4 \\ 6 \end{bmatrix} + \begin{bmatrix} 3 \\ 2 \end{bmatrix} = \begin{bmatrix} 4 + 3 \\ 6 + 2 \end{bmatrix} = \begin{bmatrix} 7 \\ 8 \end{bmatrix}$

32. $\begin{bmatrix} 2 \\ -3 \end{bmatrix} + \begin{bmatrix} 0 \\ 9 \end{bmatrix} = \begin{bmatrix} 2 + 0 \\ -3 + 9 \end{bmatrix} = \begin{bmatrix} 2 \\ 6 \end{bmatrix}$

33. $AB = \sqrt{(3 - 7)^2 + (-3 - (-3))^2 + (1 - 5)^2}$
$= \sqrt{32} = 4\sqrt{2} \approx 5.7$ units;
midpoint of $\overline{AB} = \left(\frac{3 + 7}{2}, \frac{-3 + (-3)}{2}, \frac{1 + 5}{2} \right)$ or $(5, -3, 3)$

34. $\overline{CD} = \sqrt{(2 - 0)^2 + (4 - 2)^2 + (6 - 4)^2} = \sqrt{12}$
$= 2\sqrt{3} \approx 3.5$ units;
midpoint of $\overline{CD} = \left(\frac{2 + 0}{2}, \frac{4 + 2}{2}, \frac{6 + 4}{2} \right) = (1, 3, 5)$

35. $(x - 0)^2 + (y - 0)^2 + (z - 0)^2 = 5^2$
$x^2 + y^2 + z^2 = 25$

36. $(x - (-1))^2 + (y - 2)^2 + (z - (-3))^2 = 4^2$
$(x + 1)^2 + (y - 2)^2 + (z + 3)^2 = 16$

Page 690 Applications and Problem Solving

37.

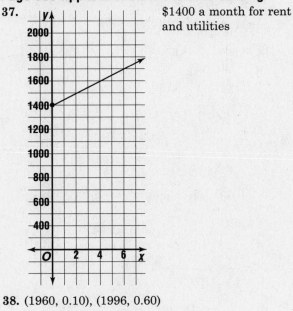

$1400 a month for rent and utilities

38. $(1960, 0.10), (1996, 0.60)$
$m = \frac{0.6 - 0.1}{1996 - 1960} = \frac{0.5}{36} = 0.0139$
$c - 0.10 = 0.0139(t - 1960)$
$c = 0.1 + 0.0139(t - 1960)$
Sample answer: $c = 0.1 + 0.0139(2010 - 1960)$
$c = \$0.80$

39a.

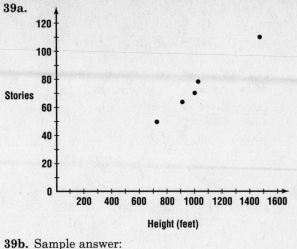

39b. Sample answer:
$m = \frac{78 - 50}{1028 - 722} \approx 0.09$
$y - 50 = 0.09(x - 722)$
$y = 0.09x - 14.98$
or $y = 0.09x - 15$

39c. $y = 0.09(745) - 15 = 52.05$
Sample answer: 52 stories.
The tower actually has 54 stories.

Page 691 Alternative Assessment: Thinking Critically

• Vector addition is commutative. The proof is as follows.
Let $a = (a_1, a_2)$ and $b = (b_1, b_2)$.
$(a + b) = (a_1, a_2) + (b_1, b_2)$
$= (a_1 + b_1, a_2 + b_2)$
Addition of real numbers is commutative.
$(a_1 + b_1, a_2 + b_2) = (b_1 + a_1, b_2 + a_2)$
$= b + a$

College Entrance Exam Practice, Chapters 1–12

Pages 692–693

1. $4^a = 16$
$4^a = 4^2$
$a = 2$
$2^a \cdot 2 = 2^2 \cdot 2 = 8$ **(B)**

2. $V = s^3$
$125 = s^3$
$5 = s$
$T = Ph + 2B$
$= 4(5)(5) + 2(5^2)$
$= 100 + 50$
$= 150 \text{ cm}^2$ **(B)**

3. $2 \# a = a \# 3$

$2(2) + a = 2(a) + 3$

$4 + a = 2a + 3$

$1 = a$ (C)

4. x is a fraction between 0 and 1.

I. As x increases, $x + 1$ increases

II. As x increases, x^2 increases, so $1 - x^2$ decreases

III. As x increases, $\frac{1}{x}$ decreases approaching 1. (A)

5. $x + 2 = 0$ $x^3 = (-2)^3 = -8$

$x = -2$ (D)

6. $x + x + x = 90$ $x + y = 90$

     $3x = 90$ $30 + y = 90$

       $x = 30$ $y = 60$

$y - x = 60 - 30 = 30$ (C)

7. $P = 4s$ $A = s^2$

$\frac{x}{3} = 4s$ $= \left(\frac{x}{12}\right)^2$

$\frac{x}{12} = s$ $= \frac{x^2}{144}$ (A)

8. $V = \pi r^2 h$

$= \pi(6)^2(8)$ $\frac{904.8}{231} = 3.9$ gallons

$= 904.8$ (A)

9. $\frac{(a + 5) + + (2a - 4) + (3a + 8)}{3} = \frac{6a + 9}{3} = 2a + 3$ (C)

10. $\frac{BC}{EF} = \frac{AC}{DF}$

$\frac{9}{24} = \frac{21}{DF}$

$9DF = 21(24)$

$DF = 56$ units

11. $V = \pi r^2 h$

$= \pi(3x)^2(6x)$

$= 54\pi x^3$ meters^3

12. $x + 52° + 52° = 180°$

$x = 76°$

13. $\frac{\frac{4}{3}\pi r^3}{2\pi r^3} = 0.\overline{6} = 66\frac{2}{3}\%$

14. $d = \sqrt{(-1 - 2)^2 + (2 - 4)^2 + (-3 - (-1))^2}$

$= \sqrt{(-3)^2 + (-2)^2 + (-2)^2}$

$= \sqrt{17}$ units

15. $\frac{\text{Volume cone}}{\text{Volume cylinder}} = \frac{\frac{1}{3}Bh}{Bh} = \frac{\frac{1}{3}\pi r^2 h}{\pi r^2 h} = \frac{1}{3}$

16. $A_{\text{rectangle}} - A_{\text{triangle}} = \ell w - \frac{1}{2}bh$

$= 10(12) - \frac{1}{2}(10 - 8)(12 - 6)$

$= 120 - 6 = 114$ ft^2

17. $P = 4(9x)$ $P = 3(12x)$

$= 36x$ $= 36x$ (C)

18. $3y - x = 8$

$\underline{y + x = 2}$ $x + y = 2$

      $4y = 10$ $x + 2.5 = 2$ $x < y$

        $y = 2.5$ $x = -0.5$ (B)

19. $V_{\text{sphere}} = \frac{4}{3}\pi r^3 = \frac{4}{3}\pi(2)^3 = \frac{32}{3}\pi$

$V_{\text{hemisphere}} = \frac{2}{3}\pi r^3 = \frac{2}{3}\pi(4)^3 = \frac{128}{3}\pi$ (B)

20. $2x > x^2$ (A)

21. $V_{\text{cylinder}} = \pi r^2 h$

The height is not given.   (D)

CHAPTER 13 Investigating Loci and Coordinate Transformations

Page 699 Check for Understanding

1. Both a locus and a geometric figure are a set of points that satisfy given conditions.

2. all points in a plane a given distance *r* from a point

3. In a plane, the locus could be 1- or 2-dimensional. In space, the locus could be 1-, 2-, or 3-dimensional.

4.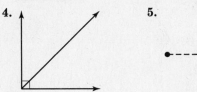

the angle bisector

5.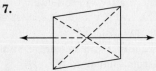

the perpendicular bisector of the segment that joins the two points

6.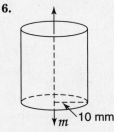

a cylindrical surface of radius 10 mm with line *m* as the axis

7.

a line perpendicular to the plane of the square through the point of intersection of the diagonals

8. a pair of parallel lines, one on each side of *m*, and each 10mm from *m*

9. the perpendicular bisector of $\overline{AB}$ and $\overline{DC}$ in plane *R*

10a.

10b. the interior of a rectangle that makes up the basketball court, minus two semicircles with centers at the midpoint of the ends with the basket and a radius of 19 ft 9 in.

Pages 700–701 Exercises

11.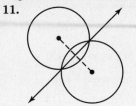

the line that joins the two points of intersection

12.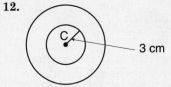

concentric circle *C* with radius 3 cm

13.

a pair of parallel lines, one on each side of ℓ, and each *r* units from ℓ

14.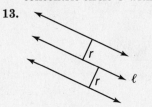

a pair of parallel lines *a* units from the base

15.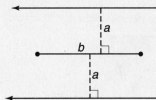

center of the pentagon

16.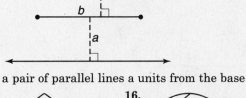

center of the circle

17.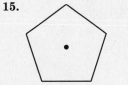

concentric circle of radius $s + \frac{(r - s)}{2}$

18.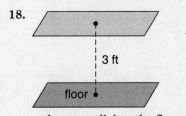

a plane parallel to the floor and 3 ft from the floor which contains a part of the desks

19.

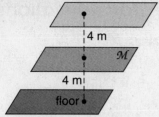

a pair of parallel planes, one on each side of $\mathcal{M}$ and each 4 m from $\mathcal{M}$

20.

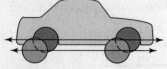

set of two parallel lines parallel to the plane of the road and through the center of the wheels

21.

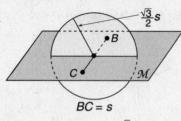

a circle with radius $\frac{\sqrt{3}}{2}s$ units in a plane perpendicular to the base with center on the midpoint of the base

22.

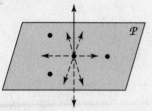

a line perpendicular to P through the circumcenter of the points

23.

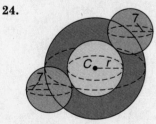

a plane perpendicular to the line containing the opposite vertices of the cube

24.

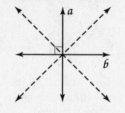

sphere of radius $14 + r$ with center C

25. a plane midway between two parallel lines, perpendicular to the plane containing the two parallel lines

26.

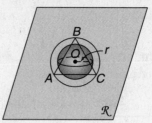

sphere with center O and radius r

27.

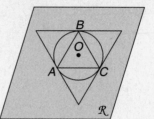

a triangle similar to $\triangle ABC$ containing points A, B, and C

28.

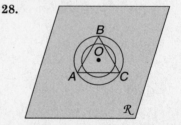

a concentric circle with radius of given length and center O

29. the rays that bisect $\angle ABD$ and $\angle BCD$

30. concentric circles in the plane perpendicular to the segment joining the two points with center at the midpoint of that segment

31. a pair of circles with radius a and center on h in two parallel planes perpendicular to the hypotenuse

32. a sphere with center $(a, 0)$

33a. a curve, parabola with ordinate one-half that of $y = x^2$

33b. $y = \frac{x^2}{2}$

34. the angle bisectors of the right angles

Geometry Chapter 13

35.

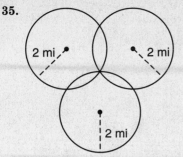

When three or more circles are tangent there is an area among them that is not covered, therefore the circles must overlap in order to cover all of the area. This would then put some of the buildings within two miles of more than one fire station.

36. points along the perpendicular bisector of the segment connecting the two homes

37. half of a sphere with a radius of 300 ft

38.

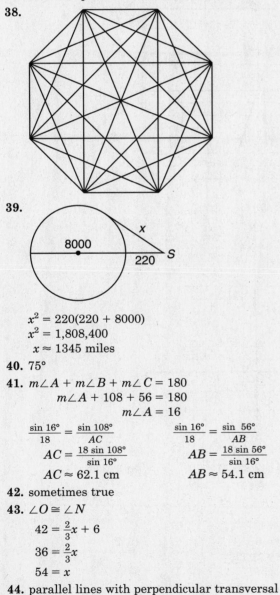

39.

$$x^2 = 220(220 + 8000)$$
$$x^2 = 1{,}808{,}400$$
$$x \approx 1345 \text{ miles}$$

40. 75°

41. $m\angle A + m\angle B + m\angle C = 180$
$m\angle A + 108 + 56 = 180$
$m\angle A = 16$

$\dfrac{\sin 16°}{18} = \dfrac{\sin 108°}{AC}$ $\dfrac{\sin 16°}{18} = \dfrac{\sin 56°}{AB}$

$AC = \dfrac{18 \sin 108°}{\sin 16°}$ $AB = \dfrac{18 \sin 56°}{\sin 16°}$

$AC \approx 62.1$ cm $AB \approx 54.1$ cm

42. sometimes true

43. $\angle O \cong \angle N$

$42 = \frac{2}{3}x + 6$

$36 = \frac{2}{3}x$

$54 = x$

44. parallel lines with perpendicular transversal

45.

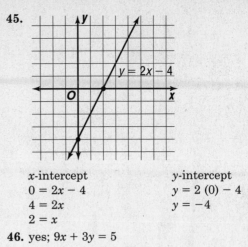

x-intercept	y-intercept
$0 = 2x - 4$	$y = 2(0) - 4$
$4 = 2x$	$y = -4$
$2 = x$	

46. yes; $9x + 3y = 5$

13-2 | Integration: Algebra Locus and Systems of Linear Equations

Page 706 Check for Understanding

1. No; a point that is outside of the locus does not satisfy the conditions. This is an if and only if situation.

2. no points when the lines are parallel, one point when the lines intersect, all points when the lines are the same line

3. The line passes through (15, 160) and (40, 140).

$m = \dfrac{140 - 160}{40 - 15} = \dfrac{-20}{25} = \dfrac{-4}{5}$

$y - 140 = \dfrac{-4}{5}(a - 40)$

$y - 140 = \dfrac{-4}{5}a + 32$

$y = \dfrac{-4}{5}a + 172$

4. Sample answer: substitution, solve for x in the second equation.

5. **6.**

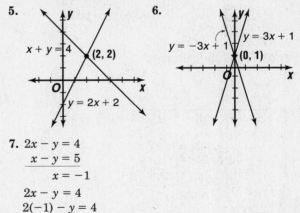

7. $2x - y = 4$
   $\underline{x - y = 5}$
   $x = -1$

$2x - y = 4$
$2(-1) - y = 4$
$-2 - y = 4$
$-y = 6$
$y = -6$

$(-1, -6)$

8. $y = \frac{1}{3}x - 4$

$y = -x + 1$

$-x + 1 = \frac{1}{3}x - 4$

$5 = \frac{4}{3}x$

$\frac{15}{4} = x$

$y = -x + 1$

$y = -\left(\frac{15}{4}\right) + 1$

$y = \frac{-11}{4}$

$\left(\frac{15}{4}, \frac{-11}{4}\right)$

9. $y = 4x$

$x + y = 10$

$x + (4x) = 10$

$5x = 10$

$x = 2$

$y = 4x$

$y = 4(2)$

$y = 8$

$(2, 8)$

10. $12 - 3y = 4x \quad \rightarrow \quad -4x - 3y = -12$

$40 + 4x = 10y \quad \rightarrow \quad \underline{4x - 10y = -40}$

$-13y = -52$

$y = 4$

$12 - 3y = 4x$

$12 - 3(4) = 4x$

$0 = 4x$

$0 = x$

$(0, 4)$

11. $y = \frac{-68,000}{10x} + 505,616$

$y = \frac{33,000}{10x} + 372,242$

$y = -6800x + 505,616$

$y = 3300x + 372,242$

$3300x + 372,242 = -6800x + 505,616$

$10100x = 133,374$

$x \approx 13.2$

in about 13 years or $1990 + 13 \approx 2003$

Pages 706–708 Exercises

12.

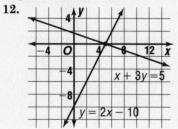

13.

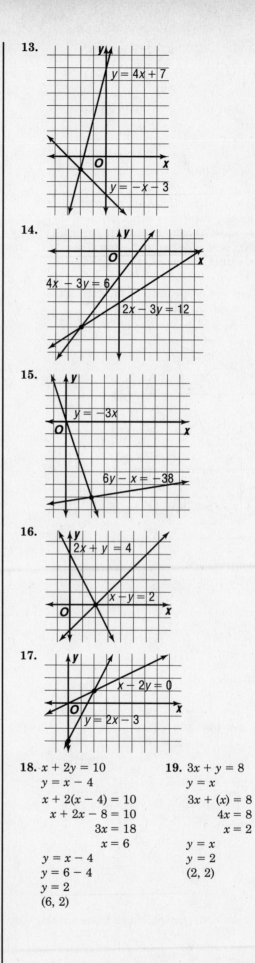

18. $x + 2y = 10$

$y = x - 4$

$x + 2(x - 4) = 10$

$x + 2x - 8 = 10$

$3x = 18$

$x = 6$

$y = x - 4$

$y = 6 - 4$

$y = 2$

$(6, 2)$

19. $3x + y = 8$

$y = x$

$3x + (x) = 8$

$4x = 8$

$x = 2$

$y = x$

$y = 2$

$(2, 2)$

Geometry Chapter 13

20. $x + y = 4$
$y = x + 6$
$x + (x + 6) = 4$
$\quad\quad 2x = -2$
$\quad\quad\quad x = -1$
$y = x + 6$
$y = -1 + 6$
$y = 5$
$(-1, 5)$

21. $2x + y = 9$
$x = 4y$
$2(4y) + y = 9$
$8y + y = 9$
$9y = 9$
$y = 1$
$x = 4y$
$x = 4(1)$
$x = 4$
$(4, 1)$

22. $y = -x + 1$
$y = 6$
$6 = -x + 1$
$5 = -x$
$x = -5$
$(-5, 6)$

23. $y = -2x + 2$
$y = \frac{x}{2} + 2$
$\frac{x}{2} + 2 = -2x + 2$
$\frac{5x}{2} = 0$
$x = 0$
$y = -2x + 2$
$y = -2(0) + 2$
$y = 2$
$(0, 2)$

24. $3x - y = 11$
$\underline{x + y = 5}$
$4x = 16$
$x = 4$

$x + y = 5$
$4 + y = 5$
$y = 1$
$(4, 1)$

25. $(x - 4y = 9)2 \quad \rightarrow \quad 2x - 8y = 18$
$2x - 3y = 8 \quad \rightarrow \quad \underline{2x - 3y = 8}$
$ -5y = 10$
$ y = -2$

$x - 4y = 9$
$x - 4(-2) = 9$
$x + 8 = 9$
$x = 1$
$(1, -2)$

26. $(x - 2y = 7)2 \quad \rightarrow \quad 2x - 4y = 14$
$2x + 3y = 0 \quad \rightarrow \quad \underline{-2x - 3y = 0}$
$ -7y = 14$
$ y = -2$

$x - 2y = 7$
$x - 2(-2) = 7$
$x + 4 = 7$
$x = 3$
$(3, -2)$

27. $x + 4y = 27$
$\underline{x + 2y = 21}$
$2y = 6$
$y = 3$
$x + 4y = 27$
$x + 4(3) = 27$
$x + 12 = 27$
$x = 15$
$(15, 3)$

28. $y = x + 7$
$3x + y = 8$
$3x + (x + 7) = 8$
$4x + 7 = 8$
$4x = 1$
$x = \frac{1}{4}$
$y = x + 7$
$y = \frac{1}{4} + 7$
$y = \frac{29}{4}$
$\left(\frac{1}{4}, \frac{29}{4}\right)$

29. $y = \frac{1}{3}x$
$x + 2y = -3$
$x + 2\left(\frac{1}{3}x\right) = -3$
$\frac{5}{3}x = -3$
$x = \frac{-9}{5}$
$y = \frac{1}{3}x$
$y = \frac{1}{3}\left(\frac{-9}{5}\right)$
$y = \frac{-3}{5}$
$\left(\frac{-9}{5}, \frac{-3}{5}\right)$

30a. $y = 3$
$y = 2x$
$3 = 2x$
$1.5 = x \quad (1.5, 3)$
$y = 3$
$y = 2x - 13$
$3 = 2x - 13$
$16 = 2x$
$x = 8 \quad (8, 3)$

 $y = 7$
$y = 2x$
$7 = 2x$
$3.5 = x \quad (3.5, 7)$
$y = 7$
$y = 2x - 13$
$7 = 2x - 13$
$20 = 2x$
$x = 10 \quad (10, 7)$

30b. $b = \sqrt{(8 - 1.5)^2 + (3 - 3)^2}$
$ = \sqrt{(6.5)^2}$
$ = 6.5$
$h = \sqrt{(3.5 - 3.5)^2 + (7 - 3)^2}$
$h = \sqrt{4^2}$
$h = 4$
$A = bh$
$ = (6.5)(4)$
$ = 26$

30c. There is no point that satisfies all equations.

31. $(x + 3)^2 - (y + 4)^2 = 9$
$ x = 2$
$(2 + 3)^2 - (y - 4)^2 = 9$
$25 - y^2 + 8y - 16 = 9$
$y^2 - 8y = 0$
$y(y - 8) = 0$
$y = 0 \text{ or } y - 8 = 0$
$\phantom{y = 0 \text{ or } y - 8} y = 8$

$(2, 8) \text{ and } (2, 0)$

32. midpoint of $\overline{AG}$ is $\left(\frac{-1+9}{2}, \frac{-3+0}{2}\right) = \left(4, \frac{-3}{2}\right)$

slope of $\overline{AG} = \frac{0 - (-3)}{9 - (-1)} = \frac{3}{10}$

slope of perpendicular is $\frac{-10}{3}$

$y - \left(\frac{-3}{2}\right) = \frac{-10}{3}(x - 4)$

$y + \frac{3}{2} = \frac{-10}{3}x + \frac{40}{3}$

$6y + 9 = -20x + 80$

$20x + 6y = 71$

33. $y = (x - 1)^2$

$y = x + 1$

$x + 1 = (x - 1)^2$

$x + 1 = x^2 - 2x + 1$

$0 = x^2 - 3x$

$0 = x(x - 3)$

$x = 0$ or $x = 3$

$y = x + 1$	$y = x - 1$
$y = 0 + 1$	$y = 3 + 1$
$y = 1$	$y = 4$
(0, 1)	and (3, 4)

34. See students' work.

35. Let x = tickets for children under 12.

Let y = tickets for children 12 and over.

$1.50x + 2.50y = 405 \quad \rightarrow$

$(1.00x + 4.00y = 550)(-1.5) \quad \rightarrow$

$ 1.50x + 2.50y = 405$

$ \underline{-1.50x - 6.00y = -825}$

$ -3.5y = -420$

$ y = 120$

$ 1.00x + 4.00y = 550$

$1.00x + 4.00(120) = 550$

$ x = 70$

(70, 120)

36. Pennsylvania: (1,908,000, 1993)

 (2,303,000, 2020)

$m = \frac{2020 - 1993}{2,303,000 - 1,908,000} = \frac{27}{395,000}$

$y - 1993 = \frac{27}{395,000}(x - 1,908,000)$

Texas: (1,835,000, 1993)

 (3,640,000, 2020)

$m = \frac{2020 - 1993}{3,640,000 - 1,835,000} = \frac{27}{1,805,000}$

$y - 1993 = \frac{27}{1,805,000}(x - 1,835,000)$

$\frac{27}{395,000}(x - 1,908,000) = \frac{27}{1,805,000}(x - 1,835,000)$

$9747(x - 1,908,000) = 2133(x - 1,835,000)$

$9747x - 18,597,276,000 = 2133x - 3,914,055,000$

$7614x = 14,683,221,000$

$x \approx 1,928,450$

$y - 1993 = \frac{27}{395,000}(1,928,450 - 1,908,000)$

$y \approx 1994.397$

Yes; in 1994, Texas and Pennsylvania will both have about 1,928,000 people age 65 or older. The locus will be the point of intersection of the graphs of the two equations representing the number of people age 65 or older.

37.

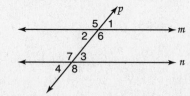

a circle with radius $\frac{DC}{2}$ and the midpoint of $\overline{DC}$ as its center

38. $g + 2g + 1.5g + 0.5g + g = 360$

$ 6g = 360$

$ g = 60$

60, 2(60) = 120, 1.5(60) = 90, 0.5(60) = 30, 60

39. $(x - 2)^2 + (y - 3)^2 = 25$

$(6 - 2)^2 + (j - 3)^2 = 25$

$4^2 + (j - 3)^2 = 25$

$16 + j^2 - 6j + 9 = 25$

$j^2 - 6j = 0$

$j(j - 6) = 0$

$j = 0$ or $j - 6 = 0$

$\phantom{j = 0 \text{ or } } j = 6$

40. $\frac{4}{x} = \frac{x}{19}$ $\frac{4}{y} = \frac{y}{23}$

$x^2 = 76$ $y^2 = 92$

$x = \sqrt{76} \approx 8.7$ $y = \sqrt{92} \approx 9.6$

$\frac{19}{z} = \frac{z}{23}$

$z^2 = 437$

$z = \sqrt{437} \approx 20.9$

41. trapezoid; Sample answer:

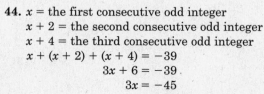

42. $m\angle 1 + m\angle 2 + 60 = 180$

$ m\angle 1 = m\angle 2$

$2(m\angle 1) + 60 = 180$

$2(m\angle 1) = 120$

$m\angle 1 = 60, \ m\angle 2 = 60$; equiangular and equilateral

43. Sample answer:

all odd-numbered angles have measure 145

44. x = the first consecutive odd integer

$x + 2$ = the second consecutive odd integer

$x + 4$ = the third consecutive odd integer

$x + (x + 2) + (x + 4) = -39$

$3x + 6 = -39$

$3x = -45$

$x = -15$

$x + 2 = -13$

$x + 4 = -11$

45.
$$\frac{r-3}{2-0}=\frac{3}{2}$$
$$2(r-3)=3(2)$$
$$2r-6=6$$
$$2r=12$$
$$r=6$$

Page 708 Mathematics and Society

1. The close-up photo would show the same basic patterns (turns, branches, etc.) as the long-range photo, but on a smaller scale. The position of each pattern can be described in terms of sliding, rotating, or reflecting a given pattern to another place on the plane.

2. The best place to build may be the locus of points equidistant from quickly growing areas. Population trends, housing needs, transportation, size and location of shopping facilities, schools needed, employment centers and trends, land use and availability are factors that might be considered.

3. See students' work.

13-3 Intersection of Loci

Page 709 Modeling Mathematics

a. yes   **b.** the same result   **c.** no

Page 712 Check for Understanding

1. by graphing or algebraically

2. intersection could be no points, one point, or two points

3. at most two   **4.** See students' work.

5. none, a point, two points, or a circle

6.
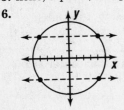
The locus is four points in the intersection of the circle of radius 5 units and center (0, 0) and the parallel lines 3 units on either side of the *x*-axis.

7.
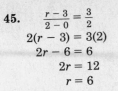
The locus is a point on the angle bisector 7 in. from the vertex.

8.
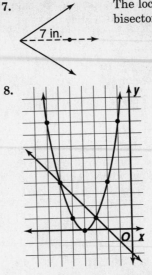
The locus is two points, (−3, 1) and (−6, 4).

9. a plane that is perpendicular to the *xy*-plane intersecting the *xy*-plane at $x = 5$

10. a cylinder with radius 4 and an axis passing through the point (2, 5, 0)

11. Construct the perpendicular bisectors of each side of the triangle formed by these three cities. This intersection area is the area that should be considered; Columbus, Ohio area.

Pages 712–714 Exercises

12a. none; two   **12b.** two; two

12c. two; two   **12d.** one; two

13. none or a point   **14.** none, a point, or a line

15. none, a point, two points, or a line segment

16. none, a point, a circle, or a sphere

17.
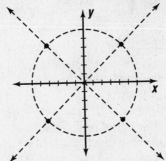
The locus is four points whose coordinates are $(\pm3\sqrt{2}, \pm3\sqrt{2})$.

18.
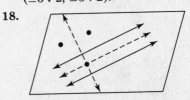
The locus is the intersection of the perpendicular bisector of the segment connecting two points and the line halfway between two parallel lines.

19. 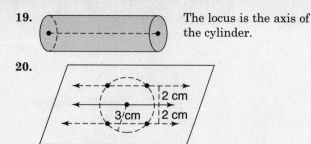 The locus is the axis of the cylinder.

20.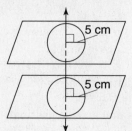

2 cm

3 cm | 2 cm

The locus is four points that are the intersection of the two parallel lines 2 cm from the given line and a circle of radius 3 cm whose center is the given point on the line.

21.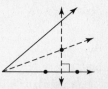

5 cm

5 cm

The locus is two circles with a radius of 5 cm that each line in the parallel planes and whose centers are the intersection of the perpendicular line with each plane.

22. 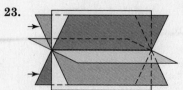 The locus is the intersection of the perpendicular bisector of the segment whose endpoints are the two points and the angle bisector.

23. The locus is a set of two intersecting planes.

24. a plane perpendicular to the xy-plane whose intersection with the xy-plane is the line $y = -3x + 11$

25. a parabola that opens up with vertex at $(9, 0)$

26. a plane perpendicular to the xy-plane whose intersection with the xy-plane is the line $y = -x$.

27. a circle with center $(4, 1)$ and radius 5.

28. a sphere with center $(-6, 3, 1)$ and radius 5

29. a sphere with center $(3, 4, 5)$ and radius 4

30. one

31. $(x + 3)^2 + (y - 1)^2 = 25$
$y = -3x - 13$
$(x + 3)^2 + (-3x - 13 - 1)^2 = 25$
$x^2 + 6x + 9 + 9x^2 + 84x + 196 = 25$
$10x^2 + 90x + 180 = 0$
$x^2 + 9x + 18 = 0$
$(x + 3)(x + 6) = 0$
$x = -3$ or $x = -6$

$y = -3(-3) - 13$ $y = -3(-6) - 13$
$y = 9 - 13$ $y = 18 - 13$
$y = -4$ $y = 5$
$(-3, -4)$ $(-6, 5)$

32. $x + y = 6$ $\rightarrow$ $y = 6 - x$
$(x - 1)^2 + y^2 = 17$
$(x - 1)^2 + (6 - x)^2 = 17$
$x^2 - 2x + 1 + 36 - 12x + x^2 = 17$
$2x^2 - 14x + 20 = 0$
$x^2 - 7x + 10 = 0$
$(x - 5)(x - 2) = 0$
$x = 5$ or $x = 2$

$y = 6 - 5$ $y = 6 - 2$
$y = 1$ $y = 4$
$(5, 1)$ $(2, 4)$

33. $x^2 + y^2 = 4$
$y = x + 6$
$x^2 + (x + 6)^2 = 4$
$x^2 + x^2 + 12x + 36 = 4$
$2x^2 + 12x + 32 = 0$
$x^2 + 6x + 16 = 0$
no points

34. points on and in the interior of the circle that lie above the x-axis

35.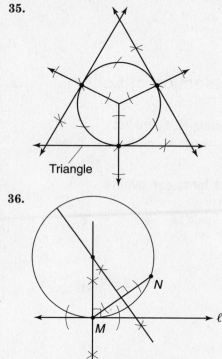

Triangle

36.

M   N ℓ

37. There would be many solutions.

38. Place the point at the intersection of the two lines.

39. the corner of E St. and 3rd St.

40. on the midline of the field so that the circle formed is at least tangent to the short side of the rectangle

41. a semicircle with radius 80 ft and center at the center of the goal

Geometry Chapter 13

42. $(9x + y = 20)(-3) \rightarrow -27x - 3y = -60$

$ 3x + 3y = 12 \qquad \underline{3x + 3y = 12}$

$ -24x = -48$

$ x = 2$

$ 9x + y = 20$

$ 9(2) + y = 20$

$ 18 + y = 20$

$ y = 2$

$ (2, 2)$

43. 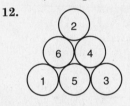 The locus is the perpendicular bisector of the segment connecting the two points of intersection.

44. $r = \sqrt{[4 - (-2)]^2 + [-3 - (-5)]^2 + (-2 - 7)^2}$

$ r = \sqrt{6^2 + 2^2 + (-9)^2}$

$ r = \sqrt{121} = 11$

$ (x - 4)^2 + [y - (-3)]^2 + [z - (-2)]^2 = 11^2$

$ (x - 4)^2 + (y + 3)^2 + (z + 2)^2 = 121$

45. $ C = 2\pi r$

$ 15.7 = 2\pi r$

$ 2.499 = r$

$ T = 4\pi r^2$

$ \approx 4\pi(2.499)^2$

$ \approx 78.5 \text{ m}^2$

$ V = \frac{4}{3}\pi r^3$

$ \approx \frac{4}{3}\pi(2.499)^2$

$ \approx 65.4 \text{ m}^3$

46. $A = \frac{1}{2}(b_1 + b_2)h$

length of median $= \frac{1}{2}(b_1 + b_2)$

$ A = 17.5(18) = 315 \text{ cm}^2$

47.

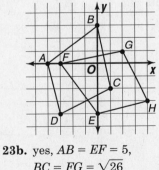

$c^2 = a^2 + b^2 - 2ab \cos C$

$(AB)^2 = 17^2 + 15^2 - 2(17)(15) \cos 39°$

$(AB)^2 \approx 117.66$

$ AB \approx 10.8$

48. $P_{\triangle FGE} = 2 \cdot P_{\triangle ABC}$

$\phantom{48.P_{\triangle FGE}} = 2(4 + 4.1 + 3.8) = 2(11.9) \text{ or } 23.8$

49. $\angle A \cong \angle C, \angle B \cong \angle D, \angle C \cong \angle E, \overline{AB} \cong \overline{CD},$

$\overline{BC} \cong \overline{DE}, \overline{AC} \cong \overline{CE}$

50. $ x^2 + 8x - 5 = 0$

$ x^2 + 8x = 5$

$ x^2 + 8x + 16 = 5 + 16$

$ (x + 4)^2 = 21$

$ x + 4 = \pm\sqrt{21}$

$ x = -4 \pm \sqrt{21}$

51. $x^2 + 5x - 3 = 0$

$ a = 1 \;\; b = 5 \;\; c = -3$

$ x = \dfrac{-5 \pm \sqrt{5^2 - 4(1)(-3)}}{2(1)}$

$ = \dfrac{-5 \pm \sqrt{37}}{2}$

$ \approx \dfrac{-5 \pm 6.08}{2}$

$\dfrac{-5 \pm 6.08}{2} \approx 0.54, \dfrac{-5 - 6.08}{2} \approx -5.54$

13-4 | Mappings

Page 718 Check for Understanding

1. because there are actually three transformations

2. The preimage and the image of both isometries and enlargements are similar figures. Those that have isometry preserve congruence and those that are enlargements don't preserve congruence.

3. See students' work.

4. They organize data, which makes analysis more efficient.

5. $\overline{CD}$ **6.** $\angle RUT$ **7.** $\angle STU$ **8.** $\overline{BC}$

9. two reflections or a rotation

10. reduction, rotation

11. Yes; all angles and sides are congruent.

12.

```
        ( 2 )
     ( 6 ) ( 4 )
  ( 1 ) ( 5 ) ( 3 )
```

Pages 718–721 Exercises

13. $\angle BAC$ **14.** $\angle D$ **15.** $\overline{ED}$ **16.** $\overline{CA}$

17. enlargement and reflection

18. rotation or reflection

19. enlargement, reflection

20. translation

21. Yes; all angles and sides are congruent.

22. no, $GH \neq AF$ and $DE \neq JI$

23a. rotation

23b. yes, $AB = EF = 5,$

$ BC = FG = \sqrt{26}$

$ CD = GH = \sqrt{20}$

$ AD = EH = \sqrt{17}$

24. $\triangle MNO$
26. $\triangle TXY$
28. $\triangle IJK$

25. quadrilateral $SRUT$
27. $\triangle GIH$
29. quadrilateral $HIJK$

30.

$\triangle ABC$		$\triangle A'B'C'$	
x	y	x	y
-5	-1	-5	1
0	2	0	-2
3	1	3	-1

$A'(-5, 1)$, $B'(0, -2)$, $C'(3, -1)$

31.

quadrilateral $ABCD$		quadrilateral $A'B'C'D'$	
x	y	x	y
-3	1	3	-3
-1	2	1	-2
-2	0	2	-4
-4	-1	4	-5

$A'(3, -3)$, $B'(1, -2)$, $C'(2, -4)$, $D'(4, -5)$

32a.

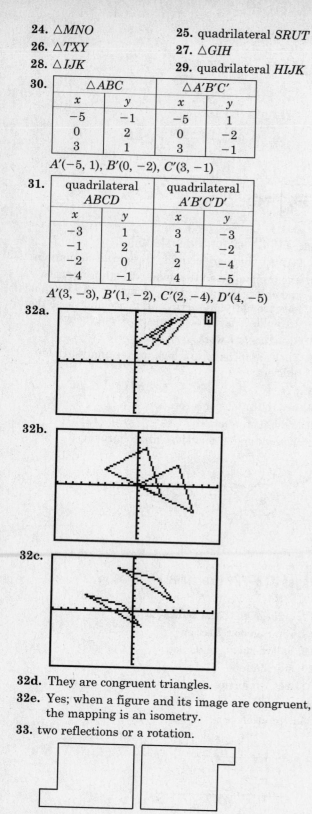

32b.

32c.

32d. They are congruent triangles.

32e. Yes; when a figure and its image are congruent, the mapping is an isometry.

33. two reflections or a rotation.

34. rotation

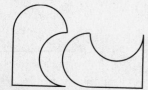

35. reflection of order and reflection of L and J

36. See students' work.   **37.** reflections
38. two points

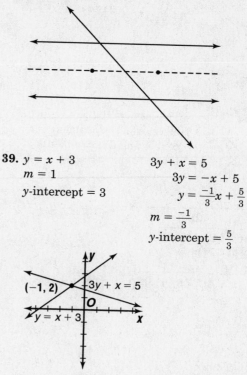

39. $y = x + 3$
$m = 1$
y-intercept $= 3$

$3y + x = 5$
$3y = -x + 5$
$y = \frac{-1}{3}x + \frac{5}{3}$
$m = \frac{-1}{3}$
y-intercept $= \frac{5}{3}$

40. The locus is two circles concentric to the given circle, one with a radius of 2 in. and the other with a radius of 8 in.

41. $m = \frac{-2 - 6}{3 - 7} = \frac{-8}{-4} = 2$
$y - 6 = 2(x - 7)$
$y - 6 = 2x - 14$
$y = 2x - 8$

42. always

43. $YZ = \frac{1}{2}(XY) = \frac{1}{2}(10)$ or 5
$XZ = \sqrt{3}(YZ) = 5\sqrt{3}$

44. $m = \frac{7 - 4}{2 - 1} = 3$
$f(x) = 3x + 1$

45. $\frac{29.29 - 21.75}{21.75} = \frac{7.54}{21.75} = .34\overline{6} \approx 35\%$

Page 721 Self Test

1. The locus is the circle that is the intersection of the cylindrical surface with axis ℓ and radius 8 cm, and the sphere with center R and radius 8 cm.

2. The locus is the two points that are the intersection of the perpendicular bisector of $\overline{PQ}$ and circle P with radius 8 cm.

3. $(x - 7y = 13)(-3)$ → $\quad -3x + 21y = -39$

$\ 3x - 5y = 23 \quad$ → $\quad \underline{3x - 5y = 23}$

$$16y = -16$$
$$y = -1$$

$$x - 7y = 13$$
$$x - 7(-1) = 13$$
$$x + 7 = 13$$
$$x = 6$$

$(6, -1)$

4. $x = 8 + 3y$

$$2x - 5y = 8$$
$$2(8 + 3y) - 5y = 8$$
$$16 + 6y - 5y = 8$$
$$y = -8$$

$$x = 8 + 3y$$
$$x = 8 + 3(-8)$$
$$x = -16$$

$(-16, -8)$

5. one point; $(-3, 1)$

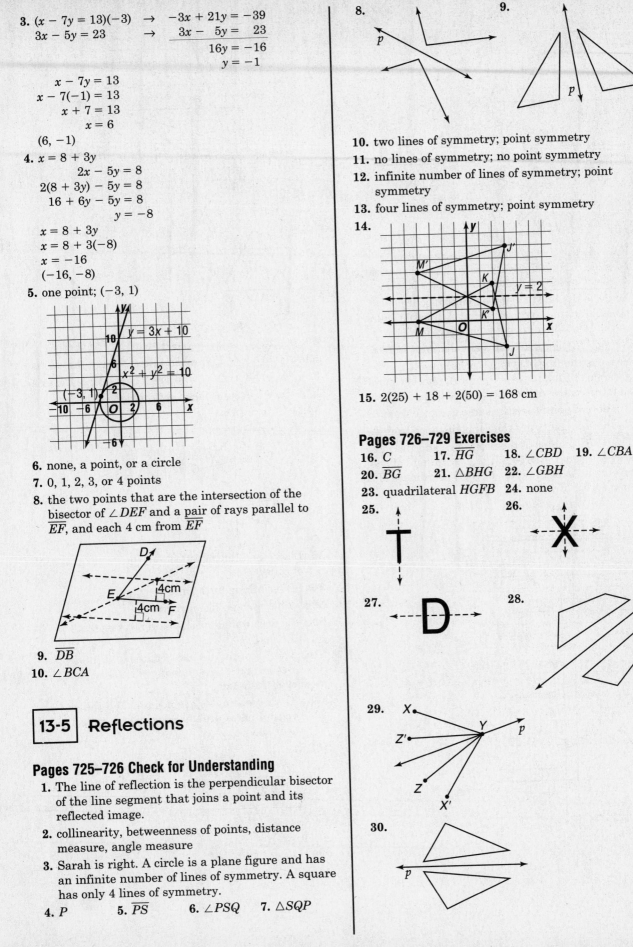

6. none, a point, or a circle

7. 0, 1, 2, 3, or 4 points

8. the two points that are the intersection of the bisector of $\angle DEF$ and a pair of rays parallel to $\overline{EF}$, and each 4 cm from $\overline{EF}$

9. $\overline{DB}$

10. $\angle BCA$

13-5 Reflections

Pages 725–726 Check for Understanding

1. The line of reflection is the perpendicular bisector of the line segment that joins a point and its reflected image.

2. collinearity, betweenness of points, distance measure, angle measure

3. Sarah is right. A circle is a plane figure and has an infinite number of lines of symmetry. A square has only 4 lines of symmetry.

4. P **5.** $\overline{PS}$ **6.** $\angle PSQ$ **7.** $\triangle SQP$

8.

9.

10. two lines of symmetry; point symmetry

11. no lines of symmetry; no point symmetry

12. infinite number of lines of symmetry; point symmetry

13. four lines of symmetry; point symmetry

14.

15. $2(25) + 18 + 2(50) = 168$ cm

Pages 726–729 Exercises

16. C **17.** $\overline{HG}$ **18.** $\angle CBD$ **19.** $\angle CBA$

20. $\overline{BG}$ **21.** $\triangle BHG$ **22.** $\angle GBH$

23. quadrilateral $HGFB$ **24.** none

25.

26.

27.

28.

29.

30.

31.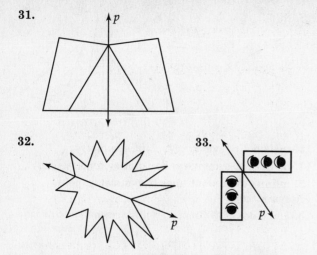

32. 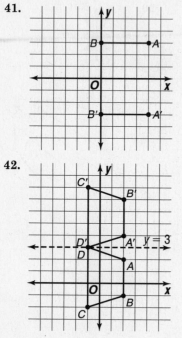 **33.**

34. Yes; ℓ is the line of symmetry because it is possible to find, for every point A, another point B so that ℓ is the perpendicular bisector of $\overline{AB}$.

35. Yes; ℓ is the line of symmetry because it is possible to find, for every point A, another point B so that ℓ is the perpendicular bisector of $\overline{AB}$.

36. No; not all points are the same distance from ℓ.

37. Yes; ℓ is the line of symmetry because it is possible to find, for every point A, another point B so that ℓ is the perpendicular bisector of $\overline{AB}$.

38. No; not all points are the same distance from ℓ.

39. No; not all points are the same distance from ℓ.

40. The x-coordinates of the pre-image and the image stay the same. However, the y-coordinate of the pre-image is negated to get the y-coordinate of the image.

41.

42.

43.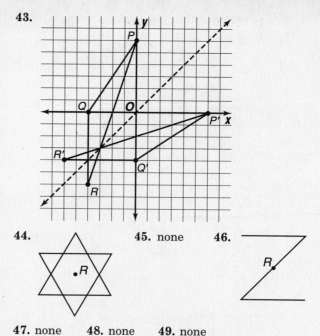

44. 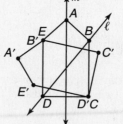 **45.** none **46.**

47. none   **48.** none   **49.** none

50. point symmetry   **51.** both   **52.** both

53a. $(x, y) \rightarrow (-x, y)$ when reflected over the y-axis

53b. $(x, y) \rightarrow (x, -y)$ when reflected over the x-axis

53c. $(x, y) \rightarrow (y, x)$ when reflected over the line $y = x$

54.

55. Line m is a line of reflection; the vertex is a point of reflection.

56a. interlocking hexagons; no

56b. a honeycomb-like structure

56c. Figures would overlap and not tessellate correctly.

57a. The y-coordinates are negated and the x-coordinates are unchanged. It is reflected over the x-axis.

57b. The x-coordinates are negated and the y-coordinates are unchanged. It is reflected over the y-axis.

58.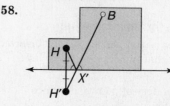

59a. $\angle S$ **59b.** $\overline{CD}$

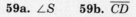

60.

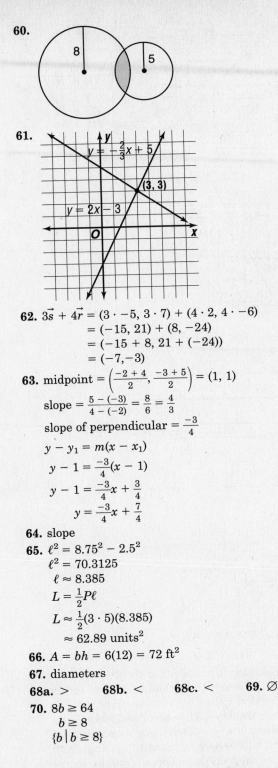

61.

$y = -\frac{2}{3}x + 5$

(3, 3)

$y = 2x - 3$

62. $3\vec{s} + 4\vec{r} = (3 \cdot -5, 3 \cdot 7) + (4 \cdot 2, 4 \cdot -6)$
$= (-15, 21) + (8, -24)$
$= (-15 + 8, 21 + (-24))$
$= (-7, -3)$

63. midpoint $= \left(\frac{-2 + 4}{2}, \frac{-3 + 5}{2}\right) = (1, 1)$

slope $= \frac{5 - (-3)}{4 - (-2)} = \frac{8}{6} = \frac{4}{3}$

slope of perpendicular $= \frac{-3}{4}$

$y - y_1 = m(x - x_1)$

$y - 1 = \frac{-3}{4}(x - 1)$

$y - 1 = \frac{-3}{4}x + \frac{3}{4}$

$y = \frac{-3}{4}x + \frac{7}{4}$

64. slope

65. $\ell^2 = 8.75^2 - 2.5^2$
$\ell^2 = 70.3125$
$\ell \approx 8.385$
$L = \frac{1}{2}P\ell$
$L \approx \frac{1}{2}(3 \cdot 5)(8.385)$
≈ 62.89 units^2

66. $A = bh = 6(12) = 72$ ft^2

67. diameters

68a. > **68b.** < **68c.** < **69.** $\varnothing$

70. $8b \geq 64$
$b \geq 8$
$\{b \mid b \geq 8\}$

13-6A Modeling Mathematics: Reflections and Translations

Page 730

1. The orientation remains unchanged.

2. yes

3. $AA'' = BB'' = CC'' = 2$(distance from ℓ to m)

4. Use a translation.

5a. See students' work.

5b. The image is a translation of the preimage.

5c. yes

13-6 Translations

Page 732 Modeling Mathematics

a. It is hidden from view. **b.** 3

c. 3 rectangles

Pages 733–734 Check for Understanding

1. Collinearity, betweenness of points, distance measure, angle measure; each of these properties are also preserved in a translation.

2. A translation is like sliding a figure in one direction such that all points move the same number of units.

3. Sample answer: yes; the designs on wallpaper keep repeating. The pictures are usually translations of each other. While hanging wallpaper, it is important to match parts of the repeating pattern.

4. $(2, -5)$ **5a.** 5

5b. There will be an addition x number of rectangular faces after the translation, where x is the number of sides on the polygon that is the base. There will be 2 base faces of a given polygoral shape.

6. Yes; $\overline{TU}$ is a glide of $\overline{PQ}$.

7. No; $\triangle HGK$ is not turned correctly.

8. $S'(1, 2)$

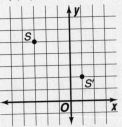

9. $E'(4, 1), F'(7, 3), G'(7, 1)$

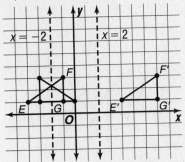

10. $H'(1, 1), I'(5, 3), J'(5, 1) K'(1, 1)$

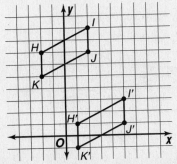

237 *Geometry* Chapter 13

11. It is a move of 15 ft away from the wall and 21 ft to the left and rotated.

Pages 734–737 Exercises

12. R **13.** T **14.** Q

15. U **16.** S **17.** none

18. Yes; it is one reflection after another with respect to two parallel lines.

19. Yes; it is one reflection after another with respect to two parallel lines.

20. Yes, it is one reflection after another with respect to two parallel lines.

21. No; it is a translation and then a reflection with respect to a line.

22. $W'(-1, 5)$ $X'(2, 2)$

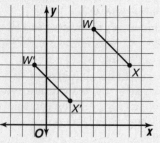

23. $A'(-8, -4)$, $B'(-3, -2)$, $C'(-4, -5)$, $D'(-7, -6)$

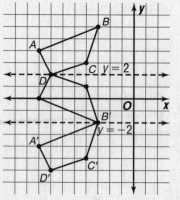

24. $C'(-10, -1)$, $A'(-8, 2)$, $T'(-6, -2)$

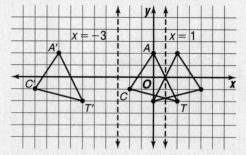

25. $N'(-4, 1)$, $I'(0, 0)$, $C'(0, 3)$, $K'(-8, -1)$

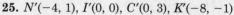

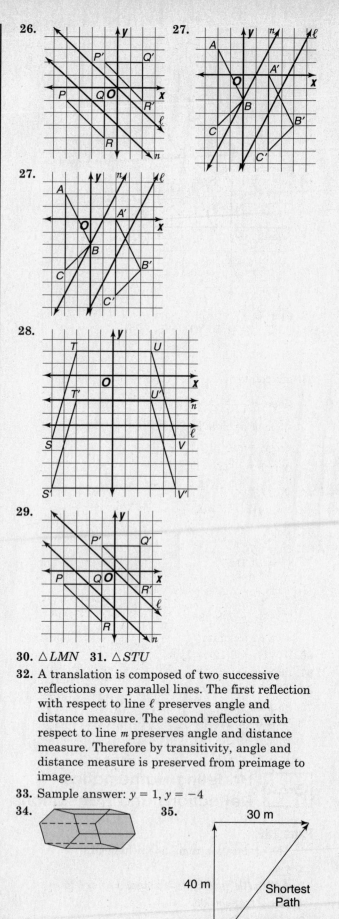

26.

27.

27.

28.

29.

30. $\triangle LMN$ **31.** $\triangle STU$

32. A translation is composed of two successive reflections over parallel lines. The first reflection with respect to line ℓ preserves angle and distance measure. The second reflection with respect to line m preserves angle and distance measure. Therefore by transitivity, angle and distance measure is preserved from preimage to image.

33. Sample answer: $y = 1$, $y = -4$

34.

35.

30 m

40 m

Shortest Path

Geometry Chapter 13

36.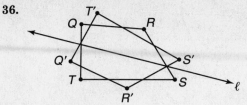

37. a circle

38.
$$(2x - 6y = 8)(2) \quad \rightarrow \quad 4x - 12y = 16$$
$$(3x + 4y = -4)(3) \quad \rightarrow \quad \underline{9x + 12y = -12}$$
$$13x = 4$$
$$x = \frac{4}{13}$$

$$2x - 6y = 8$$
$$2\left(\frac{4}{13}\right) - 6y = 8$$
$$-6y = \frac{96}{13}$$
$$y = \frac{-16}{13}$$
$$\left(\frac{4}{13}, \frac{-16}{13}\right)$$

39a. $\overrightarrow{SA}$ **b.** $\overrightarrow{QT}$ **c.** $\overrightarrow{TR}$

40. $y = \frac{3}{4}x - 3$

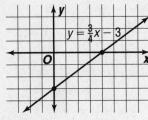

41. yes; *HL*

42. An isosceles triangle has at least two sides congruent, and an equilateral triangle has three congruent sides.

43. $8x^2 + 48xy + 72y^2 = 8(x^2 + 6xy + 9y^2)$
$$= 8(x + 3y)^2$$

44a. 42, 66, 66, 75, 83, 84, 84, 156, 158

44b. $\frac{2}{9}$ **44c.** $\frac{7}{9}$

13-6B Using Technology: Translating Polygons with Vectors

Page 738 Exercises

1. See students' work.   2. See students' work.

3. See students' work.   4a. See students' work.

4b. See students' work.   4c. See students' work.

4d. See students' work.

13-7 Rotations

Page 739 Modeling Mathematics

a. congruence of sides and angles

b. Yes; it is a congruence transformation.

Pages 741–742 Check for Understanding

1. Both a translation and a rotation are made up of two reflections. The difference is that a translation is reflected over parallel lines and a rotation is reflected over intersecting lines.

2. A rotation image can be found by reflecting the image over a line, then reflecting that image over a second line that intersects the first line. Another method is to rotate each point using the angle of rotation.

3. Yes; it is made of 6 equilateral triangles that repeat every 60°.

4a. Sample answer: midpoint of $\overline{AY}$

4b. Sample answer: a point on the perpendicular bisector of $\overline{AY}$

4c. Any point on the perpendicular bisector of $\overline{AY}$ could be a center of rotation.

5. 2(37°) = 74°   **6.** pentagon *GHIDE*

7. pentagon *PKLMN*   **8.** pentagon *LMNPK*

9. $\angle CNQ$ **10.** 2(70°) = 140°   **11.** $\overline{NK}$

12.

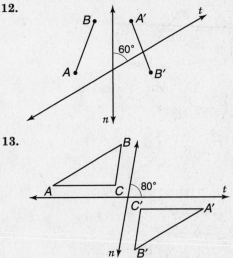

13.

14a. The *x*- and *y*-coordinates of the preimage were negated to get the coordinates of the image.

14b. This is a 180° rotation.

Pages 743–745 Exercises

15. Yes; it is a proper successive reflection with respect to two intersecting lines.

16. Yes; it is a proper successive reflection with respect to two intersecting lines.

17. 2(55°) = 110°   **18.** 2(28.5°) = 57°

19. 2(74°) = 148°

20.

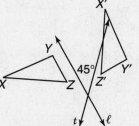

21.

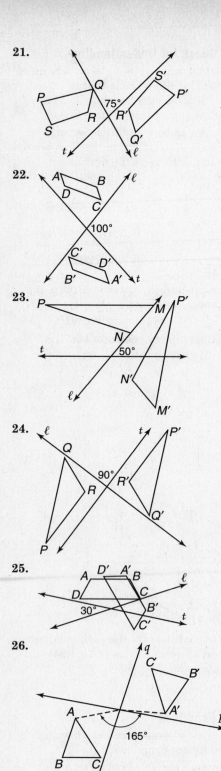

22.

23.

24.

25.

26.

27.

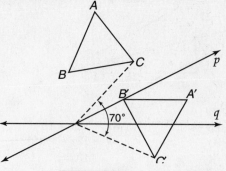

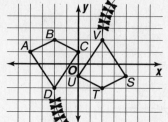

	angle measure	betweenness of points	orientation	collinearity	distance measure
28. reflection	yes	yes	no	yes	yes
29. translation	yes	yes	yes	yes	yes
30. rotation	yes	yes	no	yes	yes

31. See students' work.   **32.** See students' work.

33.

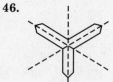

34. $360 \div 6 = 60$ **35.** $2(60) = 120$
36. two rotations   **37.** reflection
38. rotation   **39.** translation
40. reflection

41. Angles of rotation with measures of 90 or 180 would be easier on a coordinate plane because of the grids used in graphing.

42. *H, I, N, O, S, X, Z*

43a. $\frac{360}{16} \times 4 = 90$ **43b.** $\frac{360}{16} \times x = 135$
$x = 6$
$1 + 6 = \text{Seat } 7$

44a. right circular cone   **44b.** square

45. Yes; the upper left, upper right, and center quadrilaterals.

46.

47. The locus in two circles concentric to the given circle, one with radius of 2 in. and the other width radius of 8 in.

48. Given: $\overline{AD} \cong \overline{BC}$
$\overline{AB} \cong \overline{DC}$

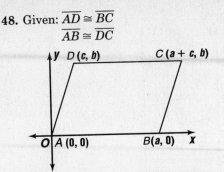

Prove: *ABCD* is a parallelogram.

Proof:

Use the distance formula to find *AB*, *DC*, *AD*, and *BC*.

$AB = \sqrt{(a-0)^2 + (0-0)^2}$
$\quad = \sqrt{a^2 + 0^2}$
$\quad = \sqrt{a^2}$
$\quad = a$

$AD = \sqrt{(c-0)^2 + (b-0)^2}$
$\quad = \sqrt{c^2 + b^2}$

$DC = \sqrt{(a+c-c)^2 + (b-b)^2}$
$\quad = \sqrt{a^2 + 0^2}$
$\quad = \sqrt{a^2}$
$\quad = a$

$BC = \sqrt{(a+c-a)^2 + (b-0)^2}$
$\quad = \sqrt{c^2 + b^2}$

Thus, $AB = DC$ and $AD = BC$. By the definition of congruence, $\overline{AB} \cong \overline{DC}$ and $\overline{AD} \cong \overline{BC}$. Therefore, *ABCD* is a parallelogram.

49. $r^2 = 20^2 - 16^2$ $V = \frac{1}{3}Bh$
$r^2 = 144$ $= \frac{1}{2}(144\pi)(16)$
$r = 12$ $= 768\pi \approx 2412.7 \text{ ft}^3$

$B = r^2 = 12^2\pi$ or 144π

50.

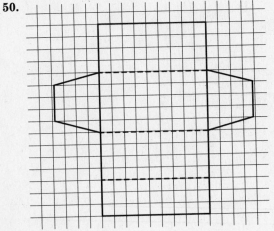

51. $x = \frac{1}{2}(75) = 37.5$

52. Yes; $m\angle S = 53$, $m\angle C = 37$

$\frac{AB}{RS} = \frac{AC}{QR}$ $\frac{AC}{QR} = \frac{CB}{QS}$
$\frac{AB}{6} = \frac{6}{8}$ $\frac{6}{8} = \frac{7.5}{QS}$
$8AB = 36$ $6QS = 60$
$AB = 4.5$ $QS = 10$

53. $\frac{1}{x+9}$

54. $3z^2 - 75 = 3(z^2 - 25)$
$\qquad\qquad\quad = 3(z+5)(z-5)$

13-8 | Dilations

Pages 749–750 Check for Understanding

1. All transformations, except dilations, produce congruent figures. The dilation image may be congruent or may be similar.

2. A dilation is an enlargement if the absolute value of the scale factor is greater than one. It is a reduction if the absolute value of the scale factor is a value between 0 and 1.

3. If the scale factor is a negative value, a dilation of *P* with center *C* would have its image point on the ray opposite $\overrightarrow{CP}$.

4. A dilation produces figures that are similar.

5. See students' work.   **6.** $6 \times 8 = 48$

7. $BC < YZ$ **8.** $32 \div 8 = 4$

9. 62   **10.** similar

11. congruence transformation

12. enlargement   **13.** reduction

14. reduction

15. Scale factor of 2:

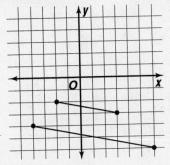

Scale factor of $\frac{1}{2}$:

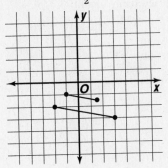

16. Scale factor of 2:

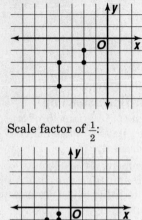

Scale factor of $\frac{1}{2}$:

17. $\frac{1}{2}$

18. $12x = 8$

$x = \frac{8}{12} = \frac{2}{3}$

She should use a scale factor of $\frac{2}{3}$.

Pages 750–753 Exercises

19. B **20.** T **21.** S **22.** F

23. $|-6| \cdot 5 = 30$ **24.** $\frac{1}{2} \cdot \frac{2}{3} = \frac{1}{3}$

25. $1.5(16) = 24$ **26.** $\frac{1}{4}(12) = 3$

27. $|-1|(3) = 3$ **28.** $|-5|(3.1) = 15.5$

29. $CD = |k|CA$ **30.** $CE = |k|CB$

$10 = |k|5$ $4 = |k|6$

$|k| = 2$, enlargement $|k| = \frac{2}{3}$, reduction

31. $DE = |k|AB$

$7 = |k|7$

$|k| = 1$, congruence transformation

32. $DE = |k|AB$ **33.** $CE = |k|CB$

$12 = |k|4$ $7 = |k|28$

$|k| = 3$, enlargement $|k| = \frac{1}{4}$

34. $CE = |k|CB$

$18 = |k|27$

$|k| = \frac{2}{3}$, reduction

35. $\frac{3}{4}$ **36.** $\frac{3}{2}$ **37.** 2

38. Scale factor of 2:

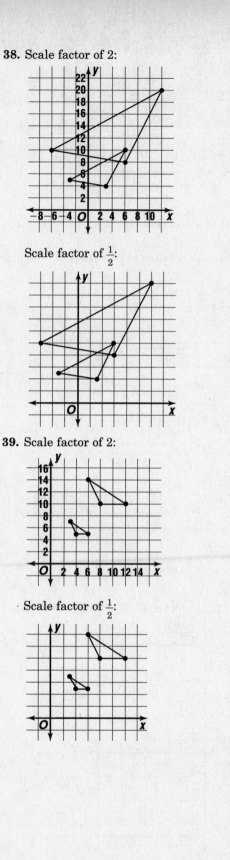

Scale factor of $\frac{1}{2}$:

39. Scale factor of 2:

Scale factor of $\frac{1}{2}$:

Geometry Chapter 13

40. Scale factor of 2:

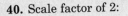
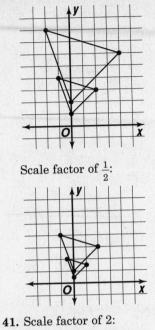

Scale factor of $\frac{1}{2}$:

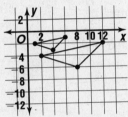

41. Scale factor of 2:

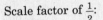

Scale factor of $\frac{1}{2}$:

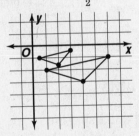

42. Scale factor of 2:

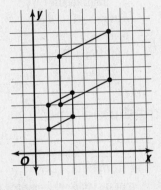

Scale factor of $\frac{1}{2}$:

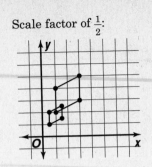

43. Scale factor of 2:

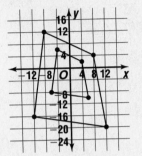

Scale factor of $\frac{1}{2}$:

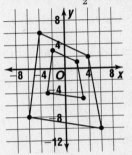

44a. The perimeter of the image will be four times the perimeter of the preimage.

44b. The area of the image will be sixteen times the area of the preimage.

45a. The surface area of the image will be nine times the surface area of the preimage.

45b. The volume of the image will be 27 times the volume of the preimage.

46. Given: dilation with center C and scale factor k

Prove: $ED = k(AB)$

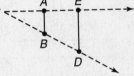

Proof:

$CE = k(CA)$ and $CD = K(CB)$ by the definition of a dilation. $\frac{CE}{CA} = k$ and $\frac{CD}{CB} = k$. So, $\frac{CE}{CA} = \frac{CD}{CB}$ by substitution. $\angle ACB \cong \angle ECD$, since congruence of angles is reflexive. Therefore, by SAS Similarity, $\triangle ACB$ is similar to $\triangle ECD$. The corresponding sides of similar triangles are proportional, so $\frac{ED}{AB} = \frac{CE}{CA}$. We know that $\frac{CE}{CA} = k$, so $\frac{ED}{AB} = k$ by substitution. Therefore, $ED = k(AB)$ by the Multiplication Property of Equality.

47.

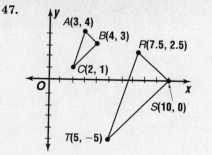

Center: (0, 5)

$BC = \sqrt{(4-2)^2 + (3-1)^2} = \sqrt{8}$

$ST = \sqrt{(10-5)^2 + (0-(-5))^2} = \sqrt{50}$

$ST = |k|BC$

$5\sqrt{2} = |k|(2\sqrt{2})$

$|k| = \frac{5}{2}$

48. $8\left(\frac{3}{4}\right) = 6$ in., $10\left(\frac{3}{4}\right) = 7.5$ in.

6 in. by 7.5 in.

49. $\dfrac{2.25 \text{ in.}}{x \text{ miles}} = \dfrac{1 \text{ in.}}{150 \text{ miles}}$

$x = 337.5$ miles

50a. Sample answer: the same fish are used at different sizes.

50b. The various fishes are tessellated so that the entire surface is covered.

51.

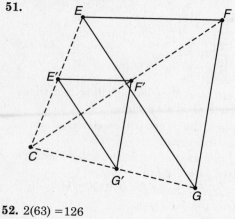

52. $2(63) = 126$

53.

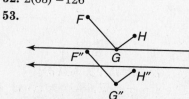

54. Read the problem carefully. Draw the given figure. Locate the points that satisfy the given conditions. Draw a smooth geometric figure. Describe the locus.

55. $LM = \sqrt{(-2-5)^2 + (3-6)^2 + [7-(-4)]^2}$

$\quad = \sqrt{(-7)^2 + (-3)^2 + 11^2}$

$\quad = \sqrt{49 + 9 + 121}$

$\quad = \sqrt{179} \approx 13.4$ units

56a. $y = 17,650 - 895x$

56b. $0 = 17,650 - 895x$

$895x = 17,650$

$x \approx 19.72 \approx 19$ h 45 min

57. $P = 6(8) = 48$

$A = \ell w$

$\quad = (40+60)(48+3)$

$\quad = 100(51) = 5100 \text{ mm}^2$

58. 45; The hypotenuse is $\sqrt{2}$ times as long as the leg, so it is a 45°−45°−90° triangle.

59. $\dfrac{GH}{HJ} = \dfrac{GK}{JK}$

$\dfrac{9}{HJ} = \dfrac{12}{10}$

$12HJ = 90$

$HJ = 7.5$

60. $(3p + 4q = -5)(3) \rightarrow \quad 9p + 12q = -15$

$5p - 12q = -27 \quad \rightarrow \quad \underline{5p - 12q = -27}$

$\qquad\qquad\qquad\qquad\qquad 14p = -42$

$\qquad\qquad\qquad\qquad\qquad\quad p = -3$

$3p + 4q = -5$

$3(-3) + 4q = -5$

$\qquad\quad 4q = 4$

$\qquad\quad\; q = 1$

$(-3, 1)$

61a.

	baked	broccoli
		peas
chicken	sweet	broccoli
		peas
	fried	broccoli
		peas
	baked	broccoli
		peas
fish	sweet	broccoli
		peas
	fried	broccoli
		peas

61b. $\frac{2}{12}$ or $\frac{1}{6}$

Chapter 13 Highlights

Page 755 Understanding and Using the Vocabulary

1. true
2. false; locus
3. true
4. false; dilation
5. false; image
6. true
7. true
8. false; reflection
9. false; preimage
10. true

Chapter 13 Study Guide and Assessment

Pages 756–758 Skills and Concepts

11. The locus is the interior of a circle with center at the given point and radius 6 cm.

12. The locus is a plane that is the perpendicular bisector of the segment joining the two points.

13. The locus is the circumcenter; the point where the three perpendicular bisectors of the segments joining A, B, and C intersect.

14.

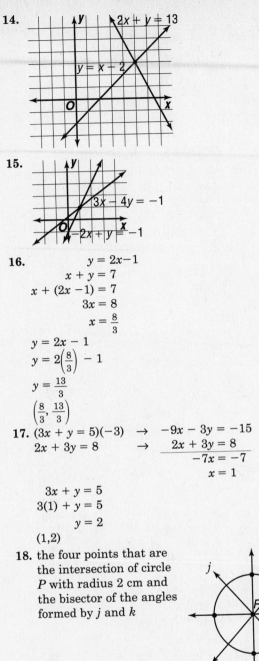

$2x + y = 13$

$y = x - 2$

15.

$3x - 4y = -1$

$-2x + y = -1$

16.
$$y = 2x - 1$$
$$x + y = 7$$
$$x + (2x - 1) = 7$$
$$3x = 8$$
$$x = \frac{8}{3}$$

$$y = 2x - 1$$
$$y = 2\left(\frac{8}{3}\right) - 1$$
$$y = \frac{13}{3}$$
$$\left(\frac{8}{3}, \frac{13}{3}\right)$$

17. $(3x + y = 5)(-3) \rightarrow -9x - 3y = -15$
$2x + 3y = 8 \rightarrow \underline{\quad 2x + 3y = 8 \quad}$
$$-7x = -7$$
$$x = 1$$

$$3x + y = 5$$
$$3(1) + y = 5$$
$$y = 2$$
$$(1, 2)$$

18. the four points that are the intersection of circle P with radius 2 cm and the bisector of the angles formed by j and k

19. the circle that is the intersection of spheres P and Q with radii 3 cm

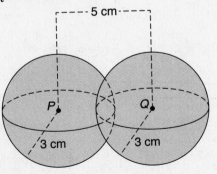

20. the point of intersection between the perpendicular bisector of the two points and the line parallel to and halfway between the two parallel lines

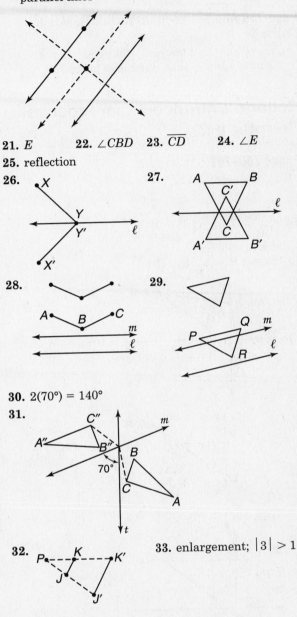

21. E **22.** $\angle CBD$ **23.** $\overline{CD}$ **24.** $\angle E$

25. reflection

26.   **27.**

28.   **29.**

30. $2(70°) = 140°$

31.

32.   **33.** enlargement; $|3| > 1$

Page 758 Applications and Problem Solving

34. The stake should be a perpendicular distance of at least 18 ft from, and all the way around, the horizontal pole if it were laying on the ground.

35. Imagine the reflection of the 5 ball with respect to the line formed by one side of the billiard table, and aim for the reflection.

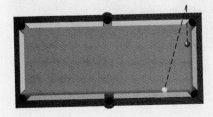

36. reflection

37. $\frac{360}{5} = 72$
$2(72) = 144$

Page 759 Alternative Assessment: Thinking Critically

• There may be none, one, a finite number of points, or an infinite number of points.

College Entrance Exam Practice, Chapter 1–13

Pages 760–761

1. perimeter of $\triangle XYZ = 8 = 3s$
$\frac{8}{3} = s$
perimeter of octagon $RSTUVWYZ =$
$8\left(\frac{8}{3}\right) = \frac{64}{3} = 21\frac{1}{3}$ (B)

2. $\frac{282}{60} = 4\frac{42}{60} = 4\frac{7}{10}$ hr (D)

3.

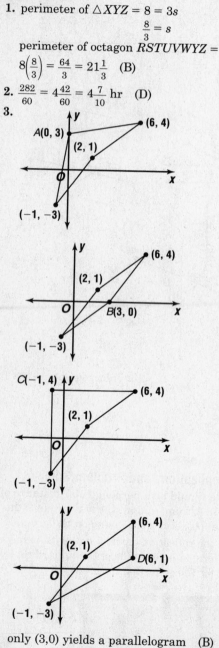

only (3,0) yields a parallelogram (B)

4. $\frac{p}{q} = \frac{2}{3} = \frac{4}{6}$ $\frac{q}{r} = \frac{6}{11}$
$p = 4$ (A)

5. $8(624) + 624 = 9(624) = 5(624) + 4(624)$ (B)

6. $-3 - x < 2x < 9 - x$
$-3 - x < 2x$ and $2x < 9 - x$
$-3 < 3x$ $3x < 9$
$-1 < x$ $x < 3$
$\{x \mid -1 < x < 3\}$ (A)

7. $\frac{a}{3a + 6} - \frac{a}{5a + 10} = \frac{2}{5}$ LCD: $15(a + 2)$
$5a - 3a = 2(3)(a + 2)$
$2a = 6a + 12$
$-4a = 12$
$a = -3$ (B)

8. $\frac{2}{1000} + \frac{3}{10} + \frac{4}{100} = 0.002 + .03 + 0.04 = 0.342$ (A)

9. $68 + x + 3x = 180$
$4x = 112$
$x = 28$
$3x = 84$

10. same as $ABCD$

11. $\frac{3}{4 - x} \div \frac{x}{x^2 - 16} = \frac{3}{-(x - 4)} \cdot \frac{(x + 4)(x - 4)}{x}$
$= \frac{-3(x + 4)}{x}$

12.

4

13. $\sqrt{y^2 - 4y + 9} = y - 1$ **14.** $x + 4x = 360$
$y^2 - 4y + 9 = (y - 1)^2$ $5x = 360$
$y^2 - 4y + 9 = y^2 - 2y + 1$ $x = 72°$
$8 = 2y$
$4 = y$ $\{4\}$

15. $1^2 + 1^2 = OM^2$
$2 = OM^2$
$OM^2 + OP^2 = MP^2$
$2 + 1 = MP^2$
$3 = MP^2$
$MP^2 + PQ^2 = MQ^2$
$3 + 1 = MQ^2$
$4 = MQ^2$
$MQ^2 + QR^2 = MR^2$
$4 + 1 = MR^2$
$5 = MR^2$
$\sqrt{5} = MR$

16. $\sqrt{3^4} = 3^2 = 9$ $9 = 9$ (C)

17. (D)

18. 30% of circle $\frac{90}{360}$ of circle (A)
25% of circle

19. Not enough information we do not know if $b < a$ or $b > a$. (D)

20. $1 \cdot 3 \cdot 5 \cdot 7 \cdot 9 = 945$ $2 \cdot 4 \cdot 6 \cdot 8 = 384$ (A)

EXTRA PRACTICE

1. $(-4, -1)$ **2.** $(3, -1)$ **3.** $(3, 4)$ **4.** $(-2, 4)$

5–7.

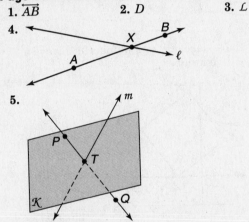

8. $(-3) \stackrel{?}{=} 2(0) - 3$
$-3 = -3$
collinear

9. $(-4) \stackrel{?}{=} 2(-0.5) - 3$
$-4 = -4$
collinear

10. $(-1) \stackrel{?}{=} 2(2) - 3$
$-1 \neq 1$
noncollinear

Page 764 Lesson 1–2

1. $\overleftrightarrow{AB}$ **2.** D **3.** $\mathcal{L}$

4.

5.

6. planes PAB, PBC, PCD, PAD, ABC
7. $\overrightarrow{AB}$, $\overrightarrow{CB}$, $\overrightarrow{PB}$

Page 764 Lesson 1–3

1. $P = 2\ell + 2w = 2(7) + 2(2) = 18$ in.
$A = \ell w = 2(7) = 14$ in^2

2. $P = 4s = 4(3.4) = 13.6$ m
$A = s^2 = (3.4)^2 = 11.56$ m^2

3. $P = 2\ell + 2w = 2(12) + 2(3) = 30$ cm
$A = \ell w = 12(3) = 36$ cm^2

4. $A = \ell w = 6(4.5) = 27$

5. $P = 2\ell + 2w = 2(12) + 2(8) = 40$

6. $\quad P = 2\ell + 2w$
$\dfrac{P - 2\ell}{2} = w$
$\dfrac{17 - 2(5.5)}{2} = w$
$3 = w$

7. $A = \ell w$
$\ell = \dfrac{A}{w}$
$= \dfrac{91}{7}$
$= 13$

For Exercises 8–10, $\ell = w = s$, because each rectangle is a square.

8. $P = 4s$ $\quad A = s^2$
$36 = 4s$ $\quad = 9^2$
$s = 9$ cm $\quad = 81$ cm^2

9. $P = 4s$ $\quad A = s^2$
$68 = 4s$ $\quad = (17)^2$
$s = 17$ in. $\quad = 289$ in.^{2}

10. $P = 4s$ $\quad A = s^2$
$118 = 4s$ $\quad = (29.5)^2$
$s = 29.5$ yd $\quad = 870.25$ yd^2

Page 765 Lesson 1–4

1. $CD = |-1 - 0| = |-1| = 1$
2. $BF = |-4 - 9| = |-13| = 13$
3. $CF = |-1 - 9| = |-10| = 10$
4. $EB = |-4 - 3| = |-7| = 7$
5. $BA = \sqrt{(-3 - 0)^2 + (-1 - 1)^2}$
$= \sqrt{9 + 4}$
$= \sqrt{13} \approx 3.61$
6. $ED = \sqrt{(-5 - 3)^2 + (3 - 4)^2}$
$= \sqrt{64 + 1}$
$= \sqrt{65} \approx 8.06$
7. $AC = \sqrt{(0 - 4)^2 + (1 - (-3))^2}$
$= \sqrt{16 + 16}$
$= \sqrt{32} \approx 5.66$
8. $CD = \sqrt{(4 - 3)^2 + (-3 - 4)^2}$
$= \sqrt{1 + 49}$
$= \sqrt{50} \approx 7.07$

9. $a^2 + b^2 = c^2$
$9^2 + 12^2 = x^2$
$81 + 144 = x^2$
$\pm\sqrt{225} = x$
$15 = x$
15 cm

10. $a^2 + b^2 = c^2$
$2^2 + 5^2 = x^2$
$4 + 25 = x^2$
$\pm\sqrt{29} = x$
$\sqrt{29} = x$
$\sqrt{29} \approx 5.39$ in.

11. $a^2 + b^2 = c^2$
$7^2 + 7^2 = x^2$
$49 + 49 = x^2$
$\pm\sqrt{98} = x$
$7\sqrt{2} = x$
$7\sqrt{2} \approx 9.90$ ft

Page 765 Lesson 1–5

1. $\dfrac{0 + 6}{2} = \dfrac{6}{2} = 3$

2. $\dfrac{-4 + 0}{2} = \dfrac{-4}{2} = -2$

3. $\dfrac{0 + 3}{2} = \dfrac{3}{2} = 1\frac{1}{2}$

4. $\left(\dfrac{x_1 + x_2}{2}, \dfrac{y_1 + y_2}{2}\right) = \left(\dfrac{-9 + 3}{2}, \dfrac{4 + (-2)}{2}\right)$
$M(-3, 1)$

5. $\left(\dfrac{x_1 + x_2}{2}, \dfrac{y_1 + y_2}{2}\right) = (-1, 8)$

$\dfrac{x_1 + x_2}{2} = -1$
$\dfrac{2 + x_2}{2} = -1$
$2 + x_2 = -2$
$x_2 = -4$

$\dfrac{y_1 + y_2}{2} = 8$
$\dfrac{6 + y_2}{2} = 8$
$6 + y_2 = 16$
$y_2 = 10$

$A(-4, 10)$

6. $\left(\dfrac{x_1 + x_2}{2}, \dfrac{y_1 + y_2}{2}\right) = (1, -5)$

$\dfrac{x_1 + x_2}{2} = 1$ $\qquad$ $\dfrac{y_1 + y_2}{2} = -5$

$\dfrac{-5 + x_2}{2} = 1$ $\qquad$ $\dfrac{-4 + y_2}{2} = -5$

$-5 + x_2 = 2$ $\qquad$ $-4 + y_2 = -10$

$x_2 = 7$ $\qquad\qquad$ $y_2 = -6$

$B(7, -6)$

7. $\left(\dfrac{x_1 + x_2}{2}, \dfrac{y_1 + y_2}{2}\right) = \left(\dfrac{7 + 2}{2}, \dfrac{3 + 4}{2}\right)$

$M(4.5, 3.5)$

8. $\quad AX = BX$
$2x + 11 = 4x - 5$
$2x = 16$
$x = 8$
$AX = 2(8) + 11 = 27$
$BX = 4(8) - 5 = 27$
$AB = AX + BX$
$AB = 27 + 27$
$AB = 54$

9. $\quad XY = YB$
$2x + 3 = 23 - 2x$
$4x = 20$
$x = 5$
$XY = 2(5) + 3 = 13$
$YB = 23 - 2(5) = 13$
$AB = 2(XY + YB)$
$\quad = 2(13 + 13)$
$\quad = 2(26)$
$\quad = 52$

10. $\quad AB = 4XY$
$5x - 4 = 4(x + 1)$
$5x - 4 = 4x + 4$
$x = 8$
$XY = 8 + 1 = 9$
$AX = 2XY$
$\quad = 2(9)$
$\quad = 18$

Page 765 Lesson 1–6

1. $\angle QRU, \angle TRU$ $\qquad$ **2.** $\angle QUT, \angle QUR, \angle TUR$

3. $\angle SRT, \angle TRU, \angle TRQ$

4. $m\angle SRU = m\angle SRT + m\angle TRU$
$m\angle SRU = 80 + 17 = 97$

5. $m\angle QRU = m\angle TRU$
$4x - 3 = 2x + 23$
$2x = 26$
$x = 13$
$m\angle QRU = 4(13) - 3 = 49$

6. $m\angle SRU + m\angle URQ = 180$
$(3y + 8) + (2y + 7) = 180$
$5y = 165$
$y = 33$
$m\angle URQ = 2y + 7 = 2(33) + 7 = 73$

7. $m\angle QRT = 2m\angle URQ$
$9n - 14 = 2(3n + 11)$
$9n - 14 = 6n + 22$
$3n = 36$
$n = 12$
$m\angle URT = m\angle URQ$
$\quad = 3n + 11$
$\quad = 3(12) + 11$
$\quad = 47$

Page 766 Lesson 1–7

1. $\angle AFB$ and $\angle EFD$ $\qquad$ **2.** $\angle ACF$

3. $\angle ACE$ and $\angle CFD$

4. adjacent, supplementary, linear pair

5. Yes; the markings on the angles indicate that they are congruent.

6. obtuse

7. Let x = measure of angle
$180 - x$ = supplement
$x = \frac{1}{3}(180 - x)$
$3x = 180 - x$
$4x = 180$
$x = 45$

8. $m\angle C + m\angle D = 90$
$(3x + 5) + (4x - 6) = 90$
$7x = 91$
$x = 13$
$m\angle C = 3(13) + 5 = 44$
$m\angle D = 4(13) - 6 = 46$

Page 766 Lesson 2–1

1. false; counterexample:

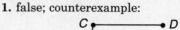
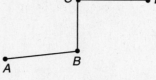

2. True; the square of a real number is always a nonnegative number.

3. True;

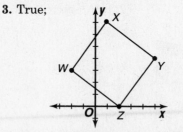

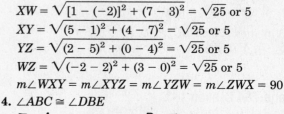

$XW = \sqrt{[1 - (-2)]^2 + (7 - 3)^2} = \sqrt{25}$ or 5
$XY = \sqrt{(5 - 1)^2 + (4 - 7)^2} = \sqrt{25}$ or 5
$YZ = \sqrt{(2 - 5)^2 + (0 - 4)^2} = \sqrt{25}$ or 5
$WZ = \sqrt{(-2 - 2)^2 + (3 - 0)^2} = \sqrt{25}$ or 5
$m\angle WXY = m\angle XYZ = m\angle YZW = m\angle ZWX = 90$

4. $\angle ABC \cong \angle DBE$

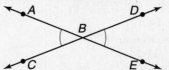

5. $\ell \perp m$

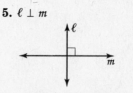

6. $\angle QRS$ and $\angle QRT$ are supplementary.

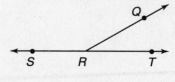

Page 766 Lesson 2–2

1. Hypothesis: a container holds 32 ounces
   Conclusion: it holds a quart
2. Hypotenuse: a candy bar is a Milky Way®
   Conclusion: it contains caramel
3. If two angles are right angles, then they are congruent.
4. If a vehicle is a car, then it has four wheels.
5. If a figure is a triangle, then it contains exactly three angles.
6. Converse: If the distance of a race is about 6.2 miles, then it is 10 kilometers; true. Inverse: If the distance of a race is not 10 kilometers, then it is not about 6.2 miles; true. Contrapositive: If the distance of a race is not about 6.2 miles, then it is not 10 kilometers; true.
7. Converse: If a food is a fruit, then it is an apple; false; Sample counterexample: Pears are fruit, but they are not apples. Inverse: If a food is not an apple, then it is not a fruit; false; Sample counterexample: Pears are not apples, but they are fruit. Contrapositive: If a food is not a fruit, then it is not an apple; true.

Page 768 Lesson 2–3

1. invalid　　2. yes; Law of Detachment
3. Basalt was formed by volcanoes; Law of Syllogism
4. no conclusion

Page 767 Lesson 2–4

1. Transitive Prop. (=)　　2. Addition Prop. (=)
3. 1. Given
   2. Multiplication Prop. (=)
   3. Distributive Prop. (=)
   4. Addition Prop. (=)
   5. Division Prop. (=)
   6. Symmetric Prop. (=)

Page 767 Lesson 2–5

1. Division Prop. (=)　　2. Addition Prop. (=)
3. Transitive Prop. (=) or Substitution Prop. (=)
4. Given: $\angle 1$ and $\angle 2$ are vertical angles.
   Prove: $\angle 1 \cong \angle 2$

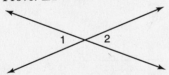

5. Given: $ABCD$ is a rectangle.
   Prove: $\overline{AC} \cong \overline{BD}$

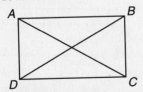

Page 768 Lesson 2–6

1. sometimes　　2. always　　3. never
4. $\angle 1$ and $\angle 4$, $\angle 2$ and $\angle 5$, $\angle 3$ and $\angle 6$

5. $\angle VWQ$ and $\angle QWS$, $\angle VWR$ and $\angle RWS$, $\angle QWR$ and $\angle RWT$, $\angle QWS$ and $\angle SWT$, $\angle SWT$ and $\angle TWV$, $\angle SWU$ and $\angle UWV$, $\angle TWU$ and $\angle UWQ$, $\angle TWV$ and $\angle VWQ$

6. $m\angle 1 = m\angle 4$
   $4x + 14 = 3x + 33$
   $x = 19$
   $m\angle 4 = 3(19) + 33 = 90$

7. $m\angle 2 + m\angle 3 = 90$
   $(2x - 14) + (x + 17) = 90$
   $3x = 87$
   $x = 29$
   $m\angle 3 = 29 + 17 = 46$

8. $m\angle UWQ + m\angle 5 = 180$
   $(8x) + (3x - 7) = 180$
   $11x = 187$
   $x = 17$
   $m\angle UWQ = 8(17) = 136$

Page 768 Lesson 3–1

1. parallel　　2. intersecting and parallel
3. skew　　4. parallel
5. True; using n as the transversal, $\angle 6$ and $\angle 11$ are on the opposite sides of the transversal and between lines ℓ and m.
6. False; $\angle 4$ and $\angle 9$ are corresponding angles, not alternate exterior angles.
7. True; using m as the transversal, $\angle 7$ and $\angle 11$ are in the same relative position and therefore corresponding.
8. k; corresponding angles
9. m; alternate exterior angles
10. k; consecutive interior angles

Page 768 Lesson 3–2

1. $m\angle 4 = m\angle 2 = 62$
2. $m\angle 3 + m\angle 1 + m\angle 2 = 180$
   $m\angle 3 + 41 + 62 = 180$
   $m\angle 3 = 77$
3. $m\angle 3 + m\angle 4 + m\angle 5 = 180$
   $77 + 62 + m\angle 5 = 180$
   $m\angle 5 = 41$
4. $m\angle 6 = m\angle 4 = 62$　　5. $m\angle 7 = m\angle 3 = 77$
6. $m\angle 7 + m\angle 8 = 180$
   $77 + m\angle 8 = 180$
   $m\angle 8 = 103$
7. $x + 68 = 180$　　$4y = x$
   $x = 112$　　　　$4y = 112$
   　　　　　　　　　$y = 28$

   $5z + 2 = x$
   $5z + 2 = 112$
   $5z = 110$
   $z = 22$
8. $(3x) + 42 = 90$　　$z = 42$
   $3x = 48$
   $x = 16$
   $(y + 7) + 2 = 90$
   $y + 7 + 42 = 90$
   $y = 41$

9. $(3x + 10) + (2x + 5) = 180$
$$5x = 165$$
$$x = 33$$

$y + (2x + 5) = 90$ $z = y$

$y + 2(33) + 5 = 90$ $z = 19$

$$y = 19$$

Page 769 Lesson 3-3

1. Line a passes through $(0, 6)$ and $(-3, 0)$.
$$\frac{6 - 0}{0 - (-3)} = \frac{6}{3} = 2$$

2. Line b passes through $(1, 6)$ and $(0, 6)$.
$$\frac{6 - 6}{1 - 0} = \frac{0}{1} = 0$$

3. Line c passes through $(1, 6)$ and $(-3, 0)$.
$$\frac{6 - 0}{1 - (-3)} = \frac{6}{4} = \frac{3}{2}$$

4. Line d passes through $(0, 0)$ and $(-4, 4)$.
$$\frac{4 - 0}{-4 - 0} = \frac{4}{-4} = -1$$

5. undefined   **6.** 2   **7.** $-\frac{2}{3}$

8.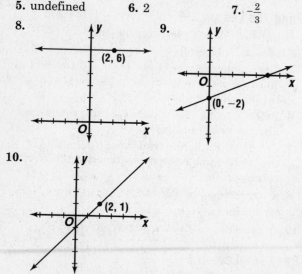

9.

10.

Page 769 Lesson 3-4

1. $\overline{GK} \parallel \overline{HL}$; If $\leftrightarrow$ and corr. $\angle$s are $\cong$, then the lines are $\parallel$.

2. $\overline{HI} \parallel \overline{KL}$; If $\leftrightarrow$ and alt. int. $\angle$s are $\cong$, then the lines are $\parallel$.

3. $\overline{FG} \parallel \overline{JK}$; If $\leftrightarrow$ and alt. int. $\angle$s are $\cong$, then the lines are $\parallel$.

4. $\overline{GJ} \parallel \overline{HL}$; If $\leftrightarrow$ and consecutive int. $\angle$s are supplementary, then the lines are $\parallel$.

5. $(3x + 20) + (5x - 8) = 180$
$$8x = 168$$
$$x = 21$$

6. $5x = 2x + 24$
$$3x = 24$$
$$x = 8$$

7. $2x + 15 = 3x - 10$
$$x = 25$$

Page 769 Lesson 3-5

1.   **2.**

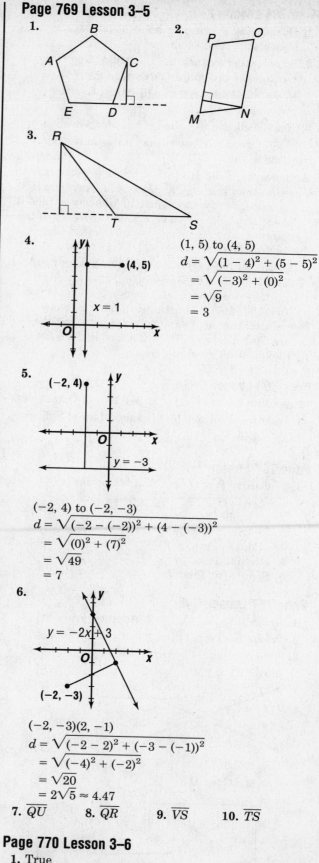

3.

4. $(1, 5)$ to $(4, 5)$
$$d = \sqrt{(1 - 4)^2 + (5 - 5)^2}$$
$$= \sqrt{(-3)^2 + (0)^2}$$
$$= \sqrt{9}$$
$$= 3$$

5. $x = 1$

$(-2, 4)$ to $(-2, -3)$
$$d = \sqrt{(-2 - (-2))^2 + (4 - (-3))^2}$$
$$= \sqrt{(0)^2 + (7)^2}$$
$$= \sqrt{49}$$
$$= 7$$

6. $y = -2x + 3$

$(-2, -3)(2, -1)$
$$d = \sqrt{(-2 - 2)^2 + (-3 - (-1))^2}$$
$$= \sqrt{(-4)^2 + (-2)^2}$$
$$= \sqrt{20}$$
$$= 2\sqrt{5} \approx 4.47$$

7. $\overline{QU}$ **8.** $\overline{QR}$ **9.** $\overline{VS}$ **10.** $\overline{TS}$

Page 770 Lesson 3-6

1. True

2. False; perpendicular great circles divide a sphere into four finite regions.

3. False; in spherical geometry, there are no parallel lines.

4. An arc of a great circle is the shortest path between 2 points.

5. A great circle is finite.

6. Intersecting great circles intersect at 2 points.

7. If 3 points are collinear, any one of the 3 points is between the other two.

Page 770 Lesson 4-1

1. $\overline{FH}$ **2.** $\angle FEH, \angle FHE$ **3.** $\overline{EH}$

4. $\angle EFH$ **5.** $\angle GHF$

6. $AB = \sqrt{(6-(-2))^2 + (4-4)^2} = \sqrt{64} = 8$
$BC = \sqrt{(-2-2)^2 + (4-7)^2} = \sqrt{25} = 5$
$AC = \sqrt{(6-2)^2 + (4-7)^2} = \sqrt{25} = 5$
$\triangle ABC$ is isosceles.

7. $PQ = \sqrt{(-3-0)^2 + (4-1)^2} = \sqrt{18} = 3\sqrt{2}$
$QR = \sqrt{(0-2)^2 + (1-3)^2} = \sqrt{8} = 2\sqrt{2}$
$PR = \sqrt{(-3-2)^2 + (4-3)^2} = \sqrt{26}$
$\triangle PQR$ is scalene.

8. sometimes   **9.** always   **10.** sometimes

Page 770 Lesson 4-2

1. $20 + x + 15 = 180$ **2.** $x + 56 = 123$
         $x = 145$ $x = 67$

3. $45 + (3x + 16) + 68 = 180$
               $3x = 51$
                $x = 17$

4. $m\angle 2 = m\angle QSR = 78$

5. $m\angle 2 + m\angle 1 + 43 = 180$
   $78 + m\angle 1 + 43 = 180$
           $m\angle 1 = 59$

6. $m\angle 3 + 78 = 180$ **7.** $56 + m\angle 4 = 78$
    $m\angle 3 = 102$ $m\angle 4 = 22$

8. $m\angle 4 + m\angle 5 = 90$ **9.** $m\angle 5 + m\angle 6 + 78 = 180$
   $22 + m\angle 5 = 90$ $68 + m\angle 6 + 78 = 180$
       $m\angle 5 = 68$ $m\angle 6 = 34$

Page 771 Lesson 4-3

1.

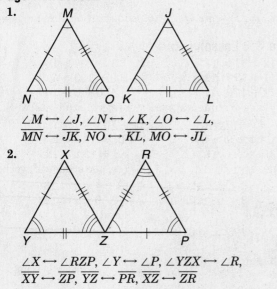

$\angle M \leftrightarrow \angle J, \angle N \leftrightarrow \angle K, \angle O \leftrightarrow \angle L,$
$\overline{MN} \leftrightarrow \overline{JK}, \overline{NO} \leftrightarrow \overline{KL}, \overline{MO} \leftrightarrow \overline{JL}$

2.

$\angle X \leftrightarrow \angle RZP, \angle Y \leftrightarrow \angle P, \angle YZX \leftrightarrow \angle R,$
$\overline{XY} \leftrightarrow \overline{ZP}, \overline{YZ} \leftrightarrow \overline{PR}, \overline{XZ} \leftrightarrow \overline{ZR}$

3.

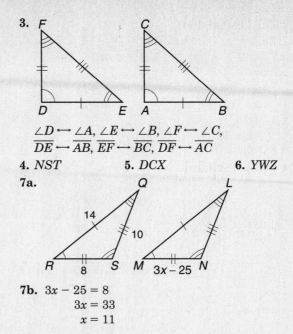

$\angle D \leftrightarrow \angle A, \angle E \leftrightarrow \angle B, \angle F \leftrightarrow \angle C,$
$\overline{DE} \leftrightarrow \overline{AB}, \overline{EF} \leftrightarrow \overline{BC}, \overline{DF} \leftrightarrow \overline{AC}$

4. NST **5.** DCX **6.** YWZ

7a.

7b. $3x - 25 = 8$
       $3x = 33$
         $x = 11$

Page 771 Lesson 4-4

1. ASA   **2.** SSS   **3.** SAS

4. $JK = \sqrt{(-3-(-8))^2 + (1-5)^2} = \sqrt{41}$
$KL = \sqrt{(-8-(-1))^2 + (5-8)^2} = \sqrt{58}$
$JL = \sqrt{(-3-(-1))^2 + (1-8)^2} = \sqrt{53}$
$ST = \sqrt{(0-4)^2 + (1-6)^2} = \sqrt{41}$
$TU = \sqrt{(4-7)^2 + (6-(-1))^2} = \sqrt{58}$
$SU = \sqrt{(0-7)^2 + (1-(-1))^2} = \sqrt{53}$
$\overline{JK} \cong \overline{ST}, \overline{JL} \cong \overline{SU}, \overline{KL} \cong \overline{TU}$, so $\triangle JKL \cong \triangle STU$.

5. $BC = \sqrt{[-4-(-1)]^2 + (1-2)^2} = \sqrt{10}$
$CD = \sqrt{[-1-(-1)]^2 + (2-4)^2} = \sqrt{4}$ or 2
$BD = \sqrt{[-4-(-1)]^2 + (1-4)^2} = \sqrt{18}$ or $3\sqrt{2}$
$NM = \sqrt{(1-0)^2 + [-1-(-3)]^2} = \sqrt{5}$
$MR = \sqrt{(0-4)^2 + [-3-(-4)]^2} = \sqrt{17}$
$NR = \sqrt{(1-4)^2 + [-1-(-4)]^2} = \sqrt{18}$ or $3\sqrt{2}$
$\triangle BCD$ and $\triangle NMR$ are not congruent.

6. Given: $\angle A \cong \angle D$
          $\overline{AO} \cong \overline{OD}$
Prove: $\triangle AOB \cong \triangle DOC$

Proof:

Statements	Reasons
1. $\angle A \cong \angle D$ $\overline{AO} \cong \overline{OD}$	1. Given
2. $\angle AOB \cong \angle DOC$	2. Vertical $\angle$s are $\cong$.
3. $\triangle AOB \cong \triangle DOC$	3. ASA

Page 771 Lesson 4-5

1. $\overline{RU}$

2. any side except $\overline{US}$; Sample answer: $\overline{ST}$

3. $\angle 7$ and $\angle 8$ **4.** Sample answer: $\angle 3$ and $\angle 5$

5. SUT; AAS

Page 772 Lesson 4–6

1. $\angle 5 \cong \angle 6$ 2. $\angle 3 \cong \angle 4$ 3. $\angle 1 \cong \angle 2$
4. $\overline{AE} \cong \overline{AG}$ 5. $\overline{FA} \cong \overline{AB}$
6. $2x + 7 = 45$ 7. $8x + 13 = 11x + 4$
   $\quad 2x = 38$ $\quad 9 = 3x$
   $\quad\; x = 19$ $\quad x = 3$
8. $3x - 10 = 2x$
   $\quad\; x = 10$

Page 772 Lesson 5–1

1.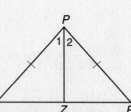
2.
3. F

4. $\overline{EH} \cong \overline{HF}$ or $\angle GHE \cong \angle GHF$ 5. $\overline{EJ} \cong \overline{JG}$
6. $\overline{EK}$ is an angle bisector   7. any triangle
8. no such triangle   9. right triangle

Page 772 Lesson 5–2

1. $\overline{QW} \cong \overline{ZX}$ 2. $\angle ABD \cong \angle CDB$ or $\angle ADB \cong \angle CBD$
3. $\overline{RS} \cong \overline{TU}$

4. $DF = PR$ 5. $m\angle F = m\angle R$
   $6x + 1 = 10x - 19$ $8x - 3 = 7x + 4$
   $\quad 4x = 20$ $\quad\; x = 7$
   $\quad\; x = 5$

Page 773 Lesson 5–3

1. Points M, N, and P are not collinear.
2. $\triangle ABC$ is a right or obtuse triangle.
3. The angle bisector of the vertex angle of an isosceles triangle is not an altitude of the triangle.
4. $m\angle 4$ 5. $m\angle 5$, because $m\angle 5 = m\angle 2 + m\angle 3$.
6. $\angle 1$ or $\angle 2$
7. Given: $\overline{PQ} \cong \overline{PR}$
          $m\angle 1 \neq m\angle 2$
   Prove: $\overline{PZ}$ is not a
          median of
          $\triangle PQR$.

   Proof:
   Assume that $\overline{PZ}$ is a median of $\triangle PQR$. $\overline{QZ} \cong \overline{ZR}$ since Z is the midpoint of $\overline{QR}$ by definition of median. We are given that $\overline{PQ} \cong \overline{PR}$ and we know that $\overline{PZ} \cong \overline{PZ}$ since the congruence of segments is reflexive. Therefore, $\triangle PZQ \cong \triangle PZR$ by SSS and $\angle 1 \cong \angle 2$ by CPCTC. If $\angle 1 \cong \angle 2$, then $m\angle 1 = m\angle 2$ by definition of congruence which is a contradiction of the given $m\angle 1 \neq m\angle 2$. Therefore, the assumption is incorrect and $\overline{PZ}$ is not a median of $\triangle PQR$.

Page 773 Lesson 5–4

1. $\angle CBA$; $\angle A$ 2. $\angle D$; $\angle CBD$
3. $\qquad m\angle P + m\angle Q + m\angle R = 180$
   $(7x + 8) + (8x - 10) + (7x + 6) = 180$
   $\qquad\qquad\qquad\qquad 22x + 4 = 180$
   $\qquad\qquad\qquad\qquad\qquad\; x = 8$

   $m\angle P = 7(8) + 8 = 64$
   $m\angle Q = 8(8) - 10 = 54$
   $m\angle R = 7(8) + 6 = 62$
   $m\angle Q < m\angle R < m\angle P$, so $PR < PQ < QR$.
   $\overline{PR}$; $\overline{PQ}$; $\overline{QR}$

4. $\qquad m\angle P + m\angle Q + m\angle R = 180$
   $(3x + 44) + (68 - 3x) + (x + 61) = 180$
   $\qquad\qquad\qquad\qquad x + 173 = 180$
   $\qquad\qquad\qquad\qquad\qquad\; x = 7$

   $m\angle P = 3(7) + 44 = 65$
   $m\angle Q = 68 - 3(7) = 47$
   $m\angle R = 7 + 61 = 68$
   $m\angle Q < m\angle P < m\angle R$, so $PR < QR < PQ$.
   $\overline{PR}$; $\overline{QR}$; $\overline{PQ}$

5. Given: $QR > QP$
          $\overline{PR} \cong \overline{PQ}$
   Prove: $m\angle P > m\angle Q$

   Prove:

Statements	Reasons
1. $QR > QP$	1. Given
2. $m\angle P > m\angle R$	2. If one side of a $\triangle$ is longer than another side, then the $\angle$ opposite the longer side is greater than the $\angle$ opposite the shorter side.
3. $\overline{PR} \cong \overline{PQ}$	3. Given
4. $\angle Q \cong \angle R$	4. Isosceles Triangle Theorem
5. $m\angle Q = m\angle R$	5. Definition of congruent angles
6. $m\angle P > m\angle Q$	6. Substitution Property (=)

Page 773 Lesson 5–5

1. $12 + 11 > 17$ 2. $5 + 100 > 100$
   $11 + 17 > 12$ $100 + 100 > 5$
   $12 + 17 > 11$ $100 + 5 > 100$
   Yes; see students' work.   Yes; see students' work.
3. $4.7 + 9 > 4.1$ 4. $2.3 + 12 > 12.2$
   $4.1 + 9 > 4.7$ $12 + 12.2 > 2.3$
   $4.1 + 4.7 \not> 9$ $2.3 + 12.2 > 12$
   no   Yes; see students' work.
5. $15 - 2 < x < 12 + 15$ 6. $13 - 4 < x < 13 + 4$
   $\quad 3 < x < 27$ $\quad 9 < x < 17$
   3 and 27   9 and 17
7. $21 - 17 < x < 21 + 17$
   $\quad 4 < x < 38$
   4 and 38

8. $AB = \sqrt{(4 - 0)^2 + (-3 - 0)^2} = \sqrt{16 + 9} = 5$
$BC = \sqrt{(0 - (-4))^2 + (0 - 3)^2} = \sqrt{16 + 9} = 5$
$AC = \sqrt{(4 - (-4))^2 + (-3 - 3)^2} = \sqrt{64 + 36} = 10$
$5 + 5 \not> 10$

No; the measures do not satisfy the Triangle Inequality Theorem.

9. $GH = \sqrt{(-2 - (-6))^2 + (4 - 5)^2} = \sqrt{16 + 1}$
$= \sqrt{17} \approx 4.12$
$HI = \sqrt{(-6 - (-3))^2 + (5 - 3)^2} = \sqrt{9 + 4}$
$= \sqrt{13} \approx 3.61$
$GI = \sqrt{(-2 - (-3))^2 + (4 - 3)^2} = \sqrt{1 + 1}$
$= \sqrt{2} \approx 1.41$
$4.12 + 1.41 > 3.61$
$4.12 + 3.61 > 1.41$
$3.61 + 1.41 > 4.12$

Yes; the measures satisfy the Triangle Inequality Theorem.

Page 774 Lesson 5–6

1. $AE > CE$ **2.** $m\angle DCE > m\angle ECB$
3. $AB > BC$
4. $5x - 14 > 0$ and $5x - 14 < 46$
    $5x > 14$ $5x < 60$
      $x > 2.8$ and $x < 12$
5. $2x - 8 < x + 2$ and $2x - 8 > 0$
      $x < 10$ $x > 4$
      $x > 4$ and $x < 10$
6. $2x + 8 < 3x - 6$
    $14 < x$
7. Given: $\overline{TR} \cong \overline{EU}$
Prove: $TE > RU$

Proof:

Statements	Reasons
1. $\overline{TR} \cong \overline{EU}$	1. Given
2. $\overline{TU} \cong \overline{TU}$	2. Congruence of segments is reflexive.
3. $m\angle 1 > m\angle 2$	3. If an $\angle$ is an ext. $\angle$ of a $\triangle$, then its measure is greater than the measure of either of its corr. remote int. $\angle$s.
4. $TE > RU$	4. SAS Inequality

Page 774 Lesson 6–1

1. $\overline{DC}$; Definition of parallelogram
2. $\overline{CB}$; Opposite sides of a $\square$ are $\cong$.
3. $\triangle CBA$; SAS or SSS
4. $\angle ABC$; Opposite $\angle$s of a $\square$ are $\cong$.
5. $\overline{EB}$; Diagonals of a $\square$ bisect each other.
6. $\angle ACD$; Alternate Interior Angles Theorem
7. $x = 80$ $z + 80 = 180$ $y = 80$
                    $z = 100$
8. $x + 35 = 60$ $y = 35$ $z = 120$
       $x = 25$

9. $x = 30$ $z + 70 = 180$
                          $z = 110$
   $x + y + z = 180$
  $30 + y + 110 = 180$
            $y = 40$

Page 774 Lesson 6–2

1. Yes; opposite sides are parallel.
2. No; we know that two side are parallel and another two sides are congruent. This is insufficient to determine if the quadrilateral is a parallelogram.
3. Yes; the diagonals bisect each other.
4. $(5x + y = 7)4 \rightarrow 20x + 4y = 28$
  $3x - 4y = 18 \rightarrow \underline{\quad 3x - 4y = 18 \quad}$
                          $23x = 46$
                            $x = 2$
      $5x + y = 7$
     $5(2) + y = 7$
      $10 + y = 7$
           $y = -3$
5. $(x + y = 5)(-2) \rightarrow -2x - 2y = -10$
  $2x + 3y = 14 \rightarrow \underline{\quad 2x + 3y = 14 \quad}$
                             $y = 4$
   $x + y = 5$
   $x + 4 = 5$
       $x = 1$
6. $x = y$ $5x + 4y = 7x + 22$
            $5x + 4x = 7x + 22$
                $2x = 22$
                $x = 11, y = 11$

Page 775 Lesson 6–3

1. $RT = 2(QP)$ **2.** $QT = RS$
    $= 2(6)$ $RS = 8$
    $= 12$
3. $PT = PS$
  $3x = 18$
    $x = 6$
4. $m\angle PQT = m\angle 2$
  $m\angle 1 + m\angle 2 + m\angle PQT = 180$
           $55 + 2(m\angle 2) = 180$
               $2(m\angle 2) = 125$
                   $m\angle 2 = 62.5$
5. $m\angle 3 + m\angle 4 = 180$
   $110 + m\angle 4 = 180$
           $m\angle 4 = 70$
6. true; a parallelogram with congruent diagonals is a rectangle.
7. false; if the diagonals of a quadrilateral bisect each other, then it is a parallelogram.
8. true; a rectangle is a quadrilateral with four right angles.
9. slope of $\overline{PQ} = \dfrac{8 - 2}{12 - 12}$ undefined
slope of $\overline{QR} = \dfrac{8 - 8}{12 - (-3)} = 0$
slope of $\overline{RS} = \dfrac{8 - 2}{-3 - (-3)}$ undefined
slope of $\overline{PS} = \dfrac{2 - 2}{12 - (-3)} = 0$ Yes; opposite sides are parallel and all right angles.

10. slope of $\overline{PQ} = \dfrac{-3-8}{0-4} = \dfrac{11}{4}$

slope of $\overline{QR} = \dfrac{8-7}{4-11} = -\dfrac{1}{7}$

slope of $\overline{RS} = \dfrac{7-(-4)}{11-7} = \dfrac{11}{4}$

slope of $\overline{PS} = \dfrac{-3-(-4)}{0-7} = -\dfrac{1}{7}$

no; not all right angles

Page 775 Lesson 6–4

1. $m\angle 1 + m\angle 3 = 90$
$m\angle 1 + 62 = 90$
$m\angle 1 = 28$

2. $m\angle 3 = m\angle 4$
$3x - 1 = 2x + 30$
$x = 31$

3. $m\angle 3 + m\angle 5 = 90$
$4(x + 1) + 2(x + 1) = 90$
$6x = 84$
$x = 14$

4. $m\angle 6 = 90$
$7x + 13 = 90$
$7x = 77$
$x = 11$

5. $m\angle LKJ = 2(m\angle 2)$
$x^2 - 17 = 2(x + 23)$
$x^2 - 17 = 2x + 46$
$x^2 - 2x - 63 = 0$
$(x + 7)(x - 9) = 0$
$x = -7 \text{ or } 9$

6. parallelogram, rectangle, rhombus, square

7. parallelogram, rectangle, rhombus, square

8. rectangle, square

Page 775 Lesson 6–5

1. $TV = \dfrac{1}{2}(PS + QR)$
$\quad = \dfrac{1}{2}(20 + 14)$
$\quad = 17$

2. $TV = \dfrac{1}{2}(PS + QR)$
$23.2 = \dfrac{1}{2}(PS + 14.3)$
$46.4 = PS + 14.3$
$32.1 = PS$

3. $TV = \dfrac{1}{2}(PS + QR)$
$x + 7 = \dfrac{1}{2}(5x + 2)$
$2x + 14 = 5x + 2$
$3x = 12$
$x = 4$

4. $m\angle QTV = m\angle RVT$
$\quad\quad\quad = 57$

5. $m\angle VTP + m\angle TPS = 180$
$a + m\angle TPS = 180$
$\quad\quad m\angle TPS = 180 - a$

6. slope of $\overline{AB} = \dfrac{1-3}{-3-1} = \dfrac{-2}{-4} = \dfrac{1}{2}$

slope of $\overline{DC} = \dfrac{-2-1}{0-6} = \dfrac{-3}{-6} = \dfrac{1}{2}$

slope of $\overline{BC} = \dfrac{1-3}{6-1} = \dfrac{-2}{5}$

slope of $\overline{AD} = \dfrac{-2-1}{0-(-3)} = \dfrac{-3}{3} = -1$

trapezoid

7. slope of $\overline{AB} = \dfrac{6-4}{5-1} = \dfrac{2}{4} = \dfrac{1}{2}$

slope of $\overline{DC} = \dfrac{3-1}{5-3} = 1$

slope of $\overline{BC} = \dfrac{6-3}{5-5}$ undefined

slope of $\overline{AD} = \dfrac{4-1}{1-3} = -\dfrac{3}{2}$

quadrilateral

8. slope of $\overline{AB} = \dfrac{-2-1}{5-1} = -\dfrac{3}{4}$

slope of $\overline{DC} = \dfrac{-2-(-5)}{-3-1} = -\dfrac{3}{4}$

slope of $\overline{AD} = \dfrac{-2-1}{-3-1} = \dfrac{3}{4}$

slope of $\overline{BC} = \dfrac{-2-(-5)}{5-1} = \dfrac{3}{4}$

parallelogram

Page 776 Lesson 7–1

1. $\dfrac{96}{74} = \dfrac{48}{37}$

2. $\dfrac{5}{15} = \dfrac{1}{3}$

3. $\dfrac{6}{9} = \dfrac{2}{3}$

4. $\dfrac{4}{n} = \dfrac{7}{8}$
$4(8) = 7n$
$32 = 7n$
$n = \dfrac{32}{7}$

5. $\dfrac{x+1}{x} = \dfrac{7}{2}$
$2(x + 1) = 7x$
$2x + 2 = 7x$
$5x = 2$
$x = \dfrac{2}{5} \text{ or } 0.4$

6. $\dfrac{5}{17} = \dfrac{2x}{51}$
$17(2x) = 5(51)$
$34x = 255$
$x = 7.5$

7. $\dfrac{AB}{PQ} = \dfrac{AD}{PS}$
$\dfrac{4}{6} = \dfrac{8}{PS}$
$4PS = 48$
$PS = 12$

8. $\dfrac{RS}{CD} = \dfrac{QR}{BC}$
$\dfrac{4.5}{6.3} = \dfrac{QR}{7}$
$6.3QR = 31.5$
$QR = 5$

9. $\dfrac{CD}{SR} = \dfrac{DA}{SP}$
$\dfrac{21.8}{33} = \dfrac{43.6}{SP}$
$21.8SP = 1438.8$
$SP = 66$

Page 776 Lesson 7–2

1. $\dfrac{12}{16} = \dfrac{x}{20}$
$16x = 240$
$x = 15$

$\dfrac{12}{16} = \dfrac{y-4}{12}$
$6(y - 4) = 144$
$16y - 64 = 144$
$y = 13$

2. $y + 92 = 123$
$y = 31$

$2x - 1 = 57$
$2x = 58$
$x = 29$

3. $\dfrac{8}{12} = \dfrac{2}{3}$

4a. $\dfrac{AD}{HE} = \dfrac{DC}{GH}$
$\dfrac{8}{12} = \dfrac{10}{GH}$
$8GH = 120$
$GH = 15$

4b. $\dfrac{AD}{HE} = \dfrac{BC}{FG}$
$\dfrac{8}{12} = \dfrac{10}{FG}$
$8FG = 120$
$FG = 15$

4c. $\dfrac{AD}{HE} = \dfrac{AB}{EF}$
$\dfrac{8}{12} = \dfrac{15}{EF}$
$8EF = 180$
$EF = 22.5$

5a. perimeter of $ABCD = 8 + 10 + 10 + 15 = 43$

5b. perimeter of $EFGH = 12 + 15 + 15 + 22.5 = 64.5$

5c. $\dfrac{\text{perimeter of } ABCD}{\text{perimeter of } EFGH} = \dfrac{43}{64.5} = \dfrac{2}{3}$

Page 776 Lesson 7–3

1. yes; AA Similarity; $\triangle GHI \sim \triangle OMN$

2. yes; SAS Similarity; $\triangle JKL \sim \triangle QRP$

3. yes; AA Similarity; $\triangle RSX \sim \triangle TUX$

4.
$$\frac{AE}{AD} = \frac{BF}{CD}$$
$$\frac{12}{18} = \frac{8}{CD}$$
$$12CD = 144$$
$$CD = 12$$

$$BC = AC - AB$$
$$BC = 22.5 - 15$$
$$BC = 7.5$$

$$\frac{AE}{AD} = \frac{AB}{AC}$$
$$\frac{12}{18} = \frac{15}{AC}$$
$$12AC = 270$$
$$AC = 22.5$$

5. $RU = ST$
$$ST = SV + VT$$
$$20 = SV + 15$$
$$SV = 5$$

$$RS = UT$$
$$RW = RS + SW$$
$$RW = 12 + 4$$
$$RW = 16$$

$$\frac{SV}{VT} = \frac{WS}{UT}$$
$$\frac{5}{15} = \frac{WS}{12}$$
$$15WS = 60$$
$$WS = 4$$

Page 777 Lesson 7–4

1. BD **2.** BF **3.** BF **4.** DF

5. false; $\dfrac{BC}{AE} = \dfrac{CD}{ED}$ **6.** true

7. $\dfrac{MX}{YM} = \dfrac{NX}{ZN}$
$$\frac{9}{6} = \frac{12}{x}$$
$$9x = 72$$
$$x = 8$$

8. $\dfrac{XN}{ZN} = \dfrac{XM}{MY}$
$$\frac{20}{16} = \frac{x-6}{20}$$
$$16(x-6) = 400$$
$$16x - 96 = 400$$
$$16x = 496$$
$$x = 31$$

9. $\dfrac{MX}{MY} = \dfrac{NX}{NZ}$
$$\frac{5}{x-2} = \frac{9}{x+6}$$
$$9(x-2) = 5(x+6)$$
$$9x - 18 = 5x + 30$$
$$4x = 48$$
$$x = 12$$

Page 777 Lesson 7–5

1. $\dfrac{AC}{BR} = \dfrac{DF}{ES}$
$$\frac{20}{BR} = \frac{12}{5}$$
$$12BR = 100$$
$$BR = 8\frac{1}{3}$$

2. BC

3. $\dfrac{AB}{BR} = \dfrac{DE}{ES}$
$$\frac{12}{BR} = \frac{5}{4}$$
$$5BR = 48$$
$$BR = 9.6$$

4. $\dfrac{AB}{AR} = \dfrac{CB}{CR}$
$$\frac{15}{6} = \frac{CB}{8}$$
$$6CB = 120$$
$$CB = 20$$

5. $\dfrac{\text{perimeter of } \triangle DEF}{\text{perimeter of } \triangle ABC} = \dfrac{DF}{AC}$
$$\frac{30}{x} = \frac{8}{12}$$
$$8x = 360$$
$$x = 45$$
perimeter of $\triangle ABC$ is 45

Page 777 Lesson 7–6

1. $\sqrt[3]{x}$ approaches 1

2. $\dfrac{1}{x^2}$ alternates between approaching infinity and approaching 0.

3. $x^{\frac{1}{2}}$ approaches 1

4.

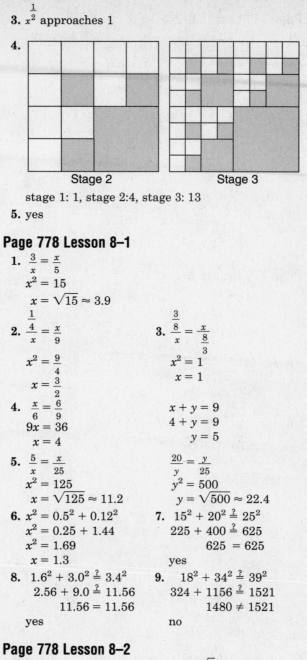

Stage 2   Stage 3

stage 1: 1, stage 2: 4, stage 3: 13

5. yes

Page 778 Lesson 8–1

1. $\dfrac{3}{x} = \dfrac{x}{5}$
$$x^2 = 15$$
$$x = \sqrt{15} \approx 3.9$$

2. $\dfrac{\frac{1}{4}}{x} = \dfrac{x}{9}$
$$x^2 = \frac{9}{4}$$
$$x = \frac{3}{2}$$

3. $\dfrac{\frac{3}{8}}{x} = \dfrac{x}{\frac{8}{3}}$
$$x^2 = 1$$
$$x = 1$$

4. $\dfrac{x}{6} = \dfrac{6}{9}$
$$9x = 36$$
$$x = 4$$

$$x + y = 9$$
$$4 + y = 9$$
$$y = 5$$

5. $\dfrac{5}{x} = \dfrac{x}{25}$
$$x^2 = 125$$
$$x = \sqrt{125} \approx 11.2$$

$$\frac{20}{y} = \frac{y}{25}$$
$$y^2 = 500$$
$$y = \sqrt{500} \approx 22.4$$

6. $x^2 = 0.5^2 + 0.12^2$
$$x^2 = 0.25 + 1.44$$
$$x^2 = 1.69$$
$$x = 1.3$$

7. $15^2 + 20^2 \stackrel{?}{=} 25^2$
$$225 + 400 \stackrel{?}{=} 625$$
$$625 = 625$$
yes

8. $1.6^2 + 3.0^2 \stackrel{?}{=} 3.4^2$
$$2.56 + 9.0 \stackrel{?}{=} 11.56$$
$$11.56 = 11.56$$
yes

9. $18^2 + 34^2 \stackrel{?}{=} 39^2$
$$324 + 1156 \stackrel{?}{=} 1521$$
$$1480 \neq 1521$$
no

Page 778 Lesson 8–2

1. $2x = 10$
$$x = 5$$

$$y = x\sqrt{3}$$
$$y = 5\sqrt{3} \approx 8.66$$

2. $x = \dfrac{7}{\sqrt{2}} = \dfrac{7\sqrt{2}}{2} \approx 4.95$ $y = x = \dfrac{7\sqrt{2}}{2} \approx 4.95$

3. $x = \dfrac{31.2}{\sqrt{3}} = \dfrac{31.2\sqrt{3}}{3} = 10.4\sqrt{3} \approx 18.01$
$$y = 2x = 2(10.4\sqrt{3}) = 20.8\sqrt{3} \approx 36.03$$

4. $d = s\sqrt{2}$
$$d = 17\sqrt{2} \approx 24.04 \text{ m}$$

5. shorter leg $= \dfrac{\frac{\sqrt{3}}{3}}{\sqrt{3}} = \dfrac{1}{3}$

side = hypotenuse $= 2\left(\dfrac{1}{3}\right) = \dfrac{2}{3}$ yd

6. $s = \dfrac{d}{\sqrt{2}} = \dfrac{6}{\sqrt{2}} = 3\sqrt{2} \approx 4.24$ in.

7. $P = 3s$ hypotenuse = 14
$$42 = 3s$$ shorter leg $= \dfrac{1}{2}(14) = 7$
$$s = 14$$ longer leg = altitude $= 7\sqrt{3} \approx 12.12$ cm

Page 778 Lesson 8–3

1. $\sin A = \frac{21}{29} \approx 0.7241$ 2. $\sin B = \frac{20}{29} \approx 0.6897$

3. $\tan A = \frac{21}{20} \approx 1.0500$ 4. $\cos B = \frac{21}{29} \approx 0.7241$

5. $\cos E = \frac{24}{40} = \frac{3}{5} = 0.6000$

6. $\tan F = \frac{24}{32} = \frac{3}{4} = 0.7500$

7. $\cos 17° = \frac{x}{9.7}$ 8. $\tan X° = \frac{16}{10}$
   $x = 9.7 \cos 17°$ $m\angle X = 58.0$
   $x \approx 9.3$

9. $\cos 22° = \frac{16.4}{x}$
   $x = \frac{16.4}{\cos 22°}$
   $x \approx 17.7$

Page 779 Lesson 8–4

1. $\sin 15° = \frac{LN}{37}$ 2. $\sin 47° = \frac{10}{AL}$
   $LN = 37 \sin 15°$ $AL = \frac{10}{\sin 47°}$
   $LN \approx 9.6$ $AL \approx 13.7$

3. $\cos 16° = \frac{13.4}{AL}$ 4. $\tan 72° = \frac{13}{LN}$
   $AL = \frac{13.4}{\cos 16°}$ $LN = \frac{13}{\tan 72°}$
   $AL \approx 13.9$ $LN \approx 4.2$

5. $\tan 74° = \frac{AN}{33.6}$
   $AN = 33.6 \tan 74°$
   $AN \approx 117.2$

6. $\tan 35° = \frac{x}{100}$
   $x = 100 \tan 35°$
   $x \approx 70$

   height of bridge $\approx 70 + 1.5 \approx 71.5$ m

7. $\cos 65° = \frac{8}{x}$ 8. $\tan 25° = \frac{150}{x}$
   $x = \frac{8}{\cos 65°}$ $x = \frac{150}{\tan 25°}$
   $x \approx 18.9$ ft $x \approx 321.7$ ft

9. $\sin X° = \frac{10}{75}$
   $m\angle X \approx 7.7$

   Angle of elevation is about 7.7°.

10. $\tan 19° = \frac{5.3}{x}$
    $x = \frac{5.3}{\tan 19°}$
    $x \approx 15.4$ mi

Page 779 Lesson 8–5

1.
   $\frac{\sin 53°}{r} = \frac{\sin 61°}{2.8}$
   $r \sin 61° = 2.8 \sin 53°$
   $r = \frac{2.8 \sin 53°}{\sin 61°}$
   $r \approx 2.6$

2.
   $\frac{\sin 98°}{36} = \frac{\sin T}{12}$
   $\sin T = \frac{12 \sin 98°}{36}$
   $m\angle T = 19.3$

3.
   $\frac{\sin 87°}{22} = \frac{\sin 70°}{r}$
   $r \sin 87° = 22 \sin 70°$
   $r = \frac{22 \sin 70°}{\sin 87°}$
   $r \approx 2.1$

4.
   $\frac{\sin 55°}{11} = \frac{\sin R}{9}$
   $11 \sin R = 9 \sin 55°$
   $\sin R = \frac{9 \sin 55°}{11}$
   $m\angle R \approx 42.1$

5. $m\angle E + m\angle F + m\angle G = 180$
   $30 + m\angle F + 70 = 180$
   $m\angle F = 80$

   $\frac{\sin 30°}{e} = \frac{\sin 70°}{8}$ $\frac{\sin 80°}{f} = \frac{\sin 70°}{8}$
   $e = \frac{8 \sin 30°}{\sin 70°}$ $f = \frac{8 \sin 80°}{\sin 70°}$
   $e \approx 4.3$ $f \approx 8.4$

6. $\frac{\sin 124°}{25} = \frac{\sin E}{10}$
   $25 \sin E = 10 \sin 124°$
   $\sin E = \frac{10 \sin 124°}{25}$
   $m\angle E \approx 19.4$
   $m\angle E + m\angle F + m\angle G = 180$
   $19.4 + m\angle F + 124 = 180$
   $m\angle F = 36.6$
   $\frac{\sin 36.6°}{f} = \frac{\sin 124°}{25}$
   $f \sin 124° = 25 \sin 36.6°$
   $f = \frac{25 \sin 36.6°}{\sin 124°}$
   $f \approx 18.0$

7. $m\angle E + m\angle F + m\angle G = 180$
   $29 + 62 + m\angle G = 180$
   $m\angle G = 89$

   $\frac{\sin 89°}{11.5} = \frac{\sin 29°}{e}$ $\frac{\sin 89°}{11.5} = \frac{\sin 69°}{f}$
   $e = \frac{11.5 \sin 29°}{\sin 89°}$ $f = \frac{11.5 \sin 69°}{\sin 89°}$
   $e \approx 5.6$ $f \approx 10.2$

8. $\frac{\sin 35°}{24} = \frac{\sin E}{7.5}$
   $24 \sin E = 7.5 \sin 35°$
   $\sin E = \frac{7.5 \sin 35°}{24}$
   $m\angle E \approx 10.3$
   $m\angle E + m\angle F + m\angle G = 180$
   $10.3 + m\angle F + 35 = 180$
   $m\angle F \approx 134.7$
   $\frac{\sin 134.7°}{f} = \frac{\sin 35°}{24}$
   $f \sin 35° = 24 \sin 134.7°$
   $f = \frac{24 \sin 134.7°}{\sin 35°}$
   $f \approx 29.7$

9. $m\angle E + m\angle F + m\angle G = 180$
$m\angle E + 36 + 119 = 180$
$m\angle E = 25$

$\dfrac{\sin 25°}{e} = \dfrac{\sin 36°}{8}$

$e = \dfrac{8 \sin 25°}{\sin 36°}$

$e \approx 5.8$

$\dfrac{\sin 119°}{g} = \dfrac{\sin 36°}{8}$

$g = \dfrac{8 \sin 119°}{\sin 36°}$

$g \approx 11.9$

10. $m\angle E + m\angle F + m\angle G = 180$
$m\angle E + 47 + 73 = 180$
$m\angle E = 60$

$\dfrac{\sin 60°}{0.9} = \dfrac{\sin 47°}{f}$

$f = \dfrac{0.9 \sin 47°}{\sin 60°}$

$f \approx 0.8$

$\dfrac{\sin 60°}{0.9} = \dfrac{\sin 73°}{g}$

$g = \dfrac{0.9 \sin 73°}{\sin 60°}$

$g \approx 1.0$

Page 779 Lesson 8–6

1.

Law of Sines;
$m\angle E + m\angle Q + m\angle R = 180$
$40 + 70 + m\angle R = 180$
$m\angle R = 70$

$\dfrac{\sin 70°}{r} = \dfrac{\sin 70°}{4}$

$r = \dfrac{4 \sin 70°}{\sin 70°}$

$r = 4$

$\dfrac{\sin 70°}{4} = \dfrac{\sin 40°}{e}$

$e = \dfrac{4 \sin 40°}{\sin 70°}$

$e \approx 2.7$

2.

Law of Cosines;
$q^2 = 10.5^2 + 11^2 - 2(10.5)(11) \cos 35°$
$q = \sqrt{10.5^2 + 11^2 - 2(10.5)(11) \cos 35°}$
$q \approx 6.5$

$\dfrac{\sin 35°}{6.5} = \dfrac{\sin E}{11}$

$\sin E = \dfrac{11 \sin 35°}{6.5}$

$m\angle E \approx 76.1$

$m\angle E + m\angle R + m\angle Q = 180$
$76.1 + m\angle R + 35 = 180$
$m\angle R \approx 68.9$

3.

Law of Sines;
$\dfrac{\sin E}{11} = \dfrac{\sin 42°}{17}$

$\sin E = \dfrac{11 \sin 42°}{17}$

$m\angle E \approx 25.7$

$m\angle E + m\angle R + m\angle Q = 180$
$25.7 + 42 + m\angle Q = 180$
$m\angle Q \approx 112.3$

$\dfrac{\sin 112.3°}{q} = \dfrac{\sin 42°}{17}$

$q = \dfrac{17 \sin 112.3°}{\sin 42°}$

$q \approx 23.5$

4.

Law of Sines;
$\dfrac{\sin 56°}{e} = \dfrac{\sin 26°}{12.2}$

$e = \dfrac{12.2 \sin 56°}{\sin 26°}$

$e \approx 23.1$

$m\angle E + m\angle R + m\angle Q = 180$
$56 + m\angle R + 26 = 180$
$m\angle R = 98$

$\dfrac{\sin 98°}{r} = \dfrac{\sin 26°}{12.2}$

$r = \dfrac{12.2 \sin 98°}{\sin 26°}$

$r \approx 27.6$

5. $\dfrac{\sin 19°}{61} = \dfrac{\sin P}{51}$

$\sin P = \dfrac{51 \sin 19°}{61}$

$m\angle P \approx 15.8$

$m\angle P + m\angle S + m\angle V = 180$
$15.8 + 19 + m\angle V = 180$
$m\angle V \approx 145.2$

$\dfrac{\sin 145.2°}{v} = \dfrac{\sin 19°}{61}$

$v = \dfrac{61 \sin 145.2°}{\sin 19°}$

$v \approx 106.9$

6. $5^2 = 12^2 + 13^2 - 2(12)(13) \cos P$

$\cos P = \dfrac{12^2 + 13^2 - 5^2}{2(12)(13)}$

$m\angle P \approx 22.6$

$\dfrac{\sin 22.6°}{5} = \dfrac{\sin S}{12}$

$\sin S = \dfrac{12 \sin 22.6°}{5}$

$m\angle S \approx 67.3$

$m\angle P + m\angle S + m\angle V = 180$
$22.6 + 67.3 + m\angle V = 180$
$m\angle V \approx 90.1$

7. $s^2 = 20^2 + 24^2 - 2(20)(24) \cos 47$

$s = \sqrt{20^2 + 24^2 - 2(20)(24) \cos 47}$

$s \approx 17.9$

$\dfrac{\sin 47°}{17.9} = \dfrac{\sin P}{20}$

$\sin P = \dfrac{20 \sin 47°}{17.9}$

$m\angle P \approx 54.8$

$m\angle P + m\angle S + m\angle V = 180$
$54.8 + 47 + m\angle V = 180$
$m\angle V \approx 78.2$

8. $m\angle P + m\angle V + m\angle S = 180$
$40 + 59 + m\angle S = 180$
$m\angle S = 81$

$\dfrac{\sin 40°}{p} = \dfrac{\sin 81°}{14}$

$p = \dfrac{14 \sin 40°}{\sin 81°}$

$p \approx 9.1$

$\dfrac{\sin 81°}{14} = \dfrac{\sin 59°}{v}$

$v = \dfrac{14 \sin 59°}{\sin 81°}$

$v \approx 12.1$

9. $345^2 = 648^2 + 442^2 - 2(648)(442) \cos P$

$\cos P = \frac{648^2 + 442^2 - 345^2}{2(648)(442)}$

$m\angle P \approx 30.0$

$\frac{\sin S}{442} = \frac{\sin 30°}{345}$

$\sin S = \frac{442 \sin 30°}{345}$

$m\angle S \approx 39.8$

$m\angle P + m\angle V + m\angle S = 180$

$30.0 + m\angle V + 39.8 = 180$

$m\angle V \approx 110.2$

10. $p^2 = 5^2 + 4.9^2 - 2(5)(4.9) \cos 29$

$p = \sqrt{5^2 + 4.9^2 - 2(5)(4.9) \cos 29}$

$p \approx 2.5$

$\frac{\sin S}{4.9} = \frac{\sin 29°}{2.5}$

$\sin S = \frac{4.9 \sin 29°}{2.5}$

$m\angle S \approx 71.8$

$m\angle P + m\angle V + m\angle S = 180$

$29 + m\angle V + 71.8 = 180$

$m\angle V \approx 79.2$

Page 780 Lesson 9–1

1. P

2. No; both endpoints are not on the circle.

3. $DB = 2(PC) = 2(6) = 12$

4. $\overline{EA}$

5. Yes; all radii of a circle are congruent.

6. $PG = \frac{1}{2}(DB) = \frac{1}{2}(17) = 8.5$

7. $d = 2(3.8) = 7.6$, $C = \pi(7.6) \approx 23.9$

8. $c = 11 = \pi d$

$d = \frac{11}{\pi} \approx 3.5$

$r = \frac{3.5}{2} \approx 1.8$

9. $r = 0.5x$; $C = \pi x$

10. $C = \pi d$

$C = 14\pi$ yd

11. $9^2 + 12^2 = d^2 \qquad C = \pi d$

$225 = d^2 \qquad\qquad = 15\pi$ cm

$15 = d$

12. $d = 3\sqrt{2}$

$C = \pi d$

$= 3\sqrt{2}\pi$ m

Page 780 Lesson 9–2

1. minor;

$m\widehat{XQ} = m\widehat{XQS} - m\widehat{QS} = 180 - 40 = 140$

2. major;

$m\widehat{VX} = m\widehat{QS} = 40$

$m\widehat{VSX} = 360 - m\widehat{VX} = 360 - 40 = 320$

3. semicircle; $m\widehat{QXV} = 180$

4. major; $m\widehat{XRT} = m\angle XRT = 90$;

$m\widehat{VT} = m\widehat{XRT} - m\widehat{VX} = 90 - 40 = 50$

$m\widehat{TSV} = 360 - m\widehat{VT} = 360 - 50 = 310$

5. length of $\widehat{XQ} = \frac{140}{360} \cdot \pi(16) \approx 19.5$

6. length of $\widehat{VSX} = \frac{320}{360} \cdot \pi(16) \approx 44.7$

7. length of $\widehat{QXV} = \frac{180}{360} \cdot \pi(16) \approx 25.1$

8. length of $\widehat{TSV} = \frac{310}{360} \cdot \pi(16) \approx 43.3$

Page 780 Lesson 9–3

1. A **2.** $\widehat{QS}$ **3.** $\overline{QV}$ **4.** $\overline{WA}$

5. $\overline{SY}$ **6.** $AC = 2(7) = 14$

7. $m\widehat{JK} = 75$ **8.** $OM^2 + MN^2 = ON^2$

$\qquad\qquad\qquad\qquad 6^2 + 8^2 = ON^2$

$\qquad\qquad\qquad\qquad 100 = ON^2$

$\qquad\qquad\qquad\qquad ON = 10$

Page 781 Lesson 9–4

1. $\widehat{GR}$

2. $m\angle GTR = \frac{1}{2}m\widehat{GR}$ **3.** $m\angle MEG = 90$

$\qquad 62 = \frac{1}{2}m\widehat{GR}$

$\qquad m\widehat{GR} = 124$

4. $m\angle GTR = \frac{1}{2}m\widehat{GER}$

$\qquad 62 = \frac{1}{2}m\widehat{GER}$

$\qquad m\widehat{GER} = 124$

$m\widehat{GTR} = 360 - m\widehat{GER} = 360 - 124 = 236$

5. Sample answer: $\angle GTR$

6. $m\angle IJG + m\angle GHI = 180$

$\qquad (2x + 10) + 2x = 180$

$\qquad\qquad\qquad 4x = 170$

$\qquad\qquad\qquad x = 42.5$

$m\angle GHI = 2x = 2(42.5) = 85$

7. $m\angle GHI = \frac{1}{2}m\widehat{GJI}$ **8.** $\quad m\angle GHJ = \frac{1}{2}m\widehat{JIH}$

$\qquad 85 = \frac{1}{2}m\widehat{GJI}$ $2(42.5) - 10 = \frac{1}{2}m\widehat{JIH}$

$\qquad m\widehat{GJI} = 170$ $150 = m\widehat{JIH}$

9. $\qquad m\angle JIH = \frac{1}{2}m\widehat{JGH}$

$180 - m\angle JGH = \frac{1}{2}m\widehat{JGH}$

$\quad 180 - 75 = \frac{1}{2}m\widehat{JGH}$

$\qquad\qquad 105 = \frac{1}{2}m\widehat{JGH}$

$\qquad\quad m\widehat{JGH} = 210$

Page 781 Lesson 9–5

1. $m\widehat{CE} = 45$ **2.** $m\angle PCG = 90$

3. $m\angle CGP = 180 - (m\angle PCG + m\angle CPG)$

$\qquad\qquad\quad = 180 - (90 + 45)$

$\qquad\qquad\quad = 45$

4. $CG = CP = AP = 8$ **5.** $m\angle FQD = 45$

6. $m\widehat{DF} = m\angle FQD = 45$ **7.** $DQ = BQ = 5$

8. $DG = DQ = 5$ **9.** $x = 12$

10. $6^2 + x^2 = (4 + 6)^2$ **11.** $x = 5 + 3 = 8$

$\quad 6^2 + x^2 = 10^2$

$\qquad\quad x^2 = 64$

$\qquad\quad x = 8$

Page 781 Lesson 9–6

1. $m\widehat{BF} = 360 - (m\widehat{BC} + m\widehat{CD} + m\widehat{DE} + m\widehat{EF})$
   $= 360 - (84 + 38 + 64 + 60)$
   $= 114$

2. $m\widehat{BDF} = 360 - m\widehat{BF} = 360 - 114 = 246$

3. $m\angle 1 = 180 - m\widehat{BF} = 180 - 114 = 66$

4. $m\widehat{BFC} = 360 - m\widehat{BC} = 360 - 84 = 276$

5. $m\angle 2 = \frac{1}{2}m\widehat{BFC} = \frac{1}{2}(276) = 138$

6. $m\angle GBC = \frac{1}{2}m\widehat{BC} = \frac{1}{2}(84) = 42$

7. $x + 35 = 180$
   $x = 145$

8. $80 = \frac{1}{2}(x = 110)$
   $160 = x + 110$
   $x = 50$

9. $x = \frac{1}{2}(45 - [180 - (110 + 45)])$
   $= \frac{1}{2}(45 - 25)$
   $= 10$

Page 782 Lesson 9–7

1. x must be positive.
   $x(5 + x) = 2(2 + 4)$
   $5x + x^2 = 12$
   $x^2 + 5x - 12 = 0$
   $x = \frac{-5 + \sqrt{25 - 4(-12)}}{2} \approx 1.8$

2. $2x(2x) = 5(20)$
   $4x^2 = 100$
   $x^2 = 25$
   $x = \sqrt{25}$ or 5

3. $9^2 = 8(x + 8)$
   $81 = 8x + 64$
   $8x = 17$
   $x \approx 2.1$

4. $NO = NM = 13$

5. $LO^2 + NO^2 = LN^2$
   $8^2 + 13^2 = LN^2$
   $233 = LN^2$
   $LN = \sqrt{233} \approx 15.3$

6. $PN = LN - LP$
   $= 15.3 - 8 = 7.3$

Page 782 Lesson 9–8

1. $(-2, 7)$, $\sqrt{81} = 9$

2. $\left(\frac{2}{3}, -4\right)$, $\sqrt{169} = 13$

3.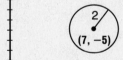

4.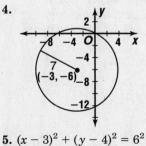

5. $(x - 3)^2 + (y - 4)^2 = 6^2$
   $(x - 3)^2 + (y - 4)^2 = 36$

6. $(x - (-2))^2 + (y - 7)^2 = (\sqrt{17})^2$
   $(x + 2)^2 + (y - 7)^2 = 17$

Page 782 Lesson 10–1

1. $180(15 - 2) = 180(13) = 2340$

2. $180(59 - 2) = 180(57) = 10{,}260$

3. $180(2t - 2) = 360t - 360$

4. $\frac{360}{24} = 15$

5. $\frac{360}{60} = 6$

6. $\frac{360}{51\frac{3}{7}} = 7$

7. $\frac{180(4 - 2)}{4} = \frac{180(2)}{4}$
   $= 90$
   $180 - 90 = 90$

8. $\frac{180(16 - 2)}{16} = \frac{180(14)}{16}$
   $= 157.5$
   $180 - 157.5 = 22.5$

9. $\frac{180(s - 2)}{s}$,
   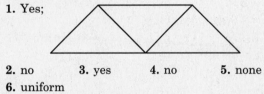
   $180 - \frac{180(s - 2)}{s} = \frac{180s - 180s + 360}{s}$
   $= \frac{360}{s}$

10. $180 - 160 = 20$
    $\frac{360}{20} = 18$

11. $180 - 177.6 = 2.4$
    $\frac{360}{2.4} = 150$

12. $180 - 120 = 60$
    $\frac{360}{60} = 6$

Page 783 Lesson 10–2

1. Yes;
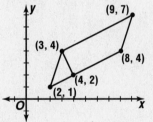

2. no
3. yes
4. no
5. none
6. uniform

Page 783 Lesson 10–3

1. $A = bh = 5(11, 2) = 56$ in^2

2. $A = bh = 9(16) = 144$ yd^2

3. $A = 1(1) + 3(3) + 6(15) = 1 + 9 + 90 = 100$ mm^2

4.

parallelogram;
length of base $= \sqrt{(8 - 2)^2 + (4 - 1)^2}$
$= \sqrt{36 + 9}$
$= \sqrt{45}$
length of height $= \sqrt{(3 - 4)^2 + (4 - 2)^2}$
$= \sqrt{1 + 4}$
$= \sqrt{5}$

$A = bh$
$= \sqrt{45}\sqrt{5}$
$= \sqrt{225} = 15$ unit^2

5.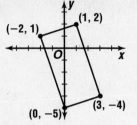

rectangle;

$$\ell = \sqrt{(0-3)^2 + (-5-(-4))^2}$$
$$= \sqrt{9+1} = \sqrt{10}$$
$$w = \sqrt{(-2-0)^2 + (1-(-5))^2}$$
$$= \sqrt{4+36}$$
$$= \sqrt{40}$$
$$A = \ell w$$
$$= \sqrt{10}\sqrt{40}$$
$$= \sqrt{400} = 20 \text{ unit}^2$$

Page 783 Lesson 10–4

1. $A = \frac{1}{2}h(b_1 + b_2)$
$$= \frac{1}{2}(5)(7 + 14)$$
$$= \frac{1}{2}(5)(21) = 52.5 \text{ ft}^2$$

2. $A = \frac{1}{2}d_1d_2 = \frac{1}{2}(8)(14) = 56 \text{ in}^2$

3. $h = \frac{s}{2}\sqrt{3} = \frac{6}{2}\sqrt{3} \text{ or } 3\sqrt{3}$
$$A = \frac{1}{2}bh = \frac{1}{2}(6)(3\sqrt{3}) = 9\sqrt{3} \approx 15.6 \text{ m}^2$$

4. $P = b_1 + b_2 + \text{leg}_1 + \text{leg}_2$
$$29 = b_1 + b_2 + 4 + 5$$
$$20 = b_1 + b_2$$
$$A = \frac{1}{2}h(b_1 + b_2)$$
$$= \frac{1}{2}(3)(20)$$
$$= 30 \text{ in}^2$$

5. $P = 4s$
$$52 = 4s$$
$$13 = s$$
$$\left(\frac{1}{2}d_1\right)^2 + \left(\frac{1}{2}d_2\right)^2 = s^2$$
$$\left[\frac{1}{2}(24)\right]^2 + \left(\frac{1}{2}d_2\right)^2 = 13^2$$
$$144 + \left(\frac{1}{2}d_2\right)^2 = 169$$
$$\left(\frac{1}{2}d_2\right)^2 = 25$$
$$\frac{1}{2}d_2 = 5$$
$$d_2 = 10$$
$$A = \frac{1}{2}d_1d_2 = \frac{1}{2}(24)(10) = 120 \text{ units}^2$$

6. $P = b_1 + b_2 + 2(\text{leg})$
$$28 = b_1 + b_2 + 2(5)$$
$$18 = b_1 + b_2$$
$$A = \frac{1}{2}h(b_1 + b_2)$$
$$36 = \frac{1}{2}h(18)$$
$$72 = 18h$$
$$h = 4 \text{ cm}$$

Page 784 Lesson 10–5

1. $\frac{1}{2}s = a\sqrt{3}$
$$\frac{1}{2}s = 5.8\sqrt{3}$$
$$s = 11.6\sqrt{3}$$
$$A = \frac{1}{2}Pa$$
$$= \frac{1}{2}[3(11.6\sqrt{3})](5.8)$$
$$\approx 174.8 \text{ cm}^2$$

2. $\frac{1}{2}s = a$
$$\frac{1}{2}s = 8$$
$$s = 16$$
$$A = s^2 = 16^2 \text{ or } 256 \text{ in}^2$$

3. $a = \frac{1}{2}s\sqrt{3}$
$$a = \frac{1}{2}(19.1)\sqrt{3}$$
$$a = 9.55\sqrt{3}$$
$$A = \frac{1}{2}Pa$$
$$= \frac{1}{2}[6(19.1)](9.55\sqrt{3})$$
$$\approx 947.8 \text{ mm}^2$$

4. central angle of pentagon = 72°
$$\tan\left[\frac{1}{2}(72°)\right] = \frac{\frac{1}{2}s}{a}$$
$$\tan 36° = \frac{6.5}{a}$$
$$a = \frac{6.5}{\tan 36°}$$
$$a \approx 8.946$$
$$A = \frac{1}{2}Pa$$
$$\approx \frac{1}{2}[5(13)](8.946)$$
$$\approx 290.8 \text{ mi}^2$$

5. $C = 2\pi r = 2\pi(18) = 36\pi \approx 113.1 \text{ in.}$
$$A = \pi r^2 = \pi(18^2) = 324\pi \approx 1017.9 \text{ in}^2$$

6. $A_{\text{shaded region}} = A_{\text{circle}} - A_{\text{square}}$
$$A = \pi(3\sqrt{2})^2 - 6^2$$
$$= 18\pi - 36$$
$$\approx 20.5 \text{ units}^2$$

7. $A_{\text{shaded region}} = A_{\text{large hexagon}} - A_{\text{small hexagon}}$
$$A = \frac{1}{2}(6 \cdot 8)(4\sqrt{3}) - \frac{1}{2}(6 \cdot 6)(3\sqrt{3})$$
$$= 96\sqrt{3} - 54\sqrt{3}$$
$$= 42\sqrt{3}$$
$$\approx 72.7 \text{ units}^2$$

8. $A_{\text{shaded region}} = A_{\text{hexagon}} - A_{\text{triangle}}$
$$A = \frac{1}{2}(6 \cdot 12)(6\sqrt{3}) - \frac{1}{2}(3 \cdot 12\sqrt{3})(6)$$
$$= 216\sqrt{3} - 108\sqrt{3}$$
$$= 108\sqrt{3}$$
$$\approx 187.1 \text{ units}^2$$

Page 784 Lesson 10–6

1. Let s = measure of side of larger square.
$$P(\text{shaded region}) = 1 - \frac{\text{area of small square}}{\text{area of large square}}$$
$$= 1 - \frac{\left(\frac{1}{2}s\sqrt{2}\right)^2}{s^2}$$
$$= 1 - \frac{\frac{1}{2}s^2}{s^2}$$
$$= 1 - \frac{1}{2} \text{ or } \frac{1}{2}$$

2. Each "petal" is composed of 2 sectors whose central angle measures 90° with a radius of 2 units less the area of the 45° − 45° − 90° triangle.

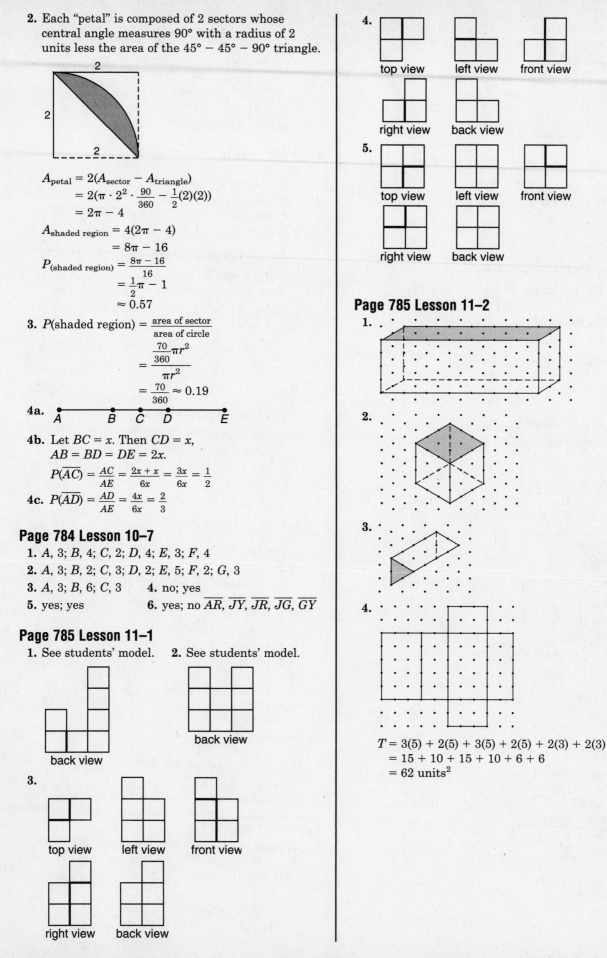

$$A_{petal} = 2(A_{sector} - A_{triangle})$$
$$= 2\left(\pi \cdot 2^2 \cdot \frac{90}{360} - \frac{1}{2}(2)(2)\right)$$
$$= 2\pi - 4$$
$$A_{shaded\ region} = 4(2\pi - 4)$$
$$= 8\pi - 16$$
$$P_{(shaded\ region)} = \frac{8\pi - 16}{16}$$
$$= \frac{1}{2}\pi - 1$$
$$\approx 0.57$$

3. $P(shaded\ region) = \dfrac{area\ of\ sector}{area\ of\ circle}$

$$= \frac{\frac{70}{360}\pi r^2}{\pi r^2}$$
$$= \frac{70}{360} \approx 0.19$$

4a.

A   B   C   D   E

4b. Let $BC = x$. Then $CD = x$, $AB = BD = DE = 2x$.

$$P(\overline{AC}) = \frac{AC}{AE} = \frac{2x + x}{6x} = \frac{3x}{6x} = \frac{1}{2}$$

4c. $P(\overline{AD}) = \dfrac{AD}{AE} = \dfrac{4x}{6x} = \dfrac{2}{3}$

Page 784 Lesson 10–7

1. A, 3; B, 4; C, 2; D, 4; E, 3; F, 4
2. A, 3; B, 2; C, 3; D, 2; E, 5; F, 2; G, 3
3. A, 3; B, 6; C, 3   **4.** no; yes
5. yes; yes   **6.** yes; no $\overline{AR}$, $\overline{JY}$, $\overline{JR}$, $\overline{JG}$, $\overline{GY}$

Page 785 Lesson 11–1

1. See students' model.   **2.** See students' model.

back view

back view

3.

top view   left view   front view

right view   back view

4.

top view   left view   front view

right view   back view

5.

top view   left view   front view

right view   back view

Page 785 Lesson 11–2

1.

2.

3.

4.

$$T = 3(5) + 2(5) + 3(5) + 2(5) + 2(3) + 2(3)$$
$$= 15 + 10 + 15 + 10 + 6 + 6$$
$$= 62\ units^2$$

5.

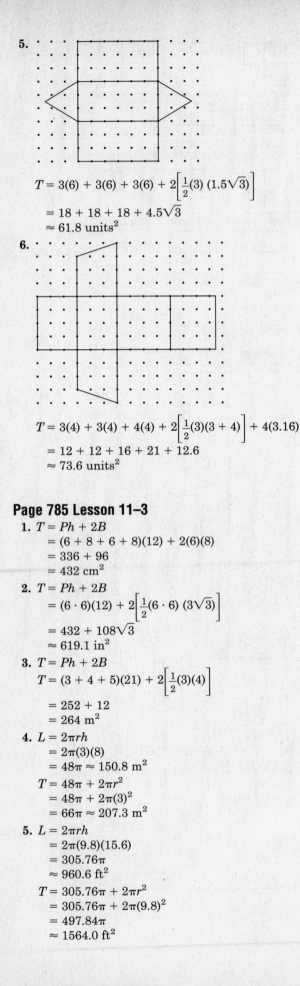

$$T = 3(6) + 3(6) + 3(6) + 2\left[\frac{1}{2}(3)(1.5\sqrt{3})\right]$$
$$= 18 + 18 + 18 + 4.5\sqrt{3}$$
$$\approx 61.8 \text{ units}^2$$

6.

$$T = 3(4) + 3(4) + 4(4) + 2\left[\frac{1}{2}(3)(3 + 4)\right] + 4(3.16)$$
$$= 12 + 12 + 16 + 21 + 12.6$$
$$\approx 73.6 \text{ units}^2$$

Page 785 Lesson 11–3

1. $T = Ph + 2B$
$$= (6 + 8 + 6 + 8)(12) + 2(6)(8)$$
$$= 336 + 96$$
$$= 432 \text{ cm}^2$$

2. $T = Ph + 2B$
$$= (6 \cdot 6)(12) + 2\left[\frac{1}{2}(6 \cdot 6)(3\sqrt{3})\right]$$
$$= 432 + 108\sqrt{3}$$
$$\approx 619.1 \text{ in}^2$$

3. $T = Ph + 2B$
$$T = (3 + 4 + 5)(21) + 2\left[\frac{1}{2}(3)(4)\right]$$
$$= 252 + 12$$
$$= 264 \text{ m}^2$$

4. $L = 2\pi rh$
$$= 2\pi(3)(8)$$
$$= 48\pi \approx 150.8 \text{ m}^2$$
$$T = 48\pi + 2\pi r^2$$
$$= 48\pi + 2\pi(3)^2$$
$$= 66\pi \approx 207.3 \text{ m}^2$$

5. $L = 2\pi rh$
$$= 2\pi(9.8)(15.6)$$
$$= 305.76\pi$$
$$\approx 960.6 \text{ ft}^2$$
$$T = 305.76\pi + 2\pi r^2$$
$$= 305.76\pi + 2\pi(9.8)^2$$
$$= 497.84\pi$$
$$\approx 1564.0 \text{ ft}^2$$

6. $L = 2\pi rh$
$$= 2\pi(6.8)(17)$$
$$= 231.2\pi$$
$$\approx 726.3 \text{ in}^2$$
$$T = 231.2\pi + 2\pi r^2$$
$$= 231.2\pi + 2\pi(6.8)^2$$
$$= 323.68\pi$$
$$\approx 1016.9 \text{ in}^2$$

Page 786 Lesson 11–4

1. $T = \pi r\ell + \pi r^2$
$$= \pi(8)(17) + \pi(8)^2$$
$$= 136\pi + 64\pi$$
$$\approx 628.3 \text{ in}^2$$

2. $T = \frac{1}{2}P\ell + B$
$$= \frac{1}{2}[(4(16)(15)] + 16(16)$$
$$= 480 + 256$$
$$= 736 \text{ cm}^2$$

3. apothem of a pentagon
$$\tan 36° = \frac{3.5}{a}$$
$$a = \frac{3.5}{\tan 36}$$
$$a \approx 4.817°$$
$$B = \frac{1}{2}Pa$$
$$\approx \frac{1}{2}(5 \cdot 7)(4.817) \approx 84.3$$
$$T = \frac{1}{2}P\ell + B$$
$$= \frac{1}{2}(5.7)(8.2) + 84.3$$
$$= 143.5 + 84.3$$
$$\approx 227.8 \text{ yd}^2$$

4. $r^2 = 19^2 - 17^2$
$$r^2 = 72$$
$$r \approx 8.485$$
$$T = \pi r\ell + \pi r^2$$
$$= \pi(8.485)(19) + \pi(8.485)^2$$
$$= 233.215\pi$$
$$\approx 732.7 \text{ m}^2$$

5. $\ell^2 = 3^2 + 5^2$
$$\ell^2 = 34$$
$$\ell \approx 5.831$$
$$T = \pi r\ell + 2\pi rh + \pi r^2$$
$$= \pi(3)(5.831) + 2\pi(3)(10) + \pi(3)^2$$
$$= 17.493\pi + 60\pi + 9\pi$$
$$\approx 271.7 \text{ in}^2$$

6. $T = Ph + \frac{1}{2}P\ell + B$
$$= 16(6) + \frac{1}{2}(16)(5) + 4(4)$$
$$= 96 + 40 + 16$$
$$= 152 \text{ m}^2$$

Page 786 Lesson 11–5

1. $h^2 = 36^2 - 20^2$
$$h^2 = 896$$
$$h \approx 29.933$$
$$V = Bh$$
$$= \frac{1}{2}(40)(29.933)(25)$$
$$\approx 14{,}966.6 \text{ ft}^3$$

2. $h^2 = 17^2 - 8^2$
$$h^2 = 225$$
$$h = 15$$
$$V = Bh$$
$$= \pi r^2 h$$
$$= \pi(4)^2(15)$$
$$\approx 754.0 \text{ cm}^3$$

3. $V = 15(10)(3) + 5(10)(3)$
   $= 450 + 150$
   $= 600 \text{ m}^3$

4. $V = Bh$
   $= (17.5)(14)$
   $= 245 \text{ cm}^3$

5. $V = \pi r^2 h$
   $= \pi(3.2)^2(10.5)$
   $= 107.52\pi$
   $\approx 337.8 \text{ cm}^3$

6. $V = Bh$
   $= 16(4.2)$
   $= 67.2 \text{ ft}^3$

7. $V = s^3$ $\quad d = s\sqrt{2}$
   $= (6\sqrt{2})^3$ $\quad 12 = s\sqrt{2}$
   $\approx 610.9 \text{ cm}^3$ $\quad s = \dfrac{12}{\sqrt{2}} \text{ or } 6\sqrt{2}$

Page 786 Lesson 11–6

1. $V = \frac{1}{3}Bh$
   $= \frac{1}{3}\pi r^2 h$
   $= \frac{1}{3}\pi(5)^2(12)$
   $= 100\pi$
   $\approx 314.2 \text{ in}^3$

2. $V = \frac{1}{3}Bh$
   $= \frac{1}{3}(30)(12)(8)$
   $= 960 \text{ m}^3$

3. $V = \frac{1}{3}Bh$
   $= \frac{1}{3}\left(\frac{1}{2} \cdot 4 \cdot 6\right)(8)$
   $= 32 \text{ ft}^3$

4. $V = \frac{1}{3}\pi r^2 h$
   $= \frac{1}{3}\pi(8)^2(21)$
   $= 448\pi$
   $\approx 1407.4 \text{ cm}^3$

5. $h = \frac{1}{2}\ell\sqrt{3} = 11\sqrt{3}$
   $V = \frac{1}{3}\pi r^2 h$
   $= \frac{1}{3}\pi(11)^2(11\sqrt{3})$
   $\approx 2414.2 \text{ yd}^3$

6. $V = \pi r^2 h + \frac{1}{3}\pi r^2 h$
   $= \pi(2)^2(8) + \frac{1}{3}\pi(2)^2(8)$
   $= 32\pi + \frac{32}{3}\pi$
   $\approx 134.0 \text{ cm}^3$

Page 787 Lesson 11–7

1. true   **2.** false   **3.** true   **4.** true

5. $RS^2 = PS^2 - PR^2$
   $RS^2 = 15^2 - 9^2$
   $RS^2 = 144$
   $RS = 12$

6. $PR^2 = PS^2 - PR^2$
   $PR^2 = 26^2 - 24^2$
   $PR^2 = 100$
   $PR = 10$

7. $T = 4\pi r^2$
   $= 4\pi(200)^2$
   $= 160000\pi$
   $\approx 502{,}654.8 \text{ ft}^2$

   $V = \frac{4}{3}\pi r^3$
   $= \frac{4}{3}\pi(200)^3$
   $= 10666666\frac{2}{3}\pi$
   $\approx 33{,}510{,}321.6 \text{ ft}^3$

8. $C = 2\pi r$ $\qquad T = 4\pi r2$
   $18.84 = 2\pi r$ $\qquad = 4\pi(2.998)^2$
   $r = 2.998$ $\qquad \approx 113.0 \text{ m}^2$

   $V = \frac{4}{3}\pi r^3$
   $= \frac{4}{3}\pi(2.998)^3$
   $\approx 112.9 \text{ m}^3$

Page 787 Lesson 11–8

1. neither   **2.** similar

3. $\dfrac{3m}{3m} = \dfrac{4m}{4m} = \dfrac{6m}{6m} = 1$, congruent

4. $\dfrac{\text{surface area of small prism}}{\text{surface area of large prism}} = \dfrac{2^2}{5^2} = \dfrac{4}{25}$ or 4:25

5. $\dfrac{\text{volume of small prism}}{\text{volume of larger prism}} = \dfrac{2^3}{5^3} = \dfrac{18}{x}$
   $8x = 2250$
   $x = 281.25 \text{ m}^3$

Page 787 Lesson 12–1

1. x-intercept $\qquad\qquad$ y-intercept
   $4x - y = 4$ $\qquad\qquad$ $4x - y = 4$
   $4x - 0 = 4$ $\qquad\qquad$ $4(0) - y = 4$
   $4x = 4$ $\qquad\qquad\quad$ $-y = 4$
   $x = 1$ $\qquad\qquad\qquad$ $y = -4$

   slope
   $4x - y = 4$
   $-y = -4x + 4$
   $y = 4x - 4$
   $m = 4$

2. x-intercept: 4 $\qquad\qquad$ y-intercept: none
   slope: undefined

3. x-intercept $\qquad\qquad$ y-intercept
   $x + 2y = 6$ $\qquad\qquad$ $x + 2y = 6$
   $x + 2(0) = 6$ $\qquad\qquad$ $0 + 2y = 6$
   $x = 6$ $\qquad\qquad\qquad$ $y = 3$

   slope
   $x + 2y = 6$
   $2y = -x + 6$
   $y = \dfrac{-1}{2}x + 3$
   $m = -\dfrac{1}{2}$

4. x-intercept $\qquad\qquad$ y-intercept
   $3x - 6y = 6$ $\qquad\qquad$ $3x - 6y = 6$
   $3x - 6(0) = 6$ $\qquad\qquad$ $3(0) - 6y = 6$
   $3x = 6$ $\qquad\qquad\qquad$ $-6y = 6$
   $x = 2$ $\qquad\qquad\qquad$ $y = -1$

   slope
   $3x - 6y = 6$
   $-6y = -3x + 6$
   $y = \dfrac{1}{2}x - 1$
   $m = \dfrac{1}{2}$

5. $y = 4x - 2$
   $m = 4, b = -2$

Graph of $y = 4x - 2$

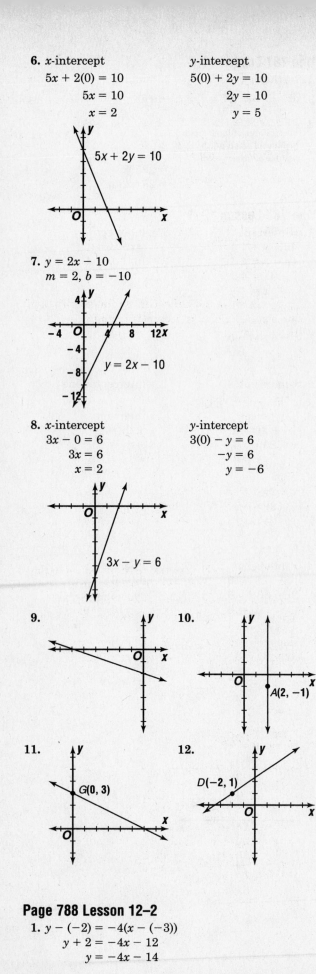

6. *x*-intercept

$5x + 2(0) = 10$
$5x = 10$
$x = 2$

y-intercept

$5(0) + 2y = 10$
$2y = 10$
$y = 5$

7. $y = 2x - 10$
$m = 2, b = -10$

8. *x*-intercept

$3x - 0 = 6$
$3x = 6$
$x = 2$

y-intercept

$3(0) - y = 6$
$-y = 6$
$y = -6$

9.

10.

11.

12.

Page 788 Lesson 12–2

1. $y - (-2) = -4(x - (-3))$
$y + 2 = -4x - 12$
$y = -4x - 14$

2. $y - (-3) = \frac{1}{6}(x - 12)$
$y + 3 = \frac{1}{6}x - 2$
$y = \frac{1}{6}x - 5$

3. $y - 7 = 0(x - 6)$
$y - 7 = 0$
$y = 7$

4. $m = \frac{3}{4}; (0, 8)$
$y = \frac{3}{4}x + 8$

5. slope $= -4$
$y - 1 = -4(x - (-3))$
$y - 1 = -4x - 12$
$y = -4x - 11$

6. slope $= 0$
$y - 2 = 0(x - (-8))$
$y - 2 = 0$
$y = 2$

7. $m = \frac{3 - (-3)}{0 - 4} = \frac{6}{-4}$ or $-\frac{3}{2}$
$y - 3 = -\frac{3}{2}(x - 0)$
$y - 3 = -\frac{3}{2}x$
$y = -\frac{3}{2}x + 3$

Page 788 Lesson 12–3

1. slope of $\overleftrightarrow{AB} = \frac{2 - 0}{4 - 9} = -\frac{2}{5}$
slope of $\overleftrightarrow{BC} = \frac{-1 - 2}{2 - 4} = \frac{3}{2}$
not collinear

2. slope of $\overleftrightarrow{XY} = \frac{-1 - 9}{3 - 6} = \frac{10}{3}$
slope of $\overleftrightarrow{YZ} = \frac{0 - (-1)}{4 - 3} = \frac{1}{1}$ or 1
not collinear

3. slope of $\overleftrightarrow{LM} = \frac{4 - 3}{0 - 2} = -\frac{1}{2}$
slope of $\overleftrightarrow{MN} \ \frac{3 - 6}{2 - (-4)} = \frac{-3}{6}$ or $\frac{-1}{2}$
collinear

4a.

Tax Due / Taxable Income

4b. Sample answer: (11,905, 1789)(7412, 1114)
$m = \frac{1789 - 1114}{11,905 - 7412} = \frac{675}{4493} \approx 0.15$
$y - 1114 = 0.15(x - 7412)$
$y = 0.15x + 3$

4c. Sample answer: $y = 0.15 (12982) + 3 = \$1950.30$

5. midpoint of $\overline{ST} = \left(\frac{6 + (-6)}{2}, \frac{4 + 10}{2}\right)$ or $(0, 7)$

midpoint of $\overline{RS} = \left(\frac{-6 + 6}{2}, \frac{-8 + 4}{2}\right)$ or $(0, -2)$

midpoint of $\overline{RT} = \left(\frac{-6 + (-6)}{2}, \frac{-8 + 10}{2}\right)$ or $(-6, 1)$

equation of median through R:

slope $\frac{-8 - 7}{6 - 0} = \frac{-15}{-6} = \frac{5}{2}$

$y - 7 = \frac{5}{2}(x - 0)$

$y - 7 = \frac{5}{2}x$

$\quad y = \frac{5}{2}x + 7$

equation of median through S:

slope $= \frac{4 - 1}{6 - (-6)} = \frac{3}{12} = \frac{1}{4}$

$y - 1 = \frac{1}{4}(x - (-6))$

$y - 1 = \frac{1}{4}x + \frac{3}{2}$

$\quad y = \frac{1}{4}x + \frac{5}{2}$

equation of median through T:

slope $= \frac{10 - (-2)}{-6 - 0} = \frac{12}{-6} = -2$

$y - 10 = -2(x - (-6))$

$y - 10 = -2x - 12$

$\quad y = -2x - 2$

6. slope of $\overline{ST} = \frac{4 - 10}{6 - (-6)} = \frac{-6}{12} = \frac{-1}{2}$

slope of perpendicular is 2

equation of altitude through R:

$y - (-8) = 2(x - (-6))$

$\quad y + 8 = 2x + 12$

$\qquad y = 2x + 4$

slope of $\overline{RS} = \frac{-8 - 4}{-6 - 6} = 1$

slope of perpendicular is -1

equation of altitude through T:

$y - 10 = -1(x - (-6))$

$y - 10 = -x - 6$

$\quad y = -x + 4$

slope of $\overline{RT} = \frac{-8 - 10}{-6 - (-6)} =$ undefined

slope of perpendicular is 0

equation of altitude through S:

$y - 4 = 0(x - 6)$

$y - 4 = 0$

$\quad y = 4$

Page 788 Lesson 12–4

1. $R(-b, 2b)$ **2.** $C(a - b, c), D(0, 0)$

3. Given: $\triangle ABC$

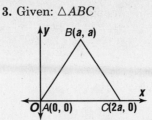

Prove: $\triangle ABC$ is isoscelels.

Proof:

Use the distance formula to find AB and CB.

$AB = \sqrt{(a - 0)^2 + (b - 0)^2}$

$\quad = \sqrt{a^2 + b^2}$

$CB = \sqrt{(a - 2a)^2 + (b - 0)^2}$

$\quad = \sqrt{a^2 + b^2}$

Thus, $AB = CB$ and $\overline{AB} \cong \overline{CB}$. By the definition of isosceles, $\triangle ABC$ is an isosceles triangle.

4. Given: $\triangle PQR$

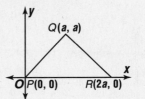

Prove: $\triangle PQR$ is a right triangle

Proof:

Find the slope of $\overline{PQ}$ and $\overline{RQ}$.

$m(\overline{PQ}) = \frac{a - 0}{a - 0} \qquad\qquad m(\overline{RQ}) = \frac{a - 0}{a - 2a}$

$\qquad\quad = \frac{a}{a} \qquad\qquad\qquad\quad = \frac{a}{-a}$

$\qquad\quad = 1 \qquad\qquad\qquad\qquad = -1$

Thus, the slopes are negative reciprocals of each other. So, $\overline{PQ}$ and $\overline{RQ}$ are perpendicular. By definition of perpendicular lines, the angles formed are right angles. Therefore, $\triangle PQR$ is a right triangle.

Page 789 Lesson 12–5

1.

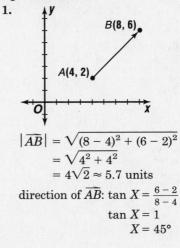

$|\overline{AB}| = \sqrt{(8 - 4)^2 + (6 - 2)^2}$

$\quad = \sqrt{4^2 + 4^2}$

$\quad = 4\sqrt{2} \approx 5.7$ units

direction of $\overline{AB}$: $\tan X = \frac{6 - 2}{8 - 4}$

$\qquad\qquad\qquad \tan X = 1$

$\qquad\qquad\qquad\qquad X = 45°$

2.

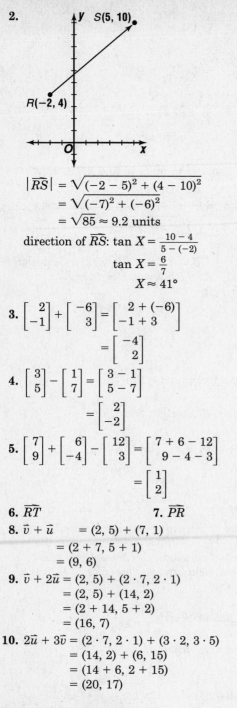

$$|\overrightarrow{RS}| = \sqrt{(-2-5)^2 + (4-10)^2}$$
$$= \sqrt{(-7)^2 + (-6)^2}$$
$$= \sqrt{85} \approx 9.2 \text{ units}$$

direction of $\overrightarrow{RS}$: $\tan X = \dfrac{10-4}{5-(-2)}$

$$\tan X = \dfrac{6}{7}$$
$$X \approx 41°$$

3. $\begin{bmatrix} 2 \\ -1 \end{bmatrix} + \begin{bmatrix} -6 \\ 3 \end{bmatrix} = \begin{bmatrix} 2+(-6) \\ -1+3 \end{bmatrix}$

$$= \begin{bmatrix} -4 \\ 2 \end{bmatrix}$$

4. $\begin{bmatrix} 3 \\ 5 \end{bmatrix} - \begin{bmatrix} 1 \\ 7 \end{bmatrix} = \begin{bmatrix} 3-1 \\ 5-7 \end{bmatrix}$

$$= \begin{bmatrix} 2 \\ -2 \end{bmatrix}$$

5. $\begin{bmatrix} 7 \\ 9 \end{bmatrix} + \begin{bmatrix} 6 \\ -4 \end{bmatrix} - \begin{bmatrix} 12 \\ 3 \end{bmatrix} = \begin{bmatrix} 7+6-12 \\ 9-4-3 \end{bmatrix}$

$$= \begin{bmatrix} 1 \\ 2 \end{bmatrix}$$

6. $\overrightarrow{RT}$ **7.** $\overrightarrow{PR}$

8. $\vec{v} + \vec{u} = (2, 5) + (7, 1)$
$$= (2+7, 5+1)$$
$$= (9, 6)$$

9. $\vec{v} + 2\vec{u} = (2, 5) + (2 \cdot 7, 2 \cdot 1)$
$$= (2, 5) + (14, 2)$$
$$= (2+14, 5+2)$$
$$= (16, 7)$$

10. $2\vec{u} + 3\vec{v} = (2 \cdot 7, 2 \cdot 1) + (3 \cdot 2, 3 \cdot 5)$
$$= (14, 2) + (6, 15)$$
$$= (14+6, 2+15)$$
$$= (20, 17)$$

Page 789 Lesson 12–6

1.

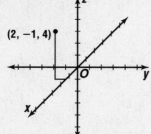

2.

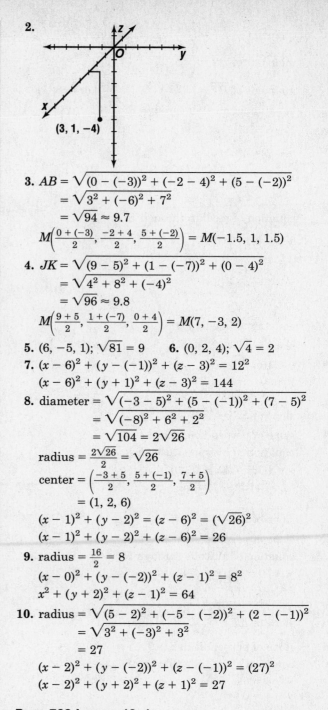

3. $AB = \sqrt{(0-(-3))^2 + (-2-4)^2 + (5-(-2))^2}$
$$= \sqrt{3^2 + (-6)^2 + 7^2}$$
$$= \sqrt{94} \approx 9.7$$
$$M\left(\dfrac{0+(-3)}{2}, \dfrac{-2+4}{2}, \dfrac{5+(-2)}{2}\right) = M(-1.5, 1, 1.5)$$

4. $JK = \sqrt{(9-5)^2 + (1-(-7))^2 + (0-4)^2}$
$$= \sqrt{4^2 + 8^2 + (-4)^2}$$
$$= \sqrt{96} \approx 9.8$$
$$M\left(\dfrac{9+5}{2}, \dfrac{1+(-7)}{2}, \dfrac{0+4}{2}\right) = M(7, -3, 2)$$

5. $(6, -5, 1); \sqrt{81} = 9$ **6.** $(0, 2, 4); \sqrt{4} = 2$

7. $(x-6)^2 + (y-(-1))^2 + (z-3)^2 = 12^2$
$$(x-6)^2 + (y+1)^2 + (z-3)^2 = 144$$

8. diameter $= \sqrt{(-3-5)^2 + (5-(-1))^2 + (7-5)^2}$
$$= \sqrt{(-8)^2 + 6^2 + 2^2}$$
$$= \sqrt{104} = 2\sqrt{26}$$

radius $= \dfrac{2\sqrt{26}}{2} = \sqrt{26}$

center $= \left(\dfrac{-3+5}{2}, \dfrac{5+(-1)}{2}, \dfrac{7+5}{2}\right)$
$$= (1, 2, 6)$$
$$(x-1)^2 + (y-2)^2 = (z-6)^2 = (\sqrt{26})^2$$
$$(x-1)^2 + (y-2)^2 + (z-6)^2 = 26$$

9. radius $= \dfrac{16}{2} = 8$
$$(x-0)^2 + (y-(-2))^2 + (z-1)^2 = 8^2$$
$$x^2 + (y+2)^2 + (z-1)^2 = 64$$

10. radius $= \sqrt{(5-2)^2 + (-5-(-2))^2 + (2-(-1))^2}$
$$= \sqrt{3^2 + (-3)^2 + 3^2}$$
$$= 27$$
$$(x-2)^2 + (y-(-2))^2 + (z-(-1))^2 = (27)^2$$
$$(x-2)^2 + (y+2)^2 + (z+1)^2 = 27$$

Page 789 Lesson 13–1

1.

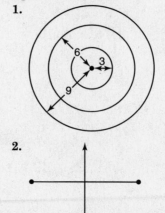

two concentric circles, one with a radius of 3 in. and one with a radius of 9 in.

2.

the perpendicular bisector of the line segment

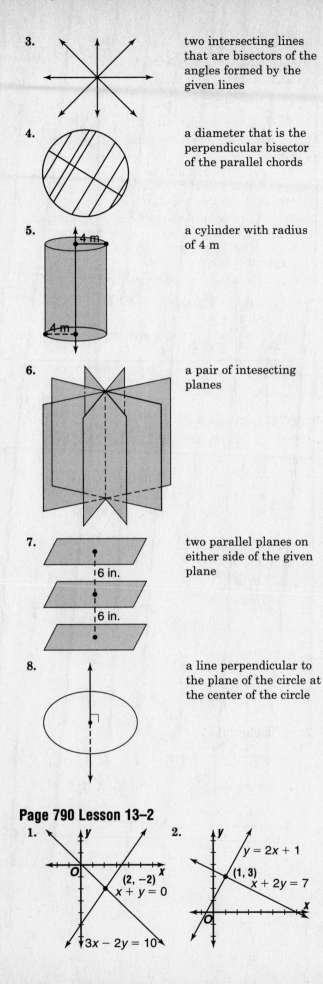

3. two intersecting lines that are bisectors of the angles formed by the given lines

4. a diameter that is the perpendicular bisector of the parallel chords

5. a cylinder with radius of 4 m

4 m

4 m

6. a pair of intesecting planes

7. two parallel planes on either side of the given plane

6 in.

6 in.

8. a line perpendicular to the plane of the circle at the center of the circle

Page 790 Lesson 13–2

1.

O   *x*

(2, −2)
x + *y* = 0

3*x* − 2*y* = 10

2.

y = 2*x* + 1

(1, 3)
x + 2*y* = 7

O   *x*

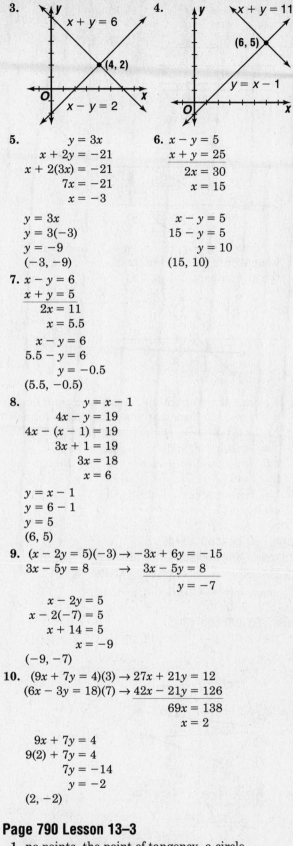

3.

x + *y* = 6

(4, 2)

O   *x*

x − *y* = 2

4.

x + *y* = 11

(6, 5)

y = *x* − 1

O   *x*

5.
$$y = 3x$$
$$x + 2y = -21$$
$$x + 2(3x) = -21$$
$$7x = -21$$
$$x = -3$$

$$y = 3x$$
$$y = 3(-3)$$
$$y = -9$$
$$(-3, -9)$$

6.
$$x - y = 5$$
$$\underline{x + y = 25}$$
$$2x = 30$$
$$x = 15$$

$$x - y = 5$$
$$15 - y = 5$$
$$y = 10$$
$$(15, 10)$$

7.
$$x - y = 6$$
$$\underline{x + y = 5}$$
$$2x = 11$$
$$x = 5.5$$

$$x - y = 6$$
$$5.5 - y = 6$$
$$y = -0.5$$
$$(5.5, -0.5)$$

8.
$$y = x - 1$$
$$4x - y = 19$$
$$4x - (x - 1) = 19$$
$$3x + 1 = 19$$
$$3x = 18$$
$$x = 6$$

$$y = x - 1$$
$$y = 6 - 1$$
$$y = 5$$
$$(6, 5)$$

9. $(x - 2y = 5)(-3) \rightarrow -3x + 6y = -15$
$3x - 5y = 8 \qquad \rightarrow \quad \underline{3x - 5y = 8}$
$$y = -7$$

$$x - 2y = 5$$
$$x - 2(-7) = 5$$
$$x + 14 = 5$$
$$x = -9$$
$$(-9, -7)$$

10. $(9x + 7y = 4)(3) \rightarrow 27x + 21y = 12$
$(6x - 3y = 18)(7) \rightarrow \underline{42x - 21y = 126}$
$$69x = 138$$
$$x = 2$$

$$9x + 7y = 4$$
$$9(2) + 7y = 4$$
$$7y = -14$$
$$y = -2$$
$$(2, -2)$$

Page 790 Lesson 13–3

1. no points, the point of tangency, a circle
2. no points, 1, 2, 3, or 4 points
3. no points, 1 or 2 points
4. no points, 1 or 2 points, a circle

5. 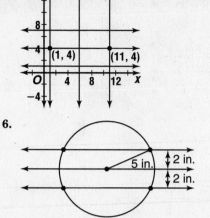   (1, 4) and (11, 4)

6.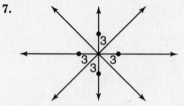

4 points 5 in. from the given point that are located on 2 parallel lines 2 in. above and below the given line

7.

4 points 3 units from the intersection point on the 2 intersecting lines that bisect the angles formed by the given lines

8. The locus is a cylinder with radius 6 units whose axis is perpendicular to the xy-plane through the point at $(2, -4, 0)$.

9. The locus is a sphere with radius 4 units and center at $(3, 4, 5)$.

Page 790 Lesson 13–4

1. rotation, translation   2. dilation, translation
3. $\triangle RQS$ 4. $\triangle EFD$ 5. $\triangle NMW$ 6. $\triangle YXZ$
7. quadrilateral $CDAB$ 8. $\triangle KLM$

Page 791 Lesson 13–5

1. L 2. J 3. $\overline{JL}$ 4. $\triangle CXA$
5. N 6. $\angle MNJ$

7.

8.

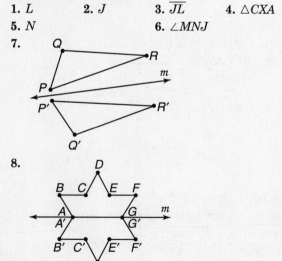

9.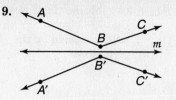

10. No; not all points are the same distance from p.

11. Yes; for any point A on the figure on one side of p, it is possible to find another point B on the figure on the other side of p so that p is the perpendicular bisector of $\overline{AB}$.

12. Yes; for any point A on the figure on one side of p, it is possible to find another point B on the figure on the other side of p so that p is the perpendicular bisector of $\overline{AB}$.

13.   **14.**

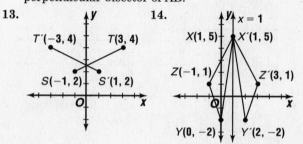

Page 791 Lesson 13–6

1. yes   2. No; the green image is incorrect.
3. yes
4. $R'(5, 1)$, $S'(-1, -6)$ 5. $A'(2, 5)$, $B'(0, 8)$

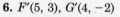

6. $F'(5, 3)$, $G'(4, -2)$

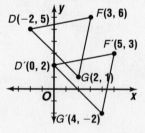

Geometry Extra Practice

7. $X'(-1, 2)$, $Y'(0, 7)$, $Z'(1, 5)$

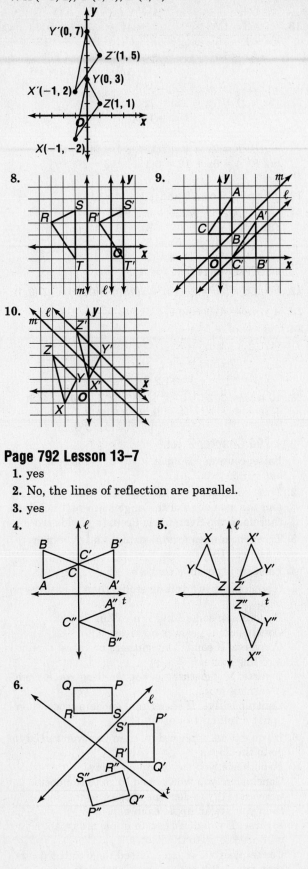

7.

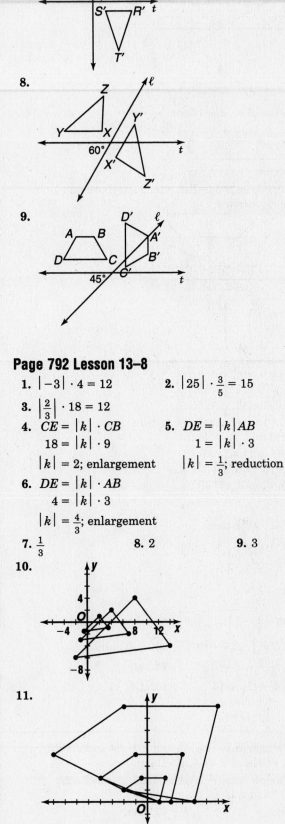

8.

9.

Page 792 Lesson 13–7

1. yes
2. No, the lines of reflection are parallel.
3. yes
4.   5.

6.

Page 792 Lesson 13–8

1. $\left|-3\right| \cdot 4 = 12$ 2. $\left|25\right| \cdot \frac{3}{5} = 15$
3. $\left|\frac{2}{3}\right| \cdot 18 = 12$
4. $CE = \left|k\right| \cdot CB$ 5. $DE = \left|k\right| AB$
   $18 = \left|k\right| \cdot 9$ $1 = \left|k\right| \cdot 3$
   $\left|k\right| = 2$; enlargement $\left|k\right| = \frac{1}{3}$; reduction
6. $DE = \left|k\right| \cdot AB$
   $4 = \left|k\right| \cdot 3$
   $\left|k\right| = \frac{4}{3}$; enlargement
7. $\frac{1}{3}$ 8. 2   9. 3
10.

11.

Chapter Tests

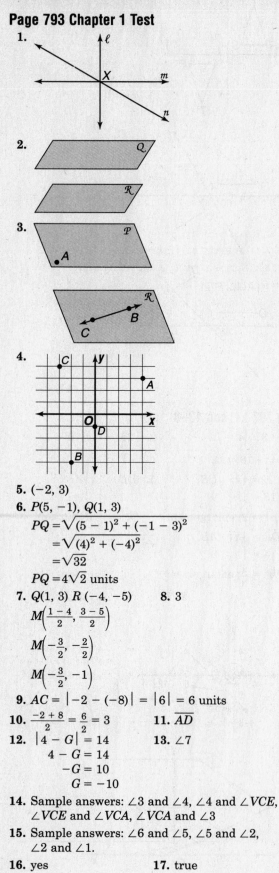

1.

2.

3.

4.

5. $(-2, 3)$

6. $P(5, -1), Q(1, 3)$

$$PQ = \sqrt{(5-1)^2 + (-1-3)^2}$$
$$= \sqrt{(4)^2 + (-4)^2}$$
$$= \sqrt{32}$$
$$PQ = 4\sqrt{2} \text{ units}$$

7. $Q(1, 3) \; R(-4, -5)$ **8.** 3

$$M\left(\frac{1-4}{2}, \frac{3-5}{2}\right)$$
$$M\left(-\frac{3}{2}, -\frac{2}{2}\right)$$
$$M\left(-\frac{3}{2}, -1\right)$$

9. $AC = |-2 - (-8)| = |6| = 6$ units

10. $\frac{-2+8}{2} = \frac{6}{2} = 3$ **11.** $\overline{AD}$

12. $|4 - G| = 14$ **13.** $\angle 7$
$$4 - G = 14$$
$$-G = 10$$
$$G = -10$$

14. Sample answers: $\angle 3$ and $\angle 4$, $\angle 4$ and $\angle VCE$, $\angle VCE$ and $\angle VCA$, $\angle VCA$ and $\angle 3$

15. Sample answers: $\angle 6$ and $\angle 5$, $\angle 5$ and $\angle 2$, $\angle 2$ and $\angle 1$.

16. yes   **17.** true

18.

$AC = CE$	$AC = 4(3) + 1 = 13$
$4x + 1 = 16 - x$	$CE = 16 - 3 = 13$
$5x = 15$	$AE = AC + CE$
$x = 3$	$AE = 13 + 13 = 26$

19. $m\angle BVF + m\angle FVA = 180$
$$(7x - 1) + (6x + 12) = 180$$
$$13x = 169$$
$$x = 13$$
$m\angle BVF = 7x - 1 = 7(13) - 1 = 90$
$m\angle FVA = 6x + 12 = 6(13) + 12 = 90$
yes

20. $\angle 5$ and $\angle 6$ or $\angle 5$ and $\angle 1$

21.
$$m\angle 5 + m\angle 6 = m\angle FVB$$
$$(3x + 14) + (x + 30) = 9x - 11$$
$$5x = 55$$
$$x = 11$$
$$m\angle FVB = 9(11) - 11 = 88$$

22. $P = 2\ell + 2w = 2(410) + 2(780) = 2380$ ft

23. $A = \ell w = 410(780) = 319{,}800$ ft^2

24.
$$a^2 + b^2 = c^2$$
$$(410)^2 + (780)^2 = c^2$$
$$776{,}500 = c^2$$
$$c \approx 881.2 \text{ ft}$$

25. 10 totals; 3, 3, 3; 3, 3, 4; 3, 3, 9; 4, 4, 4; 4, 4, 9; 4, 9, 9; 3, 4, 4; 3, 4, 9; 9, 9, 9; 9, 9, 3

Page 794 Chapter 2 Test

1. False; counter example: $x = -1$; -1 is real, but $-(-1) > 0$.

2. True; congruent angles have the same measures, and the measures of the angles are real numbers; therefore, the Symmetric Prop. (=) holds true.

3. True; the angles form a straight angle which measures 180.

4. False; it is possible that $x = -4$.

5. If something is a rolling stone, then it gathers no moss.
Hypothesis: something is a rolling stone
Conclusion: it gathers no moss
Converse: If something gathers no moss, then it is a rolling stone.
Inverse: If something is not a rolling stone, then it gathers moss.
Contrapositive: If something gathers moss, then it is not a rolling stone.

6. If you eat an apple a day, then you won't need to go to the doctor.
Hypothesis: you eat an apple a day
Conclusion: you won't need to go to the doctor
Converse: If you don't need to go to the doctor, then you ate an apple each day.
Inverse: If you don't eat an apple a day, then you will need to go to the doctor.
Contrapositive: If you do need to go to the doctor, then you didn't eat an apple each day.

7. If two planes are parallel, then they do not intersect.
Hypothesis: two planes are parallel
Conclusion; they do not intersect
Converse: If two planes do not intersect, then they are parallel.
Inverse: If two planes are not parallel, then they intersect.
Contrapositive: If two planes intersect, then they are not parallel.

8. If there are two points, then they make a line.
Hypothesis: there are two points.
Conclusion: they make a line
Converse: If there is a line, then there are two points on it.
Inverse: If there are not two points, then there is not a line.
Contrapositive: If there is not a line, then there are not two points on that line.

9. If there are any two points, then there is exactly one straight line through them.
Hypothesis: there are any two points
Conclusion: there is exactly one straight line through them
Converse: If there is exactly one line, then there are two points on it.
Inverse: If there are not two points, then there is not exactly one straight line through them.
Contrapositive: If there is not exactly one line, then there are not two points on it.

10. Wise investments with Petty-Bates build for the future; syllogism.

11. Lines ℓ and m intersect; Law of Detachment.

12. no conclusion

13. 7 is a real number; Law of Detachment.

14. Symmetric Prop. (=)

15. Subtraction Prop. (=)

16. Division Prop. (=)

17. Substitution Prop. (=)

18a. The pattern is 3, 5, 7 · · ·, $2n - 1$. So, $2(15) - 1 = 29$.

18b. $1 + 3 + 5 + 7 + 9 + 11 + 13 + 15 + 17 + 19 = 100$ passengers

19.

Statements	Reasons
a. $\overline{AC} \cong \overline{BD}$	**a.** Given
b. $AC = BD$	**b.** Def. $\cong$ segments
c. $AB + BC = AC$ $BC + CD = BD$	**c.** Segment Addition Postulate
d. $AB + BC = BC + CD$	**d.** Subst. Prop. (=)
e. $AB = CD$	**e.** Subtr. Prop. (=)
f. $\overline{AB} \cong \overline{CD}$	**f.** Def. $\cong$ segments

20.

Statements	Reasons
a. $m\angle 1 = m\angle 3 + m\angle 4$	**a.** Given
b. $m\angle 2 = m\angle 2$	**b.** Reflexive Prop. (=)
c. $m\angle 1 + m\angle 2 = m\angle 3 + m\angle 4 + m\angle 2$	**c.** Add. Prop. (=)
d. $\angle 1$ and $\angle 2$ form a linear pair.	**d.** Def. linear pair
e. $\angle 1$ and $\angle 2$ are supplementary.	**e.** Supplement Theorem
f. $m\angle 1 + m\angle 2 = 180$	**f.** Def. suppl. $\angle$s
g. $m\angle 3 + m\angle 4 + m\angle 2 = 180$	**g.** Subst. Prop. (=)

Page 795 Chapter 3 Test

1. true; def. alt. ext. $\angle$s

2. false; def. consec. int. $\angle$s

3. false; def. vertical $\angle$s

4. true; Consecutive Interior Angles Theorem

5. true; Corresponding Angles Postulate

6. false; def. supp. $\angle$s

7. true; Consecutive Interior Angles Theorem

8. $a \parallel b$; If ⟷ so that corr. $\angle$s are $\cong$, then the lines are $\parallel$.

9. $m \parallel n$; If ⟷ so that a pair of alt. int. angles is $\cong$, then the lines are $\parallel$.

10. $a \parallel b$; If ⟷ so that a pair of consec. int. $\angle$s is supp., then the lines are $\parallel$.

11. $\dfrac{2 - (-2)}{5 - (-3)} = \dfrac{4}{8} = \dfrac{1}{2}$

12. $\dfrac{5 - (-3)}{-2 - 1} = -\dfrac{8}{3}$

13. $\dfrac{1 - (-3)}{-2 - 5} = -\dfrac{4}{7}$

14. $\dfrac{-2 - 2}{-3 - 5} = \dfrac{-4}{-8} = \dfrac{1}{2}$, -2

15. $\overline{FD}$ **16.** $\overline{AC}$ **17.** $\overline{DC}$

18. Given: $\angle 1 \cong \angle 2$
$\overline{ST} \parallel \overline{PR}$

Prove: $\angle P \cong \angle R$

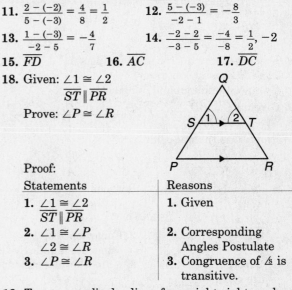

Proof:

Statements	Reasons
1. $\angle 1 \cong \angle 2$ $\overline{ST} \parallel \overline{PR}$	**1.** Given
2. $\angle 1 \cong \angle P$ $\angle 2 \cong \angle R$	**2.** Corresponding Angles Postulate
3. $\angle P \cong \angle R$	**3.** Congruence of $\angle$s is transitive.

19. Two perpendicular lines form eight right angles.

20.

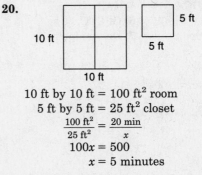

10 ft by 10 ft = 100 ft² room
5 ft by 5 ft = 25 ft² closet
$$\frac{100 \text{ ft}^2}{25 \text{ ft}^2} = \frac{20 \text{ min}}{x}$$
$$100x = 500$$
$$x = 5 \text{ minutes}$$

Page 796 Chapter 4 Test

1. $\triangle PSQ$, $\triangle PST$ 2. $\triangle QRS$ 3. $\overline{PS}$
4. $\triangle QRS$ 5. $m\angle 8 = 90$
6. $m\angle 6 = m\angle 9$
$$m\angle 3 + m\angle 9 + m\angle 8 = 180$$
$$30 + m\angle 9 = 60$$
$$m\angle 9 = 60$$
$$m\angle 6 = 60$$
7. $m\angle 2 + m\angle 6 + m\angle 7 = 180$
$$m\angle 2 + 60 + 90 = 180$$
$$m\angle 2 = 30$$
8. $m\angle 9 + m\angle 10 = 180$
$$60 + m\angle 10 = 180$$
$$m\angle 10 = 120$$
9. $m\angle H = m\angle L$
$$m\angle 4 + m\angle 10 + m\angle L = 180$$
$$20 + 120 + m\angle L = 180$$
$$m\angle L = 40$$
$$m\angle H = 40$$
10. $M\angle 1 + m\angle 5 + m\angle H = 180$
$$m\angle 1 + 120 + 40 = 180$$
$$m\angle 1 = 20$$
11. $\angle 10$ and $\angle 5$ or $\angle 11$ and $\angle 4$
12. $\triangle PRO$; AAS 13. $\triangle RQO$, SSS
14. $\triangle QOR$; ASA 15. $\triangle PQO$; SAS
16. $x + (2x - 1) + 43 = 180$
$$3x = 138$$
$$x = 46$$
17. $5x - 7 = 3x + 1$
$$2x = 8$$
$$x = 4$$
18. Umeko —Drama Club, delivery person;
Jim—Spanish Club, tutor;
Gwen—marching band, lifeguard
19. Given: $\overline{AC} \perp \overline{BD}$
$\angle B \cong \angle D$
Prove: C is the midpoint of $\overline{BD}$.
Proof:

Statements	Reasons
1. $\overline{AC} \perp \overline{BD}$ $\angle B \cong \angle D$	1. Given
2. $\overline{CA} \cong \overline{CA}$	2. Congruence of segments is reflexive.
3. $\angle BCA$ and $\angle DCA$ are rt. $\angle$s	3. $\perp$ lines form 4 rt. $\angle$s.
4. $\angle 3 \cong \angle 4$	4. All right $\angle$s are $\cong$.
5. $\triangle BCA \cong \triangle DCA$	5. AAS
6. $\overline{BC} \cong \overline{DC}$	6. CPCTC
7. C is the midpoint of $\overline{BD}$.	7. Def. midpoint

20. Given: $m\angle ACB = 110$
$m\angle DAC = 40$
Prove: $\triangle ACD$ is isosceles.

Proof:

Statements	Reasons
1. $m\angle ACB = 110$; $m\angle DAC = 40$	1. Given
2. $m\angle D + m\angle DAC = m\angle ACB$	2. Exterior Angle Theorem
3. $m\angle D + 40 = 110$	3. Subst. Prop. (=)
4. $m\angle D = 70$	4. Subtr. Prop. (=)
5. $m\angle ACD + m\angle D + m\angle DAC = 180$	5. Angle Sum Theorem
6. $m\angle ACD + 70 + 40 = 180$	6. Subst. Prop. (=)
7. $m\angle ACD = 70$	7. Subtr. Prop. (=)
8. $m\angle ACD = m\angle D$	8. Subst. Prop. (=)
9. $\angle ACD \cong \angle D$	9. Def. $\cong$ $\angle$s
10. $\overline{AD} \cong \overline{AC}$	10. If 2 $\angle$s of a $\triangle$ are $\cong$, the sides opp. the $\angle$s are $\cong$.
11. $\triangle ACD$ is isosceles.	11. Def. isosceles $\triangle$

Page 797 Chapter 5 Test

1. $\overline{HQ} \perp \overline{AW}$, so, $m\angle AQH = 90$.
2. $m\angle A + m\angle AHQ = 90$
$$64 + m\angle AHQ = 90$$
$$m\angle AHQ = 26$$
3. $m\angle PWA = \frac{1}{2}(m\angle AWH) = \frac{1}{2}(36) = 18$
$$m\angle PWA + m\angle A + m\angle APW = 180$$
$$18 + 64 + m\angle APW = 180$$
$$m\angle APW = 98$$
4. $m\angle XWQ + m\angle WXQ + m\angle XQW = 180$
$$18 + m\angle WXQ + 90 = 180$$
$$m\angle WXQ = 72$$
$$m\angle WXQ + m\angle HXW = 180$$
$$72 + m\angle HXW = 180$$
$$m\angle HXW = 180$$
5. $AP = PH$
$$3y + 11 = 7y - 5$$
$$4y = 16$$
$$y = 4$$
$$AP + PH = AH$$
$$(3y + 11) + (7y - 5) = AH$$
$$10y + 6 = AH$$
$$10(4) + 6 = AH$$
$$46 = AH$$
6. $>$ 7. $<$ 8. $>$ 9. $<$
10. $AB = DB$
$$2x = 5x - 24$$
$$3x = 24$$
$$x = 8$$
11. $AE = CD$
$$2x + 13 = 4x - 5$$
$$2x = 18$$
$$x = 9$$
12. $m\angle NAL$, $m\angle NLA$ 13. $\angle 4$, $\angle 5$, $\angle 8$

14.
$$m\angle A + m\angle B + m\angle C = 180$$
$$(5x + 31) + (74 - 3x) + (4x + 9) = 180$$
$$6x + 114 = 180$$
$$x = 11$$

$m\angle A = 5x + 31 = 5(11) + 31 = 86$

$m\angle B = 74 - 3x = 74 - 3(11) = 41$

$m\angle C = 4x + 9 = 4(11) + 9 = 53$

Since $m\angle A$ is greatest, the side opposite $\angle A$ is longest—$\overline{BC}$.

15. $AB = \sqrt{(1 - 7)^2 + (-1 - 7)^2} = \sqrt{36 + 64} = 10$

$BC = \sqrt{(7 - 2)^2 + (7 - (-5))^2} = \sqrt{25 + 144} = 13$

$AC = \sqrt{(1 - 2)^2 + (-1 - (-5))^2}$
$\quad = \sqrt{1 + 16} \approx 4.12$

$10 + 13 > 4.12$

$13 + 4.12 > 10$

$4.12 + 10 > 13$

Yes; the measures satisfy the Triangle Inequality Theorem.

16. $4x - 10 < 3x + 20$
$\quad\quad x < 30$

17. $13x - 5 > 7x + 25$
$\quad\quad 6x > 30$
$\quad\quad\quad x > 5$

18. Given: $\overline{FM}$ is a median of $\triangle DEF$.
$\quad\quad m\angle 1 > m\angle 2$

Prove: $DF \neq EF$

Proof:

Assume $DF = EF$. M is the midpoint of $\overline{DE}$ and $\overline{DM} \cong \overline{EM}$ since it is given that $\overline{FM}$ is a median of $\triangle DEF$. $\overline{FM} \cong \overline{FM}$ by the Reflexive Prop. (=) and $m\angle 1 > m\angle 2$ is given, so $DF > EF$ by SAS Inequality. But $DF = EF$ by assumption. This contradicts the Comparison Prop. Therefore, the assumption is false, and $DF \neq EF$.

19. Given: $NO = QP$
$\quad\quad PN > OQ$

Prove: $MP > MO$

Proof:

Statements	Reasons
1. $NO = QP$	1. Given
2. $\overline{NO} \cong \overline{QP}$	2. Def. $\cong$ segments congruence
3. $\overline{OP} \cong \overline{OP}$	3. Congruence of segments is reflexive.
4. $PN > OQ$	4. Given
5. $m\angle MOP > m\angle MPO$	5. SSS Inequality
6. $MP > MO$	6. If one $\angle$ of $\triangle$ is greater than another, the side opp. the greater $\angle$ is longer than the side opp. the lesser $\angle$.

20. Given: $\overline{AD} \perp \overline{DC}$
$\quad\quad \overline{AB} \perp \overline{BC}$
$\quad\quad AB = DC$

Prove: $\overline{DC} \perp \overline{BC}$

Proof:

Statements	Reasons
1. $\overline{AD} \perp \overline{DC}$, $\overline{AB} \perp \overline{BC}$, $AB = DC$	1. Given
2. $\overline{AB} \cong \overline{DC}$	2. Def. $\cong$ segments
3. $\overline{AC} \cong \overline{AC}$	3. Congruence of segments is reflexive.
4. $\angle D$ and $\angle B$ are rt $\angle$s.	4. $\perp$ lines form 4 rt. $\angle$s.
5. $\triangle ADC$ and $\triangle CBA$ are rt $\triangle$s.	5. Def. rt. $\triangle$
6. $\triangle ADC \cong \triangle CBA$	6. HL
7. $\angle ACD \cong \angle CAB$	7. CPCTC
8. $\overline{AB} \parallel \overline{CD}$	8. If $\overleftrightarrow{}$ and alt. int. $\angle$s are $\cong$, lines are $\parallel$.
9. $\overline{DC} \perp \overline{BC}$	9. Perpendicular Transversal Theorem

Page 798 Chapter 6 Test

1. $\overline{EG}$; the diagonals of a parallelogram bisect each other.

2. $\angle FGH$; opposite angles of a parallelogram are congruent.

3. $\overline{GH}$; def. of parallelogram.

4. $\triangle HGD$; SAS

5. $\overline{FH}$; the diagonals of a rhombus are perpendicular.

6. $\angle FDH$, $\angle FGH$; each diagonal of a rhombus bisects each pair of opposite angles.

7. 729

8. slope of $\overline{AB} = \dfrac{6 - 11}{-2 - 2} = \dfrac{5}{4}$

slope of $\overline{BC} = \dfrac{11 - 8}{2 - 3} = -3$

slope of $\overline{CD} = \dfrac{8 - 3}{3 - (-1)} = \dfrac{5}{4}$

slope of $\overline{DA} = \dfrac{3 - 6}{-1 - (-2)} = -3$

$ABCD$ is a parallelogram because the slopes of the opposite sides are equal.

9. slope of $\overline{AB} = \dfrac{-3 - (-2)}{7 - 4} = \dfrac{-1}{3}$

slope of $\overline{BC} = \dfrac{-2 - 4}{4 - 6} = 3$

slope of $\overline{CD} = \dfrac{4 - 2}{6 - 12} = \dfrac{-1}{3}$

slope of $\overline{DA} = \dfrac{2 - (-3)}{12 - 7} = 1$

$ABCD$ is not a parallelogram because the slopes of both pairs of opposite sides are not equal.

10. true

11. false; sample answer:

12. false; sample answer:

13. true

14. $2x - 4 = 10$
$2x = 14$
$x = 7$

$-3y = 12 - y$
$-2y = 12$
$y = -6$

15. $4x = 78$ $3y = 4x + 42$
$x = 19.5$ $3y = 78 + 42$
                   $y = 40$

16. $TV = \frac{1}{2}(PS + QR)$
$26 = \frac{1}{2}(32 + QR)$
$52 = 32 + QR$
$QR = 20$

17. $m\angle QTV + m\angle TVS = 180$
$79 + m\angle TVS = 180$
$m\angle TVS = 101$

18. $TV = \frac{1}{2}(PS + QR)$
$= \frac{1}{2}(9x + 13x)$
$= 11x$

19. $TV = \frac{1}{2}(PS + QR)$
$3x - 10 = \frac{1}{2}(2x + 4 + x - 3)$
$6x - 20 = 3x + 1$
$3x = 21$
$x = 7$
$TV = 3(7) - 10 = 11$
$PS = 2(7) + 4 = 18$
$QR = 7 - 3 = 4$

20. $m\angle MPS = m\angle OPS$
$4x + 7 = 7x - 38$
$3x = 45$
$x = 15$

Page 799 Chapter 7 Test

1. $\frac{x}{28} = \frac{60}{16}$
$16x = 28(60)$
$x = 105$

2. $\frac{21}{1 - x} = \frac{7}{x}$
$21x = 7(1 - x)$
$21x = 7 - 7x$
$28x = 7$
$x = 0.25$

3. $\frac{14}{25} = \frac{x}{1600}$
$25x = 14(1600)$
$x = 896$ students

4. true

5. False; all angles in isosceles $\triangle$s are not the same measure.

6. yes, SSS Similarity; $\triangle JKL \sim \triangle RST$

7. yes, SAS Similarity; $\triangle ABC \sim \triangle PKM$

8. $\frac{AF}{FE} = \frac{AG}{GD}$
$\frac{3x + 1}{18} = \frac{8}{9}$
$9(3x + 1) = 8(18)$
$27x + 9 = 144$
$27x = 135$
$x = 5$

9. $DC = FB$
$4x - 7 = 17$
$4x = 24$
$x = 6$

10. converges to 1

11. slope $\overline{AC}$ = slope $\overline{BC} = \frac{4 - 3}{3 - 0} = \frac{1}{3}$

$AC = 3(BC)$, so slope of $AC = \frac{3}{3}\left(\frac{1}{3}\right)$ or $\frac{3}{9}$.

From C, go down 3 and left 9 to get to A.

$A(3 - 9, 4 - 3)$ or $A(-6, -1)$

slope $\overline{CD}$ = slope $\overline{CE} = \frac{4 - 2}{3 - 2} = \frac{2}{1}$

$CE = 3(CD)$, so slope of $CE = \frac{3}{3}\left(\frac{2}{1}\right)$ or $\frac{6}{3}$.

From C, go down 6 and left 3 to get to E.

$E(3 - 3, 4 - 6)$ or $E(0, -2)$

12. $\frac{7}{4} = \frac{\text{perimeter of } \triangle BKA}{\text{perimeter of } \triangle JKL}$
$\frac{7}{4} = \frac{4z}{\text{perimeter of } \triangle JKL}$

perimeter of $\triangle JKL = \frac{4(42)}{7}$ or 24

$(2x + 6) + (3x - 1) + 4 = 24$
$5x + 9 = 24$
$5x = 15$
$x = 3$

13. $\frac{PW}{ST} = \frac{QW}{SU}$
$\frac{x}{x + 5} = \frac{1}{5}$
$5x = x + 5$
$4x = 5$
$x = 1\frac{1}{4}$

14. $\frac{SW}{SV} = \frac{RS}{SU}$
$\frac{3}{2} = \frac{1\frac{1}{3}}{x + \frac{2}{3}}$
$\frac{8}{3} = 3x + \frac{6}{3}$
$\frac{2}{3} = 3x$
$\frac{2}{9} = x$

15. Given: $\triangle ABC \sim \triangle RSP$
D is the midpoint of $\overline{AC}$.
Q is the midpoint of $\overline{PR}$.
Prove: $\triangle SPQ \sim \triangle BCD$

Proof:

Statements	Reasons
1. $\triangle ABC \sim \triangle RSP$ D is the midpoint of $\overline{AC}$. Q is the midpoint of $\overline{PR}$.	1. Given
2. $\angle RSP \cong \angle ABC$	2. Def. ~ polygons
3. $\overline{BD}$ is a median of $\triangle ABC$. $\overline{QS}$ is a median of $\triangle RSP$.	3. Def. median
4. $\dfrac{SQ}{BD} = \dfrac{SP}{BC} = \dfrac{PR}{AC}$	4. If 2 $\triangle s$ are ~, then the measures of corr. medians are proportional to the measures of corr. sides.
5. $PQ = QR$ $DC = DA$	5. Def. midpoint
6. $AD + DC = AC$ $PQ + QR = PR$	6. Seg. Add. Post.
7. $2(DC) = AC$ $2(PQ) = PR$	7. Subst. Prop. (=)
8. $\dfrac{2(PQ)}{2(DC)} = \dfrac{SQ}{BD}$	8. Subst. Prop. (=)
9. $\dfrac{PQ}{DC} = \dfrac{SQ}{BD}$	9. Subst. Prop. (=)
10. $\triangle SPQ \sim \triangle BCD$	10. SSS Similarity

1. $\dfrac{3}{x} = \dfrac{x}{12}$
$x^2 = 36$
$x = 6$

2. $\dfrac{5}{x} = \dfrac{x}{4}$
$x^2 = 20$
$x = \sqrt{20} \approx 4.5$

3. $\dfrac{28}{x} = \dfrac{x}{56}$
$x^2 = 1568$
$x = 28\sqrt{2} \approx 39.6$

4. $\dfrac{8}{QS} = \dfrac{QS}{5}$
$QS^2 = 40$
$QS = \sqrt{40} \approx 6.3$

5. $\dfrac{9.5}{QP} = \dfrac{QP}{12.5}$
$QP^2 = 118.75$
$QP = \sqrt{118.75} \approx 10.9$

6. $10^2 + 24^2 \stackrel{?}{=} 26^2$
$100 + 576 \stackrel{?}{=} 676$
$676 = 676$ ✓
yes

7. $12^2 + 19^2 \stackrel{?}{=} 27^2$
$144 + 361 \stackrel{?}{=} 729$
$505 \neq 729$
no

8. $39^2 + 80^2 \stackrel{?}{=} 89^2$
$1521 + 6400 \stackrel{?}{=} 7921$
$7921 = 7921$ ✓
yes

9. $x = \dfrac{7}{\sqrt{2}} = \dfrac{7\sqrt{2}}{2} \approx 4.9$

10. $4.2^2 + 5.1^2 = x^2$
$17.64 + 26.01 = x^2$
$x = \sqrt{43.65} \approx 6.6$

11. $x = \dfrac{1}{2}s\sqrt{3}$
$= \dfrac{1}{2}(6.8)\sqrt{3}$
$= 3.4\sqrt{3} \approx 5.9$

12. $P = 3s$
$51 = 3s$
$s = 17$
$\dfrac{1}{2}s = 8.5$
$h = \dfrac{1}{2}s\sqrt{3} = 8.5\sqrt{3} \approx 14.72$ in.

13. $\sin d° = \dfrac{11}{61} \approx 0.1803$ **14.** $\tan c° = \dfrac{60}{11} \approx 5.4545$

15. $11^2 + 16^2 = WZ^2$
$WZ = \sqrt{377}$
$\cos a° = \dfrac{16}{\sqrt{377}} = \dfrac{16\sqrt{377}}{377} \approx 0.8240$

16. $\tan b° = \dfrac{16}{11} \approx 1.4545$

17. $\sin X = \dfrac{28}{36}$
$m\angle X \approx 51$

18. $45° + 79 + X = 180$
$m\angle X = 56$

$\dfrac{\sin 79°}{30} = \dfrac{\sin 56°}{x}$
$x = \dfrac{30 \sin 56°}{\sin 79°}$
$x \approx 25.3$

$\dfrac{\sin 79°}{30} = \dfrac{\sin 45°}{y}$
$y = \dfrac{30 \sin 45°}{\sin 79°}$
$y \approx 21.6$

19. $28^2 = 22^2 + 22^2 - 2(22)(22) \cos X$
$\cos X = \dfrac{22^2 + 22^2 - 28^2}{2(22)(22)}$
$m\angle X \approx 79$

20. Sample answer: making a list; $\dfrac{5}{50}$ or $\dfrac{1}{10}$ 1, 9, 25, 49, 81

1. $\overline{NA}, \overline{NB}, \overline{NC},$ or $\overline{ND}$ **2.** isosceles

3. No; $\overline{AD}$ is a diameter. **4.** $\dfrac{1}{2}(21) = 10\dfrac{1}{2}$

5. $C = 2\pi r = 2\pi(5) = 10\pi \approx 31.4$

6. $C = \pi d$
$126.5 = \pi d$
$d = \dfrac{126.5}{\pi} \approx 40.3$

7. $r = \dfrac{8}{\sqrt{2}} = 4\sqrt{2}$
$C = 2\pi r = 2\pi 4\sqrt{2} = 8\sqrt{2}\pi$

8. $r = \dfrac{6}{\sqrt{3}} = 2\sqrt{3}$
$C = 2\pi r = 2\pi 2\sqrt{3} = 4\sqrt{3}\pi$

9. $x = 10\sqrt{2}$

10. $x = 15$

11. $r^2 + 8^2 = (x+6)^2$
$6^2 + 8^2 = (x+6)^2$
$100 = x^2 + 12x + 36$
$0 = x^2 + 12x - 64$
$0 = (x-4)(x+16)$
$x = 4$ or $x = -16$
Disregard $x = -16$

12. $5x = 6(8)$
$x = 9.6$

13. $6^2 = x(x+5)$
$36 = x^2 + 5x$
$0 = x^2 + 5x - 36$
$0 = (x+9)(x-4)$
$x = 4$

14. $5(5+x) = 4(4+7)$
$25 + 5x = 44$
$5x = 19$
$x = 3.8$

15. $m\widehat{AC} = m\widehat{BD} = 42$

16. $m\widehat{CD} = 180 - m\widehat{AC} - m\widehat{BD}$
$\phantom{m\widehat{CD}} = 180 - 42 - 42$
$\phantom{m\widehat{CD}} = 96$

17. $m\angle BDF = m\widehat{BF} = m\widehat{AC} = 42$

18. $m\angle CPD = m\widehat{CD} = 96$

19. $m\widehat{AF} = 180 - m\widehat{BF}$
$\phantom{m\widehat{AF}} = 180 - 42$
$\phantom{m\widehat{AF}} = 138$

20. $m\widehat{EF} = m\widehat{BF} - m\widehat{BE}$
$\phantom{m\widehat{EF}} = 42 - 12$
$\phantom{m\widehat{EF}} = 30$
$m\angle G = \frac{1}{2}(m\widehat{CD} - m\widehat{EF})$
$ = \frac{1}{2}(96 - 30)$
$ = 33$

21. $m\angle FCD = \frac{1}{2}(m\widehat{DB} + m\widehat{BF})$
$ = \frac{1}{2}(42 + 42)$
$ = 42$

22. $m\angle EDC = \frac{1}{2}(m\widehat{EF} + m\widehat{FEC})$
$ = \frac{1}{2}(30 + 180)$
$ = 105$

23. $x^2 + 3^2 = 5^2$
$x^2 = 16$
$x = 4$ in.

24. How parents wake up their children:

Call to them 43%
Other 19%
Alarm clock 22%
Kids wake on own 16%

25. $x(8-x) = 2.5(2.5)$
$8x - x^2 = 6.25$
$x^2 - 8x + 6.25 = 0$
$x = \frac{8 \pm \sqrt{(-8)^2 - 4(6.25)}}{2} \approx 7.1$ in.

Page 802 Chapter 10 Test

1. hexagon   **2.** concave

3. Not regular; polygon is not convex and all angles are not congruent.

4. $180(12-2) = 180(10)$
$ = 1800$

5. $\frac{180(15-2)}{15} = \frac{180(13)}{15} = 156$
$180 - 156 = 24$

6. See students' work.   **7.** uniform, semi-regular

8. 727

9. $A = bh$
$ = (4.95)(0.51)$
$ = 2.5245$ ft^2

10. $P = 4s$ $A = s^2$
$258 = 4s$ $= (64.5)^2$
$s = 64.5$ in. $= 4160.25$ in^2

11. $A = \frac{1}{2}bh$
$ = \frac{1}{2}(16)(30.6)$
$ = 244.8$ ft^2

12. $A = \frac{1}{2}bh$
$3x^2 + 6x = \frac{1}{2}b(3x+6)$
$6x^2 + 12x = b(3x+6)$
$b = 2x$ units

13. length of median $= \frac{1}{2}(b_1 + b_2)$
$A = \frac{1}{2}(b_1 + b_2)h$
$ = 13.5(10)$
$ = 135$ ft^2

14. $a = \frac{1}{2}s\sqrt{3}$ $A = \frac{1}{2}Pa$
$ = \frac{1}{2}(10)\sqrt{3}$ $= \frac{1}{2}(6 \cdot 10)(5\sqrt{3})$
$ = 5\sqrt{3}$ ≈ 259.8 cm^2

15. $r = \frac{1}{2}(4.5) = 2.25$ **16.** $C = \pi d$
$A = \pi r^2$ $= \pi(4.5)$
$ = \pi(2.25)^2$ ≈ 14.1 in.
$ = 5.0625\pi$
$ \approx 15.9$ in^2

17. $A = \frac{N}{360}\pi r^2$
$ = \frac{30}{360}\pi(2.25)^2$
$ = 1.3$ in^2

18. probability $= \frac{\text{area of bull's eye}}{\text{area of target}}$
$ = \frac{\pi(1.5)^2}{\pi(9)^2}$
$ = \frac{2.25}{81} = \frac{1}{36} = 2.78\%$

19. probability = $\dfrac{\text{area of blue ring}}{\text{area of target}}$

$\qquad = \dfrac{\pi(5.5)^2 - \pi(1.5)^2}{\pi(9)^2}$

$\qquad = \dfrac{28}{81} \approx 34.57\%$

20a. See students' work.

20b. See students' work.

20c. See students' work

Page 803 Chapter 11 Test

1.

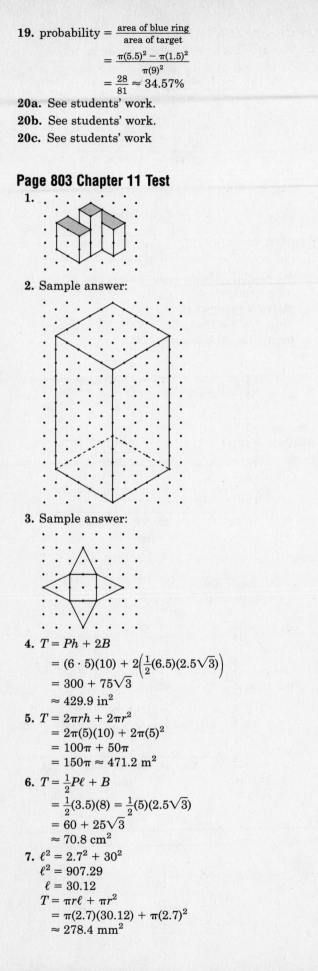

2. Sample answer:

3. Sample answer:

4. $T = Ph + 2B$

$\qquad = (6 \cdot 5)(10) + 2\left(\frac{1}{2}(6.5)(2.5\sqrt{3})\right)$

$\qquad = 300 + 75\sqrt{3}$

$\qquad \approx 429.9 \text{ in}^2$

5. $T = 2\pi rh + 2\pi r^2$

$\qquad = 2\pi(5)(10) + 2\pi(5)^2$

$\qquad = 100\pi + 50\pi$

$\qquad = 150\pi \approx 471.2 \text{ m}^2$

6. $T = \frac{1}{2}P\ell + B$

$\qquad = \frac{1}{2}(3.5)(8) = \frac{1}{2}(5)(2.5\sqrt{3})$

$\qquad = 60 + 25\sqrt{3}$

$\qquad \approx 70.8 \text{ cm}^2$

7. $\ell^2 = 2.7^2 + 30^2$

$\qquad \ell^2 = 907.29$

$\qquad \ell = 30.12$

$\qquad T = \pi r\ell + \pi r^2$

$\qquad = \pi(2.7)(30.12) + \pi(2.7)^2$

$\qquad \approx 278.4 \text{ mm}^2$

8. $T = 4\pi r^2$

$\qquad = 4\pi(3)^2$

$\qquad = 36\pi$

$\qquad \approx 113.1 \text{ in}^2$

9. $V = Bh$

$\qquad = \frac{1}{2}(8 \cdot 4\sqrt{3})(4)$

$\qquad = 64\sqrt{3}$

$\qquad \approx 110.9 \text{ yd}^3$

10. $V = \frac{1}{3}Bh$

$\qquad = \frac{1}{3}\pi r^2 h$

$\qquad = \frac{1}{3}\pi(19.5)^2(50)$

$\qquad \approx 19{,}909.8 \text{ cm}^3$

11. $\qquad h^2 + a^2 = \ell^2$

$\qquad h^2 + \left(\dfrac{11.5}{\sqrt{3}}\right)^2 = 40^2$

$\qquad\qquad h^2 = 1600 - 44.08$

$\qquad\qquad h \approx 39.445$

$\qquad V = \frac{1}{3}Bh$

$\qquad = \frac{1}{3}\left[\frac{1}{2}(23 \cdot 11.5\sqrt{3})\right](39.445)$

$\qquad = 3011.8 \text{ cm}^3$

12. $V = \pi r^2 h$

$\qquad = \pi(19.5)^2(50)$

$\qquad = 19{,}012.5\pi$

$\qquad \approx 59{,}729.5 \text{ cm}^3$

13. $V = \frac{4}{3}\pi r^3$

$\qquad = \frac{4}{3}\pi(18)^3$

$\qquad = 7776\pi$

$\qquad \approx 24{,}429.0 \text{ mm}^3$

14. Area of walkway = $(12)(6) - 10(4)$

$\qquad\qquad = 72 - 40$

$\qquad\qquad = 32 \text{ m}^2$

$\qquad V = 32(h) = 32(0.1) = 3.2 \text{ m}^3$

15. $L = Ph$

$\qquad = (6 + 8 + 10)(16)$

$\qquad = 24(16)$

$\qquad = 384 \text{ in}^2$

$\qquad c^2 = 6^2 + 8^2$

$\qquad c^2 = 36 + 64$

$\qquad c^2 = 100$

$\qquad c = 10$

Page 804 Chapter 12 Test

1.

$x + 2y = 6$

$\qquad 2y = -x + 6$

$\qquad\quad y = -\frac{1}{2}x + 3$

$-\frac{1}{2}; 3$

2.

$x = 3$

none; none

3.

$y = -5x$

$-5; 0$

4. $y - (-2) = -4(x - 3)$
$\qquad y + 2 = -4x + 12$
$\qquad\quad y = -4x + 10$

5. $m = \frac{11 - 3}{-4 - (-6)} = \frac{8}{2} = 4$
$\qquad y - 11 = 4(x - (-4))$
$\qquad y - 11 = 4x + 16$
$\qquad\quad y = 4x + 27$

6. $m = 2$ 　　　　　　**7.** $m = $ undefined
$\quad y - (-4) = 2(x - (-1))$ 　　$x = -4$
$\qquad y + 4 = 2x + 2$
$\qquad\quad y = 2x - 2$

8. $\vec{a} + \vec{b} = (-3, 5) + (0, 7)$
$\qquad\quad = (-3 + 0, 5 + 7)$
$\qquad\quad = (-3, 12)$

9. $\vec{b} - 3\vec{a} = (0, 7) - (3 \cdot (-3), 3 \cdot 5)$
$\qquad\quad = (0, 7) - (-9, 15)$
$\qquad\quad = (0 - (-9), 7 - 15)$
$\qquad\quad = (9, -8)$

10. $(4, 5, -2)$; $\sqrt{81} = 9$ 　**11.** $(0, 0, 0)$; $\sqrt{7} \approx 2.6$

12. $|\vec{v}| = \sqrt{[0 - (-5)]^2 + [0 - (-3)]^2}$
$\qquad = \sqrt{5^2 + 3^2}$
$\qquad = \sqrt{34} \approx 5.8$ units

13. $|\overrightarrow{AB}| = \sqrt{[3 - (-2)]^2 + (7 - 5)^2}$
$\qquad = \sqrt{5^2 + 2^2}$
$\qquad = \sqrt{29} = 5.4$ units

14. $\sqrt{(2 - 2)^2 + (4 - 4)^2 + (5 - 7)^2}$
$\qquad = \sqrt{0^2 + 0^2 + (-2)^2}$
$\qquad = \sqrt{4} = 2$ units

15. $M\left(\frac{0 + 3}{2}, \frac{-4 + 0}{2}, \frac{2 + 2}{2}\right) = M\left(\frac{3}{2}, -2, 2\right)$

16. diameter $= \sqrt{(-3 - 5)^2 + [5 - (-1)]^2 + (7 - 5)^2}$
$\qquad = \sqrt{(-8)^2 + 6^2 + 2^2}$
$\qquad = \sqrt{104} = 2\sqrt{26}$
radius $= \frac{2\sqrt{26}}{2}, = \sqrt{26}$
center $= \left(\frac{-3 + 5}{2}, \frac{5 + (-1)}{2}, \frac{7 + 5}{2}\right)$
$\qquad = (1, 2, 6)$
equation of sphere:
$(x - 1)^2 + (y - 2)^2 + (z - 6)^2 = (\sqrt{26})^2$
$(x - 1)^2 + (y - 2)^2 + (z - 6)^2 = 26$

17. slope of segment $= \frac{-4 - 2}{1 - 5} = \frac{-6}{-4}$ or $\frac{3}{2}$
slope of perpendicular $= \frac{-2}{3}$
midpoint of segment $= \left(\frac{5 + 1}{2}, \frac{2 + (-4)}{2}\right)$
$\qquad = (3, -1)$
equation of perpendicular bisector:
$y - (-1) = \frac{-2}{3}(x - 3)$
$\qquad y + 1 = \frac{-2}{3}x + 2$
$\qquad\quad y = \frac{-2}{3}x + 1$

18. $(a + b, c)$

19. Given: $\triangle LOM$
Prove: $\overrightarrow{NK}$ is a perpendicular bisector of $\overline{OM}$.

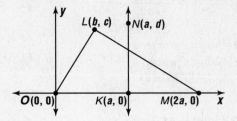

Proof:
slope of $\overrightarrow{NK} = \frac{d - 0}{a - a} = \frac{d}{0}$; undefined
slope of $\overline{OM} = \frac{0 - 0}{0 - 2a} = \frac{0}{-2a} = 0$
$\overrightarrow{NK} \perp \overline{OM}$ because vertical and horizontal lines are perpendicular.
$OK = \sqrt{(a - 0)^2 + (0 - 0)^2} = a$
$KM = \sqrt{(2a - a)^2 + (0 - 0)^2} = a$
Since $OK = KM$ and $\overrightarrow{NK} \perp \overline{OM}$, $\overrightarrow{NK}$ is a perpendicular bisector of $\overline{OM}$.

20a.

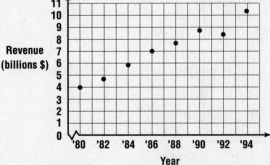

20b. Sample answer; (1984, 5.9)(1980, 4)
$m = \frac{5.9 - 4}{1984 - 1980} = \frac{1.9}{4} = 0.475$
$y - 4,000,000,000 = 0.475(x - 1980)$

20c.

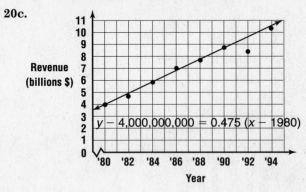

1. two lines parallel to ℓ, each 5 inches from ℓ

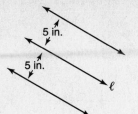

2. a circle with a radius of 3.5 cm, centered at the vertex of the rhombus

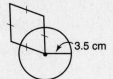

3. a quarter of a half sphere

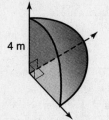

4. a cylinder whose axis is line n with a radius of 10 feet

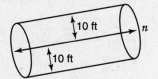

5. 0, 1, 2, 3, or 4 points

6. 0 points, 1 point, 2 points, a circle, 2 circles

7. (1,4)

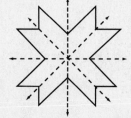

8. $3x - 2y = 10$
$(x + y = 0)(2)$

$\qquad$ $3x - 2y = 10$
$\qquad$ $\underline{2x + 2y = 0}$
$\qquad\qquad$ $5x = 10$
$\qquad\qquad\quad$ $x = 2$

$x + y = 0$
$2 + y = 0$
$\quad\; y = -2$
$(2, -2)$

9. $x - 4y = 7$
$(2x + y = -4)(4)$

$\qquad$ $x - 4y = 7$
$\qquad$ $\underline{8x + 4y = -16}$
$\qquad$ $9x = -9$
$\qquad\quad x = -1$

$\quad\; x - 4y = 7$
$(-1) - 4y = 7$
$\qquad\; -4y = 8$
$\qquad\qquad y = -2$
$(-1, -2)$

10. yes $\qquad$ **11.** yes $\qquad$ **12.** yes $\qquad$ **13.** no

14. reflection $\quad$ **15.** rotation $\quad$ **16.** translation

17.

18. reduction

19. congruence transformation

20. Let x = number of correct answers
$7x - 5(24 - x) = 0$
$7x - 120 + 5x = 0$
$\qquad\qquad 12x = 120$
$\qquad\qquad\quad\; x = 10$ questions answered correctly

279